Intermediate Algebra

Concepts Through Applications

Mark Clark

Palomar College

Brooks/Cole

Thomson Learning

Editor: Janey Moeller
Publishing Services Supervisor: Donna Brown
Graphic Designer: Krista Pierson
Rights and Permissions Specialist: Kalina Ingham Hintz
Project Coordinator: Mary Snelling
Marketing Manager: Sara L. Hinckley

Printed in the United States of America.

Thomson Custom Publishing
5191 Natorp Blvd.
Mason, Ohio 45040
USA

For information about our products, contact us:
1-800-355-9983
http://www.thomsoncustom.com

International Headquarters
Thomson Learning
International Division
290 Harbor Drive, 2ⁿᵈ Floor
Stamford, CT 06902-7477
USA

UK/Europe/Middle East/South Africa
Thomson Learning
Berkshire House
168-173 High Holborn
London WCIV 7AA

Asia
Thomson Learning
60 Albert Street, #15-01
Albert Complex
Singapore 189969

Canada
Nelson Thomson Learning
1120 Birchmount Road
Toronto, Ontario MIK 5G4
Canada
United Kingdom

Visit us at www.thomsoncustom.com and learn more about this book and other titles published by Thomson Learning Custom Publishing.

ISBN 0-759-34467-1

The Adaptable Courseware Program consists of products and additions to existing Custom Publishing products that are produced from camera-ready copy. Peer review, class testing, and accuracy are primarily the responsibility of the author(s).

For permission to use material from this text or product, submit a request online at http://www.thomsonrights.com
Any additional questions about permissions can be submitted by email to thomsonrights@thomson.com

This book is dedicated to
my wonderful wife
Christine and son Will.
Thank you both for your
support and love.

I love you both!

PREFACE

INTRODUCTION

Intermediate Algebra: Concepts and Applications is designed to help college and university students apply traditional mathematical skills in real-world contexts. The text is application-driven and uses current technology to empower students while they master algebraic concepts, critical thinking, and math communication skills.

Most of the examples in *Intermediate Algebra: Concepts and Applications* are applications-based using real-world data. Section exercises are ordered and balanced in a way that is consistent with the importance of applying and understanding the mathematics within a context. The writing style is carefully geared to the learner's thinking process to emphasize and demonstrate how to *think* through a problem and apply the skills presented.

Pedagogically, the text is consistent with the AMATYC and NCTM standards to successfully prepare and transition students for subsequent math and science courses. ***Access to a graphing calculator is required.***

KEY FEATURES OF THE TEXT

Applications Driven

The material is presented through discussion, examples, and homework problems set in a real-world context. Cognitive psychology research has shown that learning math skills in context helps students make better connections between mathematics and other disciplines and life. Linear, quadratic, and exponential functions are investigated through modeling data by using an "eyeball best fit." These models are tools to investigate questions in the context of real life situations. Creating models by hand forces students to analyze the parts of each function and how they affect the attributes of the function's graph. Graphing calculators are used to plot data and check the fit of each model. Regression is not used in this text but could be easily incorporated at the instructor's discretion.

Communication Focused

Examples and questions ask the student to explain the meaning of their solution in the context of the problem. Most application problems require a complete-sentence answer thereby encouraging students to consider the reasonableness of their solution. Model breakdown is discussed and is seen in many of the examples and problems throughout each chapter. Students are asked to explain the meaning within the context of basic concepts such as slope, intercept, and vertex. Requiring verbal explanation helps the student communicate mathematical concepts and applications in a precise way which will facilitate adaptation of math skills to other disciplines and coursework such as psychology, chemistry, business, and so on.

Concept Investigations

Directed discovery activities can be used as group work during class or as individual assignments to further investigate the concepts being presented. Inserted at key points within the chapter, they allow the student to discover connections between the graphical and algebraic representations of the functions being studied. The graphing calculator helps the student visualize the concepts being presented in that section.

Section Problems

Given throughout each section these problems allow students to practice what has been taught in the preceding discussion or examples. The solutions to these problems are provided at the end of each section to allow the learner to check their work and understanding. These can be done in class as a way to check student progress and provide more examples for discussion.

Skill Connections

Located in the margin, Skill Connections, present basic examples to reinforce skills taught within the section through in-context examples. The margin is also utilized to provide calculator tips and vocabulary help.

Key Points Review

The end of each section contains a summary of the key points along with all formulas and definitions. This provides students with an easily accessible reference to information important for overall understanding of the section material.

Exercise Sets

The exercise sets include a balance of both applications and skill-based problems. Modeling problems using real life data are the focus with some additional skill problems provided when needed. Generally my students have remarked that the practice they gain from the applications is enough to have the math skills sink in and be understood. Additional skill problems are available to students through the online or CD tutorial.

Chapter Projects

There are projects for each chapter that can be assigned either individually or as group work. Instructors can choose which projects best suit the focus of their class and give their students the chance to show how well they can pull all of a chapter's concepts together. Some of these projects include online research or activities that students must perform to analyze the data and make conclusions. These projects are available online; ask your Brooks/Cole sales representative for more information.

Intermediate Algebra
Concepts Through Applications

Chapter 1 Linear Functions

Chapter 2 Systems of Linear Equations

Chapter 3 Quadratic Functions

Chapter 4 Exponential and Logarithmic Functions

Chapter 5 Rational Functions

Chapter 6 Radical Functions

Appendix A

Appendix F

Section 1.1   Solving Linear Equations

• **Solving Linear Equations** • **Writing Complete Solutions to Applications**

Equations can be used to represent many things in life. One of the uses of Algebra is to solve equations for an unknown quantity, or variable. In this section you will learn how to solve linear equations for a missing variable and to write a complete solution. Complete sentence answers that give the units and the meaning of the solution you found will provide the reader with a clear understanding of that solution.

Example 1

Given the following equation
$$U = 19.95 + 0.59m$$
where U is the total cost in dollars to rent a 10ft truck from U-Haul for the day, and m is the number of miles the truck is driven.

a. Determine how much it will cost to rent a 10ft truck from U-Haul and drive it 75 miles.

b. Determine the number of miles you can travel for a total cost of $135.00.

Solution

a. Since the number of miles driven was given, you can replace the variable m in the equation with the number 75 and solve for the missing variable U as follows:

$$U = 19.95 + 0.59m$$
$$U = 19.95 + 0.59(75)$$
$$U = 19.95 + 44.25$$
$$U = 64.20$$

This solution indicates that renting a 10ft truck from U-Haul and driving it 75 miles would cost you $64.20.

b. Since the total cost of $135.00 is given in the statement we can substitute 135.00 for the variable U and solve for the missing variable m.

$$U = 19.95 + 0.59m$$

$$135.00 = 19.95 + 0.59m$$

$$\underline{-19.95 \quad -19.95} \qquad \text{Subtract 19.95 from both sides.}$$

$$115.05 = 0.59m$$

$$\frac{115.05}{0.59} = \frac{0.59m}{0.59} \qquad \text{Divide both sides by 0.59.}$$

$$195 = m$$

This solution indicates that for a cost of $135.00 you can rent a 10ft truck from U-Haul for a day and drive it 195 miles.

Problem 1

A team of engineers is trying to pump down the pressure in a vacuum chamber. They know the following equation represents the pressure in the chamber.
$$P = 35 - 0.07s$$
where P is the pressure in pounds per square inch (psi) of a vacuum chamber and s is the time in seconds.

a. What will the pressure be after 150 seconds?

b. When will the pressure inside the chamber be 1psi?

Solution   See page 7

Skill Connection:
When solving an equation for a variable the goal is to isolate the variable (by itself) on one side of the equation and simplify the other side.

SC-Example 1: *Solve*
$$w = 5 + 7$$

Solution:
Since w is already isolated on the left side of the equation the only thing left to do is simplify the right side.
$$w = 5 + 7$$
$$w = 12$$

SC-Example 2: *Solve*
$$15 = 3k$$

Solution:
Since k is not by itself on the right side of the equation we need to isolate it. Since k is being multiplied by the 3 we need to use division to eliminate it.
$$15 = 3k$$
$$\frac{15}{3} = \frac{3k}{3}$$
$$5 = k$$

Many of the applications in this book will investigate applications that involve money and business. We must understand some business terms in order to understand these applications and communicate clearly the meaning of the solutions we find. The three main concepts in business are **Revenue**, **Cost** and **Profit**. A simple definition of revenue is the amount of money that is brought into the business through sales. For example if a pizza place sells 10 pizzas for $12 each their revenue would be 10 pizzas · $12 per pizza = $120. A definition for cost would be amount of money paid out for expenses. Expenses often are categorized in two ways: fixed costs and variable costs. The same pizza place would probably have fixed costs such as rent, utilities and perhaps salaries and would have variable costs of supplies and food ingredients per pizza made. The cost for the business would be the fixed costs and the variable costs added together. The Profit for a business is the revenue minus the cost. If this pizza place had $100 in cost when making the 10 pizzas they would have a profit of $120 - $100 = $20. These definitions should help you understand some of the following examples and exercises throughout this book.

Skill Connection:

When you have more than one number on the same side of the equation as the variable you are solving for, start by eliminating any addition or subtraction. After addition and subtraction you can eliminate multiplication and division.

SC-Example 3: *Solve*

$$5z + 16 = 3$$

Solution:

Once again the variable z is not isolated on a side of the equation so we need to move the 16 and the 5 to the other side of the equation. The 16 is being added so we should eliminate it first. Since it is being added we will subtract 16 from both sides.

$$
\begin{array}{r}
5z + 16 = 3 \\
-16 \quad -16 \\
\hline
5z = -13
\end{array}
$$

$$\frac{5z}{5} = \frac{-13}{5}$$

$$z = -\frac{13}{5}$$

Once the 16 was moved we divided both sides by 5 to finish isolating the variable. Some instructors will want this solution in a reduced fraction or a mixed number.

$$z = -2\frac{3}{5}$$

Example 2

You are in charge of creating and purchasing t-shirts for a local summer camp. After calling a local silk-screening company you find that to purchase 100 or more t-shirts there will be a $150 setup fee and a $5 per t-shirt charge.

a.   Write an equation for the total cost, C, of making, t, t-shirts.

b.   How much would 300 t-shirts cost?

c.   How many t-shirts can you purchase with a budget of $1500?

Solution

a.   First we should determine the variables given, since we want to find the total cost and the number of t-shirts let
C = Total Cost of t-shirts, in dollars.
t = Number of t-shirts produced.
Since each t-shirt will cost $5 we need to multiply 5 by t (the number of t-shirts produced). That leaves the $150 setup fee that needs to be added to that to get the total.

$$C = 5t + 150$$

b.   The number of t-shirts is given so we can substitute 300 in for t and solve for the total cost C.

$$C = 5t + 150$$
$$C = 5(300) + 150$$
$$C = 1500 + 150$$
$$C = 1650$$

The total cost to produce 300 t-shirts will be $1650.

c.   The total budget represents the total cost of the t-shirts, so we can substitute 1500 for C, and solve for the number of t-shirts, t.

$$C = 5t + 150$$
$$1500 = 5t + 150$$

$$
\begin{array}{rr}
-150 \qquad\qquad -150 & \text{Subtract 150 from both sides.}
\end{array}
$$

$$1350 = 5t$$

$$\frac{1350}{5} = \frac{5t}{5} \qquad\qquad \text{Divide both sides by 5.}$$

$$270 = t$$

For a budget of $1500 you can purchase 270 t-shirts.

SC-Example 4: *Solve*

$$\frac{2}{3}x + \frac{5}{6} = 7$$

Solution:
In this case to eliminate the fractions we can multiply by the common denominator 6 and then continue solving.

$$\frac{2}{3}x + \frac{5}{6} = 7$$

$$6\left(\frac{2}{3}x + \frac{5}{6}\right) = 6(7)$$

$$6\left(\frac{2}{3}x\right) + 6\left(\frac{5}{6}\right) = 6(7)$$

$$\overset{2}{6}\left(\frac{2}{\overset{}{3}}x\right) + \overset{}{6}\left(\frac{5}{\overset{}{6}}\right) = 6(7)$$

$$4x + 5 = 42$$

$$\underline{-5 \quad -5}$$

$$4x = 37$$

$$\frac{4x}{4} = \frac{37}{4}$$

$$x = \frac{37}{4}$$

Once the fractions were eliminated we finished isolating the variable. Again the solution can also be given as a mixed number.

$$x = 9\frac{1}{4}$$

In both of the previous examples it is important to pay attention to the definition of each variable. This helps you to determine the variable whose value was given and which variable you need to solve for. In some questions you will need to define your own variables, be sure to give units (how the quantity is measured). Use variables that will be easy to remember what they represent. For example;

- t = time in years
- h = hours after 12 noon
- p = population of San Diego (in thousands)
- P = profit of IBM (in millions of dollars)

Units are very important in communicating what a variable represents. The meaning of $P = 100$ is very different if profit for IBM is measured in dollars and not millions of dollars. The same for $S = 6.5$. If S represents your salary for your first job out of college it would be great if S were measured in millions of dollars per year and not dollars per hour. As you can see units can make a large difference in the meaning of a quantity.

Problem 2

Rockapella, a small town rock band, wants to produce a CD before their next summer concert series. They have looked into a local recording studio and found that it will cost them $1500 to produce the master recording and then an additional $1.50 to make each CD up to 500.

a. Write an equation for the total cost, C, in dollars, of producing n, CD's.

b. How much will it cost Rockapella to make 250 CD's?

c. If Rockapella has $2000 to produce CD's how many can they order?

Solution   See page 7

Example 3

A small bicycle company produces high tech bikes for international race teams. The company has fixed costs of $5000 per month for rent, salary and utilities. For every bike they produce it costs them $755 in materials and other costs. The company can sell each bike for an average price of $1995, but can only produce a maximum of 20 bikes per month.

a. Find an equation for the monthly cost of producing b bikes.

b. How much does it cost the bicycle company to produce 20 bikes?

c. Find an equation for the monthly revenue from selling b bikes.

d. How much revenue will the bicycle company make if they sell 10 bikes?

e. Find an equation for the monthly profit the company makes if they produce and sell b bikes. (You can assume they will sell all the bikes they make.)

f. What is the profit of producing and selling 15 bikes?

g. How many bikes does the company have to produce and sell in order to make $15,000 profit?

h. How many bikes does the company have to produce and sell in order to make $30,000 profit?

Skill Connection:
Many equations will involve several operations and thus will require more steps to solve.

SC-Example 5: *Solve*

$$4t - 2(3.4t + 7) = 5t - 17.3$$

Solution:
To start solving we need to distribute the negative 2 through the parenthesis and then combine like terms before isolating the variables.

$$4t - 2(3.4t + 7) = 5t - 17.3$$
$$4t - 6.8t - 14 = 5t - 17.3$$
$$-2.8t - 14 = 5t - 17.3$$
$$\underline{2.8t \qquad\qquad 2.8t}$$
$$-14 = 7.8t - 17.3$$
$$\underline{17.3 \qquad\qquad 17.3}$$
$$3.3 = 7.8t$$
$$\frac{3.3}{7.8} = \frac{7.8t}{7.8}$$
$$0.423 = t$$

You can check this answer by substituting it back into the equation and verifying that the two sides are equal. Because of rounding the two sides will not be exactly the same but should be very close.

$$4t - 2(3.4t + 7) = 5t - 17.3$$
$$-15.1844 = -15.185$$

Solution

a.   First define the variables in the problem.

    C = The monthly cost, in dollars, to produce b, bikes.

    b = The number of bikes produced each month. (Remember a maximum of 20 bikes can be produced each month.)

Each bike cost \$755 for materials and other costs so we need to multiply b by 755, and then the fixed costs need to be added in order to get the total monthly cost. This gives the following equation.

$$C = 755b + 5000$$

b.   The number of bikes produced is given so we can substitute 20 for b and solve for C.

$$C = 755b + 5000$$
$$C = 755(20) + 5000$$
$$C = 20100$$

A monthly production of 20 bikes will result in a total monthly cost of \$20,100.

c.   First define the variables in the problem.

    R = The monthly revenue, in dollars, from selling b, bikes.

    b = The number of bikes sold in the month.

The bicycle company can sell each bike for an average price of \$1995 so the revenue can be calculated using the equation

$$R = 1995b$$

d.   The number of bikes is given so we can substitute 10 for b.

$$R = 1995b$$
$$R = 1995(10)$$
$$R = 19950$$

The total monthly revenue from selling 10 bikes is \$19,950.

e.   Profit is calculated by taking the revenue and subtracting off any costs incurred.

    P = The monthly profit, in dollars, from producing and selling b, bikes.

Thus we can use the equations for revenue and cost we found earlier.

$$P = R - C$$
$$P = (1995b) - (755b + 5000) \qquad \text{Substitute for } R \text{ and } C.$$

This Profit equation can be simplified by distributing the negative and combining like terms.

$$P = (1995b) - (755b + 5000)$$
$$P = 1995b - 755b - 5000 \qquad \text{Distribute the negative sign.}$$
$$P = 1240b - 5000 \qquad \text{Combine like terms.}$$

f.   The number of bikes is given so we can substitute 15 for b.

$$P = 1240(15) - 5000$$
$$P = 13600$$

The monthly profit from producing and selling 15 bikes is \$13,600.

g.   The amount of profit desired is given so we can substitute 15000 for P.

$$P = 1240b - 5000$$

$$15000 = 1240b - 5000$$

$$\underline{\quad 5000 \qquad\qquad\qquad 5000 \quad}$$ Add 5000 to both sides.

$$20000 = 1240b$$

$$\frac{20000}{1240} = \frac{1240b}{1240}$$ Divide both sides by 1240.

$$16.129 = b$$

Since we found a decimal answer we need to compare the profits for the whole bikes represented on both sides of this decimal.

$$P = 1240(16) - 5000$$

$$P = 14840$$

$$P = 1240(17) - 5000$$

$$P = 16080$$

If we want to make at least $15,000 profit for the month we will need to produce at least 17 bikes. We round up since producing 16 bikes would not quite make $15,000 profit.

h.   The amount of profit desired is given so we can substitute 30000 for P.

$$P = 1240b - 5000$$

$$30000 = 1240b - 5000$$

$$\underline{\quad 5000 \qquad\qquad\qquad 5000 \quad}$$ Add 5000 to both sides.

$$35000 = 1240b$$

$$\frac{35000}{1240} = \frac{1240b}{1240}$$ Divide both sides by 1240.

$$28.226 = b$$

The algebra once again came out with a decimal answer so we would need to round to the whole number of bikes that will produce the desired profit. That would give us 29 bikes produced in a month. This is not possible since the problem stated that the company could only produce a maximum of 20 bikes per month. Therefore the correct answer is that the company cannot make $30,000 profit in a month with its current production capacity.

This last example shows that you need to check each answer to determine if it is a reasonable solution or not. Many times this is something that only requires some common sense and other times a restriction stated in the problem will need to be considered.

We use formulas in many areas of our lives. These formulas are set up to calculate a value given certain values of other types. For example $D = rt$ is a formula to calculate the distance traveled when you are given the rate at which you are traveling and for how long (time) you traveled that rate. This formula can be re-arranged (solved) for one of the other variables in order to make it easier to use to find rate if you know the distance and time or find the time if you know the distance and rate. Solving formulas for other variables works the same way that other solving does except that many of the calculations will not be able to be completed until values for the variables are known.

Example 4

Solve the following formulas for the variable indicated.

a. $D = rt$ for r.

b.   Distance in Free-fall: $D = \frac{1}{2}Gt^2$ for G.

c. $y = mx + b$ for m.

Solution

a.   Since r is being multiplied by t we need to divide both sides by t.

$$D = rt$$

$$\frac{D}{t} = \frac{rt}{t} \qquad \text{Divide both sides by } t.$$

$$\frac{D}{t} = r$$

b.   We want to solve for G.

$$D = \frac{1}{2}Gt^2$$

$$2D = 2\left(\frac{1}{2}Gt^2\right) \qquad \text{Multiply both sides by 2 to remove the } 1/2.$$

$$2D = Gt^2$$

$$\frac{2D}{t^2} = \frac{Gt^2}{t^2} \qquad \text{Divide both sides by } t \text{ squared.}$$

$$\frac{2D}{t^2} = G$$

c.   We want to solve for m so we will need to isolate the term with m and then divide both sides by x.

$$y = mx + b$$
$$\underline{-b \qquad\qquad -b}$$
$$y - b = mx$$

Subtract b from both sides to isolate the mx term. Since y and b are not the same variable we cannot subtract them but must leave the left side as $y - b$.

$$\frac{y - b}{x} = \frac{mx}{x}$$

Divide both sides by x to isolate the m.

$$\frac{y - b}{x} = m$$

Problem 3

Solve the following for the indicated variable.

a.   Velocity in Free-fall: $V = Gt$ for t.

b.   Velocity: $v = v_o + at$ for a. (note v_o is the initial velocity)

Solution   See page 8

Section 1.1 Problem Solutions

Problem 1   Solution

a. Substitute 150 for s and solve for P.[

$$P = 35 - 0.07s$$

$$P = 35 - 0.07(150)$$

$$P = 35 - 10.5$$

$$P = 24.5$$

The pressure inside the vacuum chamber will be 24.5psi after 150 seconds.

b. Substitute 1 for P and solve for s.

$$P = 35 - 0.07s$$

$$1 = 35 - 0.07s$$

$$\underline{-35 \quad -35} \qquad\qquad \text{Subtract 35 from both sides.}$$

$$-34 = -0.07s$$

$$\frac{-34}{-0.07} = \frac{-0.07s}{-0.07} \qquad\qquad \text{Divide both sides by -0.07.}$$

$$485.714 = s$$

It will take 485.7 seconds to pump the vacuum chamber down to 1psi.

Problem 2   Solution

a. Define the variables

C = Rockapella's total cost, in dollars of producing n, CD's.

n = Number of CD's produced by Rockapella.

It cost \$1.50 per CD plus the additional \$1500 for the production of the master recording.

$$C = 1.50n + 1500$$

b. Substitute 250 for n and solve for C.

$$C = 1.50n + 1500$$

$$C = 1.50(250) + 1500$$

$$C = 1875$$

The total cost for Rockapella to produce 250 Cd's will be \$1875.

c. Substitute 2000 for C and solve for n.

$$C = 1.5n + 1500$$

$$2000 = 1.5n + 1500$$

$$\underline{-1500 \qquad\qquad -1500} \qquad\qquad \text{Subtract 1500 from both sides.}$$

$$500 = 1.5n$$

$$\frac{500}{1.5} = \frac{1.5n}{1.5} \qquad\qquad \text{Divide both sides by 1.5.}$$

$$333.33 = n$$

Rockapella can make up to 333 CD's for \$2000.

Problem 3   Solution

a.

$$V = Gt$$

$$\frac{V}{G} = \frac{Gt}{G} \qquad \text{Divide both sides by } G.$$

$$\frac{V}{G} = t$$

b.

$$v = v_0 + at$$

$$\underline{\quad -v_0 \qquad\qquad -v_0 \quad} \qquad \text{Subtract } v_0 \text{ from both sides.}$$

$$v - v_0 = at$$

$$\frac{v - v_0}{t} = \frac{at}{t} \qquad \text{Divide both sides by } t.$$

$$\frac{v - v_0}{t} = a$$

1.1 Exercises

1. The number of homicides, N, of 15-19 year-olds in the U.S. t years after 1990, can be represented by the equation $N = -315.9t + 4809.8$

   source: Based on data from Statistical Abstract 2001

   a. Find the number of homicides of 15-19 year-olds in the U.S. in 1992. (1992 is 2years after 1990 so $t = 2$)

   b. Find the number of homicides of 15-19 year-olds in the U.S. in 2002.

   c. When was the number of homicides 7337?

2. The number of students who are enrolled in math classes at a local college can be represented by $E = -17w + 600$ where E represents the math class enrollment at the college w weeks after the start of the Fall semester.

   a. Find the total enrollment in math classes at the college at the beginning of the Fall semester. (hint since the semester is just starting $w = 0$)

   b. What week will the total enrollment be 430 students?

   c. What will the total enrollment be in math classes after 8 weeks?

3. The gasoline prices in Southern California can increase very quickly during the summer months. The following equation represents the gasoline prices p in dollars per gallon w weeks after the beginning of summer. $p = 1.299 + 0.03w$

   a. What does gasoline cost after 5 weeks of summer?

   b. When will gasoline cost $1.66 per gallon?

4. $P = 20.5b - 500.5$ represents the profit in dollars from selling b books.

   a. How much profit will you earn if you sell 25 books?

   b. How much profit will you earn if you sell 50 books?

   c. How many books must you sell in order to make $3600 in profit?

5. Sales people often work for commissions on the sales that they make for the company. As a new salesperson at a local technology company you are told you will make an 8% commission on all sales you make after the first $1000. Your pay can be represented by $p = 0.08(s - 1000)$ dollars when s is the amount of sales you make in dollars.

   a. How much will you earn from $2000 in sales?

   b. How much will you earn from $50,000 in sales?

   c. If you need at least $500 per week to pay your bills, what sales do you need per week?

6. After calling U-Hual truck rental you decided to compare their prices to Budget truck rental. Budget charges $29.95 for the day and $0.55 per mile driven to rent a 15ft moving truck.

   source: Budget.com

   a. Let B be the cost of renting a 15ft moving truck from Budget for a day and driving the truck m miles. Find an equation for the cost of renting from Budget.

   b. How much would it cost to rent a 15ft truck from Budget if you were to drive it 75 miles?

   c. How many miles could you drive the truck if you could only pay $100 for the rental?

7. A local cell phone company has a pay as you talk plan that cost $10 per month and $0.20 per minute you talk on the phone.

   a. Write an equation for the total monthly cost C of this plan if you talk for m minutes.

   b. Use your equation to determine the total monthly cost of this plan if you talk for 200 minutes.

   c. How many minutes did you talk on the phone if your bill for June was $37?

8. If you are in sales and guaranteed $250 per week plus a 7% commission on all your sales find the following:

   a. Write an equation for your pay per week, P, if you make s dollars of sales.

   b. What will your pay be if you have sales of $4000?

   c. How many dollars of sales do you need to make in order to have a weekly pay of $750?

9. You are planning a trip to Las Vegas and need to calculate your expected costs for the trip. You found that you can take a tour bus trip for up to 7 days and it will cost you $125 for the round trip. You figure that you can stay at a hotel and eat for about $100 per day.

   a. Write an equation for the total cost of this trip depending on the number of days you stay. (We will ignore the gambling budget)

   b. How much will it cost for a 3 day trip?

   c. If you have $700 and want to gamble half of it how many days can you stay in Las Vegas, assuming you do not win any money?

10. A professional photographer has several costs involved in taking pictures at an event such as a wedding. The film cost about $3.39 per roll and costs about $15 per roll to develop the proofs. The photographer also has to pay salaries for the day of $500.

   a. Find an equation for the total cost to shoot a wedding depending on the number of rolls of film used.

b. How much will it cost if the photographer shoots 15 rolls of film?

c. How many rolls of film can the photographer shoot if the total cost cannot exceed a budget of $750?

11. The photographer from the previous problem charges her clients a $45 fee per roll of film plus a flat fee of $400 for the wedding.

   a. Find an equation for the total revenue for shooting the wedding depending on the number of rolls of film used.

   b. How much will the photographer charge the client for a wedding that she shot 15 rolls of film for?

   c. Find an equation for the profit made by the photographer depending on the number of rolls of film used.

   d. How much profit will the photographer make on a wedding that she shot 15 rolls of film for?

   e. How many rolls of film must the photographer shoot in order to break-even? (break-even means profit = 0)

12. Enviro-Safe Pest Management charges new clients $150 for an in home inspection and initial treatment for ants. Each month pre-planned treatments cost $38.

   a. Find an equation for the total cost for pest management from Enviro-Safe Pest Management depending on the number of months your house is treated.

   b. If your house has an initial treatment and then is treated for 11 more months how much will Enviro-Safe charge you?

13. The population of the United States during the 1990's can be estimated by the equation $P = 2.57t + 249.78$, where P is the population in millions t years since 1990.

   source: Based on data from Statistical Abstract 2001

   a. What was the population of the United States in 1993?

   b. When was the population of the United States 270,000,000?

   c. When did the population of the United States reach 300 million?

14. A small golf club manufacturer is concerned about their monthly costs. The workshop costs $23,250 per month to run in addition to the $145 in materials per set of irons produced.

   a. Find an equation for the monthly cost of this club manufacturer.

   b. What are the monthly costs for this company if they make 100 sets of irons?

c. How many sets of irons does this manufacturer need to produce for their costs to be $20,000?

d. If this company wants to break-even making 100 sets of irons per month, what should they charge for each set?

15. The percent P of companies that are still in business t years after the fifth year in operation can be represented by the equation.

$$P = -3t + 50$$

   a. What percent of companies are still in business after 1 year in operation?

   b. What percent of companies are still in business after 25 years in operation?

   c. After how many years are there only 35% of companies still in business?

Math

Tutorial

More practice problems like exercises 16 through 30 can be found in section 1.1 of the CD Tutorial.

For exercises 16 through 30 solve each equation.

16. $5x + 60 = 2x + 90$

17. $1.25d - 3.4 = -2.3(5d + 4)$

18. $\frac{2}{5}d + 6 = 14$

19. $3(c + 5) - 21 = 107$

20. $5k + 7 = 2(6k - 14) + 56$

21. $-3x - 6 = 14 + 8x$

22. $1.7d + 5.7 = 29.7 + 5d$

23. $\frac{1}{3}m + \frac{4}{3} = 4$

24. $\frac{3}{7}(2z - 5) = \frac{4}{7}(-3z + 9)$

25. $2.1m + 3.4 = 7.2 - 9.4m$

26. $-3(2v + 9) - 3(3v - 7) = 4v + 6(2v - 8)$

27. $\frac{5}{7}d - \frac{3}{10} = \frac{4}{7}d + 4$

28. $4.5w - 3.25 = 7.5$

29. $-\frac{8}{9}(3t + 5) = \frac{2}{3}t - 12$

30. $5r - 9 = 18r + 2$

For exercises 31 through 40 solve for the indicated variable.

31. Force: $F = ma$ for a.

32. Weight (N): $W = mg$ for m.

33. Impulse: $J = Ft$ for F.

34. Angular Acceleration: $\omega = \omega_0 + \alpha t$ for α (note ω is the Greek symbol omega and α is the Greek symbol alpha.)

35. $y = mx + b$ for b.

36. Rotational kinetic energy (J): $K = \frac{1}{2}I\omega^2$ for I.

37. Elastic potential energy (J): $U = \frac{1}{2}kx^2$ for k.

38. Kinetic energy (J): $K = \frac{1}{2}mv^2$ for m.

39. $ax + by = c$ for y.

40. $ax + 5 = y$ for x.

Section 1.2   Using Data to Create Scattergrams

• Using Data to Create Scattergrams • Intercepts • Domain and Range • Graphical Models

Data is collected in many ways and places around us. Grocery stores collect data on how and what we buy in their store. Scientists collect data during experiments to study different characteristics of the subject. Historians collect data in order to study trends in past events. The Center of Disease Control (CDC) collects data on cases of infectious diseases in order to predict when an outbreak has occurred or how dangerous a virus might be. Governments collect population data to predict future trends in public funds and needs for services.

After data is collected it needs to be organized and presented in a useful form. Most data is organized as a table.

Example 1

Table 1.2.1

Year	Number of Deaths
1994	3532
1995	3262
1996	2894
1997	2601
1998	2283
1999	2093

source: Center for Disease Control and Prevention (CDC)

This table alone does not give enough information about the context of the situation to be of much help. The number of deaths in this table could represent many different things. Some possibilities may include:

• Number of Deaths due to jay-walking.

• Number of Deaths caused by poisoning.

• Number of Deaths of bears living in Canada.

• Number of Homicides of 15-19 year olds in the United States.

This data was collected by the Center for Disease Control and Prevention and actually does represents the number of homicides of 15-19 year olds in the United States.

Although a table is useful to display data sometimes it is better to graph the data giving a more visual picture of the situation. To do this we first define the variables involved and determine which variable depends on the other. In cases like renting a U-haul truck and driving it m miles for the day it is clear that the cost U depends on how many miles you drive the truck. In many cases it is not as clear which variable depends on the other. You may find that it is often easier to determine which variable is independent rather than dependent. In the Number of Deaths data given in **Table 1.2.1** we could define the following variables:

N = Number of Homicides of 15-19 year olds in the U. S.

t = Year

Since the year does not depend on the number of homicides committed we would call t the **independent variable** (input variable), thus making N the **dependent variable** (output variable). Someone might say that N depends on t. It is important to note that the number of homicides are not caused by what year it is but the number of homicides depends on what year you are wanting to discuss.

Say What?

The following words or phrases all mean the same thing. We will discuss some of these in later sections.

Independent Variable:
• independent variable
• input variable
• input
• domain value
• usually x

Dependent Variable:
• dependent variable
• output variable
• output
• range value
• usually y

Scattergram:
• scattergram
• scatterplot
• statplot

Now that we know which variable depends on the other we can build a **scattergram**. The independent variable is usually placed on the horizontal axis and the dependent variable on the vertical axis. It is best to label each axis with at least the units for each variable being represented.

The next thing that needs to be decided is the **scale** (spacing) for each axis. Please note that the scale does not need to be the same on the horizontal and vertical axis. The scale must remain equal on any one axis. For the horizontal axis, representing the year, the scale can be 1 and start at about 1990, and for the vertical axis, representing the number of deaths, the scale could be 200 starting at about 2000. This results in **Graphic 1.2.1**.

Graphic 1.2.1

Homicides of 15-19 Year Olds in the U.S.

You should notice that both axes in this case do not start at 0 so a zig-zag pattern is placed at the beginning of the axis to show a jump in the numbering. This is a valid way of making the graph easier to create but it does distort how the relationship looks. With this scale the decrease in homicides appears very steep. Using a different scale would cause this same decrease to appear much less drastic. By adjusting the definitions of the variables and the data you can get a accurate graph that is not distorted. One option for such changes would be

N = Number of Homicides of 15-19 year olds in the U. S. (in thousands)

t = Time in years since 1990

This change will result in the following adjusted data:

Table 1.2.2

t	N
4	3.532
5	3.262
6	2.894
7	2.601
8	2.283
9	2.093

This type of change allows for smaller labels on the axes and often a more readable graph. The years have been based on the year 1990 being year 0. You can choose any year you would like for the base year in a problem. This base year only gives you a place to start counting from it does not determine the starting year of the data. Choosing a "nice" year like 1990 or 1980 makes it easier to figure out what each number represents. For example for a base year 1990 t = 7 represents 1997, for a base year 1980, 1997 would have been represented by t = 17.

Be careful that once you define your variables you stay consistent with the values you use for each variable.

The above change in data will result in **Graphic 1.2.2**. Both of these graphs are reasonable but **Graphic 1.2.2** is easier to read and will be easier to use in the future.

Graphic 1.2.2

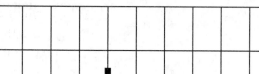

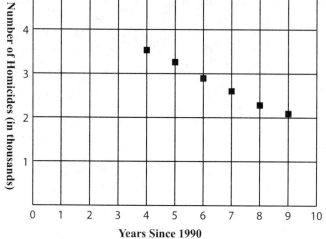

Problem 1

The state of Arizona's population for various years is given in the table.

Table 1.2.3

Year	Population of Arizona
1990	3679056
1991	3762394
1992	3867333
1993	3993390
1994	4147561
1995	4306908
1996	4432308
1997	4552207
1998	4667277
1999	4778332

source: U.S. Census Bureau

a.   Define variables for this data.

b.   Adjust the data.

c.   Create a scattergram.

Solution   see page 18

The data shown thus far would be considered **linearly related**, because the data generally falls along the path of a straight line. In the next example we will draw an "Eye-ball Best Fit" line through the data points on the scattergram. This is best done with a small clear ruler and you want to choose a line that comes as close to all the points plotted as possible. The points that miss the line should be equally spread out above and below the line. This will allow for each missing point to be balanced out by anther missing point.

Example 2

a. Using the data in **Table 1.2.2** draw a scattergram of the data and draw an "Eye-ball Best Fit" line through the data.

b. Using your "Eye-ball Best Fit" line make a prediction for the number of homicides of 15-19 year olds in 1993.

Solution

a. See **Graphic 1.2.3**

Graphic 1.2.3

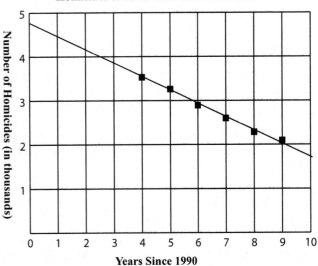

Homicides of 15-19 Year Olds in the U.S.

Number of Homicides (in thousands)

Years Since 1990

Remember that the "Eye-ball Best Fit" line will not necessarily hit any points on the graph but will be as close to ALL the points as possible. This line can be considered a **graphical model** of the data. A mathematical model is used to gain additional information about the situation described by the data. Models may also be used to make predictions beyond the given data.

b. We may want to estimate the number of homicides in 1993. From the graph we can see that in 1993 the number of homicides was approximately 3.8 thousand (slightly less than 4 thousand).

Problem 2

Draw an "Eye-ball Best Fit" line for the Population of Arizona data you graphed in **Problem 1**.

Solution   see page 19

The points that a graph crosses the axes are called **intercepts**. The **vertical intercept** (or N - intercept in this case) for **Graphic 1.2.3** is about (0, 4.75). This means that when $t = 0$, $N = 4.75$. This can be translated, "In 1990 there were about 4,750 homicides of 15-19 year olds in the United States". An intercept can be recognized by the fact that one variable will always be equal to zero. The **horizontal intercept** (or t - intercept) for this graph cannot be seen since the line never reaches the t - axis. To see the t - intercept you will need to expand the values on the horizontal axis and extend the line until it reaches the t - axis. This is one reason to make your graph extend past the data given in the problem.

Say What?
The following words or phrases all mean the same thing.

Vertical Intercept:
Where the graph crosses the vertical axis.
- vertical intercept
- y - intercept
- Can take on the name of the variable representing the vertical axis, such as N - intercept in example 2.

Dependent Variable:
Where the graph crosses the horizontal axis.
- horizontal intercept
- x - intercept
- Can take on the name of the variable representing the horizontal axis, such as t - intercept in example 2.

Definition 1.2.1

Vertical Intercept: Where the graph crosses the vertical axis.
   This will always occur when the input variable is zero.

Horizontal Intercept: Where the graph crosses the horizontal axis.
   This will always occur when the output variable is zero.

The values of the independent variable (inputs) that result in reasonable values for the dependent variable (outputs) are considered the **domain** of the model. The resulting outputs from a given domain are called the **range** of the model. When using an "Eye-ball Best Fit" line that you have drawn on a scattergram the domain and range will be estimated according to the graph and what you are comfortable with. This means that every student's domain and range may be different but still equally correct. Since a model is usually meant to be used to predict a future or past value the domain should extend beyond the data whenever reasonable. The main thing you will want to avoid is model breakdown. Model breakdown is when a domain value results in an output that cannot make sense in the context of the situation or cannot be used mathematically. In this course rarely will you find any input values that could not be used mathematically but you will find many input values that will result in outputs that do not make sense in the context.

Definition 1.2.2

Domain and Range of a Model

Domain: The values of the independent variable which will result in reasonable output values and no model breakdown. Input values that are reasonable.

Range: The values of the dependent variable resulting from the given domain values. The outputs that come from the given domain's input values.

Model Breakdown: When input values give you outputs that could not make sense in the context of the problem.

Example 3

The price of a share of Johnson and Johnson (JNJ) stock has been rising on a very consistent pace since the early 90's. The following table gives share prices (in dollars) for Johnson and Johnson stock on the first trading day of the year.

Table 1.2.4

Year	Share Price ($)
1994	11.3125
1995	16.325
1996	21.91
1997	25.125
1998	32.53
1999	41.31
2000	44.41
2001	48.31
2002	58.14

source: BigCharts.Marketwatch.com

a. Create a scattergram for this data and draw an "Eye-ball Best Fit" line through the data.

b. Determine the t - intercept for this model and explain its meaning in this context.

c. Find a reasonable domain and range for this model.

d. According to your model what is a reasonable JNJ stock price for the beginning of 2003?

Solution

a. First we need to define the variables.
P = Price per share of Johnson and Johnson Stock (in dollars) on the first day of trading t years since 1990.
t = Time in years since 1990.
We use the year 1990 because it is an easy year to count from and will make the input values smaller. The outputs are already reasonable so no adjustment is needed.

Table 1.2.5

t	P
4	11.3125
5	13.625
6	21.91
7	25.125
8	32.53
9	41.34
10	44.41
11	48.31
12	58.14

Graphic 1.2.4

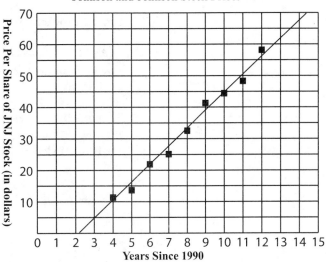

b. The t - intercept for this model is when the line crosses the t - axis (horizontal axis) at approximately (2.25,0). The 2.25 represents early 1992 and the 0 represents a stock price of $0. Together this means that in early 1992 the stock price for JNJ was $0. This does not make any sense in this context since Johnson and Johnson is a large long standing company, so we must have model breakdown.

c. Since this model does a reasonable job representing this data we should be able to extend the domain beyond the given data. One possible domain for this model would be [3, 14]. The range that results from that model would be the prices the model predicts for this stock between the years 1993 and 2004. From the graph we can estimate that the lowest price represented during those years is about $5 and the highest price represented is about $67. This results in a range of [5, 67].

d. 2003 would be represented by $t = 13$ and according to the graph the model is at approximately $62.50 when $t = 13$. Thus in 2003 you could expect the price per share of Johnson and Johnson stock to be about $62.50.

Domain and range are essential parts of any model and help the user of that model know when it is appropriate to use that model and when it is not. Be sure to pay special attention in the coming sections to any domain and range questions and examples.

Section 1.2 Key Points

- Define your variables carefully and with proper units.
- The independent variable holds the input values and is related to the domain.
- The dependent variable holds the output values and is related to the range. The dependent variable is determined by the value of the independent variable.
- The intercepts are where the graph crosses the axes and will always have zero as part of their coordinates.
- Domain will usually be determined first based on the data given and whether it is reasonable to expand beyond the input values of the data.
- Range on a graphical model will be estimated from the graph and will start at the lowest output value on the graph and go to the highest output value based on the domain..

Section 1.2 Problem Solutions

Problem 1   Solution

There are many possible correct answers, only one of these possibilities is given here.

a. To make the values easier to plot we can define the variables as
P = The population of Arizona (in millions)
t = Time in years since 1990

b. Using these definitions both the input and output values will need to be adjusted.

Table 1.2.6

t	Population of Arizona (in millions)
0	3.679
1	3.762
2	3.867
3	3.993
4	4.148
5	4.307
6	4.432
7	4.552
8	4.667
9	4.778

Problem 1   *Solution Continued*
c.   Graphic 1.2.5

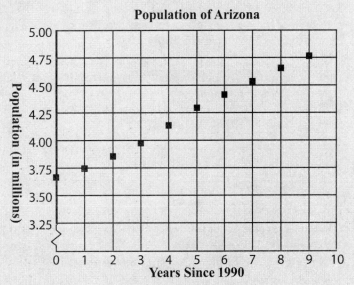

Problem 2   *Solution*
a.   Graphic 1.2.6

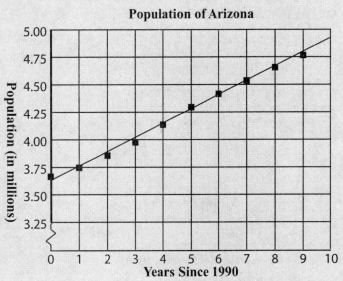

1.2 Exercises

1. Quiksilver Inc., the makers of the Quiksilver and Roxy clothing lines, has had steadily increasing profits over the past several years. The profits for Quicksilver Inc. are given in **Table 1.2.7**

Table 1.2.7

Year	Profits for Quiksilver Inc. (in millions of dollars)
1998	126.7
1999	175.6
2000	199.8
2001	232.7

source: CBS.Marketwatch.com

   a. Define the variables for this problem.
   b. Adjust the data if needed.
   c. Create a scattergram and draw an "Eye-ball Best Fit" line through the data.
   d. Using your graphical model estimate the profit for Quiksilver Inc. in 2003.
   e. What is a reasonable domain and range for your graphical model?

2. The population of the United States throughout the 90's is given in **Table 1.2.8**

Table 1.2.8

Year	Population of the U.S. (in millions)
1990	249.46
1991	252.15
1992	255.03
1993	257.78
1994	260.33
1995	262.80
1996	265.23
1997	267.78
1998	270.25
1999	272.69

source: U.S. Census Bureau

   a. Define the variables for this problem.
   b. Adjust the data if needed.
   c. Create a scattergram and draw an "Eye-ball Best Fit" line through the data.
   d. Using your graphical model estimate the population of the U.S. in 2000.
   e. What is a reasonable domain and range for your graphical model?
   f. What is the vertical intercept for your model and what does it mean in this context?

3. The percentage of events won on the Senior Golf Tour by 50 - 52 year olds during certain five year periods is given in **Table 1.2.9** (note: you will want to adjust the data carefully. i.e. 85 - 89 could be represented by the middle year 87.)

Table 1.2.9

Years	Percentage of Events Won
1985 - 1989	54.9
1990 - 1994	52.4
1995 - 1999	50.8
2000 - 2002	48.9

source: Golf Magazine Sept. 2002

   a. Define the variables for this problem.
   b. Adjust the data if needed.
   c. Create a scattergram and draw an "Eye-ball Best Fit" line through the data.
   d. Using your graphical model estimate the percentage of Senior Tour events 50 - 52 year olds will win between 2005 and 2009.
   e. What is a reasonable domain and range for your graphical model?

4. The stock prices for International Business Machines, IBM, for various years are given in **Table 1.2.10**

Table 1.2.10

Year	1996	1997	1998	2001
Stock Price ($)	22.72	38.31	52.81	84.81

source: Bigcharts.Marketwatch.com

   a. Create a graphical model for this data. (remember to define variables)
   b. Using your model estimate the stock price for IBM in 2000.
   c. What year did the stock price for IBM reach $65?
   d. What is a reasonable domain and range for your graphical model?

5. The death rate (per 100,000 people) for motor vehicle related injuries for males in the U.S., for various years is given in **Table 1.2.11**

Table 1.2.11

Year	1995	1996	1997	1999
Death Rate	23.1	22.8	22.4	21.8

source: CDC

   a. Find a graphical model for this data.
   b. According to your model when will the Death Rate be approximately 20 deaths per 100,000 people.
   c. What is a reasonable domain and range for your model.
   d. What does your model predict the death rate to be in 1998?
   e. What is the vertical intercept for your model and what does it mean in this context?

In exercises 6 through 9 use the graph to answer the questions.

6.

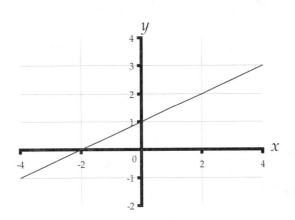

a. Estimate the vertical intercept.
b. Estimate the horizontal intercept.
c. Estimate the input value that makes the output of this graph equal 1.5.
d. Estimate the input value that makes the output of this graph equal -1.
e. Estimate the output value of this graph when the input value is 3.

7.

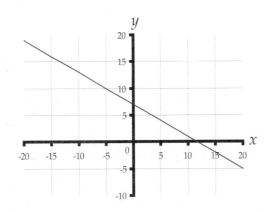

a. Estimate the vertical intercept.
b. Estimate the horizontal intercept.
c. Estimate the input value that makes the output of this graph equal 15.
d. Estimate the input value that makes the output of this graph equal -2.
e. Estimate the output value of this graph when the input value is -10.

8.

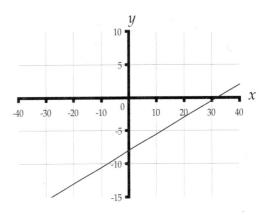

a. Estimate the y-intercept.
b. Estimate the x-intercept.
c. Estimate the value of x that results in $y = -5$.
d. Estimate the value of x that results in $y = -10$.
e. Estimate the value of y when $x = 20$

9.

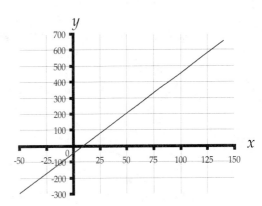

a. Estimate the x-intercept.
b. Estimate the y-intercept.
c. Estimate the value of x that results in $y = 500$.
d. Estimate the value of x that results in $y = -200$.
e. Estimate the value of y when $x = 100$.

Section 1.3   Introduction to Linear Equations

• Slope and its Meaning • Finding Equations of Lines • Graphing Lines by Hand

In section 1.2 we created scattergrams of data by hand and drew an "Eyeball Best Fit" line on that scattergram to give us an approximate graphical model for the data and situation we were considering. Although the graphical model is useful to estimate some values it is often easier to find values for a model if we know an algebraic equation for it. In this section we will investigate the different characteristics of a linear equation and its graph. We will also learn to find linear equations and graph them by hand.

We are going to do a few Concept Investigations in order to see some of the characteristics of a line and how they are related to the equation of a line.

Concept Investigation 1

Use your graphing calculator to examine the following.
Start by setting up your calculator by doing the following steps.

i   Change the window to a standard window. (press [zoom], [6](ZStandard))

ii   Clear all equations from the Y= screen. (press [Y=], [CLEAR])

Now your calculator is ready to graph equations. The Y= screen is where equations will be put into the calculator to graph them or evaluate them at input values. We are now going to graph several simple equations in order to investigate how the graph of an equation for a line reacts to changes in the equation. (Note that your calculator uses y as the dependent (output) variable and x as the independent (input) variable.)

a. Graph the following equations on a standard window. Enter each equation in its own row (Y1, Y2, Y3, ...)

    i $y = x$ (note: To enter an x you use the [X,T,θ ,n] key next to the green [ALPHA] key.)

    ii $y = 2x$

    iii $y = 5x$

    iv $y = 8x$

In your own words describe what the coefficient (number in front) of x does to the graph.

b. Now graph the following equations that have negative coefficients.

    i $y = -x$

    ii $y = -2x$

    iii $y = -5x$

    iv $y = -8x$

In your own words describe what a negative coefficient of x does to the graph.

c. Graph the following equations with coefficients that are between zero and one.

i $y = x$

ii $y = \dfrac{1}{5}x$

iii $y = \dfrac{1}{2}x$

iv $y = \dfrac{2}{3}x$

v $y = 0.9x$

Describe in your own words what a coefficient of x between zero and one does to the graph.

These three sets of graphs demonstrate the concept of **slope** of a line. Slope can be described in several ways and is basically the direction or steepness of the line. The graph of a line will have the same steepness (direction) over the entire graph. When considering slope or direction of a graph always look from Left to Right. Here are some ways of thinking about slope of a line.

- The steepness of a line

- The direction a line is traveling in (left to right).

- How fast something is changing.

   In mathematics we calculate the slope of a line as a ratio (fraction) of the vertical change and horizontal change. This ratio must stay constant no matter where on the line you are. Change in mathematics is the difference between two quantities or variables and is calculated by subtraction. This concept results in some of the following ways to remember how to calculate the slope of a line. m is often the letter that is used to represent the slope of a line.

- $m = \dfrac{\text{rise}}{\text{run}}$ The vertical rise divided by the horizontal run.

- $m = \dfrac{\text{change in outputs}}{\text{change in inputs}}$

- $m = \dfrac{\text{change in } y}{\text{change in } x} = \dfrac{\Delta y}{\Delta x}$ (note: the symbol Δ means change)

- $m = \dfrac{y_2 - y_1}{x_2 - x_1}$ where (x_1, y_1) and (x_2, y_2) are two distinct points on the line.

All of these descriptions can be used to remember the idea of slope and how to calculate it. If you use one of the word descriptions, remember that change in mathematics is most often measured using subtraction. When interpreting the slope of a model remember that slope is a measurement of how fast something is changing.

In particular the slope measures the increase, or decrease in the output variable for a unit change in the input variable. This is often stated as the increase, or decrease in y for a unit change in x.

Definition 1.3.1

Slope:
- The ratio of the vertical change and horizontal change of a line.
- The increase or decrease in y for a unit change in x.
- For a line going through the two distinct points (x_1, y_1) and (x_2, y_2)

$$\text{slope} = \frac{\text{change in } y}{\text{change in } x} = \frac{\text{rise}}{\text{run}} = \frac{y_2 - y_1}{x_2 - x_1}$$

- In a context slope represents the amount the output variable is changing for every unit change in the input variable.

Example 1

a. Estimate the slope of the line shown in the graph

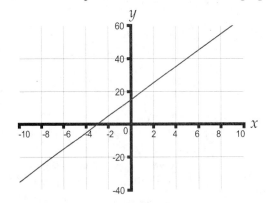

b. Estimate the slope of the line shown in the graph

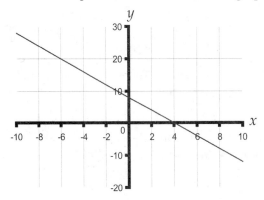

c. Find the slope of the line passing through the points given in the table.
   Table 1.3.1

x	y
0	5
1	9
2	13
3	17
4	21

d. Find the slope of the line passing through the points given in the table.

Table 1.3.2

x	y
0	20
2	14
4	8
6	2
8	-4

Solution

a. Reading the graph it appears that the points $(1, 20)$ and $(5, 40)$ lie on the line.

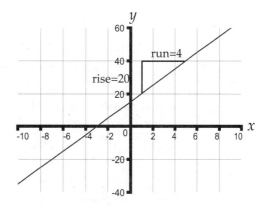

Using these two points we can see that the rise is 20 when the run is 4. This gives us a slope of $m = \dfrac{20}{4} = 5$. If we picked another set of points on this line we should get the same slope. Since this line is going up from left to right it confirms that the slope should be positive. We say this line is increasing.

b. Reading this graph it appears that the points $(-6, 20)$ and $(4, 0)$ lie on the line.

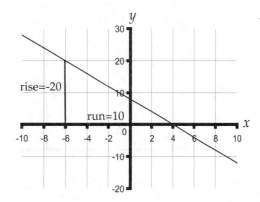

Using these points we can see that the rise is -20 when the run is 10. This gives us a slope of $m = \dfrac{-20}{10} = -2$. This could also have been calculated using the formula for slope resulting in

$$m = \frac{20 - 0}{-6 - 4} = \frac{20}{-10} = -2$$

Since this line is going down from left to right it confirms that the slope should be negative. We say this line is decreasing.

c.   If we calculate the change in the values given in the table we can find the slope. Since each input is 1 unit more than the next we can subtract each consecutive y value and divide by 1 to find the slope.

Table 1.3.3

x	y	Slope
0	5	
1	9	$\dfrac{9-5}{1} = 4$
2	13	$\dfrac{13-9}{1} = 4$
3	17	$\dfrac{17-13}{1} = 4$
4	21	$\dfrac{21-17}{1} = 4$

Since the change between any two points is the same we know that these points would all lie on a line with a slope of 4.

d.   In this table each input is 2 more than the previous so we will have to divide each output change by the input change of 2.

Table 1.3.4

x	y	Slope
0	20	
2	14	$\dfrac{14-20}{2} = -3$
4	8	$\dfrac{8-14}{2} = -3$
6	2	$\dfrac{2-8}{2} = -3$
8	-4	$\dfrac{-4-2}{2} = -3$

All of the calculations are equal to -3 and thus confirm that these points would all lie on a line with slope -3.

Problem 1

a.   Estimate the slope of the line shown in the graph.

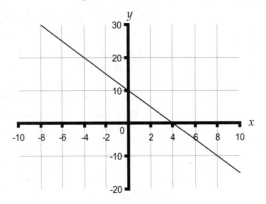

b. Find the slope of the line passing through the points given in the table.
Table 1.3.5

x	y
0	140
5	100
10	60
15	20
20	-20

Solution   See page 34

Next we will investigate another important characteristic of linear equations.

Concept Investigation 2

Start by clearing the equations from the Y= screen.

a. Graph the following equations:

   i $y = x$

   ii $y = x + 1$

   iii $y = x + 2$

   iv $y = x + 3$

   v $y = x + 7$

Describe in your own words what the constant term does to the graph.

b. Graph the following equations:

   i $y = x$

   ii $y = x - 1$

   iii $y = x - 2$

   iv $y = x - 3$

   v $y = x - 7$

Describe what a negative constant term does to the graph.

The constant term of a linear equation in this form represents the vertical intercept of the linear graph. In mathematics we let b represent the vertical intercept. With the slope and vertical intercept an equation of a line can be easily written. Every line can be described with two pieces of information, the slope of the line and a point on the line. Both of these are needed since a slope does not tell you where the line is and a point does not tell you where to go.

An equation for a line can be written in many forms but the **slope-intercept form** is the most common and most useful form. In a graphing calculator the slope-intercept form is the easiest to use. The slope-intercept form of an equation of a line is represented by the equation $y = mx + b$. In this equation m represents the slope of the line and b represents the y - intercept (vertical intercept). The variables x and y are the independent and dependent variables respectively. Any equation that can be simplified into this form is the equation of a line.

> **Slope-Intercept Form of a line:**
> $$y = mx + b$$
> **Slope:** The increase, or decrease in the output variable for a unit change in the input variable.
> The steepness of the line.
> In the slope-intercept form of a line slope is represented by m.
>
> **Vertical Intercept:** where the line crosses the vertical axis.
> In the slope-intercept form of a line the vertical intercept is $(0, b)$. This is often called the y - intercept.

Say What?

Slope:
- slope
- rate of change
- m in the slope-intercept form of a line.

When asked for the slope of the line $y = 4x + 9$ be sure to only give the constant 4 as the slope. The variable x is not part of the slope.

Example 2
Find the slope and y - intercept of the following lines.

a. $y = 2x + 5$

b. $y = \frac{3}{2}x - \frac{7}{2}$

c. $2x + 5y = 20$

Solution

a. The slope is 2 and the y - intercept is $(0, 5)$.

b. The slope is $\frac{3}{2}$ and the y - intercept is $\left(0, -\frac{7}{2}\right)$.

c. This equation should be put into slope-intercept form before we try to read the slope and intercept.
$$2x + 5y = 20$$
$$\underline{-2x \qquad\quad -2x} \qquad \text{Isolate } y.$$
$$5y = -2x + 20$$
$$\frac{5y}{5} = \frac{-2x + 20}{5}$$
$$y = -\frac{2}{5}x + 4$$

Therefore the slope is $-\frac{2}{5}$ and the y - intercept is $(0, 4)$.

Problem 2
Find the slope and y - intercept of the following lines.

a. $y = -3x + 7$

b. $y = \frac{2}{7}x - 8$

c. $3x - 4y = 15$

Solution   See page 35

Using the information gained from the slope-intercept form of a line we can graph linear equations. Use the vertical intercept as a starting point on the line and then use the slope as the direction you should follow to find additional points on the line. Remember that slope is the rise over the run that the line takes from one point to another. Once you have two or three points you can draw the entire line by connecting these points and extending the line in both directions.

Example 3

Sketch the graph of the following lines.

a. $y = 2x + 5$

b. $y = \dfrac{2}{3}x - 2$

c. $3y = 5x - 8$

d. $y = -3x + 2$

Solution

a. The y - intercept is $(0, 5)$ and the slope is $2 = \dfrac{2}{1}$ so the rise is 2 when the run is 1. Using this information we get the following graph.

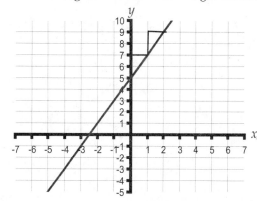

Starting at (0,5) and going up 2 and over 1 we get to (1,7). Doing this again gets us to (2,9). Using these three points we connect the point s and extend the line in both directions.

b. The vertical intercept is $(0, -2)$ and the slope is $\dfrac{2}{3}$ so the rise is 2 when the run is 3. Using this information we get the following graph

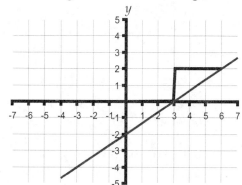

Starting at (0,-2) and going up 2 and over 3 we get to (3,0). Doing this again gets us to (6,2). Using these three points we connect the point s and extend the line in both directions.

c. To start we must isolate the output variable y and put the equation into slope-intercept form.

$$3y = 5x - 8$$

$$\frac{3y}{3} = \frac{5x - 8}{3}$$

$$y = \frac{5}{3}x - \frac{8}{3}$$

The vertical intercept is $\left(0, -\dfrac{8}{3}\right)$ and the slope is $\dfrac{5}{3}$ so the rise is 5 when the run is 3. Using this information we get the following graph

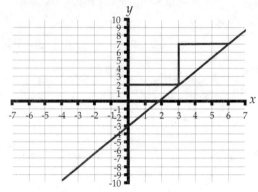

You will need to approximate the location of the intercept and other points from there.

d. The y - intercept is $(0, 2)$ and the slope is $-3 = \dfrac{-3}{1}$ so the rise is -3 when the run is 1. Since the rise is negative the graph will actually go down when looking from left to right. Using this information we get the following graph

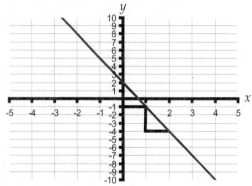

The slope is negative so the graph will go down.

Problem 3
Graph the following lines.

a. $y = 4x - 5$

b. $y = -\dfrac{3}{2}x + 6$

Solution   See page 35

Now that we have learned the basic characteristics of a line and know how to find the slope of a line we can use the slope-intercept form of a line to find the equation of any line we may need. Unless we are given the slope of the line we are looking for we will need two points to find the slope and thus the equation of the line that we want.

Example 4

a. Find the equation of the line that passes through the points $(2, 5)$ and $(4, 9)$.

b. Find the equation of the line that passes through the points in the table

Table 1.3.6

x	y
2	7
4	15
6	23
8	31

c. Find the equation of the line shown in the graph.

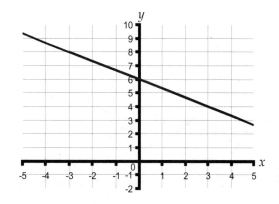

Solution

a. First we can find the slope using the two given points.

$$m = \frac{9-5}{4-2} = \frac{4}{2} = 2$$

Now using the slope and one of the points we can substitute them into the slope-intercept form of a line and find b.

$$y = 2x + b$$
$$5 = 2(2) + b$$
$$5 = 4 + b$$
$$1 = b$$

Now we can substitute the slope and the y - intercept into the slope-intercept form and we will have the equation of the line. $y = 2x + 1$. We can check our equation by substituting in the points we were given and confirm that they are solutions to the equation.

$$y = 2x + 1$$
$$5 = 2(2) + 1 \qquad \text{The point (2,5) is a solution.}$$
$$5 = 5$$

$$9 = 2(4) + 1 \qquad \text{The point (4,9) is also a solution so we have found the}$$
$$9 = 9 \qquad \qquad \text{correct equation for the line.}$$

b. First we can find the slope of the line from the table and then use one of the points listed in the table to find the vertical intercept.

Table 1.3.7

x	y	slope
2	7	
4	15	$\dfrac{15-7}{2} = \dfrac{8}{2} = 4$
6	23	$\dfrac{23-15}{2} = 4$
8	31	$\dfrac{31-23}{2} = 4$

$$y = 4x + b \qquad \text{Substitute the value of the slope in for m.}$$
$$7 = 4(2) + b \qquad \text{Substitute the point (2,7) into the equation and solve}$$
$$7 = 8 + b \qquad \text{for b.}$$
$$-1 = b$$

$$y = 4x - 1 \qquad \text{Write the equation of the line.}$$

We can check this equation by substituting in a couple of points from the table into the equation.

$$y = 4x - 1$$
$$15 = 4(4) - 1 \qquad \text{The point (4,15) is a solution.}$$
$$15 = 15$$

$$23 = 4(6) - 1 \qquad \text{The point (6,23) is also a solution thus we should}$$
$$23 = 23 \qquad \text{have the correct equation for the line.}$$

c. Using the graph we can estimate that the points $(-3, 8)$ and $(3, 4)$ are on the line.

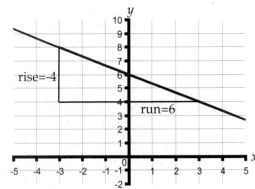

A rise of -4 and run of 6 gives us a slope of $-\frac{2}{3}$

We can also estimates y - intercept to be $(0,6)$.

Using this slope and the estimate for the y - intercept we get the equation $y = -\frac{2}{3}x + 6$. The graph goes in a downward direction so the slope should be negative and the y - intercept seems to be 6 so we should have the correct equation for the line.

> **Steps to find the equation of a line:**
> i   Use two points to calculate the slope.
> ii   Substitute in the slope and use a point to find the vertical intercept, b.
> iii Write the equation
> iv   Check your equation by plugging in the points to be sure they are solutions.

Problem 4

a. Find the equation of the line that passes through the points $(5, 4)$ and $(20, 7)$.

b. Find the equation of the line that passes through the points in the table.

Table 1.3.8

x	y
1	6
4	1
7	-4
10	-9

Solution   See page 36

There are two types of linear equations that are unique. These two types are vertical and horizontal lines. Vertical lines will have an undefined slope since they have no horizontal change. Having no horizontal change and thus a run of zero results in a division by zero which is undefined. The general equation for a vertical line is $x = k$ where k is a constant. Horizontal lines on the other hand will have a slope of zero since there is no vertical change. No vertical change implies the rise is zero and thus when calculating slope you will always get slope equal to zero. The general equation for a horizontal line is $y = k$ where k is a constant.

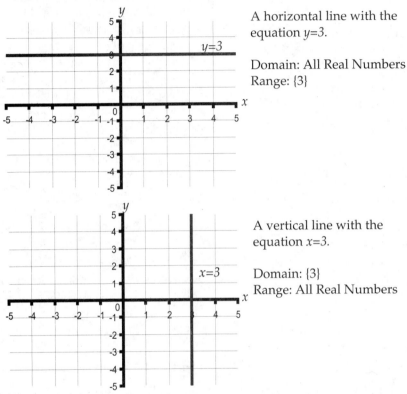

A horizontal line with the equation $y=3$.

Domain: All Real Numbers
Range: {3}

A vertical line with the equation $x=3$.

Domain: {3}
Range: All Real Numbers

The horizontal line $y = k$ will have a domain of All Real Numbers but will have a range of only $\{k\}$. This is because no value of x will affect the output of the function which is always k. A vertical line $x = k$ has a domain and range that is just the reverse. The domain will be $\{k\}$ since that is the only value x can have but the range will be All Real Numbers.

All lines that are not vertical or horizontal and do not involve a context will have the same domain and range. Because any real number can be substituted in for the input variable the domain will be All Real Numbers. The resulting range will also be All Real Numbers since any real number output value can be found if the right input value is given.

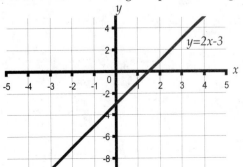

Domain: All Real Numbers
Range: All Real Numbers

Section 1.3 Key Points

- Slope of a line is the steepness of the line.

    - $m = \dfrac{\text{rise}}{\text{run}} = \dfrac{\text{change in outputs}}{\text{change in inputs}} = \dfrac{\text{change in } y}{\text{change in } x}$

        - How fast the quantity is changing.
- Slope-Intercept Form of a line.
    - $y = mx + b$
    - m is the slope of the line.
    - $(0,b)$ is the vertical intercept of the line.
- In a context slope represents the change in the output variable per a change in the input variable
- Steps to find the equation of a line.
    - **i**   Use two points to calculate the slope.
    - **ii** Substitute in the slope and use a point to find the value of b.
    - **iii** Write the equation
    - **iv** Check your equation by plugging in the points to be sure they are solutions.
- The domain and range of a line that is not vertical or horizontal and has no context.
    - Domain: All Real Numbers
    - Range: All Real Numbers
- The domain and range of a vertical line $x = k$
    - Domain: $\{k\}$
    - Range: All Real Numbers
- The domain and range of a horizontal line $y = k$.
    - Domain: All Real Numbers
    - Range: $\{k\}$

Section 1.3 Problem Solutions

Problem 1   Solution

a.

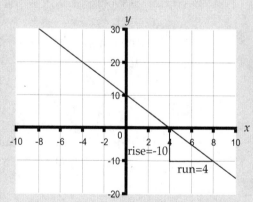

With a rise of -10 and run of 4 we have a slope of $-\dfrac{10}{4} = -\dfrac{5}{2}$

Problem 1   Solution Continued

b. Find the difference between the outputs and divide by the difference between the inputs. In this case each output is 40 less than the previous and each input is 5 greater than the previous. This gives us a slope of -8.

Table 1.3.9

x	y	slope
0	140	
5	100	$\dfrac{100 - 140}{5} = -8$
10	60	$\dfrac{60 - 100}{5} = -8$
15	20	$\dfrac{20 - 60}{5} = -8$
20	-20	$\dfrac{-20 - 20}{5} = -8$

Problem 2   Solution

a. The slope is -3 and the y - intercept is $(0, 7)$.

b. The slope is $\dfrac{2}{7}$ and the y - intercept is $(0, -8)$.

c. We first need to isolate y and put the equation into slope-intercept form.

$$3x - 4y = 15$$

$$\underline{-3x \qquad\qquad -3x}$$

$$-4y = -3x + 15$$

$$\dfrac{-4y}{-4} = \dfrac{-3x + 15}{-4}$$

$$y = \dfrac{3}{4}x - \dfrac{15}{4}$$

The slope is $\dfrac{3}{4}$ and the y - intercept is $\left(0, -\dfrac{15}{4}\right)$

Problem 3   Solution

a. The vertical intercept is -5 so the graph will pass through the point $(0, -5)$. The slope is 4 so the graph will rise 4 for every run of 1.

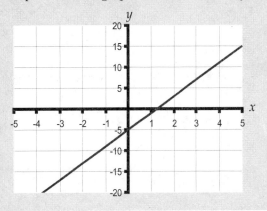

Problem 3   Solution Continued

b. The y - intercept is $(0, 6)$. The slope is $-\dfrac{3}{2}$ so the rise is -3 when the run is 2.

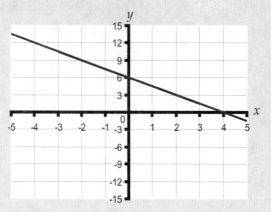

Problem 4   Solution

c.

$$m = \frac{7-4}{20-5} = \frac{3}{15} = \frac{1}{5}$$ Use the two given points to calculate the slope.

$$y = \frac{1}{5}x + b$$ Substitute the slope and use one point to solve for b.

$$7 = \frac{1}{5}(20) + b$$

$$7 = 4 + b$$

$$3 = b$$

$$y = \frac{1}{5}x + 3$$ Write the equation.

$$7 = \frac{1}{5}(20) + 3$$ Check the equation using the two points.

$$7 = 7$$

$$4 = \frac{1}{5}(5) + 3$$

$$4 = 4$$ Both points work so the equation is correct.

Problem 4   Solution Continued

d. Start by using the table to calculate the slope.

Table 1.3.10

x	y	slope
1	6	
4	1	$\dfrac{1-6}{3} = -\dfrac{5}{3}$
7	-4	$\dfrac{-4-1}{3} = -\dfrac{5}{3}$
10	-9	$\dfrac{-9-(-4)}{3} = -\dfrac{5}{3}$

$y = -\dfrac{5}{3}x + b$ Substitute the slope into the slope-intercept form

$6 = -\dfrac{5}{3}(1) + b$ Use another point to solve for b.

$6 + \dfrac{5}{3} = b$

$\dfrac{23}{3} = b$

$y = -\dfrac{5}{3}x + \dfrac{23}{3}$ Write the equation.

$1 = -\dfrac{5}{3}(4) + \dfrac{23}{3}$ Use another point to check the equation.

$1 = -\dfrac{20}{3} + \dfrac{23}{3}$

$1 = 1$

1.3 Exercises

1. Use the graph to find the following:.

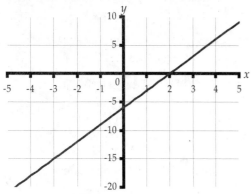

a. Find the slope of the line.
b. Estimate the vertical intercept.
c. Estimate the horizontal intercept.
d. Find the equation of the line.

2. Use the graph to find the following:.

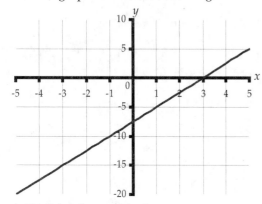

a. Find the slope of the line.
b. Estimate the y-intercept
c. Estimate the x-intercept
d. Find the equation of the line.

3. Use the graph to find the following:.

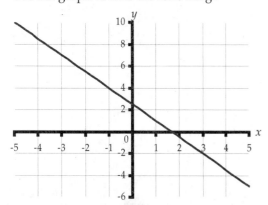

a. Find the slope of the line.
b. Estimate the y-intercept
c. Estimate the x-intercept
d. Find the equation of the line.

4. Use the graph to find the following:.

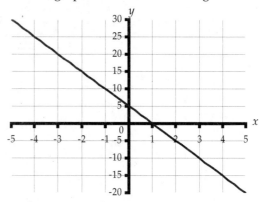

a. Find the slope of the line.
b. Estimate the vertical intercept.
c. Estimate the horizontal intercept.
d. Find the equation of the line.

5. Use the table to find the following:
Table 1.3.11

x	y
0	7
2	11
4	15
6	19
8	23

a. Find the slope of the line passing through the points.
b. Find the y-intercept.
c. Find the equation of the line passing through the points.

6. Use the table to find the following:
Table 1.3.11

x	y
-4	-18
0	-4
4	10
8	24
12	38

a. Find the slope of the line passing through the points.
b. Find the y-intercept.
c. Find the equation of the line passing through the points.

7. Use the table to find the following:
    Table 1.3.11

x	y
-2	29
0	15
2	1
4	-13
6	-27

    a. Find the slope of the line passing through the points.
    b. Find the y-intercept.
    c. Find the equation of the line passing through the points.

8. Use the table to find the following:
    Table 1.3.11

x	y
-3	14.25
0	9
3	3.75
6	-1.5
9	-6.75

    a. Find the slope of the line passing through the points.
    b. Find the y-intercept.
    c. Find the equation of the line passing through the points.

9. Use the table to find the following:
    Table 1.3.11

x	y
2	-18
5	-6
8	6
11	18
14	30

    a. Find the slope of the line passing through the points.
    b. Find the y-intercept.
    c. Find the equation of the line passing through the points.

10. Use the table to find the following:
    Table 1.3.11

x	y
4	7
9	-5.5
14	-18
19	-30.5
24	-43

    a. Find the slope of the line passing through the points.
    b. Find the y-intercept.
    c. Find the equation of the line passing through the points.

11. Find the equation of the line that passes through the points $(3, 5)$ and $(7, 14)$.

12. Find the equation of the line that passes through the points $(-2, 4)$ and $(5, 18)$.

13. Find the equation of the line that passes through the points $(7, 6)$ and $(21, 1)$.

14. Find the equation of the line that passes through the points $(-5, -2)$ and $(-3, -10)$.

For exercises 15 through 35 sketch the graph on graph paper, label the vertical and horizontal intercept. Round your answers to 2 decimal places.

15. $y = 2x - 7$

16. $y = 3x - 12$

17. $y = \frac{4}{5}x - 6$

18. $y = \frac{2}{3}x + 4$

19. $y = -2x + 5$

20. $y = -4x - 3$

21. $y = -\frac{7}{5}x + 11$

22. $y = 0.5x + 4$

23. $y = -0.25x + 2$

24. $y = -\frac{2}{5}x + \frac{3}{5}$

25. $y = \frac{1}{4}x - \frac{3}{4}$

26. $y = -0.75x + 2.5$

27. $2x + 4y = 8$

28. $3x - 5y = 15$

29. $4x + 2y = 20$

30. $-3x + 2y = 16$

31. $-2x - 4y = -20$

32. $y - 5 = 3(x - 4)$

33. $y + 4 = 2(x + 3)$

34. $y - 4 = \frac{1}{2}(x + 1)$

35. $y + 7 = \frac{2}{3}(x - 9)$

Section 1.4   Finding Linear Models

• Using a Calculator to Create Scattergrams • Finding Linear Models

Creating scattergrams by hand can be very tedious, slow and inaccurate. Using some type of technology to help us create scattergrams and investigate models can be a great tool and help. There are many computer programs such as Excel that we can do this with but in this section we will discuss how to create scattergrams on a Texas Instruments TI 83 calculator. We will also begin to find algebraic linear models using the data and these scattergrams. Algebraic models are equations that can represent the graphical model we learned about in section 1.2. These models can be used more accurately and often more easily than a graphical model. In this text the word model will refer to an algebraic model unless otherwise stated.

After you have defined the variables and adjusted the data you are ready to create a scattergram. To create a scattergram, or statplot, on the calculator you need to accomplish the following tasks.

i   Input the adjusted data into the calculator.

ii   Set a window (tell the calculator where to look in order to see the data).

iii   Set up the stat plot and graph it.

Example 1

Create a scattergram for the population data for Arkansas in various years given in **Table 1.4.1**.

Table 1.4.1

Year	Population of Arkansas
1990	2,354,343
1991	2,370,666
1993	2,423,743
1995	2,480,121
1997	2,524,007
1998	2,538,202
1999	2,551,373

source: Census Bureau 2001

Solution

First we will define the variables as

P = The population of Arkansas (in millions)

t = Years since 1990

The adjusted data is in **Table 1.4.2**

Table 1.4.2

t	Population of Arkansas (in millions)
0	2.35
1	2.37
3	2.42
5	2.48
7	2.52
8	2.54
9	2.55

To input this data into the calculator you push the [STAT] button and then [1] (EDIT) for the edit screen. You should get the following two screens.

Graphic 1.4.1.

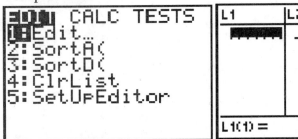

The second screen shows you the first three lists (L1, L2, and L3) in which we can input data. You will see a black cursor in the first list ready for your first input value. Now you just need to enter your first input value and then press [ENTER]. Repeat this for all the input data and then use the right arrow key to move over to list 2 and do this again for the output data.

Graphic 1.4.2

Now that the data is entered the window (graphing area the calculator is going to show you) needs to be set. Press the [WINDOW] button at the top of the calculator and enter Xmin, Xmax, Ymin, and Ymax values. The best way to choose these is as follows:

- Xmin = A slightly smaller value than your smallest input.
- Xmax = A slightly larger value than your largest input.
- Ymin = A slightly smaller value than your smallest output.
- Ymax = A slightly larger value than your largest output

Graphic 1.4.3.

Remember that there are many windows that will show you your data you just need to be sure the min and max are surrounding your data values. Note that Xscl, Yscl , and Xres can all stay 1. Now that the window is fixed we need to set up the statplot and graph it. To set up the statplot we need to press the [STAT PLOT] button which is actually in yellow above the [Y=] button. To activate a yellow feature you need to first press the yellow [2nd] button on the left side of the calculator. If you press [2nd] and then [STAT PLOT] you get the following screen.

Graphic 1.4.4

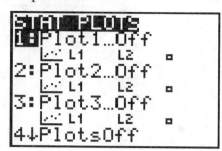

On the STAT PLOT screen you will want to select the plot you want to work with. You can either highlight the plot you want and press [ENTER] or press the number of the plot. By pressing [1] you will get the plot setup screen below.

Graphic 1.4.5

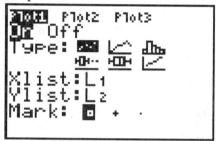

On the plot setup screen you will want to use the arrow keys to move around. First turn the plot on by moving the cursor over the word on and pressing [ENTER]. The the Type of plot should be the first one with dots. The Xlist and Ylist needs to have the titles for the lists that you put your input and output data into respectively. The Mark you use should probably be squares or plus signs. The dot is very hard to read. Once your screen is set like the one above press the [GRAPH] button on the top right corner of the calculator and you should get a scattergram like this

Graphic 1.4.6.

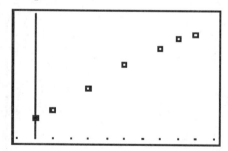

This entire process will get easier with practice and will be a vital part of most problems throughout this textbook.

Problem 1

Practice using the calculator to create scattergrams on the following two sets of data.

a.

Table 1.4.3

r	M
25	972.5
32	1235
37	1422.5
45	1722.5
59	2247.5

b.

Table 1.4.4

g	T
-30	1307
-24	1161.2
-5	699.5
0	578
9	359.2
16	189.2
28	-102.4
37	-321.1
51	-661.3

Table 1.2.1

Year	Number of Deaths
1994	3532
1995	3262
1996	2894
1997	2601
1998	2283
1999	2093

source: Center for Disease Control and Prevention (CDC)

Table 1.4.1

Year	Population of Arkansas
1990	2,354,343
1991	2,370,666
1993	2,423,743
1995	2,480,121
1997	2,524,007
1998	2,538,202
1999	2,551,373

source: Census Bureau 2001

Solution   page 47

Since we are creating scattergrams using the calculator we can not draw by hand an "Eye-ball Best Fit" line on the calculator screen, so we need another method to create a model from our data. In the last section we learned about the slope-intercept of a line and how to find the equation of a line. In perfect linear relationships the data will have an equal amount of change between them. When working with real life data this change should still be somewhat equal but will typically have some variation in it. The number of homicides per year in **Table 1.2.1** were decreasing by about 300 deaths per year. The population of Arkansas data from **Table 1.4.1** was increasing by about 23,270 people per year. These amounts of change are somewhat consistent throughout the data. Although linearly related data will have a fairly consistent amount of change for each equal amount of change in inputs you will need to look at the scattergram in order to pick two points that will make a good "Eye-ball Best Fit" line. Consider the next example to see how the steps from the last section works with scattergrams to help find a linear model and check its reasonableness.

Example 2

Table 1.4.5 gives the stock price for Nike Inc. (NKE) at the beginning of various years. (Note some prices were adjusted for splits in the stock.)

Table 1.4.5

Year	Price Per Share ($)
1993	11.47
1994	18.66
1997	39.75
1998	40.56
1999	49.12
2000	55.81

source: Bigcharts.Marketwatch.com

a. Find a model for the data.

b. Using your model estimate the price per share of Nike stock in 2001.

c. What is the slope of your model and what does it mean in this context?

d. Determine a reasonable domain and range for the model.

Solution

a. Finding a model will take several steps.

Step 1 Define the variables.

N = The price per share of Nike stock at the beginning of the year (in dollars)

t = Years since 1990

Step 2 Adjust the data.

Table 1.4.6

t	Price Per Share ($)
3	11.47
4	18.66
7	39.75
8	40.56
9	49.12
10	55.81

Step 3 Create a scattergram

Graph 1.4.7.

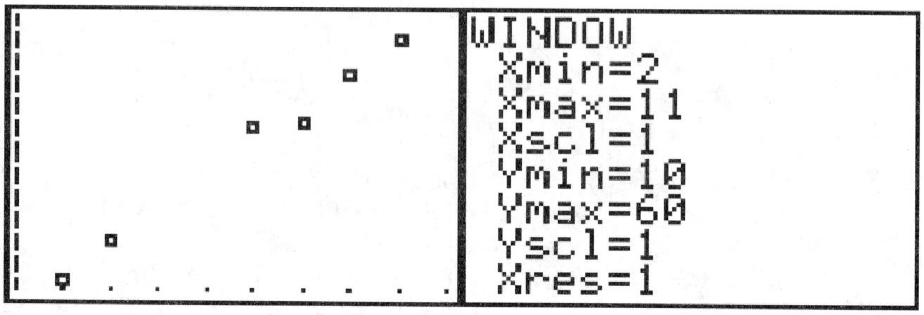

```
WINDOW
Xmin=2
Xmax=11
Xscl=1
Ymin=10
Ymax=60
Yscl=1
Xres=1
```

Step 4 Select a model type.

This data seems to be linearly related so we will find a linear model.

Step 5 Pick two points that will make a good "Eye-ball Best Fit" and calculate the slope.

Using a clear ruler we can choose the second point and the next to the last point because they seem to line up well with the rest of the data.

$(4, 18.66)$ and $(9, 49.12)$

$$m = \frac{\text{change in outputs}}{\text{change in inputs}}$$

$$m = \frac{49.12 - 18.66}{9 - 4}$$

$$m = \frac{30.46}{5}$$

$$m = 6.092$$

Step 6 Substitute the slope into the slope-intercept form and use one point to find the vertical intercept, b.

$$N = mt + b$$

$$N = 6.092t + b$$

Substituting the point (4, 18.66)

$$18.66 = 6.092(4) + b$$

$$18.66 = 24.368 + b$$

$$\underline{-24.368 \quad -24.368} \qquad \text{Subtract 24.368 from both sides.}$$

$$-5.708 = b$$

Step 7 Use the slope and vertical intercept to write the model.

$$N = 6.092t - 5.708$$

Step 8 Check your model for a good fit.

To check your model you will want to enter the model into the Y= screen and graph it with the data. To do this press the [Y=] and enter the equation using the $[X, T, \theta, n]$ key for the input variable. After you enter the equation press the [GRAPH] key to view the graph.

Graph 1.4.8.

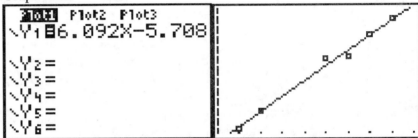

This equation gives us a line that comes close to all the points in the data and looks like a good fit with the points that are not on the model are well balanced on the top and bottom of the line. If the line did not fit well we could adjust the slope or vertical intercept to try and get a better fit.

b. The year 2001 is represented by $t = 11$, so we substitute 11 for t and solve for N.

$$N = 6.092t - 5.708$$

$$N = 6.092(11) - 5.708$$

$$N = 61.304$$

At the beginning of 2001 the stock price for Nike inc. was approximately $61.30

c. The slope for this model is 6.092. The stock price of Nike Inc. was increasing approximately $6.09 per year.

d. Let the domain be $[2, 12]$, then the range can be found by looking for the lowest and highest points on the function within that domain. Looking at the graph the lowest point occurs when $t = 2$ since we now have an equation we can calculate this point and get

$$N = 6.092(2) - 5.708$$

$$N = 6.476$$

The highest point within this domain occurs at $t = 12$ and using the equation we get

$$N = 6.092(12) - 5.708$$

$$N = 67.396$$

Using these values the range is $[6.476, 67.396]$

Modeling Steps:
1.   Define the variables. (be sure to use units)
2.   Adjust the data. (if needed)
3.   Create a scattergram. (on calculator)
4.   Select a model type. (for now we only have linear)
5.   Pick two points and calculate the slope.
6.   Substitute in the slope and use a point to find the vertical intercept, b.
7.   Write the model.
8.   Check your model by graphing it on the calculator.

Many mistakes that occur in the modeling process can be avoided by checking your work along the way. When calculating the slope in step 5 be sure to think about the slope you found and consider whether it agrees with the trend you see in your scattergram. If your data is going down from left to right the slope should be negative.

When explaining the meaning of the slope you can follow this simple pattern:

"Definition of the output variable" **is** "increasing/decreasing" **by approximately** "value of the slope" "unit for the output variable" **per** "unit for the input variable".

In the U-haul example the slope was 0.59. Using the pattern above the meaning of this slope could be given as:

The cost for renting a 10-ft truck from U-haul for the day increases by 0.59 dollars per mile driven.

If the variables are defined, writing this sentence is just a matter of putting the pieces together properly.

Example 3

Find the slope and give its meaning in the context of the given model.

a.   Let $P = 115b - 4000$ be the profit in dollars Bicycles Galore makes from selling b bikes.

b.   Let $S = -0.76a + 33.04$ be the percentage of women a years old who smoked cigarettes during their pregnancy.
    source: U.S. National Center for Health Statistics, National Vital Statistics Reports.

Solution

a.   The slope of this model is 115. The output variable is P profit in dollars and the input variable is b bikes sold. Therefore the slope means: The profit for Bicycles Galore in increasing by $115 per bike sold.

b.   The slope of this model is -0.76. The output variable is S percent of women who smoked cigarettes during their pregnancy and the input variable is a years old. Therefore the slope means: The percent of women who smoke cigarettes during their pregnancy is decreasing by 0.76 percentage points per year of age. In other words the older the women get the fewer of them that smoke during pregnancy.

Note that when a model is measuring a percentage the slope will typically measure the number percentage points the output is changing not the percent itself.

Problem 2

Table 1.4.7 gives the total prize money given out at professional rodeo events in the United States.

Table 1.4.7

Year	Total Prize Money (millions of dollars)
1995	24.5
1997	28.0
1998	29.9
1999	31.1
2000	32.3

source: Statistical Abstract 2002.

a. Find a model for the data.

b. Using your model estimate the total prize money given out in 2004.

c. What is the slope of your model and what does it mean in this context?

d. Determine a reasonable domain and range for this model.

Solution   See page 47

Section 1.4 Key Points

- Creating scattergrams on the calculator.
- Steps to the modeling process.
  - **i**   Define the variables. (be sure to use units)
  - **ii**   Adjust the data. (if needed)
  - **iii** Create a scattergram. (on calculator)
  - **iv**   Select a model type. (for now we only have linear)
  - **v**   Pick two points and calculate the slope.
  - **vi**   Substitute in the slope and use a point to find the vertical intercept, b.
  - **vii** Write the model.
  - **viii** Check your model by graphing it on the calculator.
- In a context slope represents the change in the output variable per a change in the input variable

Section 1.4 Problem Solutions

Problem 1   Solution

a.

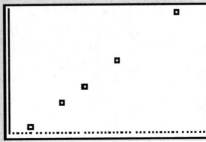

Problem 1   Solution Continued

b.

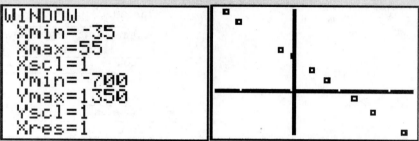

Problem 2   Solution

a.

Step 1 Define the variables.
P = The total prize money given out at professional rodeo events in millions of dollars.
t = Years since 1990

Step 2 Adjust the data.

Table 1.4.8

t	Price Per Share ($)
5	24.5
7	28.0
8	29.9
9	31.1
10	32.3

Step 3 Create a scattergram.

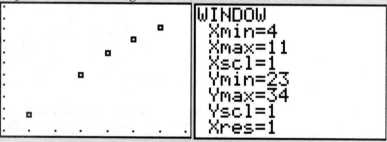

Step 4 Select a model type.
This data seems to be linearly related so we will find a linear model.

Step 5 Pick two points that will make a good "Eye-ball Best Fit" and calculate the slope.
Using a clear ruler we can choose the first point and the next to the last point because they seem to line up well with the rest of the data.

$$(5, 24.5) \text{ and } (9, 31.1)$$

$$m = \frac{\text{change in outputs}}{\text{change in inputs}}$$

$$m = \frac{31.1 - 24.5}{9 - 5}$$

$$m = 1.65$$

Problem 2   Solution Continued

a.

Step 6 Substitute the slope into the slope-intercept form and use one point to find the vertical intercept, b.

$$P = mt + b$$

$$P = 1.65t + b$$

Substituting the point (5, 24.5)

$$24.5 = 1.65(5) + b$$

$$24.5 = 8.25 + b$$

$$\underline{-8.25 \quad -8.25} \qquad \text{Subtract 8.25 from both sides.}$$

$$16.25 = b$$

Step 7 Use the slope and vertical intercept to write the model.

$$P = 1.65t + 16.25$$

Step 8 Check your model for a good fit.

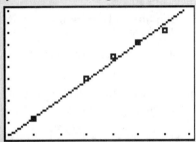

This model fits the data well and the points that miss are well balanced above and below the line. This is a good "Eye-ball Best Fit" model.

b. 2004 is represented by $t = 14$ so we get

$$P = 1.65(14) + 16.25$$

$$P = 39.35$$

In 2004 professional rodeos gave out a total of about $39.35 million in prize money.

c. The slope is 1.65. The total prize money given out at profession rodeo events is increasing by about 1.65 million dollars per year.

d. A reasonable domain would be $[3, 14]$. The lowest point within this domain will occur at $t = 3$ using the equation we get

$$P = 1.65(3) + 16.25$$

$$P = 21.2$$

The highest value within this domain for the model will occur when $t = 14$ giving us

$$P = 1.65(14) + 16.25$$

$$P = 39.35$$

Therefore the range would be $[21.2, 39.35]$.

1.4 Exercises

1. The amount of beef consumption by Americans is given in **Table 1.4.7**

   Table 1.4.7

Year	Beef Consumption (in millions of pounds)
1990	24031
1995	25534
1999	26932
2000	27290

   source: Statistical Abstract 2001

   a. Find a model for this data.

   b. According to your model how much beef was consumed by Americans in 1997?

   c. Give a reasonable domain and range for this model.

   d. What is the slope of your model? Explain its meaning in this context.

2. The net sales of Outback Steakhouse Inc. for various years is given in **Table 1.4.8**

   Table 1.4.8

Year	Net Sales (millions of $)
1998	1402.6
1999	1646.0
2000	1906.0
2001	2127.1

   source: CBS MarketWatch

   a. Find a model for this data.

   b. Give a reasonable domain and range for this model.

   c. According to your model when will Outback Steakhouse Inc.'s net sales be 2500 million dollars?

   d. What is the slope of your model? Explain its meaning in this context.

   e. According to your model what was Outback Steakhouse Inc.'s net sales in 1995?

3. The recent annual gross profits for Burlington Industries Inc., the owners of Burlington Coat Factories, is given in **Table 1.4.9**

   Table 1.4.9

Year	Gross Profit (in millions of $)
1999	225.4
2000	185.4
2001	131.2

   source: CBS MarketWatch

   a. Find a model for this data.

   b. What is the slope of this model? Explain its meaning in this context.

   c. Estimate the gross profits for Burlington Industries in 2003.

4. According to Transport Canada the cumulative total lives saved, in Canada, by seat belts since 1990 is given in **Table 1.4.10**

   Table 1.4.10

Year	Net Seat Belt Savings
1990	973
1991	2,009
1992	3,065
1993	4,179
1994	5,271
1995	6,439
1996	7,510
1997	8,561
1998	9,563
1999	10,625
2000	11,690

   source: Transport Canada

   a. Find a model for this data.

   b. Give a reasonable domain and range for this model.

   c. What will the cumulative total lives saved in Canada be in 2005?

   d. What is the slope of your model? Explain its meaning in this context.

5. The amount of chicken consumption by Americans is given in **Table 1.4.11**

   Table 1.4.11

Year	Chicken Consumption (in millions of pounds)
1980	11189
1985	13575
1990	17762
1995	21238
1999	24630
2000	24963

   source: Statistical Abstract 2001

   a. Find a model for this data.

   b. According to your model how much chicken was consumed by Americans in 1987?

   c. Give a reasonable domain and range for this model.

   d. What is the slope of your model? Explain its meaning in this context.

6. The recent annual gross profits for Nextel Communications Inc. is given in **Table 1.4.12**

    Table 1.4.12

Year	Gross Profit (in millions of $)
1998	1077.0
1999	2207.0
2000	3542.0
2001	4820.0

    source: CBS MarketWatch

    a. Find a model for this data.

    b. What is the slope of this model? Explain its meaning in this context.

    c. Estimate the gross profits for Nextel in 1995.

The number of European Internet Users, in millions, is given in **Table 1.4.13** Use this data for Exercises 7 through 10.

Table 1.4.13

Year	UK	Spain	Finland
1998	6.7	0.6	1.43
1999	12.5	2.8	1.7
2000	18.0	5.4	1.9
2001	24.0	7.4	2.2

source: NetStatistica.com

7. Find models for the number of internet users in the UK, Spain and Finland.

8. Give a reasonable domain for the models you found in exercise 7.

9. According to your models found in exercise 7, which country has the fastest growing internet user population? Explain.

10. What is the horizontal intercept for Spain's internet users model found in exercise 7? Explain its meaning in this context.

11. The gross profit for Airborne Inc. for several years is given in **Table 1.4.14**

    Table 1.4.14

Year	Gross Profit (in millions of $)
1998	736.7
1999	684.4
2000	589.7
2001	539.0

    source: CBS MarketWatch

    a. Find a model for this data.

    b. Give a reasonable domain and range for this model.

    c. What is the slope of your model? Explain its meaning in this context.

    d. Estimate the gross profit for Airborne Inc. in 1995.

12. The total operating expenses for United Parcel Service Inc. has been increasing steadily for the past several years. The operating expenses for UPS is given in **Table 1.4.15**

    Table 1.4.15

Years Since 1995	Total Operating Expenses (in millions of $)
3	7666.0
4	8090.0
5	8918.0
6	9471.0

    source: CBS MarketWatch

    a. Find a model for this data.

    b. Give a reasonable domain and range for this model.

    c. What is the slope of your model? Explain its meaning in this context.

    d. Estimate the operating expenses for UPS in 2003.

    e. What is the vertical intercept for this model and what does it mean in this context.

13. The number of gallons of milk consumed per person in the United States is given in **Table 1.4.16**

    Table 1.4.16

Year	Gallons Per Person
1980	27.6
1985	26.7
1990	25.6
1995	24.3

    source: Statistical Abstract 2001

    a. Find a model for this data.

    b. Give a reasonable domain and range for this model.

    c. What is the vertical intercept for this model? Explain its meaning in this context.

    d. In what year did Americans drink 30 gallons per person?

    e. What is the horizontal intercept for your model? Explain its meaning in this context.

14. The net income for Anheuser-Busch Companies Inc. is given in **Table 1.4.17**

Table 1.4.17

Year	Net Income (in millions of $)
1998	1233.3
1999	1402.2
2000	1551.6
2001	1704.5

source: CBS MarketWatch

a. Find a model for this data.

b. Give a reasonable domain and range for this model.

c. Estimate the net income for Anheuser-Busch in 2003.

d. What is the slope of your model? Explain its meaning in this context.

15. The amount spent by individuals on health care expenses in the United States is given in **Table 1.4.18**

Table 1.4.18

Year	National Health Expenditures by Individuals (in billions $)
1980	58
1985	96
1990	138
1995	149
1999	187

source: Statistical Abstract 2001

a. Find a model for this data.

b. Give a reasonable domain and range for this model.

c. What is the slope of your model? Explain its meaning in this context.

d. Estimate the amount spent by individual Americans on health care in 2002.

e. When will the amount spent be $250 billion?

16. Quiksilver Inc., the makers of the Quiksilver and Roxy clothing lines, has had steadily increasing profits over the past several years. The profits for Quicksilver Inc. are given in **Table 1.4.19**

Table 1.4.19

Year	Profits for Quiksilver Inc. (in millions of dollars)
1998	126.7
1999	175.6
2000	199.8
2001	232.7

source: CBS.Marketwatch.com

a. Find a model for this data.

b. Use your model to estimate the profit for Quiksilver Inc. in 2003.

c. Give a reasonable domain and range for this model.

d. What is the slope for your model? Explain what this means in this context.

17. The population of the United States throughout the 90's is given in **Table 1.4.20**

Table 1.4.20

Year	Population of the U.S. (in millions)
1990	249.46
1991	252.15
1992	255.03
1993	257.78
1994	260.33
1995	262.80
1996	265.23
1997	267.78
1998	270.25
1999	272.69

source: U.S. Census Bureau

a. Find a model for this data.

b. Using your model estimate the population of the U.S. in 2000.

c. Give a reasonable domain and range for this model.

d. What is the vertical intercept for your model and what does it mean in this context?

e. Estimate when the U.S. population will reach 300 million.

18. The percentage of events won on the Senior Golf Tour by 50 - 52 year olds during certain five year periods is given in **Table 1.4.21** (note: you will want to adjust the data carefully. i.e. 85 - 89 could be represented by the middle year 87.

Table 1.4.21

Years	Percentage of Events Won
1985 - 1989	54.9
1990 - 1994	52.4
1995 - 1999	50.8
2000 - 2002	48.9

source: Golf Magazine Sept. 2002

a. Find a model for this data.

b. Estimate the percentage of Senior Tour events won by 50 - 52 year olds in 2005 - 2009.

c. Give a reasonable domain and range for this model.

19. The stock prices for International Business Machines, IBM, for various years are given in **Table 1.4.22**

Table 1.4.22

Year	Stock Price (in dollars)
1996	22.72
1997	38.31
1998	52.81
2001	84.81

source: Bigcharts.Marketwatch.com

a. Find a model for this data.

b. Estimate the stock price for IBM in 2000.

c. What year did the stock price for IBM reach $65?

d. Give a reasonable domain and range for this model.

e. What is the slope of this model? Explain its meaning in this context.

20. The death rate (per 100,000 people) for motor vehicle related injuries for males in the U.S., for various years is given in **Table 1.4.23**

Table 1.4.23

Year	Death Rate (per 100,000 people)
1995	23.1
1996	22.8
1997	22.4
1999	21.8

source: CDC

a. Find a model for this data.

b. According to your model when will the Death Rate be approximately 20 deaths per 100,000 people.

c. What is a reasonable domain and range for your model.

d. What does your model predict the death rate to be in 1998?

e. What is the vertical intercept for your model and what does it mean in this context?

Section 1.5   Functions

• **Relations**   • **Function Notation**

The way that things in life are related to one another is important to understand. In mathematics we are also concerned with how different sets are related. These relationships can be as simple as the relationship between a person and their height, age, or weight. We might consider the relationship between a person's height and weight, or age and height. We could look at the day of the week and the number of work absences at a certain company. We might want to know the names of the brothers and sisters of each student in this class. Another relationship we might consider is the number of units each student is taking this semester. All of these represent what we in mathematics would call a **relation**. A relation is any connection between a set of input(s) and a set of output(s) and is typically represented by a set of ordered pairs.

Definition 1.5.1

Relation: A set of ordered pairs.
$$(1, 5), (3, 7), (9, 4), (-2, 4), (3, -1)$$
In a context a relation may represent a correspondence between one set of quantities and another set of quantities.

A special type of relation would be one where each input is related to only one output. That is, when you put in one value you only get out one value. This type of relation is called a **function** in mathematics. The important thing to consider when determining if a relation is a function is whether each and every input has exactly one output associated with it. In the following example we will determine which relations are functions and which are not.

Definition 1.5.2

Function: A relation where each input is related to only one output.
For every input value in the domain you must have one and only one output value in the range.

Example 1

Determine if the following relations are functions or not. Explain your reasoning.

a.   The set $S = \{(1, 3), (5, 7), (7, 9), (15, 17)\}$

b.   The set $S = \{(2, 8), (2, 7), (3, 16), (4, 11)\}$

c.   The relationship between a person's age and their height at any point in time.

d.   The amount of profit a company makes each month of a year.

e.   The advertised prices of Sony 32" TVs in this Sunday's newspaper.

f.   The population of California each year.

Solution

In each situation we need to consider whether for each input value there is one output.

a.   This set is a function since each input only goes to one output value.

b.   This set is not a function since the input 2 goes to two different output values.

c.   Each person will have only one height at any one point in time so this is a function.

d. A company will have only one amount of profit each month so this is a function.

e. Sony 32″ TVs were advertised for several different prices so this is a relation but not a function.

f. California will have one total population each year so this relation is a function.

In mathematics knowing that a relation is a function makes doing some things with it much easier. We will see some of these things later. Most of the equations we will work with in this class will also be functions. If you consider the data sets from the last two sections you will see that they all represent functions since each input value only resulted in one output value. Any set of data can be considered a function if it holds to the requirement that each input only has one output associated with it.

Example 2

Consider the following tables of data and equations and determine wether they are functions or not.

a.

Table 1.5.1

Day	1	2	5	7
Height of Plant (in cm)	3	5	12	17

b.

Table 1.5.2

Age of Student	7	8	7	6	6	9	10
Grade Level	2nd	3rd	3rd	1st	1st	4th	4th

c. $P = 2.57t + 65$

d. $W = 2g^2 + 5g - 9$

Solution

a. Each day that is given in **Table 1.5.1** has one plant height associated with it so this represents a function.

b. In **Table 1.5.2** the age of the student could go to more than one grade level. The 7 year olds in this table go to either 2nd or 3rd grade and so this relation is not a function.

c. This is a linear equation and we know from working with these that every input, t, results in only one output value, P. Thus this equation represents a function.

d. This equation is not linear yet still has only one output, W, associated with each input value, g. Therefore it also is a function.

When working with tables of data you can determine wether the data represents a function or not by just looking at the data carefully. When you are given an equation to consider it seems harder to determine whether or not the equation represents a function. When given an equation look for anything that is out of the ordinary, such as a ± symbol which might result in two answers for any one input. Most things we will consider in this class will be functions, but it is best to have a way of recognizing when something is not a function. One way to determine wether something is a function or not is to look at its graph.

Graphic 1.5.1.

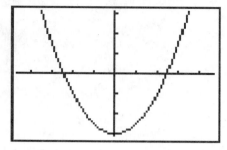

Looking at this graph we want to determine if each input has exactly one output associated with it. Pick a point on the horizontal-axis and draw an imaginary vertical line at that location and see how many times it hits the graph.

Graphic 1.5.2

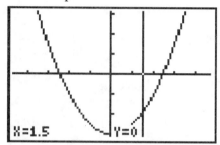

In this example we chose the input 1.5 and drew a vertical line which only hit the graph in one place below the axis. Now if you can do that with any vertical line you choose than you have the graph of a function. In this graph you can see that all of the vertical lines hit the graph only once, thus this is the graph of a function.

Graphic 1.5.3.

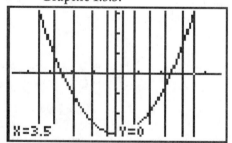

This process of testing vertical lines through a graph is called **The Vertical Line Test**. This test can be used with most equations as long as you can graph them or put them in a graphing calculator and see its graph. When using the vertical line test using a calculator you should be sure to get a viewing window that show the overall characteristics of the graph or you may incorrectly decide that the graph passes the vertical line test. Although the graphing calculator is a great tool it can only show us what we ask it to and thus we can mislead ourselves if we are not thorough and very careful.

Definition 1.5.3

The Vertical Line Test for a Function: If any vertical line intersects the graph more than once than that graph does not represent a function.

Problem 1

Determine wether the following tables, equations and graphs represent functions or not. Explain your reasoning.

a.

Table 1.5.3

Units Produced	100	150	200	250	300	350	400
Total Cost ($)	789	1565	2037	2589	3604	4568	5598

b.

Table 1.5.4

First Name of Student	John	Mary	Mark	Fred	Juan	Karla	John
No. of Units	10	12	9	15	16	21	4

c.

Table 1.5.5

Name of Student	Mary	Mark	Karla	Fred	Mark
Gender	Female	Male	Female	Male	Male

d.

Graphic 1.5.4

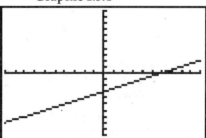

e.

Graphic 1.5.5

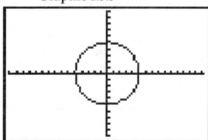

f. $C = 3.59u + 1359.56$

g. $H = 17.125 \pm \sqrt{3.5m}$ This can be entered in the equation as two equations one using the plus the other using the minus.

Solution   See page 62

Function notation was developed as a short-hand way of providing a great deal of information in a very compact form. If variables are defined properly with units and clear definitions then function notation can be used to communicate what you want to do with the function and what input and/or output values you are considering.

Let's define the following variables:

P = Population of Colorado (in millions).

t = Years since 1990.

Then the population can be represented by the following function.

$P(t) = 0.085t + 3.298$

The $P(t)$ is read P "of" t, and has a lot of information built into it. $P(t)$ represents a function named "P" which depends on the variable t. In real world applications the variable P usually represents the output variable and the variable t represents the input variable. You can see this if you consider the P, outside the parentheses, thus the output, and the t, inside the parentheses, thus the input. There is not much of a difference between this function notation and the equation: $P = 0.085t + 3.298$, but when you want to use this equation it becomes much clearer to communicate using the function notation. If you are given the variable definitions above you can make the following statements or ask the following questions in a couple of ways.

i   In words:

  i   Use the given equation to determine what the population of Colorado was in 1995.

  ii   Use the given equation to determine when the population of Colorado will be 4 million.

ii   Using function notation:

  i   Find $P(5)$.

  ii   Find $P(t) = 4$

Using the function notation allows you to communicate what the input variable or output variable is equal to without words. $P(5)$ is asking you to substitute 5 for the input variable t, and determine the value of the function $P(t)$. $P(t) = 4$ tells you that the output variable P is equal to 4 and wants you to determine the value of the input variable t, that gives you a population of 4 million people.

Function notation can be a simple way to communicate information in a short and simple way but you must be careful when interpreting the information. Be sure to know how your variables are defined and use these definitions as a basis for interpreting any results.

Example 3

Given the following definitions write sentences interpreting the following mathematical statements.

$G(t) =$ The number of guests at a local beach resort during year t.

$P(b) =$ The profit, in millions of dollars, from the sale of b bombers.

a. $G(1995) = 1990$

b. $P(10) = 7$

Solution

a.   In this notation it is important to consider which number is where. The 1995 is inside the parentheses so it must be the value of t. Therefore 1995 must be the year and since 1990 is what $G(t)$ is equal to this must represent the number of guests at the beach resort. The final interpretation might say, "In 1995 there were 1990 guests at this local beach resort."

b.   10 must be the number of bombers since it is in the parentheses and 7 must be the profit in millions. The profit from the sale of 10 bombers is 7 million dollars.

Problem 2

Given the following definitions, write sentences interpreting the following mathematical statements.

$C(m)$ = The cost, in hundreds of dollars, for producing m, miracle mops.

$P(t)$ = The population of South Dakota, in millions, t, years since 1990.

a. $C(2500) = 189$

b. $P(7) = 7.3$

Solution   See page 62

If you are careful in determining which number represents which variable you can interpret the meaning of the results by referring back to the definitions of each variable. Be sure to pay close attention to the units involved in each problem. If the profit from making bombers was measured in dollars and not millions of dollars they probably would not be made.

Function notation will change the modeling process given in the last section only in that you should now write your model in function notation and use that notation in showing your work.

Example 4

Table 1.5.6 gives the population of Colorado, in millions, for various years.

Table 1.5.6

Year	Population (in millions)
1990	3.30
1991	3.37
1992	3.46
1993	3.56
1994	3.65
1995	3.74
1996	3.81
1997	3.89
1998	3.97
1999	4.06

source: US Census Bureau

Let P be the population of Colorado, in millions, t years since 1990.

a.   Find a model for this data. Write your model in function notation.

b.   Determine a reasonable Domain and Range for your model.

c.   Find $P(11)$ and interpret its meaning in this context.

d.   Find when $P(t) = 4.35$ and interpret its meaning in this context.

Solution

a.

Step 1   Define the variables as
P = Population of Colorado in millions
t = Years since 1990.

Steps 2 and 3   Adjust the data and create a scattergram:

Graphic 1.5.6

L1	L2	L3	3
0	3.3		
1	3.37		
2	3.46		
3	3.56		
4	3.65		
5	3.74		
6	3.81		

L3(1)=

```
WINDOW
Xmin=-1
Xmax=10
Xscl=1
Ymin=3
Ymax=4
Yscl=1
Xres=1
```

Steps 4 and 5   This looks linear so pick two points and calculate the slope: we could pick the 3rd and 7th points.

$$(2, 3.46) \text{ and } (6, 3.81)$$

$$m = \frac{3.81 - 3.46}{6 - 2}$$

$$m = \frac{0.35}{4}$$

$$m = 0.0875$$

Step 6   Substitute the slope and use a point to find the vertical intercept, b.

$$P = 0.0875t + b$$

$$3.46 = 0.0875(2) + b$$

$$3.46 = 0.175 + b$$

$$\underline{-0.175 \quad -0.175} \qquad\qquad \text{Subtract 0.175 from both sides.}$$

$$3.285 = b$$

Step 7   Write the model.

$$P = 0.0875t + 3.285$$

Step 8   Check the model by graphing.

Graphic 1.5.7

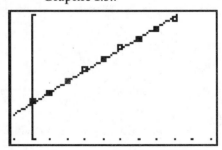

The model in function notation will be $P(t) = 0.0875t + 3.285$

b. From the data given and the close fit we obtained with our model we should be able to expand our domain beyond the data. Giving us a possible domain of [−2, 12] Looking at the graph we can see that the lowest output value is going to be on the left side of the domain and the highest output value is going to be on the right side of the domain. This tells us that we need to evaluate the function at -2 and 12 to get the lowest and highest range values respectively. Since $P(-2) = 3.11$ and $P(12) = 4.335$ the range corresponding to the domain is $[3.11, 4.335]$.

c. Substituting 11 for the input variable results in
$$P(11) = 0.0875(11) + 3.285$$
$$P(11) = 4.2475$$
This means that in 2001 the population of Colorado was about 4.25 million.

d. Setting the function equal to 4.35 results in
$$4.35 = 0.0875t + 3.285$$

$$\underline{-3.285 \qquad\qquad -3.285} \qquad \text{Subtract 3.285 from both sides.}$$

$$1.065 = 0.0875t$$

$$\frac{1.065}{0.0875} = \frac{0.0875t}{0.0875} \qquad \text{Divide both sides by 0.0875.}$$

$$12.17 = t$$

This means that the population of Colorado will reach approximately 4.35 million in 2002.

When choosing a domain and range for a model in a context you must consider model breakdown something to be avoided. When considering the domain and range of a function not in any context model breakdown will not need to be considered. This makes the domain and range much less restricted and allows for as broad a domain and range as possible. The only restrictions to the domain of a function will be any real number that results in the function being undefined. Since all non vertical linear equations are defined for all real numbers their domain will be all real numbers. Therefore since a linear graph will continue to go up and down forever the range of any non horizontal linear function will also be all real numbers. All real numbers can also be expressed using interval notation as $(-\infty, \infty)$.

Definition 1.5.3

Domain of a Function: All real numbers that do not make the function undefined.
You need to avoid division by zero and negatives under a radical.

Range of a Function: All output values resulting from values of the domain.

Domain and Range of linear functions that are not vertical or horizontal:
Domain: All Real Numbers $(-\infty, \infty)$
Range: All Real Numbers $(-\infty, \infty)$

Example 5

Determine the domain and range of the following functions:

a. $f(x) = 5x + 2$

b. $g(x) = -0.24x + 9$

c. $f(x) = 10$

Solution

a. Since this is a linear function all real number inputs will result in real number outputs. Therefore the domain is $(-\infty, \infty)$ and its range is also $(-\infty, \infty)$.

b. Since this is also a linear function its domain is $(-\infty, \infty)$ and its range is $(-\infty, \infty)$.

c. This function represents a horizontal line so its domain is still $(-\infty, \infty)$ but the range is $[10]$ since the only output value for this function is 10.

Section 1.5 Key Points

- A relation is any relationship between a set of inputs and outputs.
- A function is a relation in which each input has exactly one output.
- The vertical line test can be used to determine if a graph represents a function.
- Function notation establishes the role of each variable as input or output.
- Use caution when interpreting function notation and remember to use units.

Section 1.5 Problem Solutions

Problem 1   Solution

a. The table does represent a function since each input relates to an output.

b. This table does not represent a function because the name John goes to two separate output values.

c. This table does represent a function because each input is associated with only one output. It is ok for more than one input to go to the same output, just not the same input to more than one output.

d. This graph passes the vertical line test and thus represents a function.

e. This graph does not pass the vertical line tests since almost every vertical line drawn would hit the graph in more than one place.

f. This equation is a function since any input value u will result in only one output value.

g. This equation does not represent a function since the plus/minus symbol, $\pm$, will give two outputs for almost any input given.

Problem 2   Solution

a. 2500 is the value of the input variable and thus the number of miracle mops produced and 189 is the cost in hundreds of dollars. Therefore a good interpretation of this notation is "The cost of producing 2500 miracle mops is $18,900."

b. In 1997 the population of South Dakota was 7.3 million people.

1.5 Exercises

For each of the relations in Exercises 1 through 10, specify the input and output variables and their definition and units. Determine whether each relation is a function.

1. $G(t)$ = Your letter grade in this class when you study an average of t hours per week.

2. $S(h)$ = The salary, in dollars, of Barry Bonds when he hits h homeruns the previous season.

3. $H(a)$ = The heights, in inches, of children attending Mission Meadows Elementary School who are a years old.

4. $P(w)$ = The postage, in dollars, it takes to mail a first class package weighing w ounces.

5. $I(t)$ = The interest earned, in dollars, on an investment after t years.

6. $P(t)$ = The price, in dollars, of Nike shoes during the year t.

7. $S(y)$ = The song at the top of the pop charts during the year y.

8. $B(m)$ = The number of students in this class who have a birthday during the mth month of the year.

9. $T(t)$ = The amount of taxes, in dollars, you paid in year t.

10. $A(m)$ = The number of tourists visiting Arizona, in thousands, during the mth month of any year.

Determine whether the tables in Exercises 11 through 15 represent functions. Assume that the input is in the left column.

11.

Table 1.5.7

Month	Cost (dollars)
Jan.	5689.35
Feb.	7856.12
May	2689.15
June	1005.36

12.

Table 1.5.8

Person's height	Person's Weight (kg)
5'10"	86.4
6'2"	92
5'5"	70
5'7"	82
5'10"	91
6'1"	90

13.

Table 1.5.9

Age	Death Rate for HIV (per 100,000)
1-4 years	0.2
5-14 years	0.2
15-24 years	0.5
25-34 years	7.2
35-44 years	13.9
45-54 years	10.9
55-64 years	4.9
65-74 years	2.2
75-84 years	0.6

source: CDC

14.

Table 1.5.10

Year	Number of Business Failures in US
1990	60,432
1991	88,140
1992	97,069
1993	85,982
1994	71,558
1995	71,194
1996	71,931
1997	83,384

source: U.S. Small Business Administration

15.

Table 1.5.11

Day of Week	Amount Spent on Lunch ($)
Monday	4.78
Tuesday	5.95
Wednesday	0
Thursday	4.99
Friday	15.26
Monday	5.75
Tuesday	6.33
Wednesday	0
Thursday	4.25
Friday	20.36

16. List the domain and range of the relation given in exercise 11.

17. List the domain and range of the relation given in exercise 12.

18. List the domain and range of the relation given in exercise 14.

19. Use the relation given in exercise 13 to determine the death rate from HIV for 20 year olds.

20. Use the relation given in exercise 13 to determine the death rate from HIV for 30 year olds.

21. Use the relation given in exercise 14 to find the number of business failures in 1994.

Determine whether the equations in Exercises 22 through 27 represent functions.

22. $W = -9.2g + 7.5$

23. $Q = 2v^2 - 6.5$

24. $8 = x^2 + y^2$

25. $y = \frac{23}{5}x - \frac{2}{5}$

26. $K = 5c^3 + 6c^2 - 9$

27. $Z = \pm(6d + 9)$

Determine whether the graphs in Exercises 28 through 31 represent functions.

28.

Graph 1.5.8

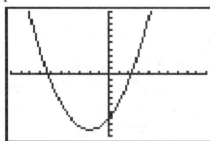

29.

Graph 1.5.9

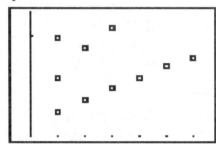

30.

Graph 1.5.10

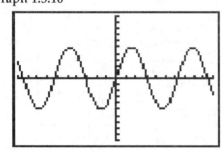

31.

Graph 1.5.11

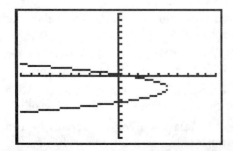

32. $W(d)$ is the weight in kilograms of a person d days after starting a diet. Write sentences interpreting the following mathematical statements.

  a. $W(0) = 86.5$

  b. $W(10) = 82$

  c. $W = 75$ when $d = 30$

  d. $W(100) = 88$

33. $P(s)$ is the population (in millions) of state s in 2001. Write the following statements in function notation.
    source: US Census Bureau

  a. The population of Wyoming was 494,423 in 2001.

  b. The population of Texas was 21,325,018 in 2001.

  c. The population of Ohio was 11.37 million in 2001.

34. $F(t)$ is the value of fresh fruits exported (in millions of dollars) in year t. Write sentences interpreting the following mathematical statements.
    source: Statistical Abstract 2001

  a. $F(1995) = 1973$

  b. $F = 1971$ when $t = 1996$

  c. $F(2000) = 2077$

35. **Table 1.5.12** lists the average monthly Social Security benefit in dollars for various years.

Table 1.5.12

Year	Benefit ($)
1995	720
1997	765
2000	845

source: Statistical Abstract 2001

  a. Let $B(t)$ be the average monthly Social Security benefit in dollars t years since 1990. Find a model for the data given. Write your model in function notation.

  b. Find $B(9)$ (remember to explain its meaning in this context.)

  c. Find $B(t) = 900$ interpret your result.

  d. Give a reasonable domain and range for this model.

  e. What is the B intercept for this model and what does it mean in this context.

36. **Table 1.5.13** lists the percent of total personal consumption Americans spent on recreation for various years.

Table 1.5.13

Year	Percent of Total Personal Consumption
1995	8.1
1996	8.2
1997	8.3
1998	8.4
1999	8.5

source: Statistical Abstract 2001

a. Let $P(t)$ be the percent of total personal consumption Americans spent on recreation t years since 1990. Find a model for this data. Write your model in function notation.

b. Give a reasonable domain and range for this model.

c. Find the P intercept for this model and explain its meaning in this context.

d. In 1990 Americans spent 7.4% of their total personal consumption on recreation. How does this compare to your result from part c?

e. Find $P(12)$ interpret your result.

f. Find $P(t) = 10$, interpret your result.

37. $f(x) = 2x - 7$

a. Find $f(5)$

b. Find $f(-10)$

c. Find $f(x) = -1$

d. Give the domain and range for $f(x)$

38. $g(x) = \frac{1}{5}x + \frac{3}{5}$

a. Find $g(20)$

b. Find $g(12)$

c. Find $g(x) = 10$

d. Give the domain and range for $g(x)$

39. $h(x) = 12.4$

a. Find $h(5)$

b. Find $h(-123)$

c. Give the domain and range for $h(x)$

40. $g(x) = -4.3x - 5$

a. Find $g(15)$

b. Find $g(-20)$

c. Find $g(x) = -45.6$

d. Give the domain and range for $g(x)$

41. $h(x) = 14x + 500$

a. Find $h(105)$

b. Find $h(x) = -140$

c. Give the domain and range for $h(x)$.

For exercises 42 and 43 use the graph of the function to answer the questions.

42.

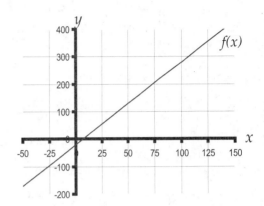

a. Estimate $f(25)$

b. Estimate $f(100)$

c. Estimate $f(x) = 200$

d. Give the domain and range for $f(x)$

e. Estimate the vertical and horizontal intercepts for $f(x)$

43.

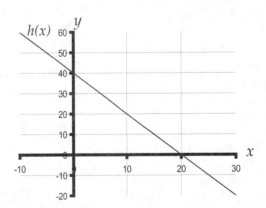

a. Estimate $h(5)$

b. Estimate $h(20)$

c. Estimate $h(x) = 20$

d. Give the domain and range for $h(x)$

e. Estimate the vertical and horizontal intercept for $h(x)$

Section 1.6   Combining Functions

• Adding, Subtracting, Multiplying, and Dividing Functions • Composing Functions

Since functions can represent many things in our lives it is often helpful to be able to combine them using different operations such as adding, subtracting, multiplying or dividing. Many functions can be combined to make more complicated functions or to create one function that gives you the information that you want without having to work with several functions at once.

Example 1

In Section 1.1 Example 3 we found the following functions for a small bicycle company:

$$C(b) = 755b + 5000$$
$$R(b) = 1995b$$

where C is the monthly cost, in dollars, to produce b, bikes and R is the monthly revenue, in dollars, from selling those bikes.

a. Find a monthly profit function for this company.

Solution

a. Since profit is a combination of revenue and cost we can determine the profit function by subtracting these two functions. Let P be the monthly profit, in dollars, from producing and selling b, bikes.

$$P(b) = R(b) - C(b)$$
$$P(b) = 1995b - (755b + 5000)$$
$$P(b) = 1995b - 755b - 5000 \qquad \text{Distribute the negative.}$$
$$P(b) = 1200b - 5000 \qquad \text{Combine like terms.}$$

This new function represents the monthly profit from producing and selling bikes. This function comes from combining the two functions of revenue and cost. It is important to note that both the revenue and cost functions had the same input variable and the output variables were also measured with the same units. This must be the case or you cannot add or subtract these functions.

Whenever you are considering if you can combine two functions by addition, subtraction, multiplication or division be sure that the input variables are the same and that you can combine the output variables the way that you would like. Units are the key to combining functions in any application.

Say What?

When adding, subtracting, multiplying or dividing functions you can write these operations in function notation in a couple of ways.

Addition:
$$f(x) + g(x)$$
$$(f + g)(x)$$

Subtraction:
$$f(x) - g(x)$$
$$(f - g)(x)$$

Multiplication:
$$f(x)g(x)$$
$$fg(x)$$

Division:
$$\frac{f(x)}{g(x)}$$
$$f(x) \div g(x)$$
$$\frac{f}{g}(x)$$

When combining functions without a context or meaning for the variables, you are free to combine any functions you are given as long as the input variables are the same. The only caution would be that you can divide as long as you don't divide by zero. This is a typical restriction that is assumed in many cases.

Combining Functions: Using Addition, Subtraction, Multiplication, or Division
- The inputs for both functions must be the same.
- To Add or Subtract: The outputs must be measured in the same units.
- To Multiply or Divide: The outputs need to make sense together when combined.

  i   feet • feet = square feet.

  ii   pounds • $\dfrac{\text{dollars}}{\text{pound}}$ = dollars

  iii hours • $\dfrac{\text{miles}}{\text{hour}}$ = miles

  iv   dollars ÷ people = $\dfrac{\text{dollars}}{\text{person}}$ = dollars per person

Skill Connection:

SC-Example 1: *Combine the following functions.*

$f(x) = 5x + 6$

$g(x) = 2x - 9$

$h(x) = 3x + 4$

a. $f(x) + g(x)$
b. $g(x) - f(x)$
c. $h(x) - g(x)$
d. $f(x)g(x)$
e. $\dfrac{g(x)}{h(x)}$

Solution:

a. To add these two functions we just need to combine like terms and simplify.
$(f + g)(x) = (5x + 6) + (2x - 9)$
$(f + g)(x) = 7x - 3$

b. When subtracting functions be careful to distribute the negative throughout the second function.
$(g - f)(x) = (2x - 9) - (5x + 6)$
$(g - f)(x) = 2x - 9 - 5x - 6$
$(g - f)(x) = -3x - 15$

c.
$(h - g)(x) = (3x + 4) - (2x - 9)$
$(h - g)(x) = 3x + 4 - 2x + 9$
$(h - g)(x) = x + 13$

d. When multiplying two functions be sure to use the distributive property.
$fg(x) = (5x + 6)(2x - 9)$
$fg(x) = 10x^2 - 45x + 12x - 54$
$fg(x) = 10x^2 - 33x - 54$

e. For now we will only set up the fraction and we will learn to simplify these later.
$\dfrac{g(x)}{h(x)} = \dfrac{2x - 9}{3x + 4}$

Example 2

Use the following functions to write a new function that will give you the result requested.

$U(t)$ = The population of the United States t years since 1900.

$F(t)$ = The number of females in the United States t years since 1900.

$D(t)$ = The United States National Debt in dollars t years since 1900.

$A(t)$ = The Average dollars spent per person on dining out t years since 1900.

a. The Total amount spent by Americans on dining out t years since 1900.

b. The number of males in the United States t years since 1900.

c. The average amount that each American would have to pay in order to pay the national debt t years since 1900.

Solution

a. $U(t) \bullet A(t)$ = The Total amount spent by Americans on dining out, in dollars, t years since 1900.

To get the total we needed to take the average amount spent and multiply by the total number of people. The units of dollars per person times people works out to dollars, which makes sense in this situation.

b. $U(t) - F(t)$ = The number of males in the United States t years since 1900.

Subtracting the number of females in the US from the total population gives us the number of males.

c. $\dfrac{D(t)}{U(t)}$ = The average amount that each American would have to pay in order to pay the national debt t years since 1900.

Dividing the national debt by the number of people in the US gives an average amount for each person.

Problem 1

Use the following functions to write a new function that will give you the result requested.

$F(t)$ = The number of people employed by Ford Motor Company in year t.

$I(t)$ = The average cost, in dollars per employee, for health insurance at Ford Motor Company in year t.

$V(t)$ = The total cost, in dollars, for vacations taken by Ford Motor Companies non management employees in year t.

$M(t)$ = The number of employees of Ford Motor Company who are in management in year t.

a. The total amount spent on health insurance for Ford Motor Companies employees in year t.

b. The number of non-management employees at Ford Motor Company in year t.

c. The average cost per non-management employee for vacations at Ford Motor Company in year t.

Solution See page 71

Many things in life require you to do a step by step process where a subsequent step requires the result of the previous step or steps. Whenever this situation occurs we are combining two or more steps together. A simple example of this would be if you are trying to get a drink from a vending machine that does not take dollar bills. If all you have is dollar bills you will need to first get change for that bill and then use that change to purchase the drink. The process of buying that drink is a combination of getting change and using the vending machine to get the drink. Today most vending machines have combined these two steps into one by combining a change machine and the vending machine together into one so that dollar bills can be used to make a purchase.

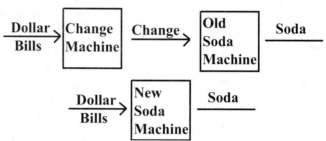

In Mathematics this way of combining functions is called a **composition** of functions. Whenever one function, or the output of the function, is substituted into another function, you are composing the two functions.

Example 3

A company knows the following two functions:

$C(e)$ = The cost of health insurance in dollars for a company with e employees.

$E(t)$ = The number of employees at the company in year t.

Find a function that will tell the companies cost for health insurance in year t.

Solution
If the company wants to know the cost for health insurance for a certain year they cannot immediately get that information from either of these functions. To use $C(e)$ they need to know the number of employees which they do not have. But they can use $E(t)$ to find the number of employees in year t and then substitute that amount into $C(e)$. This would be, in effect, a composition of these two functions and could be written as $C(E(t))$. $C(E(t))$ is the cost of health insurance for this company in year t.

This notation is can be read by starting from the very inside parentheses and working your way out. $C(E(t))$ says that t is the input for the function and C is the final output of the function. The E is a middle step that when all is done together is never noticed.

Example 4

NatureJuice Inc. is a small juice processor whom squeezes oranges for several Florida growers. They are concerned with their annual cost projections and are working with the following two functions.

$$C(t) = 135.87t + 25000$$

where $C(t)$ is the annual cost, in dollars, to process t thousand tons of oranges per year.

$$P(y) = 2.4y - 4500$$

where $P(y)$ is the annual production of oranges, in thousands of tons, in year y.

a. Find a function that will calculate the annual cost to process all oranges in year y.

b. Find the annual cost to process oranges in 1995.

c. When was the annual cost to process oranges $66,000?

Solution

a. NatureJuice Inc. wants a function that has an output of annual cost but an input of years. Since the function $P(y)$ depends on the year y and has an output of thousand of tons of oranges we can compose it with $C(t)$ to get the annual cost when given the year y. $C(P(y))$ will give the annual cost, in dollars, to process all oranges in year y.

$$C(P(y)) = 135.87(2.4y - 4500) + 25000$$
$$C(P(y)) = 326.088y - 611415 + 25000 \quad \text{Distribute 135.87.}$$
$$C(P(y)) = 326.088y - 586415 \quad \text{Combine like terms.}$$

b. We can do this problem two ways. We will do it once using the two functions given separately and then a second time using the newly composed function we found in part a.

i Using the two equations separately we first must find the number of oranges produced in 1995.

$$P(y) = 2.4y - 4500$$
$$P(1995) = 2.4(1995) - 4500$$
$$P(1995) = 4788 - 4500$$
$$P(1995) = 288$$

Thus 288 thousand tons of oranges were produced in 1995. Now we must substitute this into the cost equation.

$$C(t) = 135.87t + 25000$$
$$C(288) = 135.87(288) + 25000$$
$$C(288) = 39130.56 + 25000$$
$$C(288) = 64130.56$$

Therefore the annual cost to process oranges in 1995 was about $64,130.56.

ii Using the new composed function:

$$C(P(y)) = 326.088y - 586415$$
$$C(P(1995)) = 326.088(1995) - 586415$$
$$C(P(1995)) = 650545.56 - 586415$$
$$C(P(1995)) = 64130.56$$

This is the same result as the first method it just takes much less effort once the two functions have been composed. If you needed to do this same calculation for several years, perhaps to show a trend in the costs from year to year, the composed function would be much more efficient.

c.   Using the new composed function we have

$$C(P(y)) = 326.088y - 586415$$

$$66000 = 326.088y - 586415$$

$$\underline{586415 \qquad\qquad\qquad 586415}$$

$$652415 = 326.088y$$

$$\frac{652415}{326.088} = \frac{326.088y}{326.088}$$

$$2000.73 = y$$

In the year 2000 the annual cost to process oranges was about $66,000.

Problem 2

Consider the following functions for a metropolitan area in the U.S.

$$P(t) = 1.2t + 3.4$$

where $P(t)$ is the population of the metropolitan area in millions of people t years since 1990.

$$A(n) = 15480n - 2400$$

where $A(n)$ is the amount of air pollution in parts per million when n million people live in the metropolitan area.

a.   Find the population of this metropolitan area in 1995.

b.   Find the amount of air pollution for this metropolitan area in 1995.

c.   Find a new function that will give the amount of air pollution for this metropolitan area depending on the number of years since 1990.

d.   Use the function you found in part c to find the air pollution in 1995, 1997 and 2000.

Solution   See page 71

When composing two functions it is very important that you check that the output of one function is the same as the input needed by the other function. This is the only way that you can compose the two functions together.

Combining Functions: Using composition:
- The inputs do **not** need to be the same.
- The input for one function must be the same as the output of the other function.

Because functions can be combined together in so many ways it is important to pay close attention to the input and output of each function. These will usually determine what operation you should use to combine them.

Section 1.6 Key Points
- Functions can be combined using addition, subtraction, multiplication, division and composition. In a problem with no context you can combine any two functions.
- To add or subtract two functions within a context you need the following:
    i   The Input variables must be the same.
    ii   The Outputs must have the same units.
- To multiply or divide two functions within a context you need the following:
    i   The Input variables must be the same.
    ii   The Output units must make sense once combined.
- To compose two functions within a context you need the following:
    i   The Input do not need to be the same.
    ii   The Input for one function must be the same as the Output of the other.

Section 1.6 Problem Solutions

Problem 1   Solution

a. $F(t) \bullet I(t)$ = The total amount spent on health insurance for Ford Motor Companies employees in year t.

> The average cost per employee multiplied by the number of employees give the total cost.

b. $F(t) - M(t)$ = The number of non-management employees at Ford Motor Company in year t.

> The total number of employees minus the number of management employees gives the number of non-management employees.

c. $\dfrac{V(t)}{(F(t) - M(t))}$ = The average cost per non-management employee at Ford Motor Company in year t.

> The total cost divided by the number of non-management employees gives an average amount.

Problem 2   Solution

a.
$$P(t) = 1.2t + 3.4$$
$$P(5) = 1.2(5) + 3.4$$
$$P(5) = 9.4$$

This metropolitan area had a population of 9.4 million people in 1995.

b.   You know the population was 9.4 million people in 1995 from part a so substitute 9.4 for n and you get.
$$A(n) = 15480n - 2400$$
$$A(9.4) = 15480(9.4) - 2400$$
$$A(9.4) = 143112$$

This metropolitan area had air pollution levels of 143,112 parts per million in 1995.

c.   Since $P(t)$ gives the population of the metropolitan area in millions of people we can compose the two functions by substituting $P(t)$ into $A(n)$.
$$A(P(t)) = 15480(1.2t + 3.4) - 2400$$
$$A(P(t)) = 18576t + 52632 - 2400$$
$$A(P(t)) = 18576t + 50232$$

$a(t) = A(P(t))$ = The amount of air pollution in parts per million t years since 1990.

d.
$$a(t) = 18576t + 50232$$
$$a(5) = 143112$$
$$a(7) = 180264$$
$$a(10) = 235992$$

The amount of air pollution in this metropolitan area was 143,112 ppm in 1995, 180,264 ppm in 1997, and 235,992 ppm in 2000.

1.6 Exercises

1. The average pounds of fruits and vegetables per person that each American eats can be modeled by:
$$T(y) = 6.056y + 601.39$$
pounds per person y years since 1980.
The average pounds of fruit per person each American eats can be modeled by
$$F(y) = 1.43y + 265.12$$
pounds per person y years since 1980.
source: Based on data from the Statistical Abstract 2001

   a. How many pounds of fruits and vegetables did the average American eat in 2000?
   b. How many pounds of fruit did the average American eat in 2000?
   c. Using your previous results how many pounds of vegetables did the average American eat in 2000?
   d. Write a new function that will give the average pounds of vegetables each American eats per year.
   e. Using your new function how many pounds of vegetables did each American eat in 2000?
   f. Estimate the number of pounds of vegetables each American will eat in 2003, 2005, and 2010.

2. In section 1.3 exercise 15 you found a model for the amount spent by individuals on health care expenses in the United States close to
$$I(t) = 6.47t - 455.5$$
billions of dollars t years since 1900.
The amount spent by insurance companies on health care expenses in the U.S. can be modeled by
$$H(t) = 17.85t - 1372.1$$
billions of dollars t years since 1900.
source: Based on data from the Statistical Abstract 2001.

   a. How much was spent by individuals on health care in 2000?
   b. How much was spent by insurance companies on health care in 2000?
   c. What was the total amount spent by individuals and insurance companies on health care in 2000?
   d. Find a new function that gives the total amount spent on health care by individuals and insurance companies.
   e. Use your new function to determine the total amount spent on health care by individuals and insurance companies in 2000, 2005, and 2010.

3. The per capita consumption of milk products in the U.S. between 1980 and 1995 can be modeled by
$$M(t) = -0.218t + 27.71$$
gallon per person t years since 1980.
The per capita consumption of whole milk in the U.S. between 1980 and 1995 can be modeled by
$$W(t) = -0.56t + 16.45$$
gallons per person t years since 1980.
source: Based on data from the Statistical Abstract 2001.

   a. Use these models to find a new function that gives the per capita consumption of milk products other than whole milk.
   b. How much whole milk was consumed per person in 1990?
   c. How much milk other than whole milk was consumed per person in 1985, and 1995?
   d. What is the slope of $W(t)$? Explain its meaning in this context.
   e. What is the M-intercept for $M(t)$? Explain its meaning in this context.

4. West Tech Inc.'s vacation policy increases each employees vacation time based on the number of years they are employed. The number of weeks of vacation an employee gets in a year can be modeled by
$$v(y) = 0.25y + 1.5$$
weeks of vacation after working for the company for y years.
West Tech Inc.'s cost of an employee's vacation time in a year can be modeled by
$$C(w) = 1500w + 575$$
dollars when w weeks of vacation are taken.

   a. Find the number weeks a West Tech employee will get per year after working with the company for 10 years.
   b. What is West Tech's cost for a 10 year employee's vacation.
   c. Use these functions to find a new function that determines the cost for vacation taken by an employee that has been with the company for y years. Assume the employee will take all their vacation time.
   d. What is West Tech's cost for a 20 year employee's vacation.
   e. What is West Tech's cost for a 30 year employee's vacation.

5. Far North Manufacturing is starting to manufacture a new line of toys for this Christmas season. The number of toys they can manufacture each week can be modeled by
$$T(w) = 500w + 3000$$
where $T(w)$ represents the number of toys manufactured during week w of production.

The total weekly cost for manufacturing these toys can be modeled by

$$C(t) = 1.75t + 5000$$

where $C(t)$ represents the total weekly cost in dollars from producing t toys a week.

a. Use these models to find a new function that will give the total weekly cost for week w of production.

b. Find the number of toys produced during the fifth week of production.

c. Find the total weekly cost to produce 5000 toys.

d. Find the total weekly cost for the seventh week of production.

e. In what week will the total weekly cost reach $18,500.00?

In Exercises 6 through 12 combine the functions by adding, subtracting, multiplying, dividing, or composing the two functions. Write the function notation for the combination you use and list the units for the inputs and outputs of the new function.

6. Let $U(t)$ be the population of the United States, in millions, t years since 1900. Let $M(t)$ be the number of men in the United States, in millions, t years since 1900. Find a function for the number of women in the United States.

7. Let $S(d)$ be the average speed, in m.p.h., traveled on a cross country trip during day d of the trip. Let $T(d)$ be the time, in hours, traveled during a cross country trip on day d of the trip. Find a function for the number of miles traveled on day d of the cross country trip.

8. Let $P(b)$ be the profit, in thousands of dollars, that Pride Bike Co. makes if they sell b bikes per year. Let $B(t)$ be the number of bikes Pride Bike Co. sells in year t. Find a function for the amount of profit Pride Bike Co. makes in year t.

9. Let $U(t)$ be the population of the United States, in millions, t years since 1900. Let $D(t)$ be the national debt, in millions of dollars, t years since 1900. Find a function for the average amount of national debt per person.

10. Let $U(t)$ be the population of the United States, t years since 1900. Let $D(t)$ be the average amount of personal debt per person in the United States, t years since 1900. Find a function for the total amount of personal debt in the United States.

11. Let $D(v)$ be the amount of environmental damage, in thousands of dollars, done to a national park when v visitors come to the park in a year. Let $V(t)$ be the number of visitors who come to a national park in year t. Find a function that gives the amount of environmental damage at a national park in year t.

12. Let $P(b)$ be the profit, in thousands of dollars, that Pride Bike Co. makes if they sell b bikes per year. Let $R(b)$ be the revenue, in thousands of dollars, that Pride Bike Co. makes if they sell b bikes per year. Find a function that gives the cost that Pride Bike Co. has if they sell b bikes per year.

13. The retail prescription drug sales in the United States is a multi-billion dollar industry. Data for the total retail prescription drug sales and the mail order sales is given in **Table 1.6.1**

Table 1.6.1

Years Since 1990	Total Sales (in billions of $)	Mail Order Sales (in billions of $)
7	89.1	11.4
8	103.0	13.4
9	121.7	16.6
10	140.7	20.6

a. Find a model for the total prescription drug sales.

b. Find a model for the mail order prescription drug sales.

c. What was the total amount of prescription drug sales in 2001?

d. What was the amount of prescription drugs sold through mail order in 2001?

e. Using your two models find a new function that gives the total amount of prescription drugs sold by non-mail order retail stores.

f. What was the amount of non-mail order sales of prescription drugs in 2001 and 2002?

For Exercises 14 through 18 assume that the following functions refer to a specific tour company offering European tours and that t represents the year.

• Let $T(t)$ be the total number of people on the tour.

• Let $K(t)$ be the number of children under 12yrs old on the tour.

• Let $C(k)$ be the cost for k children under 12yrs old to take the tour.

• Let $A(a)$ be the cost for a people over 12yrs old to take the tour.

• Let $B(n)$ be the number of busses needed when n people travel on the tour.

Combine the functions by adding, subtracting, multiplying, dividing, or composing the two functions. Write the function notation for the combination you use and list the units for the inputs and outputs of the new function.

14. Find a function that gives the number of people over 12yrs old who go on the tour in year t.

15. Find a function that gives the cost for all children under 12yrs old who traveled on the tour in year t.

16. Find a function that gives the cost for all people over 12yrs old who traveled on the tour in year t.

17. Find a function that gives the total cost for all people who traveled on the tour in year t.

18. Find a function that gives the number of busses needed for the tour in year t.

19. The percent of jail inmates, who are male, in U.S. federal and state prisons during the 1990's can be modeled by $M(t) = -0.195t + 89.379$ percent t years since 1990.
source: Based on data from the Statistical Abstract 2001

  a. Let $F(t)$ be the percent of jail inmates, who are female, in U.S. federal and state prisons t years since 1990. Explain why $M(t) + F(t) = 100$

  b. Substitute the function $M(t)$ into the equation in part a and solve for $F(t)$.

  c. Find $F(5)$ and interpret it in this context.

  d. What is the slope of $F(t)$? Explain its meaning in this context.

  e. What is the M-intercept for $M(t)$? Explain its meaning in this context.

20. The percent of occupied housing units that are owner occupied is given in **Table 1.6.2**
Table 1.6.2

Year	Percent Owner Occupied
1995	64.7
1997	65.7
1998	66.3
1999	66.8
2000	67.4

source: Statistical Abstract 2001

  a. Let $O(t)$ be the percent of occupied housing units that are owner occupied, t years since 1990. Find a model for $O(t)$.

  b. Let $R(t)$ be the percent of occupied housing units that are renter occupied, t years since 1990. Using your model from part a, find a model for $R(t)$.

  c. Find $R(12)$ and explain its meaning in this context.

  d. What is the slope of $R(t)$? Explain its meaning in this context.

21. The percent of prescription drug expenditures paid by private insurance is given in **Table 1.6.3**
Table 1.6.3

Year	Percent Paid by Private Insurance
1995	44.0
1996	47.9
1997	50.9
1998	53.3

source: Statistical Abstract 2001

  a. Let $I(t)$ be the percent of prescription drug expenditures paid by private insurance, t years since 1990. Find a model for $I(t)$.

  b. Let $P(t)$ be the percent of prescription drug expenditures paid by the patient, t years since 1990. Using your model from part a, find a model for $P(t)$. (you may assume that if the insurance did not pay the patient did.)

  c. What is the slope of $P(t)$? Explain its meaning.

Math
Tutorial

More practice problems like exercises 22 through 32 can be found in section 1.5 of the CD Tutorial.

22. Let $f(x) = 3x + 8$ and $g(x) = -6x + 9$
  a. Find $f(x) + g(x)$
  b. Find $f(x) - g(x)$
  c. Find $f(x)g(x)$
  d. Find $f(g(x))$
  e. Find $g(f(x))$

23. Let $f(x) = 0.5x - 4.5$ and $g(x) = 7x - 1$
  a. Find $f(x) + g(x)$
  b. Find $g(x) - f(x)$
  c. Find $f(x)g(x)$
  d. Find $f(g(x))$
  e. Find $g(f(x))$

24. Let $f(x) = \frac{2}{3}x + \frac{1}{3}$ and $g(x) = 5x - 3$
  a. Find $f(x) + g(x)$
  b. Find $f(x) - g(x)$
  c. Find $f(x)g(x)$
  d. Find $f(g(x))$
  e. Find $g(f(x))$

25. Let $f(x) = 0.68x + 2.36$ and $g(x) = 3.57x + 6.49$

    a. Find $f(x) + g(x)$

    b. Find $g(x) - f(x)$

    c. Find $f(x)g(x)$

    d. Find $f(g(x))$

    e. Find $g(f(x))$

26. Let $f(x) = 19x + 28$ and $g(x) = -17x + 34$

    a. Find $f(x) + g(x)$

    b. Find $g(x) - f(x)$

    c. Find $f(x)g(x)$

    d. Find $f(g(x))$

    e. Find $g(f(x))$

27. Let $f(x) = -0.6x - 3.2$ and $g(x) = -7x - 4.8$

    a. Find $f(x) + g(x)$

    b. Find $f(x) - g(x)$

    c. Find $f(x)g(x)$

    d. Find $f(g(x))$

    e. Find $g(f(x))$

28. Let $f(x) = 3x + 8$ and $g(x) = -6x + 9$

    a. Find $f(5) + g(5)$

    b. Find $f(5) - g(5)$

    c. Find $f(5)g(5)$

    d. Find $f(g(5))$

    e. Find $g(f(5))$

29. Let $f(x) = 0.5x - 4.5$ and $g(x) = 7x - 1$

    a. Find $f(2) + g(2)$

    b. Find $g(2) - f(2)$

    c. Find $f(2)g(2)$

    d. Find $f(g(2))$

30. Let $f(x) = \frac{2}{3}x + \frac{1}{3}$ and $g(x) = 5x - 3$

    a. Find $f(4) + g(4)$

    b. Find $f(4) - g(4)$

    c. Find $f(4)g(4)$

    d. Find $f(g(4))$

    e. Find $g(f(4))$

31. Let $f(x) = 0.68x + 2.36$ and $g(x) = 3.57x + 6.49$

    a. Find $f(-3) + g(-3)$

    b. Find $g(-3) - f(-3)$

    c. Find $f(-3)g(-3)$

    d. Find $f(g(-3))$

    e. Find $g(f(-3))$

32. Let $f(x) = 19x + 28$ and $g(x) = -17x + 34$

    a. Find $f(2) + g(2)$

    b. Find $g(2) - f(2)$

    c. Find $f(2)g(2)$

    d. Find $f(g(2))$

    e. Find $g(f(2))$

Chapter 1 Review Exercises

1. The height of the grass used in the rough at a local golf course is given by the following equation
$$h = 0.75d + 4.5$$
   where h is the height of the grass in inches d days after the grass was cut and fertilized.
   a. What is the height of the grass 1 week after it is cut and fertilized?
   b. For a coming tournament the officials want the grass in the rough to be 12 inches high. How many days before the tournament should the golf course cut and fertilize this grass?

2. Pauley's Rental Company charges $40 per hour plus $15 per rental for insurance to rent a Bobcat tractor.
   a. Find an equation for the cost to rent a Bobcat tractor from Pauley's Rental Company.
   b. How much will it cost to rent the Bobcat for 2 hours?
   c. How much will it cost to rent the Bobcat for 3 days if a day is measured as 8 hours each?

3. The number of candles produced by the Holy Light Candle Company can be modeled by
$$C(t) = 0.56t + 4.3$$
   where $C(t)$ is the number of candles, in millions, produced t years since 1990.
   a. Find the number of candles produced by Holy Light Candle Company in 1995.
   b. Find $C(3)$ and interpret its meaning in this context.
   c. Find when $C(t) = 10$ and interpret its meaning in this context.

4. The Pharmaceutical Management Agency of New Zealand, PHARMAC, manages the amount spent on various medical conditions and drugs throughout New Zealand. **Table 1.7.1** gives the amounts spent on Anti-inflammatory Non Steroidal Drugs (NSAIDs).

Table 1.7.1

Year	Expenditures (in millions of New Zealand dollars)
1996	14.7
1997	12.1
1998	11.9
1999	9.0
2000	7.2

source: PHARMAC NZ

   a. Find a model for this data.
   b. Find the horizontal intercept of your model. Explain its meaning in this context.
   c. Find the expenditure for NSAIDs in 1994?
   d. What is the slope of this model? Explain its meaning in this context.

5. The gross profit for Costco Wholesale Corporation is given in **Table 1.7.2**

Table 1.7.2

Year	Gross Profit (in millions of $)
1998	2890.2
1999	3285.8
2000	3842.1
2001	4198.9

source: CBS.Marketwatch.com

   a. Find a model for this data.
   b. Estimate when the gross profit for Costco will be 5 billion dollars.
   c. What was the gross profit for Costco in 1995?
   d. What is the slope of this model? Explain its meaning in this context.

6. According to the U.S. Department of Labor Bureau of Labor Statistics the percent of full-time workers in private industry who filed an injury case is given in **Table 1.7.3**

Table 1.7.3

Years Since 1990	Percent
2	8.3
3	7.9
4	7.7
5	7.5
6	6.9
7	6.6
8	6.2
9	5.9

source: U.S. Bureau of Labor Statistics

   a. Find a model for this data.
   b. What is the slope for this model? Explain its meaning in this context.
   c. What percent of full-time workers in private industry will file a injury case in 2003?
   d. What is the vertical intercept for this model? What does it mean in this context?
   e. What is the horizontal intercept for this model? What does it mean in this context?

7. The number of Pre-Kindergarten through 12th grade students in California public schools is given in **Table 1.7.4**

Table 1.7.4

Year	Students
1997	5,634,519
1998	5,752,817
1999	5,870,624
2000	5,972,363

source: National Center for Education Statistics

   a. Find model for this data.
   b. What is the slope for this model? Explain its meaning in this context.

c. How many Pre-Kindergarten through 12th grade students can California expect to have in its public schools in 2005?

In Exercises 8 through 12 combine the functions by adding, subtracting, multiplying, dividing, or composing the two functions. Write the function notation for the combination you use and list the units for the inputs and outputs of the new function.

8. Let $U(t)$ be the population of the United States, in millions, t years since 1900. Let $C(t)$ be the number of children under 20 years old in the United States, in millions, t years since 1900. Find a function for the number of adults 20 years old or older in the United States.

9. Let $C(l)$ be the cost, in thousands of dollars, for Luxury Limousines Inc. to produce l limousines per year. Let $R(l)$ be the revenue, in thousands of dollars, for Luxury Limousines Inc. selling l limousines per year. Find a function for the profit of Luxury Limousines Inc. from producing and selling l limousines per year.

10. Let $E(t)$ be the number of employees of Disneyland in year t. Let $S(t)$ be the average number of sick days taken by Disneyland employees in year t. Find a function for the total number of sick days taken by Disneyland employees in year t.

11. Let $E(t)$ be the number of employees of Disneyland in year t. Let $W(e)$ be the annual workers compensation insurance cost in dollars when e employees work at Disneyland during the year. Find a function for the annual workers compensation insurance cost at Disneyland in year t.

12. Let $M(t)$ be the amount spent on treating Cancer patients throughout the U.S. in year t. Let $R(t)$ be the amount spent on Cancer research in the U.S. in year t. Find a function that represents the total amount spent on Cancer treatments and research in the U.S..

13. The number of High School, 9th -12th grade, students in California public schools is given in **Table 1.7.5**

Table 1.7.5

Year	High School Students
1997	1,578,929
1998	1,627,284
1999	1,675,778
2000	1,707,952

source: National Center for Education Statistics

a. Find a model for this data.

b. How many High School students can California expect to have in its public schools in 2005?

c. Using your model and the model from Exercise 7, find a new model for the number of California students in Pre-Kindergarten through 8th grade public schools.

d. How many students can California expect to have in its Pre-Kindergarten through 8th grade public schools in 2003, 2005, and 2010?

14. The number of people in California's labor force, and the number of these people who are unemployed is given in **Table 1.7.6**

Table 1.7.6

Year	Labor Force	Unemployment
1996	15,398,520	1,167,559
1997	15,747,435	1,061,231
1998	16,224,621	984,728
1999	16,503,004	927,430
2000	16,857,688	838,083
2001	17,246,969	807,290

source: U.S. Bureau of Labor Statistics

a. Find a model for the Labor Force data.

b. Find a model for the number of people Unemployed.

c. Estimate the number of people in the labor force in 2005.

d. Estimate the number of people unemployed in 2005.

e. Using your two models find a new model for the percent of the labor force that is unemployed.

f. What percent of the labor force is unemployed in 1998, 1999, 2000, and 2005?

15. Solve for the indicated variable.

a. Charle's Law: $V = bT$ for T.

b. $ax + by = c$ for x.

c. $2x - ay = b$ for y.

16. Sketch the graph by hand, label the vertical and horizontal intercepts.

    a. $y = 3x - 12$

    b. $y = -\dfrac{4}{5}x + 20$

    c. $3x + 5y = 20$

17. Let $f(x) = 6x + 3$ and $g(x) = -4x + 8$

    a. Find $f(x) + g(x)$

    b. Find $f(x) - g(x)$

    c. Find $f(x)g(x)$

    d. Find $f(g(x))$

    e. Find $g(f(x))$

18. Let $f(x) = 0.35x - 2.78$ and $g(x) = 2.4x - 6.3$

    a. Find $f(x) + g(x)$

    b. Find $g(x) - f(x)$

    c. Find $f(x)g(x)$

    d. Find $f(g(x))$

    e. Find $g(f(x))$

19. Let $f(x) = \dfrac{2}{5}x + \dfrac{3}{5}$ and $g(x) = 4x - 7$

    a. Find $f(x) + g(x)$

    b. Find $f(x) - g(x)$

    c. Find $f(x)g(x)$

    d. Find $f(g(x))$

    e. Find $g(f(x))$

20. Let $f(x) = \dfrac{1}{7}x + \dfrac{5}{7}$ and $g(x) = 2x - 7$

    a. Find $f(4) + g(4)$

    b. Find $f(4) - g(4)$

    c. Find $f(4)g(4)$

    d. Find $f(g(4))$

    e. Find $g(f(4))$

21. Let $f(x) = 0.6x + 2.5$ and $g(x) = 3.5x + 3.7$

    a. Find $f(-3) + g(-3)$

    b. Find $g(-3) - f(-3)$

    c. Find $f(-3)g(-3)$

    d. Find $f(g(-3))$

    e. Find $g(f(-3))$

22. Let $f(x) = 15x + 34$ and $g(x) = -17x + 34$

    a. Find $f(2) + g(2)$

    b. Find $g(2) - f(2)$

    c. Find $f(2)g(2)$

    d. Find $f(g(2))$

23. Find the equation of the line passing through the points $(2, 7)$ and $(7, 27)$.

24. Find the equation of the line passing through the points $(4, 9)$ and $(-3, 23)$.

25. Use the graph to find the following:

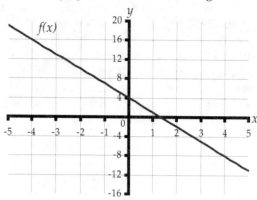

    a. Estimate the y-intercept.

    b. Estimate the x-intercept.

    c. Find the slope of the line.

    d. Find $f(4)$

    e. Find $f(x) = 16$

    f. Find an equation for $f(x)$.

26. Use the graph to find the following:

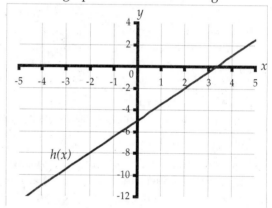

    a. Estimate the vertical intercept.

    b. Estimate the horizontal intercept.

    c. Find the slope of the line.

    d. Find $h(-2)$

    e. Find $h(x) = -2$

    f. Find an equation for $h(x)$

27. Use the table to find the following:

Table 1.7.7

x	y
-3	4
0	6
3	8
6	10
9	12

    a. The slope of the line passing through the points.

    b. The y-intercept

    c. The equation for the line passing through the points.

Chapter 1 Test

1. The number of injury cases in the U.S. private industry is given in **Table 1.1**

   Table 1.1

Year	Number of Injury Cases (in thousands)
1994	6252.2
1995	6080.6
1996	5799.9
1997	5715.8
1998	5530.9
1999	5335.0

   source: U.S. Bureau of Labor Statistics

   a. Find a model for this data.

   b. How many injury cases were there in the private industry in 2001?

   c. What is the slope of your model? Explain its meaning in this context.

   d. When was the number of injury cases in the private industry 7 million?

2. The Pharmaceutical Management Agency of New Zealand, PHARMAC, manages the amount spent on various medical conditions and drugs throughout New Zealand. The amount spent on treating Diabetes in New Zealand can be modeled by

   $$T(t) = 1.1t + 6.84$$

   where $T(t)$ represents the amount in millions of New Zealand dollars spent treating Diabetes t years since 1990. Also the amount spent on Diabetes Research in New Zealand can be modeled by

   $$R(t) = 1.3t + 0.52$$

   where $R(t)$ represents the amount in millions of New Zealand dollars spent on Diabetes Research in New Zealand t years since 1990.

   source: PHARMAC

   a. Find $T(9)$ and interpret its meaning in this context.

   b. Find $R(t) = 10$ and interpret its meaning in this context.

   c. Find a new function that represents the amount spent on both research and treatment of diabetes in New Zealand.

   d. Use the function from part c to determine the amount spent on research and treatment of diabetes in 2000.

3. Let $f(x) = 4x + 17$ and $g(x) = 2x - 7$

   a. Find $f(x) - g(x)$

   b. Find $f(x)g(x)$

   c. Find $f(g(x))$

4. Let $f(x) = 2.35x + 1.45$ and $g(x) = 2.4x - 6.3$

   a. Find $(f+g)(4)$

   b. Find $fg(-2)$

   c. Find $f(g(6))$

   d. Find $g(f(0))$

5. Sketch by hand the graph of the line
   $$y = 4x - 2$$
   Label the vertical and horizontal intercepts.

6. Sketch by hand the graph of the line
   $$2x - 4y = 10$$
   Label the vertical and horizontal intercepts.

7. Solve $ax - by = c$ for x.

8. Find the equation for the line passing through the points $(-4, 8)$ and $(6, 10)$.

9. The number of paintings John Clark sells each month can be modeled by
   $$P = 2m + 30$$
   where m is the number of months since he started selling paintings.

   a. In month 6 how many paintings will John sell?

   b. What month will he sell 50 paintings?

For Exercises 10 through 13 assume that the following functions refer to a specific summer tennis camp and that t represents the year.

- Let $T(t)$ be the total number of children at the camp.
- Let $B(t)$ be the number of boys at the camp.
- Let $C(k)$ be the total cost for k children to go to the camp.
- Let $M(k)$ be the number of matches played at a camp with k children.
- Let $A(t)$ be the average length of time, in minutes, a match takes to play.

Combine the functions by adding, subtracting, multiplying, dividing, or composing the two functions. Write the function notation for the combination you use and list the units for the inputs and outputs of the new function.

10. Find a function that gives the number of girls attending the tennis camp.

11. Find a function for the number of boys matches at the camp in year t.

12. Find a function for the total cost for the camp in year t.

13. Find the amount of time it takes for all the matches played in a certain year t.

14. The total operating expenses for Southwest Air-
     lines for the past several years is given in **Table
     1.2**

Table 1.2

Years Since 1995	Total Operating Expenses (in millions of $)
3	1559.9
4	1692.9
5	1804.2
6	1949.0

source: CBS.MarketWatch.com

a. Find a model for this data.

b. What is the vertical intercept for your model?
    Explain its meaning in this context.

c. Estimate the total operating expenses for
    Southwest Airlines in 2003.

d. When were the total operating expenses only 1
    billion dollars?

e. What is the slope of this model? Explain its
    meaning in this context.

15. Use the table to find the following:

Table 1.3

x	y
-5	16
0	12
5	8
10	4
15	0

a. The slope of the line passing through these
    points.

b. The y-intercept.

c. The x-intercept.

d. The equation for the line passing through these
    points.

16. Use the graph to find the following:

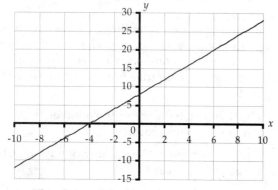

a. The slope of the line.

b. The vertical intercept.

c. The horizontal intercept.

d. An equation for the line.

Section 2.1   Introduction to Systems of Linear Equations

• **Definition of Systems** • **Graphical and Numerical Solutions** • **Types of Systems**

In many areas of life we make comparisons of two or more quantities in an attempt to make a good decision about which is best for our situation. This type of decision process can often be simplified using what mathematicians call a **system of equations**. A system of equations is a set of equations that requires a solution which will work for all of the equations in the set. This is often the case when we are trying to determine when two options are going to be equal.

Definition 2.1.1

System of Linear Equations: A set of two or more linear equations.

Solution of a System of Two Linear Equations: An ordered pair (or a set of ordered pairs) which is a solution to every equation in the system. In the graph this would be seen as the intersection of the lines.

Example 1

We began chapter 1 by considering the cost to rent a 10ft truck from U-Haul for the day. Suppose we were to compare U-Haul's prices with those of Budget Truck Rental.

U-Haul quotes you $19.95 for the day and $0.59 per mile driven.
Budget quotes you $24.95 for the day and $0.55 per mile driven.

a. Find equations for these two companies; total rental quotes for one day.

b. Graph the two equations on the same calculator screen.

c. Determine for what distance traveled the two companies will quote the same cost.

Solution

a. First we define the variables.

$U(m)$ = The total cost in dollars to rent a 10ft truck from U-Haul.

$B(m)$ = The total cost in dollars to rent a 10ft truck from Budget.

m = The number of miles traveled in rented truck.

We get the following two equations:

$$B(m) = 24.95 + 0.55m$$
$$U(m) = 19.95 + 0.59m$$

b. Put both equations into the Y= screen and be sure the stat plots are turned off. To set an appropriate viewing window let's consider the context of the situation. We are renting the truck and cannot drive less than zero miles and will probably not drive more than 200 in one day so set x-min and x-max to 0 and 200 respectively. Now for the outputs we know we will be charged at least 19.95 for the rental and that will go up from there. So if we drive the full 200 miles the cost from the companies comes to a just under $150 so let's set the y-min and y-max to 15 and 150 respectively

Graphic 2.1.1.

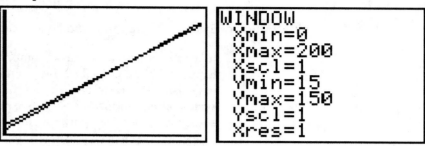

c.   Using the trace button on the calculator, see **Graphic 2.1.2**, we estimate the solution to be about 130 miles at a cost of $96.52. Therefore U-haul and Budget will both rent a 10ft truck for a day at a cost of $96.52 if you drive the truck 130 miles. In order to get a more precise solution to this system we would need to zoom in on the graph so the intersection becomes more clear or solve the system algebraically. We will learn algebraic methods to solve linear systems in the next section.

Graphic 2.1.2.

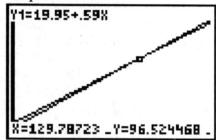

The solution to this system tells us that U-haul and Budget charge the same amount if you rent a 10ft truck for a day and drive it about 130 miles. Since U-haul charges a smaller day rate they will be cheaper than Budget up until 130 miles and over 130 miles, Budget will result in a cheaper total cost.

Problem 1

The number of American male smokers, per thousand, who are expected to die in the next 10 years from a heart attack or lung cancer can be modeled by the following two functions.

$$H(a) = 4.4a - 9$$
$$L(a) = 5.54a - 19.5$$

where $H(a)$ represents the number of American male smokers who are expected to die in the next 10 years from a heart attack per every 1,000 male smokers aged a years over 40. $L(a)$ represents the number of American male smokers who are expected to die in the next 10 years from lung cancer per every 1,000 male smokers aged a years over 40.

source: Journal of the National Cancer Institute

a.   Graph both equations on the same window.

b.   Find at what age American male smokers have the same risk of dying from a heart attack as they do from lung cancer.

Solution   see page 87

Example 2

The amount of beef and chicken consumed by Americans is given in **Table 2.1.1**.

Table 2.1.1

Year	Beef Consumption (in millions of pounds)	Chicken Consumption (in millions of pounds)
1990	24031	17762
1995	25534	21238
1999	26932	24630
2000	27290	24963

source: Statistical Abstract 2001

a. Find a model for the amount of beef consumed by Americans.

b. Find a model for the amount of chicken consumed by Americans.

c. Estimate what year the amount of beef consumed will be the same as the amount of chicken consumed.

Solution

a. To find a model for the amount of beef consumed by Americans we first need to define the variables.

> B = The amount of beef consumed by Americans, in millions of pounds.
> t = years since 1990.

Using the first and last points given we get the model

$$B(t) = 325.9t + 24031$$

b. Now for a model to find the amount of chicken consumed we define the variables.

> C = The amount of chicken consumed by Americans, in millions of pounds.
> t = years since 1990.

Using the first and next to last point we get the model

$$C(t) = 763t + 17762$$

c. Graphing the two models on one window you will need to expand the window some to see the intersection and trace the estimated answer

Graphic 2.1.3.

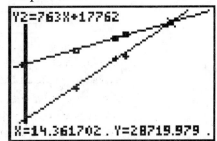

From this graph we can estimate the solution to be $(14.36, 28720)$. Thus in about 2004 the amount of chicken and beef consumed by Americans will both be approximately 28720 million pounds of each.

Using the graph and trace on your calculator is one way to check the solutions to many of the equations we will solve in this book. Another tool the calculator has that can be a great tool for both finding solutions and checking solutions you already found is the table feature. You can use the table to check a solution to a system of equations. You need to first put both equations in the Y= screen and then go to the table. Enter the input values you want to check

TI - 83 Details:

Using the TABLE Feature:

First you need to enter the function into the Y = screen as you have done to graph other problems.

To set up the table you need to press [2nd] [TBLSET] above the WINDOW button.

```
TABLE SETUP
 TblStart=0
 ΔTbl=1
Indpnt: Auto ASK
Depend: AUTO Ask
```

The only things you need to be sure are set correctly are the Indpnt and Depend settings.
Indpnt should be set to **Ask**
Depend should be set to **Auto**.

These settings will allow you to enter a value for the input variable and the calculator will automatically calculate the related output.

Now you go to the TABLE, above the GRAPH button and enter the values of *x* you want.

When the Indpnt setting is set to Auto the table will automatically fill with input values based on the TblStart setting and the ΔTbl (change in table) setting. This is good if you want a whole list but not as efficient if you want a few specific values.

and as long as the y values returned are the same you have found a solution. In the last example we used graphing and trace to find the solution of $(14.36, 28720)$. If we look at the table using these two functions and values close to 14.36 we get

X	Y₁	Y₂
14.38	28717	28734
14.37	28714	28726
14.36	28711	28719
14.35	28708	28711
14.34	28704	28703
14.33	28701	28696

X=

```
Plot1 Plot2 Plot3
\Y1▉325.9X+24031

\Y2▉763X+17762
\Y3=
\Y4=
\Y5=
\Y6=
```

From this table we can see that a more accurate solution would be $(14.34, 28703)$. In this particular application we round the answers to a whole number for the year so the table does confirm that our solution is good.

Example 3

Use the table on the calculator to numerically find the solution to the following systems of equations.

a.
$$y = 2x + 7$$
$$y = 5x - 3.5$$

b.
$$y = -9x + 177$$
$$y = 13x - 65$$

Solution

a.   Using the table we can guess a value for *x* and then adjust until we get the *y* values to be closer and eventually the same.

X	Y₁	Y₂
0	7	-3.5
2	11	6.5
4	15	16.5
3	13	11.5
3.5	14	14

X=

From this table we can see that the solution is $(3.5, 14)$.

b.

X	Y₁	Y₂
0	177	-65
2	159	-39
4	141	-13
8	105	39
10	87	65
11	78	78
12	69	91

X=8

From this table we can see that the solution is $(11, 78)$.

Remember that the table is a good way to get a solution numerically. This method can be hard if the solution is not a whole number or if you have no idea where the solution is. The table is a great place to check solutions to equations and we will use it often in the remaining chapters of this book.

Concept Investigation 1

To start turn off all your stat plots, set your window to a standard window using [zoom] [6] (ZStandard), and clear all equations from the Y= screen.

a.   Graph the following systems and answer the questions.

   i

$$y = 2x - 5$$
$$y = -5x + 9$$

   ii

$$w = \frac{2}{3}p - 2$$

$$w = \frac{1}{9}p + 3$$

   iii

$$3c - 2d = -13$$
$$5c + d = -13$$

   How many solutions does each system have? (How many places do the graphs intersect one another?)

   i   ii   iii

   Estimate the solution to each system using the trace feature of your calculator.

   i   ii   iii

b.   Graph the following systems and answer the questions.

   i

$$-x + 5y = -15$$

$$y = \frac{3}{15}x + 2$$

   ii

$$P = 2.75t - 4.25$$
$$P = 2.75t + 3$$

   How many solutions do each of these systems have?

   i   ii

   How are each of the equations in these systems related?

c.   Graph the following systems and answer the questions.

   i

$$6x + 2y = 14$$
$$21x + 7y = 49$$

   ii

$$-3.5x - 2.75y = 4.5$$
$$9.8x + 7.7y = -12.6$$

   How many solutions do each of these systems have?

   i   ii

   How are each of the equations in these systems related?

This concept investigation shows that systems of two linear equations can have three types of answers.

Mathematicians give the following names to these three types of systems.

- **Consistent System:** a system with at least one solution. The lines intersect in one place.

Graphic 2.1.4.

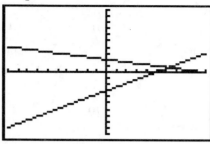

- **Inconsistent System:** a system with no solutions. The lines are parallel and thus do not intersect. Use caution when looking at the calculator since some lines may seem parallel but really are not.

Graphic 2.1.5

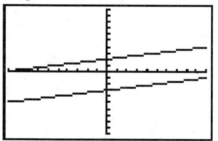

- **Dependent System:** a system with infinitely many solutions. The lines are the same and therefore intersect in infinitely many places. Use caution when looking at the calculator since some lines may seem the same but really are not. These systems are also considered consistent.

Graphic 2.1.6

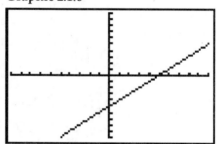

Getting an idea for the visual representation of these solutions will help in the next section when we solve systems algebraically.

Problem 2

Use the table on the calculator to numerically find the solution to the systems of equations.

a.

$$y = 2x - 8$$
$$y = -4x + 28$$

b.

$$y = -\frac{3}{5}x + 9$$

$$y = 0.6(7 - x) + 2.8$$

Solution   See page 87

Section 2.1 Key Points

- Systems of equations are a set of equations for which you are looking for a common solution.
- Solutions for systems of equations can be estimated with graphing.
- Systems can have three types of solutions.
    - **i** Consistent Systems: A system with a finite number of solutions, usually just one.
    - **ii** Dependent Systems: A system with infinitely many solutions. The equations represent the same line. These systems are also considered consistent.
    - **iii** Inconsistent Systems: A system with no solutions. The equations are parallel.

Section 2.1 Problem Solutions

Problem 1   Solution

a.

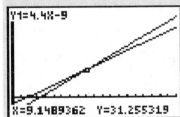

b. Since the two functions intersect at about (9 , 31.26) we have the following solution: American male smokers have the same risk of dying from a heart attack as they do from lung cancer at about age 49. At this age about 62 male smokers out of every 1000 male smokers are expected to die in the next ten years, 31 from a hear attack and 31 from lung cancer.

Problem 2   Solution

a.

X	Y₁	Y₂
0	-8	28
2	-4	20
4	0	12
6	4	4
8	8	-4
10	12	-12
12	16	-20

X=12

The solution to this system is (6,4).

b.

X	Y₁	Y₂
0	9	7
2	7.8	5.8
4	6.6	4.6
6	5.4	3.4
8	4.2	2.2
10	3	1
12	1.8	-.2

X=12

This system is inconsistent.
The two lines are always 2 units apart.
There are no solutions.

2.1 Exercises

1. The value of Records and other Magnetic Media exported and imported by the U.S. is given in **Table 2.1.2**

    Table 2.1.2

Year	Exports (in millions of $)	General Imports (in millions of $)
1997	6815	4137
1998	6057	4383
1999	5802	4703
2000	5427	5166

    source: Statistical Abstract 2001

    a. Find models for the data given.
    b. Graph both models on the same calculator screen.
    c. Estimate when the value of Records and other Magnetic Media exported by the U.S. will be equal to the value imported by the U.S..

2. The number of women enrolled in U.S. colleges has been increasing steadily since the 1970's. The number of women and men enrolled in U.S. colleges is given in **Table 2.1.3**

    Table 2.1.3

Year	Women Enrolled (in millions)	Year	Men Enrolled (in millions)
1975	4.4	1972	4.9
1976	4.7	1977	5.4
1983	6.3	1981	5.8
1985	6.6	1991	6.4
1991	7.6	1995	6.7
1997	8.6	1999	7.0

    source: Statistical Abstract 2001

    a. Find models for the number of women and men enrolled in U.S. Colleges.
    b. Graph both models on the same calculator screen.
    c. Estimate when the number of women enrolled was the same as the number of men enrolled.

3. The percent of white male and female Americans 25 years old or older who are college graduates is given in **Table 2.1.4**

    Table 2.1.4

Year	Males	Females
1980	21.3	12.3
1985	24	16.3
1990	25.3	19
1995	27.2	21
2000	28.5	23.9

    source: Statistical Abstract 2001

    a. Find models for the data given.
    b. Graph both models on the same calculator screen.

    c. Estimate when the percent of white American males with college degrees will be the same as the percent of white American women with college degrees.

4. Professional sports salaries have increased dramatically over the past few years. The average players salaries, in thousands of dollars, for the National Football League (NFL) and the National Basketball Association (NBA) are given in **Table 2.1.5**

    Table 2.1.5

Year	Average NFL Salary (in thousands)	Average NBA Salary (in thousands)
1995	714	1900
1996	791	2000
1997	725	2200
1998	1138	2600

    source: Statistical Abstract 2001

    a. Find models for the average salary data given.
    b. Graph both models on the same calculator screen.
    c. Determine when the average salary for NFL players was/will be the same as the average salary for NBA players.

5. Hope's Pottery makes clay vases to sell at a local gallery. Hope has determined the following models for her monthly revenue and costs associated with making and selling these vases.

    $$R(v) = 155v$$
    $$C(v) = 5000 + 65v$$

    where $R(v)$ represents the monthly revenue in dollars for selling v vases, and $C(v)$ represents the monthly costs in dollars for producing and selling v vases.

    a. Graph both functions on the same calculator screen.
    b. Determine the break-even point for Hope's Pottery. (The break-even point is when the revenue equals the costs.)

6. Jim's Carburetors rebuilds carburetors for local auto repair shops. Jim has determined the following models for his monthly revenue and costs associated with rebuilding these carberators.

    $$R(c) = 65c$$
    $$C(c) = 2300 + 17c$$

    where $R(c)$ represents the monthly revenue in dollars for rebuilding c carburetors, and $C(c)$ is the monthly costs in dollars for rebuilding c carburetors.

a. Graph both functions on the same calculator screen.

b. Determine the break-even point for Jim's Carberators.

7. La Opinion, a Spanish newspaper in Los Angeles County California, is one of LA's fastest growing daily newspapers. The Long Beach Press Telegram is another large daily newspaper in LA county. The daily circulation for both of these newspapers is given by the following functions;

$$O(t) = 7982t + 28489$$

$$L(t) = 726t + 97395$$

where $O(t)$ represents the daily circulation of La Opinion t years since 1990, and $L(t)$ represents the daily circulation of the Long Beach Press Telegram t years since 1990.

source: Los Angeles Almanac 2001.

a. Use graphing to estimate when the two newspapers had the same daily circulation.

b. Compare the slopes of these two functions and describe what they represent in this context.

8. A local BMW dealer has two salary options for its sales force. The sales force can choose either of the following two salary options;

$$O_1(s) = 250 + 0.03s$$

$$O_2(s) = 0.03s + 200$$

where $O_1(s)$ represents weekly salary option 1 in dollars when s dollars in sales are made per week, and $O_2(s)$ represents weekly salary option 2 in dollars when s dollars in sales are made per week.

a. Find what sales level will give the sales force the same salary with either option.

9. Harry's Flooring has two salary options for their sales people. Each sales person can choose which option they want to base their salary on.

$$O_1(s) = 500 + 0.07s$$

$$O_2(s) = 0.075s + 700$$

where $O_1(s)$ represents monthly salary option 1 in dollars when s dollars in sales are made per month, and $O_2(s)$ represents monthly salary option 2 in dollars when s dollars in sales are made per month.

Find what sales level would result in both salary options having the same monthly salary.

Math Tutorial

More practice problems like exercises 10 through 15 can be found in section 2.1 of the CD Tutorial.

For exercises 10 through 15 solve the systems by graphing. Label each system as consistent, inconsistent or dependent.

10.
$$x + y = -6$$
$$-2x + y = 3$$

11.
$$w = 8d + 54$$
$$w = \frac{3}{2}d + \frac{17}{2}$$

12.
$$p = 2.5t + 6$$
$$p = \frac{5}{2}t - 6$$

13.
$$3x - 4y = 8$$
$$0.75x - y = -2$$

14.
$$R = 2.75t + 6.35$$
$$R = -1.5t + 12.45$$

15.
$$H = 3c + 6.5$$
$$-6c + 2H = 13$$

For exercises 16 through 19 solve the systems numerically using the given tables. Label each system as consistent, inconsistent or dependent.

16.

X	Y1	Y2
0	5	19
1	8	15
2	11	11
3	14	7
4	17	3
5	20	-1

X=

17.

X	Y1	Y2
0	5	-23
-1	2	-19
-2	-1	-15
-3	-4	-11
-4	-7	-7
-5	-10	-3
-6	-13	1

X= -6

18.

X	Y1	Y2
0	5	-5
1	8	-2
2	11	1
3	14	4
4	17	7
5	20	10
6	23	13

X=6

19.

X	Y1	Y2
0	9	8
1	11	10
2	13	12
3	15	14
4	17	16
5	19	18
6	21	20

X=0

For exercises 20 through 23 solve the systems numerically. Label each system as consistent, inconsistent or dependent.

20.

$$p = 3t + 8$$
$$p = 2t + 17$$

21.

$$2.5x - 0.5y = -23.5$$
$$0.75x - 1.5y = -23.25$$

22.

$$R = 0.8t + 6$$
$$R = \frac{4}{5}t + 40.5$$

23.

$$y = 2x - 20$$
$$y = -4x + 70$$

Section 2.2   Solving Systems Algebraically

• Substitution Method • Elimination Method • Dependent Systems • Inconsistent Systems

In the last section we learned how to solve systems of two linear equations by graphing. This method can be done fairly well if done on a graphing calculator. One drawback to solving these systems by graphing is that you need to have an idea of where the intersection is going to be in order to find it on the graphing calculator screen. Example 1 is a good example of when finding an answer by graphing can be very difficult.

Example 1

Given the following system find a solution by graphing.
$$y = 0.0000005x + 12345678900$$
$$y = 0.000001x - 12345678900$$

Solution

By looking at these two equations we can see the slopes of the lines are 0.0000005 and 0.000001 since the slopes are not the same we know the lines are not the same or parallel. Therefore must be a single solution to this system. Since the slopes are so small and they both start so far from each other on the y-axis the solution is going to be at a very large value of x. Mostly this will be a guessing game so lets try a window and see what we get

Graphic 2.2.1.

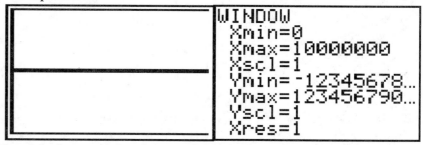

We used a large number for $x$max and tried to get both y-intercepts into the window. As you can see we did not get the lines to come anywhere close to each other. Choosing a much larger window may help. Since we are looking for where the y-values will be the same one possible approach is to use trial an error in the table on the calculator. By trying several very large numbers We found that the y-values were closest around 100,000,000,000,000,000 (1E17 in the table, the calculator is using scientific notation to write this very large number in a much shorter way. The E17 represents multiplication by 10^{17}). This helps us determine a new window that shows the intersection.

Graphic 2.2.2

X	Y₁	Y₂
1E60	1.2E10	-1E10
1E55	5E48	1E49
1E50	5E43	1E44
1E40	5E33	1E34
1E30	5E23	1E24
1E20	5E13	1E14
1E17	6.2E10	8.8E10

X=100000000000

```
WINDOW
 Xmin=100000000
 Xmax=1E17
 Xscl=1
 Ymin=0
 Ymax=880000000...
 Yscl=1
 Xres=
```

Solving by Substitution

SC-Example 1: *Solve*
$$w = 5k + 7$$
$$w = -3k + 23$$

Solution:
Since w is already isolated on the left side of at least one of the equations we can substitute the expression from the first equation into the w for the second equation.
$$w = 5k + 7$$
$$w = -3k + 23$$

Substitute and solve for k.
$$5k + 7 = -3k + 23$$

$$
\begin{array}{r}
+\,3k \qquad\quad +\,3k \\
\hline
8k + 7 = 23 \\
-7 \quad\ -7 \\
\hline
8k = 16 \\
\dfrac{8k}{8} = \dfrac{16}{8} \\
k = 2
\end{array}
$$

We know $k = 2$ so we can substitute 2 for k in either of the equations to find w.
$$w = 5k + 7$$
$$w = 5(2) + 7$$
$$w = 17$$

The solution to this system is the point $(2, 17)$. You should check this solution in both equations to be sure it is valid.
$$w = 5k + 7$$
$$17 = 5(2) + 7$$
$$17 = 17$$

$$w = -3k + 23$$
$$17 = -3(2) + 23$$
$$17 = 17$$

Graphic 2.2.3

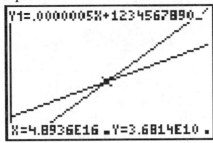

From this graph we get the solution $(4.89 \cdot 10^{16}, 3.68 \cdot 10^{10})$.

As you can see this took a lot more work than before and the window is very large and hard to find. With this type of situation when the numbers are not "nice" it can be very difficult to find the solutions graphically. Therefore we want to learn some other ways to solve systems of equations. There are two basic algebraic ways to solve systems of equations; the **substitution method** and the **elimination method**. Both of these methods are good tools to solve systems of equations and are not too difficult to master. Since most of the models we find in this text are in $y = mx + b$ form we will learn the substitution method first. The substitution method simply means to substitute the expression one equation says a variable equals into that same variable in the other equation.

Example 2

Using the models from section 2.1 for beef and chicken consumption by Americans find the year when beef and chicken consumption will be the same.
$$B(t) = 325.9t + 24031$$
$$C(t) = 763t + 17762$$
where $B(t)$ is the amount of beef consumed by Americans, in millions of pounds, t years since 1990, and $C(t)$ is the amount of chicken consumed by Americans, in millions of pounds, t years since 1990.

Solution
Since both $B(t)$ and $C(t)$ represent the amount of meat consumed by Americans and both are measured in millions of pounds we can substitute the expression that $B(t)$ equals into the position of $C(t)$.
$$B(t) = 325.9t + 24031$$
$$C(t) = 763t + 17762$$

$$
\begin{array}{ll}
325.9t + 24031 = 763t + 17762 & \text{Substitution for } C. \\
-763t \qquad\qquad\quad -763t & \text{Solve for } t. \\
\hline
-437.1t + 24031 = 17762 \\
\qquad\qquad -24031 \quad -24031 \\
\hline
-437.1t = -6269 \\
\dfrac{-437.1t}{-437.1} = \dfrac{-6269}{-437.1} \\
t = 14.34225578
\end{array}
$$

Now that we have the value of t that will give us an equal amount of meat consumed, we need to find the amount of beef and chicken consumed that year. We can do that by substituting this value for t in either equation.

$$B(t) = 325.9t + 24031$$
$$B(14.34225578) = 325.9(14.34225578) + 24031$$
$$B(14.34225578) = 28705.14116$$

or

$$C(14.34225578) = 763(14.34225578) + 17762$$
$$C(14.34225578) = 28705.14116$$

This shows that we have found the solution to this system. But since t represents a year we need to round it to the nearest whole number, in this case 14. If we substitute 14 into the variable t for these equations we will find that they are not exactly equal.

$$B(t) = 325.9t + 24031$$
$$B(14) = 325.9(14) + 24031$$
$$B(14) = 28593.6$$

or

$$C(14) = 763(14) + 17762$$
$$C(14) = 28444$$

This gives us the following approximate answer in this context. Americans will eat approximately 28,500 million pounds of both beef and chicken in 2004.

Problem 1

The Pharmaceutical Management Agency of New Zealand, PHARMAC, manages the amount spent on various medical conditions and drugs throughout New Zealand. The amount spent on treating Diabetes in New Zealand can be modeled by

$$T(t) = 1.1t + 6.84$$

where $T(t)$ represents the amount in millions of New Zealand dollars spent treating Diabetes t years since 1990. Also the amount spent on Diabetes Research in New Zealand can be modeled by

$$R(t) = 1.3t + 0.52$$

where $R(t)$ represents the amount in millions of New Zealand dollars spent on Diabetes Research in New Zealand t years since 1990.
source: PHARMAC

Find the year in which the amount spent in New Zealand on treating diabetes will be the same as the amount spent in New Zealand on diabetes research.

Solution   see page 101

Example 3

Clear Sign Designs, a local sign manufacturer, wants to give its sales force incentives to make bigger sales. In order to do this the company executives are changing the salary structure. The old system was a base salary of $1000 per month and 8% commission on sales made. The new salary structure will consist of a base salary of $500 per month with a 10% commission on sales made.

a. Find equations to represent the new and old salary structures.

b. Find what sales amount will result in the same monthly salary for the sales force.

Solving by Substitution

SC-Example 2: *Solve*
$$p = 2t - 12$$
$$p - 3t = -17$$

Solution:
p is isolated in the first equation so the expression p is equal to can be substituted into p for the second equation.
$$p = 2t - 12$$
$$p - 3t = -17$$

Substitute and solve for t.
$$(2t - 12) - 3t = -17$$
$$-1t - 12 = -17$$
$$-1t = -5$$
$$t = 5$$

We know $t = 5$ so we can substitute 5 for t in either of the equations to find p.
$$p = 2(5) - 12$$
$$p = -2$$

Therefore the solution to this system is $(5, -2)$. You should check this solution in both equations to be sure it is valid.
$$-2 = 2(5) - 12$$
$$-2 = -2$$

$$-2 - 3(5) = -17$$
$$17 = 17$$

Solution

a.   Define the variables:
N = Salary in dollars for the new salary structure.
O = Salary in dollars for the old salary structure.
s = Sales made during the month in dollars.
Changing the commission percents into decimals we get the following two equations.
$$N(s) = 500 + 0.10s$$
$$O(s) = 1000 + 0.08s$$

b.   To find the sales amount that will result in the same salary we need the new salary $N(s)$ to be equal to the old salary $O(s)$. So we can substitute the expression $500 + 0.10s$ into the second equation for $O(s)$. Solving this will give us the sales amount that will result in the same monthly salary. Using that sales amount we can find the actual monthly salary earned.

$$N(s) = 500 + 0.10s$$
$$\overline{O(s) = 1000 + 0.08s}$$

$500 + 0.10s = 1000 + 0.08s$	Substitution for O.
$\underline{-500 - 0.08s \qquad -500 - 0.08s}$	Solve for s.
$0.02s = 500$	
$\dfrac{0.02s}{0.02} = \dfrac{500}{0.02}$	
$s = 25000$	

so

$N(25000) = 500 + 0.10(25000)$	Find N when $s = 25000$
$N(25000) = 3000$	

X	Y1	Y2
25000	3000	3000

X=

Check your solution in the table.

Therefore if a salesperson has monthly sales of \$25,000 their salary will be the same, \$3000, on the new and old salary structures.

   Although most of our models we find will be in $y = mx + b$ form we will sometimes be given a linear model or equation not in this form. There are also situations that may be best modeled using another form. When this is the case we can isolate a variable in one equation and then use the substitution method. Or the system may be better suited for the elimination method.

   In the elimination method you will multiply one or both equations by constant(s) in order to make one of the variables add to zero (eliminate) when the two equations are added together. This may seem like an illegal operation but as long as you multiply both sides of the equations by the same number your equations will remain true but only look different. Your goal will be to get the coefficients of one variable to be the same but opposite signs in each equation. This will make the variable be eliminated when the two equations are added together.

Skill Connection:

Solving by Elimination

SC-Example 4: *Solve*
$$3x + 2y = 10$$
$$5x - 8y = 28$$

Solution:
Since the signs of the coefficients of y are already opposites we can eliminate the y's by multiplying the first equation by 4.
$$4(3x + 2y = 10)$$
$$5x - 8y = 28$$

$$12x + 8y = 40$$
$$5x - 8y = 28$$

Now we can add the two equations together to eliminate y.
$$12x + 8y = 40$$
$$\underline{5x - 8y = 28}$$
$$17x = 68$$
$$\frac{17x}{17} = \frac{68}{17}$$
$$x = 4$$
$$3(4) + 2y = 10$$
$$12 + 2y = 10$$
$$2y = -2$$
$$y = -1$$

The solution to this system is $(4, -1)$. You should check this solution in both equations to be sure it is valid.
$$3(4) + 2(-1) = 10$$
$$10 = 10$$

$$5(4) - 8(-1) = 28$$
$$28 = 28$$

Example 4

Fay Clark is retired and has $500,000 to invest. She needs her investments to earn $24,000 per year in interest for her to live on. She is considering depositing most of the funds in a very safe bank account that pays 3.5% simple interest per year and the rest in a more risky account that pays 10% simple interest per year.

a. Write a system of equations that will help you find the amount in each investment.

b. How much should she invest in each account in order to earn the $24,000 she needs each year?

(Note: some financial accounts are not federally insured and are thus considered more risky.)

Solution

a. There are two main factors controlling this situation; the amount of money Fay can invest and the total amount of interest she needs to earn each year. If we set up two equations using these facts we can solve the system for the amounts in each account. We need to start by defining the variables.
A = The amount invested in the account paying 3.5% simple interest
B = The amount invested in the account paying 10% simple interest.
With these definitions and the limits we were given we get the following two equations.

$$A + B = 500000 \qquad \text{The two accounts total \$500,0000.}$$
$$0.035A + 0.10B = 24000 \qquad \text{The total interest needs to be \$24,000.}$$

b. To find the amount she should deposit in each account we need to solve the system. Since neither variable is isolated in either equation we can use the elimination method.

$$A + B = 500000$$
$$0.035A + 0.10B = 24000$$

$$-0.035(A + B = 500000) \qquad \text{Multiply the first equation by}$$
$$0.035A + 0.10B = 24000 \qquad \text{-0.035, be sure to distribute all the way through.}$$

$$-0.35A - 0.035B = -17500 \quad \text{Add the two equations together,}$$
$$\underline{0.035A + 0.10B = 24000} \quad \text{thus eliminating the variable } A.$$

$$0.065B = 6500$$
$$\frac{0.065B}{0.065} = \frac{6500}{0.065} \qquad \text{Solve for } B.$$
$$B = 100000$$

so

$$A + 100000 = 500000 \qquad \text{Solve for A.}$$
$$A = 400000$$

$$\qquad\qquad \text{Check the solution in both}$$
$$400000 + 100000 = 500000 \text{ equations.}$$
$$500000 = 500000$$

$$0.035(400000) + 0.10(100000) = 24000$$
$$24000 = 24000$$

This solution tell us that Fay should deposit $400,000 into the account paying 3.5% interest and $100,000 into the more risky account paying 10% interest. This will give her a total of $24,000 in interest each year to live on.

Solving by Elimination

SC-Example 5: *Solve*

$$3g + 5h = 27$$
$$6g - 7h = -31$$

Solution:

Since the signs of the coefficients of h are already opposites we will eliminate the h's by multiplying the first equation by 7 and the second by 5.

$$3g + 5h = 27$$
$$6g - 7h = -31$$

$$7(3g + 5h = 27)$$
$$5(6g - 7h = -31)$$

Now the equations can be added together in order to eliminate h.

$$21g + 35h = 189$$
$$\underline{30g - 35h = -155}$$
$$51g = 34$$
$$\frac{51g}{51} = \frac{34}{51}$$
$$g = \frac{2}{3}$$

$$3\left(\frac{2}{3}\right) + 5h = 27$$

$$2 + 5h = 27$$
$$h = 5$$

The solution to this system is $\left(\frac{2}{3}, 5\right)$. You should check this solution in both equations to be sure it is valid.

$$3\left(\frac{2}{3}\right) + 5(5) = 27$$

$$27 = 27$$

$$6\left(\frac{2}{3}\right) - 7(5) = -21$$

$$-21 = -21$$

Problem 2

George is retiring and only has $350,000 to invest. George needs $18,000 per year more than his Social Security to live on. George has two investments that he plans to use to earn the interest he needs to live on. One investment is conservative and only pays 3.6% simple interest annually, the other is less conservative and pays 6% simple interest annually. Determine how much George should deposit into each account in order to make the interest he needs to live on each year. Note George must invest the entire $350,000.

Solution   see page 102

Example 5

Sally, a college chemistry student, needs 100ml of a 50% saline solution to do her experiment for lab today. Sally can only find saline solutions with 30% saline and 80% saline. How much of each of these solutions does Sally need to use in order to get the 100ml of 50% saline solution for her lab experiment?

Solution

Sally has two constraints that she needs to meet. She needs 100ml of the solution and she also needs 50% of that to be saline. If we define the following variables:

    A = The amount of 30% saline solution used (in ml).
    B = The amount of 80% saline solution used (in ml).

Using these variables and the two constraints given results in the following two equations.

$$A + B = 100 \qquad \text{The total solution should be 100ml}$$
$$0.30A + 0.80B = 0.50(100) \qquad \text{The percent of saline should be 50\%}$$

Solving this system of equations will give us the amounts of each solution that Sally should use.

$$A + B = 100$$
$$0.30A + 0.80B = 0.50(100)$$

$$-0.80(A + B = 100) \qquad \text{Multiply first equation by -0.80 to eliminate } B.$$
$$0.30A + 0.80B = 50$$

$$-0.80A - 0.80B = -80$$
$$\underline{0.30A + 0.80B = 50} \qquad \text{Add the equations to eliminate } B.$$

$$-0.50A = -30 \qquad \text{Solve for } A.$$
$$\frac{-0.50A}{-0.50} = \frac{-30}{-0.50}$$
$$A = 60$$

so

$$60 + B = 100 \qquad \text{Solve for } B.$$
$$B = 40$$

$$60 + 40 = 100 \qquad \text{Check the solution in both equations.}$$
$$100 = 100$$

$$0.30(60) + 0.80(40) = 0.50(100)$$
$$50 = 50$$

Sally should use 60ml of the 30% saline solution and 40ml of the 80% saline solution in order to get 100ml of 50% saline solution.

Problem 3

Jim Johnson is a local veterinarian who has prescribed a client's Great Dane a diet of 24% protein. Jim has two types of dog food but neither is 24% protein. Diamond Pet Foods Maintenance Formula has 21% protein and their Professional Formula has 30% protein. The client wants 225 pounds of food to feed their Great Dane until the next vet appointment. How much of each type of food should Jim sell his clients?

Solution   see page 103

Recall from the last section the three types of systems.

Consistent System: A system with at least one solution.

Inconsistent System: A system with no solutions. These systems have two parallel lines. Look for the same slopes.

Dependent System: A system with infinitely many solutions. These systems are also considered consistent and occur when one equation is a multiple of the other equation.

Although most systems will have a single solution, there are times when a system may be dependent or inconsistent and thus have an infinite number of solutions or no solutions, respectively. When solving a system of equations algebraically finding out when you have a dependent or inconsistent system happens rather suddenly. Keeping an eye open for systems of parallel lines (inconsistent systems) or systems with multiples of the same equation (dependent systems) is a quick way to notice these situations. But these patterns are not always clear since the equations can look very different yet be remarkably similar or the same. While solving dependent or inconsistent systems you will notice that all the variables will be eliminated and you will be left with two numbers set equal to each other. If these remaining numbers are actually equal then you have a dependent system and an infinite number of solutions since it does not matter what input or output you use. If the remaining numbers are not equal then you have an inconsistent system and no solution.

Example 6

Solve the following systems and label them as consistent, dependent, or inconsistent.

a.

$$r = 4.1t + 6.3$$
$$3r - 12.3t = 18.9$$

b.

$$5p + 2w = 4$$
$$-4p - w = -3$$

c.

$$y = 4x + 9$$
$$y = 4x - 9$$

d.

$$-3x + 2y = 7$$
$$12x - 8y = -28$$

e.

$$S = 1500 + 0.05c$$
$$S = 0.05c + 750$$

Solution

a. This system is set up well for substitution since one variable is already isolated.

$$r = 4.1t + 6.3$$
$$3r - 12.3t = 18.9$$

$$3(4.1t + 6.3) - 12.3t = 18.9 \quad \text{Substitute for } r.$$
$$12.3t + 18.9 - 12.3t = 18.9$$
$$18.9 = 18.9 \qquad \text{These numbers are equal.}$$

Since the variables both were eliminated and the remaining numbers are equal this system must be dependent and so all inputs and outputs that solve one equation will solve the other. Thus there are an infinite number of solutions that solve the equation $r = 4.1t + 6.3$.

This system is a set of two equations that in fact are only two different looking equations for the same linear function. If you put both of these equations into slope-intercept form they would look exactly the same.

b. This system is set up well for elimination since neither equation has a variable isolated.

$$5p + 2w = 4$$
$$-4p - w = -3$$

$$5p + 2w = 4$$
$$2(-4p - w = -3)$$

Multiply second equation by 2 to help eliminate the w's.

$$5p + 2w = 4$$
$$-8p - 2w = -6$$

Add the equations together to eliminate the w's

$$-3p = -2$$
$$\frac{-3p}{-3} = \frac{-2}{-3}$$

Solve for p.

$$p = \frac{2}{3}$$

$$5\left(\frac{2}{3}\right) + 2w = 4$$

Another option is to do the elimination process over again only this time eliminate the p. This will keep you from having to work with fractions very much.

$$\frac{10}{3} + 2w = 4$$

$$5p + 2w = 4$$
$$-4p - w = -3$$

$$\frac{10}{3} + 2w = 4$$

$$4(5p + 2w = 4)$$
$$5(-4p - w = -3)$$

$$-\frac{10}{3} \qquad -\frac{10}{3}$$

$$20p + 8w = 16$$
$$-20p - 5w = -15$$

$$2w = \frac{12}{3} - \frac{10}{3}$$

$$3w = 1$$

$$2w = \frac{2}{3}$$

$$w = \frac{1}{3}$$

$$w = \frac{1}{3}$$

This system has one solution at $\left(\frac{2}{3}, \frac{1}{3}\right)$, so it is a consistent system.

c. This system has two equations with the same slope but different vertical intercepts so they are parallel lines and thus this system is inconsistent. If you do not notice this at first try the substitution method and both variables will be eliminated.

$$4x + 9 = 4x - 9 \quad \text{Substitute for y.}$$

$$\underline{-4x \qquad -4x} \qquad \text{These numbers are not equal.}$$

$$9 = -9 \qquad \text{Therefore there are no solutions.}$$

d. This system is set up well for elimination since no variable is already isolated and the variables are already lined up to be eliminated.

$$-3x + 2y = 7$$
$$\underline{12x - 8y = -28}$$

$$4(-3x + 2y = 7) \quad \text{Multiply the first equation by 4.}$$
$$\underline{12x - 8y = -28}$$

$$-12x + 8y = 28 \quad \text{Add the two equations to eliminate}$$
$$\underline{12x - 8y = -28} \quad \text{the variable.}$$
$$0 = 0 \qquad \qquad \text{Both variables eliminated and the numbers are equal.}$$

Since the variables were both eliminated and the remaining numbers are equal, this system must be dependent and so all inputs and outputs that solve one equation will solve the other. Thus there are an infinite number of solutions that solve the equations $-3x + 2y = 7$ and $12x - 8y = -28$ simultaneously.

e. This system of equations is set up for substitution since the variable S is isolated in both equations.

$$S = 1500 + 0.05c$$
$$\underline{S = 0.05c + 750}$$

$$1500 + 0.05c = 0.05c + 750 \quad \text{Substitute for } S.$$
$$\underline{-0.05c \quad -0.05c}$$
$$1500 = 750 \qquad \text{All the variables were eliminated but the numbers are not equal.}$$

Since the variables were both eliminated but the remaining numbers are not equal we have an inconsistent system with no solutions.

Problem 4

Solve the following systems and label them as consistent, dependent, or inconsistent.

a.
$$a = 1.25b + 4$$
$$8.75b - 7a = 14$$

b.
$$12x + 14y = 8$$
$$-3x - 3.5y = -2$$

Solution   See page 103

Section 2.2 Key Points
- A system of equations can be solved by graphing but this may be a very difficult method and not very accurate.
- Substitution Method
    - i   Best used when a variable is already isolated in one or more equations.
    - ii   Substitute the expression representing the isolated variable from one equation into that variable in the other equation.
    - iii Remember to find the values for both variables.
- Elimination Method
    - i   Best used when neither variable is already isolated.
    - ii   Multiply one or more equations by a number in order to make the coefficients of one variable be the same size but opposite in signs.
    - iii Add the two equations together to eliminate the variable and solve.
    - iv   Remember to find the values for both variables. Sometimes solving the system again by elimination and eliminating the other variable the second time will help you avoid working with fractions.
- Inconsistent Systems
    - i   Look for equations with the same slope but different lines.
    - ii   When all variables are eliminated but the numbers remaining are not equal.
    - iii No solution.
- Dependent Systems
    - i   Look for systems with the same two equations or two equations that are multiples of each other.
    - ii   When all variable are eliminated and the remaining numbers are equal.
    - iii Infinitely Many Solutions. The equation of the line represents all solutions.

Section 2.2 Problem Solutions

Problem 1   Solution

$$T(t) = 1.1t + 6.84$$

$$R(t) = 1.3t + 0.52$$

$1.1t + 6.84 = 1.3t + 0.52$	Substitute
$-1.3t \qquad\quad -1.3t$	Solve for t.

$$-0.2t + 6.84 = 0.52$$
$$\qquad\quad -6.84 \quad -6.84$$

$$-0.2t = -6.32$$

$$\frac{-0.2t}{-0.2} = \frac{-6.32}{-0.2}$$

$$t = 31.6$$

$T(31.6) = 1.1(31.6) + 6.84$	Substitute $t = 31.6$ in and find T.
$T(31.6) = 41.6$	

X	Y₁	Y₂
31.6	41.6	41.6

X=

Check the solution with the table.

Since $t = 31.6$ we have $1990 + 31.6 = 2021.6$ giving us the following result. New Zealand will spend about 41.6 million New Zealand dollars on both diabetes research and treatments in 2021. This is probably not reasonable since the prediction is so far into the future.

Problem 2   Solution

There are two main constraints controlling this situation; the amount of money George can invest and the total amount of interest he needs to earn each year. If we set up two equations using these facts, we can solve the system for the amounts in each account. We need to start by defining the variables.

A = The amount invested in the account paying 3.6% simple interest

B = The amount invested in the account paying 6% simple interest.

With these definitions and the limits we were given we get the following equations.

$$A + B = 350000 \qquad \text{The two accounts total } \$350,0000.$$

$$0.036A + 0.06B = 18000 \qquad \text{The total interest needs to be } \$18,000.$$

$$A + B = 350000$$
$$\underline{0.036A + 0.06B = 18000}$$

$$-0.036(A + B = 350000) \qquad \text{Multiply the first equation}$$
$$\underline{0.036A + 0.06B = 18000} \qquad \text{by -0.036}$$

$$-0.036A - 0.036B = -12600 \qquad \text{Add the two equations together}$$
$$\underline{0.036A + 0.06B = 18000} \qquad \text{eliminating the variable } A.$$

$$0.024B = 5400$$

$$\frac{0.024B}{0.024} = \frac{5400}{0.024} \qquad \text{Solve for } B.$$

$$B = 225000$$

so

$$A + 225000 = 350000 \qquad \text{Solve for A.}$$

$$A = 125000$$

Check your solution in both

$$125000 + 225000 = 350000 \quad \text{equations.}$$

$$350000 = 350000$$

$$0.036(125000) + 0.06(225000) = 18000$$

$$18000 = 18000$$

George needs to deposit $125,000 in the 3.6% account and $225,000 into the account paying 6% interest.

Problem 3   Solution

Jim needs 225 pounds of the dog food that has 24% protein. Let's define the following variables:

A = The amount of Diamond Pet Foods Maintenance Formula with 21% protein.

B = The amount of Diamond Pet Foods Professional Formula with 30% protein.

Using these variables and the two constraints given results in the following two equations.

$$A + B = 225 \qquad \text{A total of 225 pounds of dog food.}$$
$$0.21A + 0.30B = 0.24(225) \qquad \text{The percent of protein should be 24\%}$$

Solving this system of equations will give us the amounts of each type of dog food Jim should use.

$$A + B = 225$$
$$\underline{0.21A + 0.30B = 0.24(225)} \qquad \begin{array}{l}\text{Multiply first equation by -0.30 to} \\ \text{eliminate } B.\end{array}$$

$$-0.30(A + B = 225)$$
$$\underline{0.21A + 0.30B = 54}$$

$$-0.30A - 0.30B = -67.5 \qquad \text{Add the equations to eliminate } B.$$
$$\underline{0.21A + 0.30B = 54} \qquad \text{Solve for } A.$$

$$-0.09A = -13.5$$

$$\frac{-0.09A}{-0.09} = \frac{-13.5}{-0.09}$$

$$A = 150$$

so   Solve for B.

$$150 + B = 225$$
$$B = 75$$
$$150 + 75 = 225 \qquad \begin{array}{l}\text{Check your solution in both} \\ \text{equations.}\end{array}$$
$$225 = 225$$
$$0.21(150) + 0.30(75) = 54$$
$$54 = 54$$

Jim should use 150 pounds of Diamond Pet Foods Maintenance Formula and 75 pounds of Diamond Pet Foods Professional Formula to make the 225 pounds of dog food with 24% protein.

Problem 4   Solution

a.

$$a = 1.25b + 4$$
$$\underline{8.75b - 7a = 14}$$

$$8.75b - 7(1.25b + 4) = 14$$
$$8.75b - 8.75b - 28 = 14$$
$$-28 = 14$$

Using substitution we find all the variables cancel but the remaining numbers do not satisfy an equality so this is a inconsistent system and has no solutions.

b.

$$12x + 14y = 8$$
$$\underline{-3x - 3.5y = -2}$$

$$12x + 14y = 8$$
$$\underline{-12x - 14y = -8}$$

$$0 = 0$$

Multiply the second equation by 4 and use elimination we find all the variable cancel and the numbers remaining are equal so this is a dependent system and has an infinite number of solutions.

2.2 Exercises

1. The student-teacher ratio for public and private schools in the U.S. is given in **Table 2.2.1**

   Table 2.2.1

Year	Public	Private
1995	17.3	14.9
1996	17.1	14.9
1997	16.8	15.1
1998	16.5	15.2

   source: Statistical Abstract 2001

   a. Find models for the student to teacher ratios at public and private schools in the U.S..

   b. Determine when the student to teacher ratio will be the same in public and private schools.

2. The number of males and females who participated in high school athletic programs for various school years is given in **Table 2.2.2**

   Table 2.2.2

School Year	Males	Females
85-86	3,344,275	1,807,121
90-91	3,406,355	1,892,316
95-96	3,634,052	2,367,936
99-00	3,861,749	2,675,874

   source: Statistical Abstract 2001

   a. Find models for the data.

   b. Determine what school year the same number of males and females will participate in high school athletic programs.

3. The percents of Caucasians and African Americans 25 years old or older who have a college degree is given in **Table 2.2.3**

   Table 2.2.3

Year	Caucasians	African Americans
1995	24	13.2
1996	24.3	13.6
1997	24.6	13.3
1998	25	14.7
1999	25.9	15.4
2000	26.1	16.5

   source: Statistical Abstract 2001

   a. Find a model for the percent of Caucasians who have a college degree.

   b. How fast is this percent growing each year?

   c. Find a model for the percent of African Americans who have a college degree.

   d. How fast is this percent growing each year?

   e. Determine when the percent of Caucasians and African Americans who have a college degree will be the same.

4. The number of American women of each age, per 1,000, who are expected to die in the next 10 years from colon cancer or breast cancer is given in **Table 2.2.4**

   Table 2.2.4

Age	Colon Cancer	Breast Cancer
60	4	7
65	6	9
70	8	10
75	11	11
80	14	12

   source: Journal of the National Cancer Institute

   a. Find models for this data.

   b. Determine at what age the risk of dying from colon cancer will be the same as the risk of dying from breast cancer.

5. Damian is investing $150,000 in two accounts to help support his daughter at college. Damian's daughter needs about $9,600 each year to supplement her part time job income. Damian decides to invest part of the money into an account paying 5% and the rest in another account paying 7.2%. How much does Damian need to invest in each account to earn enough interest to help support his daughter.

6. Henry was injured on the job and can no longer work. He received a settlement check from his company for $1.5 million that he will need to live off of for his retirement. Henry is going to pay off his debts of $125,000 and invest the rest in two accounts. One account pays 5% simple interest and the other pays 8% simple interest. Henry needs $87,500 a year in interest to continue to live at his current level.

   a. Write a system of equations that will help you find the amount invested in each account.

   b. How much should Henry invest in each account in order to earn the $87,500 he wants?

7. Joan is retiring and has $175,000 to invest. Joan needs to earn $12,000 in interest each year to supplement her Social Security and pension income. Joan plans to invest part of her money in an account that pays 9% and the rest in a safer account that pays only 5%. Determine how much Joan should invest in each account in order to earn the money she needs.

8. A chemistry student needs to make 20ml of 15% HCl solution but only has a 5% HCl solution and a 50% HCl solution to work with. How much of each solution should this student use in order to get the 20 ml of 15% HCl solution?

9. Fred needs 45ml of 12% sucrose solution in order to do his science experiment. He needs to mix a 5% sucrose solution with some 30% sucrose solution in order to get the 12% solution he wants. How much of each should Fred use?

10. Kristy is doing her chemistry lab but the student in front of her used the last of the 5% NaCl solution she needed. Kristy will have to make more 5% solution with the 2% and 10% NaCl solutions left in the lab. If Kristy needs 25 ml for her experiment how much of each solution should she use?

Math Tutorial   More practice problems like exercises 11 through 35 can be found in section 2.2 of the CD Tutorial.

For exercises 11 through 35 solve each system by elimination or substitution. Label any systems that are dependent, or inconsistent.

11.
$$w + 8s = -42$$
$$-9w - s = -48$$

12.
$$3x + y = 21$$
$$3x - y = 3$$

13.
$$3.7x + 3.5y = 5.3$$
$$y = 3.57x + 4.21$$

14.
$$p = \frac{7}{4}t + 9$$
$$4p - 7t = 36$$

15.
$$\frac{5}{3}d - \frac{3}{5}g = 52$$
$$\frac{3}{5}d + \frac{5}{3}g = -66$$

16.
$$-8x + 7y = -3$$
$$7(x - y) = 3$$

17.
$$4.1w + 3.7t = 5.1$$
$$t = 4.43w + 4.63$$

18.
$$4.5c + 2.1b = 4.7$$
$$b = 3.51c + 3.43$$

19.
$$-2x + 11y = 2$$
$$11(x - y) = -2$$

20.
$$2x - 7y = 8$$
$$y = \frac{7}{2}x + 2$$

21.
$$-3.5x + y = -16.95$$
$$y = -2.4x + 4.88$$

22.
$$2.3p + 3.5t = 7.8$$
$$11.27p + 17.15t = 38.22$$

23.
$$W = \frac{3}{7}d + 6$$
$$W = \frac{2}{7}d + 8.8$$

24.
$$3s - 2t = -2$$
$$t = -s - 9$$

25.
$$-3x + 7y = -1$$
$$3x + 9y = -2$$

26.
$$-4r + t = -1$$
$$-3r + 8t = 5$$

27.
$$-9c - 7d = 8$$
$$c - 7d = 8$$

28.
$$c - 4b = 4.7 - 17$$
$$b = 3c + 18$$

29.
$$3x + 4y = -15$$
$$y = x - 9$$

30.
$$\frac{4}{3}x + y = 13$$
$$x - \frac{7}{6}y = 4$$

31.
$$2.5x + y = 4$$
$$x - 0.4y = -5$$

32.

$$\frac{7}{4}x + y = -1$$

$$x - \frac{5}{3}y = 3$$

33.

$$W = -3.2c + 4.1$$

$$W = 2.4c - 8.8$$

34.

$$4.1x + y = -2$$

$$-2.4x + y = 2.5$$

35.

$$7r - 2c = -8$$

$$-2r - 6c = 7$$

Section 2.3   Solving Systems As Inequalities

• Solving Inequalities • Setting up Systems As Inequalities

Many times when we work with systems of equations we are not as interested in finding when the two equations are equal but rather when one equation is less than or greater than the other. Going back to the original example of U-Haul and Budget truck rentals we are not concerned with when these companies are equal but when one company is cheaper than the other. This will also be true with most comparisons we make between two quantities.

When working with inequalities in algebra you need to be cautious with what operations you perform. In most cases solving an inequality is exactly the same as solving an equation except that the answer will be expressed differently and have a different interpretation.

Say What?
Inequality Symbols:

- Less than
    <
- Greater than
    >
- Less than or equal to
    ≤
- Greater than or equal to
    ≥

Concept Investigation 1

For each inequality perform the given operations and determine if the inequality remains true.

a. $20 > 15$

i	Add 12 to both sides.	$32 > 27$	True
ii	Subtract 4 from both sides.	$16 > 11$	True
iii	Multiply both sides by 3 .	$60 > 45$	True
iv	Divide both sides by 5 .	$4 > 3$	?

b. $45 \geq 39$

i   Add –7 to both sides.

ii   Subtract –9 from both sides.

iii   Multiply both sides by –2 .

iv   Divide both sides by –3 .

c. $36 > -12$

i   Add 10 to both sides.

ii   Subtract 15 from both sides.

iii   Multiply both sides by 9 .

iv   Divide both sides by 4 .

d. $-15 \leq 7$

i   Add –5 to both sides.

ii   Subtract –6 from both sides.

iii   Multiply both sides by –6.5 .

iv   Divide both sides by –4 .

1. Which operations do not always keep the inequality true?

Skill Connection:

SC-Example 1: *Solve*
$$-5x + 7 \geq 22$$

Solution:
$$-5x + 7 \geq 22$$
$$\underline{\quad -7 \quad -7 \quad}$$
$$-5x \geq 15$$
$$\frac{-5x}{-5} \leq \frac{15}{-5}$$
$$x \leq -3$$

Therefore any number less than or equal to -3 will solve this inequality. If we want to check this we need to pick a value less than -3. We will test -5.
$$-5(-5) + 7 \geq 22$$
$$32 \geq 22$$

This is true so we believe the solution is accurate.

SC-Example 2: *Solve*
$$12w + 15 > 3w - 6$$

Solution:
$$12w + 15 > 3w - 6$$
$$\underline{-3w \qquad -3w \quad}$$
$$9w + 15 > -6$$
$$\underline{\quad -15 \ -15 \quad}$$
$$9w > -21$$
$$\frac{9w}{9} > \frac{-21}{9}$$
$$w > -2.33$$

If we test a number greater than -2.33 we will be able to check our solution. We will test $w = 0$.
$$12(0) + 15 > 3(0) - 6$$
$$15 > -6$$

Since this is true we believe our solution is valid.

Testing only one point is not good proof that your solution is correct but it will at least confirm the direction of the inequality symbol.

2. Write in your own words what to watch for when performing operations on inequalities.

3. Check your statement with other students in your class or your instructor.

Example 1

If we reconsider the U-Haul and Budget example from section 2.1, we get the following:

U = The total cost in dollars to rent a 10ft truck from U-Haul.
B = The total cost in dollars to rent a 10ft truck from Budget.
m = The number of miles traveled in rented truck.
$$B = 24.95 + 0.55m$$
$$U = 19.95 + 0.59m$$

Find the distances you can drive that will result in Budget being cheaper than U-Haul

Solution

Since we want Budget to be cheaper than U-Haul we can set the expression for the cost at Budget less than the expression for the cost at U-Haul.
$$24.95 + 0.55m < 19.95 + 0.59m$$
$$\underline{\quad -0.59m \qquad\qquad -0.59m \quad}$$
$$24.95 - 0.04m < 19.95$$
$$\underline{-24.95 \qquad\qquad -24.95 \quad}$$
$$-0.04m < -5$$
$$\frac{-0.04m}{-0.04} > \frac{-5}{-0.04} \qquad \text{Reverse the inequality symbol when you divide by a negative number.}$$
$$m > 125$$

Thus Budget will be cheaper than U-Haul for any distances more than 125 miles. We can easily check this solution and the direction of the symbol using the table.

X	Y1	Y2
110	85.45	84.85
120	90.95	90.75
125	93.7	93.7
130	96.45	96.65
140	101.95	102.55
150	107.45	108.45

$$Y_1 = 24.95 + 0.55X$$

We can see that for distances greater than 125 Budget, Y1, is less than U-Haul, Y2. Therefore our solution is correct.

You should notice in this example that the solution to the system is not one set mileage but a range of miles that make Budget cheaper than U-Haul. When solving a system as an inequality your answer will be a range of values that make the situation true.

Example 2

In section 2.2 exercise 1 we looked at the number of males and females who participated in high school athletic programs for various school years. The data is given again in **Table 2.3.1**.

Table 2.3.1

School Year	Males	Females
85-86	3,344,275	1,807,121
90-91	3,406,355	1,892,316
95-96	3,634,052	2,367,936
99-00	3,861,749	2,675,874

source: Statistical Abstract 2001

a. Find models for the data.

b. Determine when there will be more females than males participating in high school athletic programs.

Solution

a. Define Variables:

S = School Year in years since school year 1900 - 1901. i.e.. 85 represents school year 1985 - 1986.

M = The number of males in high school athletic programs.

F = The number of females in high school athletic programs.

For the number of males model we will use the first and third points.

$$(85, 3344275) \text{ and } (95, 3634052)$$

$$m = \frac{3634052 - 3344275}{95 - 85} = 28977.7$$

$$M = 28977.7S + b$$

$$3634052 = 28977.7(95) + b$$

$$3634052 = 2752881.5 + b$$

$$881170.5 = b$$

$$M = 28977.7S + 881170.5$$

Now for the model of the female data we will use the last two points.

$$(95, 2367936) \text{ and } (99, 2675874)$$

$$m = \frac{2675874 - 2367936}{99 - 95} = 76984.5$$

$$F = 76984.5S + b$$

$$2367936 = 76984.5(95) + b$$

$$2367936 = 7313527.5 + b$$

$$-4945591.5 = b$$

$$F = 76984.5S - 4945591.5$$

b. Since we want to know when the number of females will be larger than the number of males we can set up the following inequality.

$$\text{females} > \text{males}$$

$$76984.5S - 4945591.5 > 28977.7S + 881170.5$$

$$\underline{-28977.7S \qquad\qquad -28977.7S}$$

$$48006.8S - 4945591.5 > 881170.5$$

$$\underline{\qquad 4945591.5 \quad 4945591.5}$$

$$48006.8S > 5826762$$

$$\frac{48006.8S}{48006.8} > \frac{5826762}{48006.8}$$

$$S > 121.374$$

This means that the number of females will be more than the number of males participating in high school athletic programs after the school year 2021 - 2022. This could also be stated as during the school year 2022 - 2023 and beyond. Either statement is correct since the first one does not include the year 2021 - 2022 and the second starts at the next year 2022 - 2023. Either way you explain it you will need to be very careful.

When solving an inequality you may find it easiest to keep the variable on the left side of the inequality symbol. This will make the solution easier to interpret. If you do keep the variable on the left side you may run into places where you must multiply or divide by a negative number, requiring you to reverse the inequality symbol. Follow this simple rule and you will solve inequalities using the same skills you use to solve equations.

Problem 1

The percentage of college freshmen that were male or female for various years is given in **Table 2.3.2**

Table 2.3.2

Year	Percentage of Freshman who are Male	Percentage of Freshman who are Female
1980	48.8	51.2
1990	46.9	53.1
1997	45.5	54.5
2000	45.2	54.8

source: Statistical Abstract 2001

a. Find models for the data.

b. Determine for what years the number of male freshmen were greater than or equal to the number of female freshman.

Solution   See page 113

We can use a table estimate the solutions to inequalities by looking for the input value(s) that make the left side of the inequality equal to the right side of the inequality. You will start by putting the left side into Y1 and the right side into Y2 of the Y = screen of your calculator. When looking for the input value(s) that make the two sides equal notice when one side changes from being smaller than the other side to being larger. The value where these to sides are equal must be between these input values. Once you have found the input value that makes the two sides of the inequality equal look for the inequality relationship you want to be true. This inequality relationship may be when the left side is less than or greater than the right side.

You can also use a graph of the two sides of the inequality to estimate a solution by again putting one side of the inequality into Y1 and the other side into Y2 and then graphing. Once you find the intersection the graph that is vertically lower than the other is the graph that is less than. You will need to determine the values of x that make the graph you want less than or greater than the other. This will always be determined by the places where the graphs intersect. The typical solutions are either less than the x value or greater than the x value of the intersection. Look at the next example to see how this works.

Example 3

a. Solve the following inequality numerically
$$5x + 7 > 2x + 31$$

b. Solve the following inequality graphically
$$-2x + 9 \le 4x - 33$$

Solution

a. We will first put the two sides of the equation into the calculator and then use the table to estimate a solution.

From the table we can see that the two sides of the inequality are equal at $x = 8$ and that the left side (Y1) is greater than the right side (Y2) when $x > 8$ so our solution to this inequality is $x > 8$.

b. Again we will put the two sides of the inequality into the calculator but this time we will graph them both on the same window.

From the graph we can see that the two sides of the inequality are equal at $x = 7$. The graph of the left side (Y1) is lower (less than) than the graph of the right side for values of x greater than 7. Therefore the solution to this inequality is $x \leq 7$. The less than or greater to symbol is used since the original inequality had the "equal to" part included in the inequality symbol.

Problem 2

a. Jim and Martha both found the same solution to the inequality $7v + 10 < 5(2v - 7)$. Compare their solutions and determine if they made any mistakes. If they have explain what they did wrong.

Jim's Solution	Step #	Martha's Solution	Step #
$7v + 10 < 5(2v - 7)$	1	$7v + 10 < 5(2v - 7)$	1
$7v + 10 < 10v - 35$	2	$7v + 10 < 10v - 35$	2
$\underline{-10 \qquad -10}$		$\underline{-10 \qquad -10}$	
$7v > 10v - 45$	3	$7v < 10v - 45$	3
$\underline{-10v \ -10v}$		$\underline{-10v \ -10v}$	
$-3v < -45$	4	$-3v < -45$	4
$\dfrac{-3v}{-3} > \dfrac{-45}{-3}$	5	$\dfrac{-3v}{-3} > \dfrac{-45}{-3}$	5
$v > 15$	6	$v > 15$	6

b. On another problem Jim and Martha found **different** answers this time. Can you find which one made a mistake and explain what they did wrong?

Jim's Solution	Step #	Martha's Solution	Step #
$2.5n + 6.5 > -3.2n - 4.3$	1	$2.5n + 6.5 > -3.2n - 4.3$	1
$2.5n + 6.5 > -3.2n - 4.3$	2	$2.5n + 6.5 > -3.2n - 4.3$	2
$\underline{3.2n \qquad 3.2n}$		$\underline{3.2n \qquad 3.2n}$	
$5.7n + 6.5 > -4.3$	3	$5.7n + 6.5 > -4.3$	3
$\underline{-6.5 \quad -6.5}$		$\underline{-6.5 \quad -6.5}$	
$5.7n > -10.8$	4	$5.7n > -10.8$	4
$\dfrac{5.7n}{5.7} > \dfrac{-10.8}{5.7}$	5	$\dfrac{5.7n}{5.7} < \dfrac{-10.8}{5.7}$	5
$n > -1.895$	6	$n < -1.895$	6

Solution   See page 113

Section 2.3 Key Points

- In some situations systems of equations can be solved using inequalities.
    - i   When asked for one quantity greater than or less than the other.
- Solutions to inequalities will be a range of values that satisfy the situation instead of a single solution.
- When interpreting solutions to inequalities you will use phrases such as:
    - i   in "1980" and later
    - ii   after/before "1980"
    - iii for more/less than "12"
- When multiplying or dividing both sides of an inequality by a negative number you must reverse the inequality symbol.

Section 2.3 Problem Solutions

Problem 1   Solution

a. Define the variables:
    t = Time in years since 1980
    M = Percentage of college freshmen that are male.
    F = Percentage of college freshmen that are female.
    Using the first two points from each set of data you get the following two models:

$$M(t) = -0.19t + 48.8$$
$$F(t) = 0.19t + 51.2$$

b. Set up the system as an inequality with $M(t) \geq F(t)$

$$-0.19t + 48.8 \geq 0.19t + 51.2$$
$$\underline{-0.19t \qquad\qquad -0.19t}$$
$$-0.38t + 48.8 \geq 51.2$$
$$\underline{\qquad\qquad -48.8 \ -48.8}$$
$$-0.38t \geq 2.4$$
$$\frac{-0.38t}{-0.38} \leq \frac{2.4}{-0.38}$$

Reverse the inequality symbol when dividing by a negative number.

$$t \leq -6.316$$

X	Y1	Y2
-10	50.7	49.3
-8	50.32	49.68
-6.316	50	50
-4	49.56	50.44
-2	49.18	50.82
0	48.8	51.2
2	48.42	51.58

Y1■-0.19X+48.8

Check the solution and the symbol using the table.

This means that in 1973 and before the percentage of freshman who were male was greater than or equal to the percentage of freshman who were female.

Problem 2   Solution

a. Jim made mistakes on both lines 3 and 4. He should not have reversed the inequality symbol when subtracting from both sides.
b. Martha made a mistake on line 5 when she reversed the symbol while dividing by a positive number. The inequality symbol should only be reversed when multiplying or dividing by a negative number.

2.3 Exercises

1. The number of full time and part time faculty in U. S. higher education institutions is given in **Table 2.3.3**

Table 2.3.3

Year	Full Time Faculty (in thousands)	Part Time Faculty (in thousands)
1987	523	270
1989	524	300
1993	546	370
1995	551	381
1997	569	421

source: Statistical Abstract 2001

   a. Find models for the data.

   b. Find when the number of part time faculty will be greater than the number of full time faculty.

2. The populations of Afghanistan and Algeria are given in **Table 2.3.4**

Table 2.3.4

Year	Afghanistan Pop. (in thousands)	Algeria Population (in thousands)
1990	14750	25341
1995	21489	28364
2000	25889	31194
2001	26813	31736

source: Statistical Abstract 2001

   a. Find models for the populations of Afghanistan and Algeria.

   b. Determine for what years Afghanistan will have more people than Algeria.

   c. Is your prediction in part b reasonable?

3. The life expectancy of men and women at birth in the U.S. has been growing slowly. The life expectancy at birth for men and women is given in **Table 2.3.5**

Table 2.3.5

Year	Male Life Expectancy at Birth	Female Life Expectancy at Birth
1990	71.8	78.8
1991	72.0	78.9
1992	72.3	79.1
1993	72.2	78.8
1994	72.3	79.0
1995	72.5	78.9
1996	73.0	79.0
1997	73.6	79.4
1998	73.8	79.5
1999	74.1	79.7

source: Statistical Abstract 2001

   a. Find models for the life expectancy of U.S. men and women at birth.

   b. Estimate when the life expectancy of a U.S. male will be greater than the life expectancy of a female.

   c. Why do you think the life expectancy of males is growing faster than that of females?

4. The population on the continent of Africa has been growing rapidly over the past several decades. The populations of Africa and Europe are given in **Table 2.3.6**

Table 2.3.6

Year	Population of Africa (in millions)	Population of Europe (in millions)
1970	361	656
1980	472	694
1990	626	721
2000	805	729

source: Statistical Abstract 2001

   a. Find models for the population of Africa and Europe.

   b. Estimate when Africa will have a greater population than Europe.

5. The percentage of births to teenage mothers in the United States for various states is given in **Table 2.3.7**

Table 2.3.7

Year	Mass	Minn.	Wisconsin
1990	8.0	8.0	10.2
1993	7.8	8.2	10.4
1995	7.5	8.4	10.5
1997	7.4	8.7	10.7

source: Statistical Abstract 2001

   a. Find a model for the percent of births to teenage mothers in Massachusetts.

   b. What does the slope for the model in part a mean in this context?

   c. Find models for the Minnesota and Wisconsin data given.

   d. Estimate when the percent of births to teenage mothers in Minnesota will be greater than the percent in Wisconsin.

6. The revenue and cost functions for a local cabinet manufacturer are

$$R(c) = 450c$$
$$C(c) = 280c + 20000$$

where $R(c)$ represents the monthly revenue in dollars from selling c cabinets, and $C(c)$ represent the monthly cost in dollars to manufacture and sell c cabinets.

   a. Find the number of cabinets this company must sell each month in order to break even or make a profit.

7. A pre-paid service called Free-up from Verizon Wireless offers a phone for $69.99 and a rate of 30 cents per minute. Cingular Wireless offers a pre-paid service phone for $69.99 with a rate of 35 cents per minute. Virgin Mobile offers a pre-paid plan with a $79 phone and a rate of 25 cents per minute.

   a. Find models for the cost of these three plans if a person uses m minutes.

   b. When will Virgin Mobile be the cheapest plan?

8. The percent of births to unmarried women in the United States can be modeled by

$$U(t) = 1.875t + 18$$

   where $U(t)$ represents the percent of births to unmarried women in the U.S. t years since 1980. The percent of births to unmarried women in Denmark t years since 1980 can be modeled by

$$D(t) = 1.5t + 33$$

   source: Models derived from data in the Statistical Abstract 2001.

   a. Determine when the percent of births to unmarried women in the U.S. will be greater than the percent in Denmark.

9. A salesperson earns a base salary of $600 per month plus 21% commission on all sales. Find the minimum amount a salesperson would need to sell in order to earn at least $1225 for one month.

10. A salesperson earns a base salary of $725 per month plus 17% commission on all sales. Find the minimum amount a salesperson would need to sell in order to earn at least $1225 for one month.

11. Use the table to find when Y1<Y2

X	Y1	Y2
0	5	15
1	8	13
2	11	11
4	17	7
5	20	5
6	23	3

X=

12. Use the table to find when Y1>Y2

X	Y1	Y2
-6	-29	-8
-5	-24	-10
-4	-19	-12
-3	-14	-14
-2	-9	-16
-1	-4	-18

X=

13. Use the table to find when Y1>Y2

X	Y1	Y2
-10	11	-7
-9	9	-3
-8	7	1
-7	5	5
-6	3	9
-5	1	13

X=

14. Use the table to find when Y1>Y2.

X	Y1	Y2
5	-10	50
10	0	30
15	10	10
20	20	-10
25	30	-30
30	40	-50

X=

Math Tutorial
More practice problems like exercises 15 through 24 can be found in section 2.3 of the CD Tutorial.

For exercises 14 through 23 solve the inequality.

15.
$$5 + \frac{3x}{2} \le -3$$

16.
$$5x + 3 \ge 3(x - 2)$$

17.
$$4t + 3 > 2(t + 1)$$

18.
$$\frac{7d}{3} + 5 < 3$$

19.
$$2.7v + 3.69 > 1.5v - 6.5$$

20.
$$3.2 + 2.7(1.5k - 3.1) \ge 9.43k - 17.5$$

21.
$$\frac{2}{5}(w - 20) \le -\frac{3}{7}(4w - 9)$$

22.
$$8.7 - 1.4(8.2m + 6) \ge -2.3(7.1m - 4.3)$$

23.
$$2.35x + 7.42 < 1.3x - 4.75$$

24.
$$3.74x - 5.87 > 7.28x + 3.25$$

Section 2.4   Systems of Linear Inequalities

• **Graphing Linear Inequalities with Two Variables** • **Solving Systems of Linear Inequalities**

Many things in life are limited by our circumstances. When we go shopping we are limited by the amount of money we have as well as how much of something we need or want. Businesses are often limited by the production in certain plants or by the costs associated with production. Dieticians must keep their clients within a certain range of nutrients and thus must balance the types of foods and supplements they prescribe someone. All of these situations can best be looked at as inequalities since a company or person may not need to use the maximum amount of something but may use something less than that amount. When two or more constraints are considered a system of inequalities emerges. In this section we will consider some of these situations and learn to solve systems of inequalities.

Before we consider a system of inequalities we will investigate a inequality that has two variables and look at it's set of solutions.

Example 1

A bicycle plant can produce both beach cruisers and mountain bikes. The plant needs 2 hours to build one beach curser and 3.5 hours to produce a mountain bike. If the plant operates up to 60 hours per week what combinations of bikes can they produce in a week?

Solution

First we will define some variables.

   C = number of cruisers built in a week.

   M = number of mountain bikes built in a week.

Now since each curser takes 2 hours to build $2C$ is the number of hours it takes the plant to build the cruisers that week. It takes 3.5 hours to build a mountain bike so $3.5M$ is the number of hours that plant spends building mountain bikes that week. The maximum number of hours the plant operates in a week is 60 so we have the following inequality relationship.

$$2C + 3.5M \leq 60$$

This inequality can be graphed if we solve for one of the variables. You can solve for C to get

$$2C + 3.5M \leq 60$$
$$2C \leq -3.5M + 60$$
$$C \leq -1.75M + 30$$

To graph this inequality we first graph it as if it were an equation giving us the line

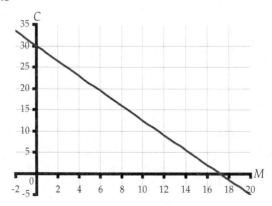

Once you have the line graphed you test a point on either side of the line to see if it is a solution to the inequality. If it is a solution you shade the side of the line the test point is on. If we test the point $(0, 0)$ it satisfies the inequality indicating that the lower portion of the graph should be shaded.

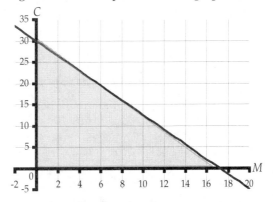

Any point within the shaded region is a solution to this inequality. Meaning that the plant can build anywhere from no bikes at all to a combination of bikes ranging from no cruisers and 17 mountain bikes to no mountain bikes but 30 cruisers. Any point on the line itself would mean that exactly 60 hours are being used a week. Any point in the shaded region means that less than 60 hours are being used and outside the shaded region implies that more than 60 would be needed to do the work.

As you can see from the example there is a large set of solutions for this situation. Working with inequalities most often means not finding a single solution but a set of possible solutions. When graphing an inequality that has two variables you can graph the inequality as if it were an equation and then decide what shading needs to be done. Deciding what side of a line to shade can be done easily using any point from one side of the line as a test. If that point is a solution to the inequality shade the side that the point is on. If the point is not a solution to the inequality then shade the other side of the line.

In this example the inequality included the equal to part so the line was drawn as a solid line. If the inequality you are graphing does not have an equal to symbol then the line is drawn as a dashed line indicating it is not a part of the solution set.

Example 2
Graph the following inequalities by hand.

a. $y < 2x - 7$

b. $y \le -\frac{3}{5}x + 6$

c. $y > -3x + 7$

Solution

a. First we will graph the line as if it is an equation. Since the inequality is a less than and not equal to we will use a dashed line.

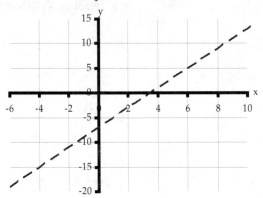

Now that we have the line we want to do the shading to show the solution set. If we choose the point $(0, 0)$ as our test point it does not satisfy the inequality because we get $0 < -7$ which is not true. So we should shade the lower portion of the graph. This agrees with the fact that this is a less symbol. Shading gives us the following graph.

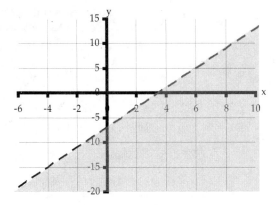

b. Again we will graph the inequality as if it were an equation. This time the line will be solid since the symbol does include an equal to.

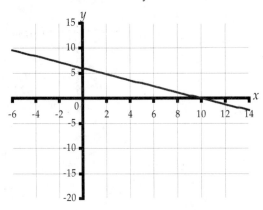

Now if we test the point $(0, 0)$ we find that it satisfies the inequality to we shade the lower portion of the graph.

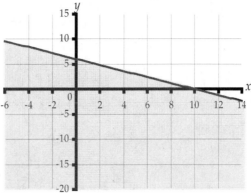

c. This inequality does not have an equal to part so we will graph the line using dashes to indicate that it is not part of the solution set but only a boundary for it.

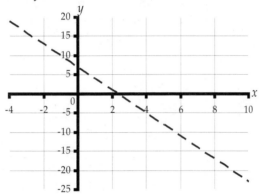

Now if we test the point $(6, 5)$, which is clearly above the line we see that it does satisfy the inequality so we will shade on that side of the line.

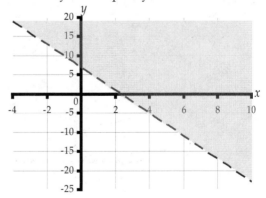

Problem 1
Graph the following inequalities by hand.

a. $y > 2x - 8$

b. $y \le -\dfrac{3}{4}x + 5$

Solution   See page 123

Now that we can graph an inequality with two variables we can consider a system of inequalities. Most situations have more than one constraint that limits what can be done. The bicycle plant from example 1 may also have a constraint that they must work at least 40 hours per week. If this is the case the situation calls for a system of inequalities, not just one inequality.

Example 3

Example 1 discussed a bicycle plant that had the time constraints that they could not exceed 60 hours of production per week. The same plant must work at least 40 hours per week in order to avoid layoffs of production staff.

a.   Create a system of inequalities to model this situation.

b.   Graph the solution set for this system.

c.   Can the plant produce 10 mountain bikes and 5 cruisers in a week?

d.   Can the plant only produce 5 mountain bikes and 10 cruisers a week?

Solution

a.   First we will define the variables the same way we did in example 1
C = number of cruisers built in a week.
M = number of mountain bikes built in a week.
The first constraint of not exceeding 60 hours per week results in the inequality

$$2C + 3.5M \leq 60$$

The new constrain of not working less than 40 hours a week results in the inequality

$$2C + 3.5M \geq 40$$

This gives us the system of inequalities

$$2C + 3.5M \leq 60$$

$$2C + 3.5M \geq 40$$

b.   We need to graph both of these inequalities at the same time being careful to shade the correct sides of each line.

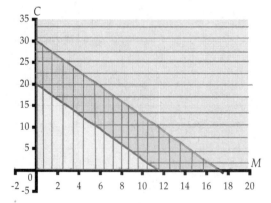

The vertical lines show the solution set for the first equation.
The horizontal lines show the solution set for the second equation

The overlap is the solution set for the system as a whole.

c.   10 mountain bikes and 5 cruisers would be the point $(10, 5)$ on the graph. This point is inside the area of the graph were the solution sets of the two inequalities overlap. Therefore this would be a reasonable amount of each bike to produce a week.

d.   5 mountain bikes and 10 cruisers would be the point $(5, 10)$ and would lie outside the overlapping section of this system. Therefore producing this combination of bikes per week would not meet the constraints.

In the last example we only needed to graph the area covered by positive numbers of bikes being produced. This is typical of many real life situations and actually adds two additional inequalities to the system. $M \geq 0$ and $C \geq 0$. We did not write these this time but could have. Common sense told us that a negative number of bikes could not be produced. Another type of application we can consider as a system of inequalities is investment questions like those we did in section 2.2.

Example 4

Mary is retiring and has $500,000 to invest in two accounts. One account pays 5% annual interest and the other pays 3.5% annual interest. How much should she invest in each account to earn at least $21,000 in interest each year?

Solution

If we define variables as

  A = the amount in the account paying 5% annual interest.
  B = the amount in the account paying 3.5% annual interest.

Since Mary can invest up to $500,000 and must earn at least $21,000 per year in interest we can write the following system of inequalities.

$$A + B \leq 500000$$

$$0.05A + 0.035B \geq 21000$$

If we graph this system we can find the possible solutions to this situaion.

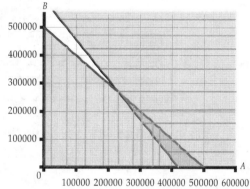

From this graph we can see that Mary can have many different investment amounts that would earn her the minimum amount of interest she needs and still not use all of her $500,000. Any combination of investments from the overlapping section of the graph can be used to meet Mary's investment goal.

In many systems of equations or inequalities the points of intersection for the lines of system are critical values of interest. In the case of Mary's investments that point of intersection is the investment that meets her needs and invests the total $500,000. This is also the investment with the least amount invested in the account paying 5% and the most money she can invest in the account paying 3.5% and still meet her minimum interest needs.

Graphing these systems can also be done using the graphing calculator. See the instructions in the TI-83 Details on the next page.

Example 5

Graph each system of inequalities.

a. $y < -2x + 5$
    $y > 3x - 5$

b. $y \geq -1.5x + 5$
    $y \leq -1.5x + 2$

c. $2x + 5y < 15$
    $3x - 2y > 6$

Solution

TI-83 Details:
To graph inequalities on your calculator you can have the calculator shade above or below the graph. To do this you use your cursor buttons to go to the left of the Y1 and press enter until you get the shade above or below symbol you are looking for.

Note that the calculator cannot use shading with dashed lines so any inequalities without the equal to part on the inequality symbol will graph with a solid line but should be interpreted as a dashed line and any points on that line should not be considered part of the solution set.

a. Since the first inequality is a less than symbol we shade below the line and the second we shade above since it is a greater than symbol. Both lines should be dashed since these inequalities do not include any equal to parts. The calculator does not show dashed lines when shading so we get

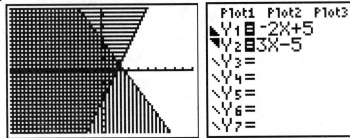

The two shaded regions intersect on the left side giving us our solution set.

b. Graphing these two inequalities gives us no intersection and thus no solution to the system.

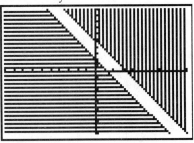

c. We first need to solve these inequalities for y and then we can graph them.

$2x + 5y < 15$

$5y < -2x + 15$ Solve the first equation for y.

$y < -\dfrac{2}{5}x + 3$

$3x - 2y > 6$ Solve the second equation for y.

$-2y > -3x + 6$

$y < \dfrac{3}{2}x - 3$ Remember to flip the inequality symbol when dividing by a negative number.

$y < -\dfrac{2}{5}x + 3$ Now graph the new system of equations.

$y < \dfrac{3}{2}x - 3$

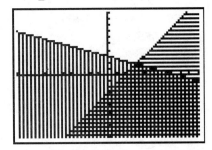

Problem 2

Graph the following systems of inequalities.

a. $y \geq x + 2$
$y \leq 2x - 3$

b. $2x - 5y > 12$
$4y > 7x - 5$

Solution   See page 124

Section 2.4 Key Points

- Graphing Linear Inequalities with Two Variables:
    1. Graph the line as if it were an equation. Use a dashed line if the inequality does not include an equal to part.
    2. Pick a point on one side of the line and test the inequality.
    3. If the point satisfies the inequality shade that side of the line if it does not satisfy the inequality shade the other side of the line.
- Graphing Systems of Linear Inequalities:
    1. Graph both inequalities on the same set of axes.
    2. The solution set is the region shaded by both inequalities in the system.

Section 2.4 Problem Solutions

Problem 1   Solution

a. Since this inequality does not have an equal to symbol we will use a dashed line. Using the point $(0, 0)$ to test we find it satisfies the inequality so we will shade above the line.

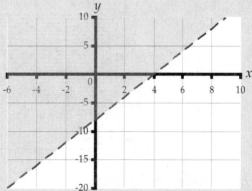

b. This inequality has an equal to symbol so the line will be solid. Using the point $(0, 0)$ to test we find it satisfies the inequality so we will shade below the line.

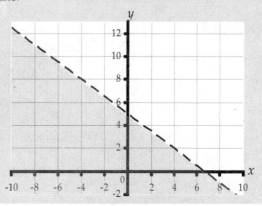

Problem 2   Solution

a. Using the calculator we get

The solution set is the region with the overlapping shading.

b. First we should solve the two equations for y and then graph them.

$$2x - 5y > 12$$

$$-5y > -2x + 12$$ Solve the first equation for y.
                       Remember to flip the inequality symbol when
$$y < \frac{2}{5}x - \frac{12}{5}$$ dividing by a negative number.

$$4y > 7x - 5$$

                       Solve the second equation for y.
$$y > \frac{7}{4}x - \frac{5}{4}$$

$$y < \frac{2}{5}x - \frac{12}{5}$$ Now graph the system.

$$y > \frac{7}{4}x - \frac{5}{4}$$

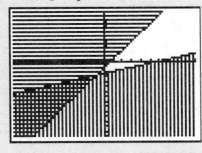

2.4 Exercises

According to the National Institutes of Health adults are considered underweight or overweight based on a combination of their height and weight. The graph below shows this relationship as a system of inequalities. Use the graph to answer questions 1 through 5.

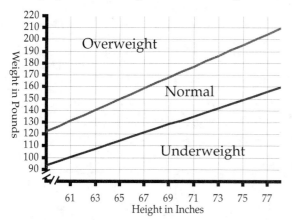

1. What category does a 5' 1" person weighing 105 pounds fall into?

2. Above what weight is a 5' 9" person considered overweight?

3. Under what weight is a 6' person considered underweight?

4. If a 150 pound person is to be considered normal how tall must they be?

5. If a person is 67" tall what is their normal weight range?

Bicycles Galore can manufacture up to 500 bikes a month in its Pittsburgh plant. Cruisers cost $75 to manufacture while mountain bikes cost $135 to manufacture. Bicycles Galore needs to keep its total monthly costs below $50,000. Use the graph of this situation to answer questions 6 through 9.

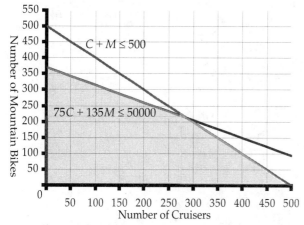

6. What is the greatest number of mountain bikes the company can build a month?

7. Can Bicycles Galore build 400 cruisers and 100 mountain bikes per month? Explain.

8. Can the company build 150 cruisers and 350 mountain bikes per month? Explain.

9. If the company wants to make 500 bikes per month what is the maximum number of mountain bikes they can build?

10. Bicycles Galore can produce up to 500 bikes per month in their Pittsburgh plant. They can make a profit of $65 per cruiser they build and $120 per mountain bike they build. The companies board of directors want to make a profit of at least $40,000 per month.

   a. Write a system of inequalities to model this situation and graph it by hand.

   b. Can Bicycles Galore meet the board of directors demand for $40,000 in profit per month?

   c. If they want to maximize their production at 500 bikes how many of each bike should they produce to make the $40,000 profit?

11. Theresa has started a small business creating jewelry to sell at boutiques. She can make a necklace in about 45 minutes and a bracelet in about 30 minutes. Theresa can only work up to 25 hours a month making the jewelry. She can make $20 profit from a necklace and $18 profit from bracelets. Theresa wants to earn at least $800 profit.

   a. Write a system of inequalities to model this situation and graph it by hand.

   b. Should Theresa make more necklaces or bracelets?

   c. Knowing that most of her customers want a bracelet and necklace combination how many of each should she make to meet her profit goal?

12. Juanita is retiring and has $750,000 to invest in two accounts. One account pays 4.5% annual interest and the other pays 3.75% annual interest. Juanita wants to know how much she should invest in each account to earn at least $30,000 in interest each year? Write a system of inequalities and graph it by hand to show the possibilities.

13. Preparing meals to eat during an all day bike race the team dietician determines that each athlete must consume at least 2000 calories and at least 350 grams of carbohydrates to sustain the energy needed to compete at peak performance. The dietician is providing each athlete a combination of power bars and sports drinks for the race. Each power bar has 240 calories and 30 grams of carbs. The sports drinks contain 300 calories and 70 grams of carbs.

   a. Write a system of inequalities for these dietary needs and graph it by hand.

   b. What is the minimum number each of these that an athlete should consume during the race.

   c. If racers can only carry 4 drinks what is the minimum number of power bars they should eat?

For Exercises 14 through 25 graph the inequalities by hand.

14. $y > 3x + 2$

15. $y < -4x + 7$

16. $y > \dfrac{5}{4}x - 2$

17. $y < \dfrac{3}{7}x + 1$

18. $y \geq \dfrac{2}{3}x + 6$

19. $y \geq \dfrac{4}{5}x - 5$

20. $y \leq -2x + 6$

21. $y \leq x + 5$

22. $2x + 5y > 10$

23. $3x + 4y < 8$

24. $12x - 4y > 8$

25. $10x - 5y < 20$

For exercises 26 through 28 find the inequality for the given graph.

26.

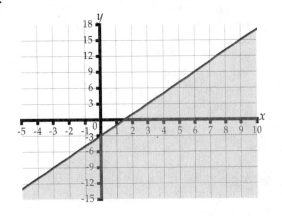

27.

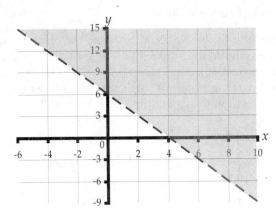

28.

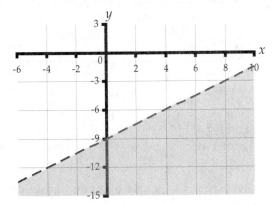

For exercises 29 through 40 graph the systems of inequalities by hand or on the calculator.

29.
$$y > 2x + 4$$
$$y < -3x + 7$$

30.
$$y < 4x + 5$$
$$y > -x + 1$$

31.
$$y < \dfrac{2}{5}x - 3$$
$$y < -\dfrac{3}{4}x + 6$$

32.
$$y \geq \dfrac{1}{3}x + 2$$
$$y \leq -\dfrac{2}{3}x + 7$$

33.
$$y \leq 2x + 5$$
$$y \geq 2x + 8$$

34.
$$y < -4x + 10$$
$$y > -4x + 2$$

35.
$$2x + 4y \leq 5$$
$$2x - 4y \leq 5$$

36.
$$-4x - 3y \geq 11$$
$$4x + 3y \geq 5$$

37.
$$5x + 3y > 7$$
$$4x + 2y < 10$$

38.
$$4x + 5y < 10$$
$$8x + 10y > 10$$

39.
$$y > \dfrac{2}{3}x - 12$$
$$6x - 4y > 12$$

40.
$$1.5x + 4.6y \leq 1.8$$
$$y \geq \dfrac{2}{17}x + 1.2$$

Chapter 2 Review Exercises

1. Frank's Shoe Repair works out of a kiosk in the local mall and has determined the following models for their monthly revenue and costs associated with repairing shoes.

$$R(s) = 7.5s$$

$$C(s) = 235 + 2.25s$$

where $R(s)$ represents the monthly revenue in dollars for repairing s shoes, and $C(s)$ is the monthly costs in dollars for repairing s shoes.

a. Graph both functions on the same calculator screen.

b. Determine the break-even point for Frank's Shoe Repair.

2. Joanne's Cosmetics Outlet has two salary options for their sales people. Each sales person can choose which option they want to base their salary on.

$$O_1(s) = 350 + 0.07s$$

$$O_2(s) = 0.065s + 450$$

where $O_1(s)$ represents monthly salary option 1 in dollars when s dollars in sales are made per month, and $O_2(s)$ represents monthly salary option 2 in dollars when s dollars in sales are made per month.

a. Graph both functions on the same calculator screen.

b. Find what sales level would result in both salary options having the same monthly salary.

3. You decide to market your own custom computer software. You must invest $3232 on computer hardware, and spend $3.95 to buy and package each disk. If each program sells for $9.00, how many copies must you sell to break-even?

4. John has cashews that sell for $4.50 a pound and peanuts that sell for $2.00 a pound. How much of each must he mix to get 100 pounds of a mixture that sells for $3.00 per pound?

5. Professional sports salaries have increased dramatically over the past few years. The average players salaries, in dollars, for the National Football League (NFL) and the National Basketball Association (NBA) are given in **Table 2.4.1**

Table 2.4.1

Year	Average NFL Salary	Average NBA Salary
1995	714,000	1,900,000
1996	791,000	2,000,000
1997	725,000	2,200,000
1998	1,138,000	2,600,000

source: Statistical Abstract 2001

a. Find models for the average salary data given.

b. Determine when the average salary for NFL players were/will be the same as the average salary for NBA players.

6. The percentage of births to teenage mothers in Delaware and Florida is given in **Table 2.4.2**

Table 2.4.2

Year	Delaware	Year	Florida
1990	11.9	1990	13.9
1993	12.5	1992	13.5
1995	13.2	1998	13.1
1998	14.2	1999	13.0

source: Statistical Abstract 2001

a. Find a model for the percent of births to teenage mothers in Delaware.

b. What does the slope for the model in part a mean in this context?

c. Find a model for the percent of births to teenage mothers in Florida.

d. Estimate when the percent of births to teenage mothers in Delaware will be greater than the percent in Florida.

For exercises 7 through 11 solve the systems by graphing. Label each system as consistent, inconsistent or dependent.

7.

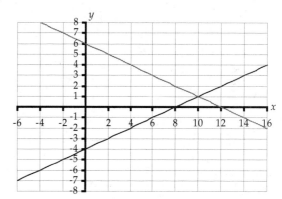

8.

$$x + 3y = -12$$
$$-5x + y = 15$$

9.

$$w = 2d + 7$$
$$w = \frac{3}{7}d + \frac{1}{2}$$

10.

$$p = 1.625t + 9$$
$$p = \frac{13}{8}t - 5$$

11.

$$5x - 4y = 28$$
$$1.25x - y = -7$$

12. The Palomar College Foundation has been given an endowment of $3 million to fund scholarships for outstanding math and science students. The foundation wants the endowment to earn enough interest each year to fund 130 $2000 scholarships. They plan to invest part of the money in a safe investment earning 7% simple interest and the rest in another account earning 11% simple interest. How much should they invest in each account in order to have enough interest to fund the 130 scholarships?

13. Brian is an agriculture scientist and is testing different applications of insecticides on tomato plants. For part of the trial he is running now he needs 150 gallons of a 12% solution of test chemical AX-14. Brian only received containers with 5% solution and 15% concentrations of test chemical AX-14. How much of each chemical should Brian mix in order to run his trial?

For exercises 14 through 24 solve each system by elimination or substitution. Label any systems that are dependent, or inconsistent.

14.
$$3x + 4y = -26$$
$$y = x - 3$$

15.
$$2w - 5t = -1$$
$$3w - 4t = 2$$

16.
$$2.35d + 4.7c = 4.7$$
$$c = -7.05d - 21.15$$

17.
$$\frac{5}{6}m + n = 25$$
$$m - \frac{4}{5}n = 5$$

18.
$$y = 4.1x - 2.2$$
$$y = -2.9x - 7.1$$

19.
$$-8x + 7y = -3$$
$$7(x - y) = 3$$

20.
$$4.1w + 3.7t = 5.1$$
$$t = 4.43w + 4.63$$

21.
$$3f + 2g = -22$$
$$g = -f - 9$$

22.
$$-6x + 15y = 5$$
$$15(x - y) = -5$$

23.
$$\frac{w}{2} + \frac{2z}{3} = 32$$
$$\frac{w}{4} - \frac{5z}{9} = 40$$

24.
$$-2.7x + y = -13.61$$
$$y = -4.28x + 5.69$$

25. The percent of births to unmarried women in Sweden can be modeled by
$$S(t) = 1.75t + 40$$
where $S(t)$ represents the percent of births to unmarried women in the Sweden t years since 1980.

The percent of births to unmarried women in Norway t years since 1980 can be modeled by
$$N(t) = 4.25t + 15$$
source: Models derived from data in the Statistical Abstract 2001.

Determine when the percent of births to unmarried women in Sweden will be less than the percent in Norway.

For exercises 26 through 33 solve the inequality.

26. Use the graph to determine when $f(x) < g(x)$

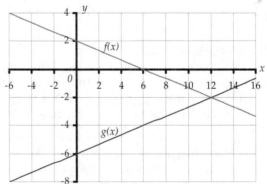

27. Use the table to find when Y1>Y2.

X	Y1	Y2
0	-4	31
2	0	25
4	4	19
6	8	13
7	10	10
8	12	7
10	16	1

X=10

28.
$$7 - \frac{9x}{11} \le -8$$

29.
$$-5x + 4 \geq 7(x - 1)$$

30.
$$3t + 4 > -6(4t + 2)$$

31.
$$\frac{3d}{5} + 7 < 4$$

32.
$$-1.5v + 2.84 > -3.2v - 1.48$$

33.
$$1.85 + 1.34(2.4k - 5.7) \geq 3.25k - 14.62$$

For exercises 34 through 37 graph the inequalities by hand.

34. $y \leq 4x - 10$

35. $y \geq 1.5x - 5$

36. $2x + 5y > 15$

37. $-3x - 4y > 12$

For exercises 38 through 41 graph the system of inequalities.

38.
$$y > 2x + 5$$
$$y < -x + 7$$

39.
$$y > 1.5x + 2$$
$$4.5x - 3y > 6$$

40.
$$4x + 5y \leq 12$$
$$2x + 8y \geq 5$$

41.
$$y > \frac{2}{3}x - 7$$
$$y < \frac{2}{3}x + 5$$

42. A college is selling tickets to a championship basketball game and has up to 12,000 tickets to sell. They can sell both regular admission tickets as well as student discount tickets. Student tickets cost $9 and regular admission tickets cost $15. The school wants to make at least $140,000 from selling tickets. Write a system of inequalities to determine the combinations of tickets they can sell to make the money they want.

43. Find the inequality for the graph.

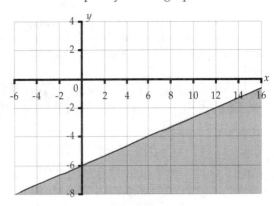

44. Find the inequality for the graph.

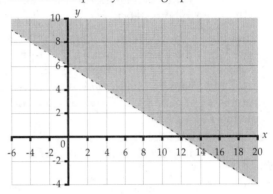

Chapter 2 Test

1. The average hourly earnings of production workers in manufacturing industries for California and Colorado are given in **Table 2.5.1**

    Table 2.5.1

Year	California (in dollars per hour)	Colorado (in dollars per hour)
1997	13.24	13.31
1998	13.66	13.74
1999	13.95	14.19
2000	14.25	14.76

    source: Statistical Abstract 2001

    a. Find models for the data.

    b. Find when the average hourly earnings were the same in both states.

2. Christine is ready to retire and has $500,000 to invest. Christine needs to earn $44,500 in interest each year in order to continue her current lifestyle. She plans to invest the money in two accounts, one paying 12% and a safer account paying 7%.

    a. Write a system of equations that will help you find the amount Christine needs to invest in each account.

    b. How much should Christine invest in each account to earn the $44,500 she wants?

3. Georgia has up to 20 hours a week to study for her math and history classes. She needs to study at least 12 hours a week to pass her math class. Write a system of inequalities to describe the possible amounts of time she can study for each subject. Graph the system by hand.

4. Wendy is working in a forensics lab and needs 2 liters of an 8% HCl solution to test some evidence. Wendy has only a 5% HCl solution and a 20% HCl solution to work with. Since she knows that the solution must be 8% for the test to be valid how much of the 5% solution and the 20% solution should she use?

For problems 5 through 7 solve the inequality

5. $5x + 7 < 12x - 8$

6. $3.2m + 4.5 \geq 5.7(2m + 3.4)$

7. $-4.7 + 6.5(a + 2.5) \leq 2.4(3.1a - 5)$

For problems 8 through 11 solve the given system.

8.
$$x + 7y = -2$$
$$3x + y = 34$$

9.
$$0.4375w + 4t = 22$$
$$-2.4t = 0.2625w - 13.2$$

10.
$$5c + 3d = -15$$
$$d = -\frac{5}{3}c - 12$$

11.
$$2.68g - 3.45f = 23.87$$
$$4.75g + 6.9f = -12.47$$

12. The amount of time the average person older than 11 spends playing home video games and on the internet is rising. The number of hours per person per year is given in **Table 2.5.2**

    Table 2.5.2

Year	Internet (hrs per person per yr)	Home Video Games (hrs per person per yr)
1998	61	43
1999	99	61
2000	135	76
2001	162	93

    source: Statistical Abstract 2001

    a. Find models for the time the average person spends on the internet and playing home video games.

    b. Determine when the time spent playing home video games was greater than time spent on the internet.

13. Use the graph to find when $f(x) \geq g(x)$.

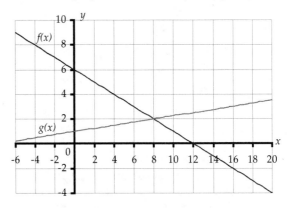

14. Scott has decided to market his custom built hammock stands. He needs to invest $7,500 on tools, and spends $395 to buy and build each stand. If each hammock stand sells for $550, how many must Scott sell to break-even?

15. Graph by hand $y > -\frac{4}{5}x + 6$

16. The revenue for local telephone service providers can be modeled by
$$L(t) = 3804.32t + 84252.07$$

where $L(t)$ represents the revenue in millions of dollars for local telephone service providers t years since 1990.

The revenue in millions of dollars for cellular telephone service providers t years since 1990 can be modeled by
$$C(t) = 6428.29t - 11553$$

Determine when the revenue for cellular telephone providers will be greater than that of local telephone providers.

17. Use the table to find when Y1<Y2.

X	Y₁	Y₂
-6	-4	-2.5
-5	-3.5	-2.75
-4	-3	-3
-3	-2.5	-3.25
-2	-2	-3.5
-1	-1.5	-3.75
0	-1	-4

X=0

Section 3.1   Introduction to Quadratics

• **Introduction to Quadratics** • **Recognizing Graphs** • **Vertex**

In this chapter we will add another type of function to our list of possible models. So far we have only found linear models and worked with systems of linear equations. We are going to start this chapter by looking at some data that takes on a different shape than the linear data we have seen before.

Concept Investigation 1

Create a scatterplot of the following data on your calculator and answer the questions.
Defining variables as

T = The average monthly temperature, °F, in San Diego, California.
m = The month of the year. i.e. $m = 5$ represents May.

a. The average monthly temperature for several months in San Diego, California is given in **Table 3.1.1**

Table 3.1.1

Month	Average Temperature (°F)
May	64
June	67
July	71
August	72
September	71
October	67
November	62
December	58

source: Weatherbase.com

i   Does this data look linear? If not describe its shape.

ii Graph the function $T(m) = -1(m-8)^2 + 72$
Describe how well this function fits the data.

iii Using the function as your model find what month San Diego is the hottest on average?

iv According to your model what is the average temperature in San Diego during the month of March? Do you think this is reasonable?

TI - 83 Details:
To enter exponents on the graphing calculator you can use two basic methods.

If you are squaring a term you can use the x^2 button on the left hand side of the calculator. All you need to enter is the number or variable you wish to square and follow that with the x^2 button.

If you want to raise a variable or number to any other power you should use the ^ button on the right side of the calculator. In this case you will need to enter the number or variable you want to raise to a power then press the ^ button followed by the power you wish to use.

[x] [^] [5]

x^5

b. The number of public branch libraries in the United States for several years is given in **Table 3.1.2**

Table 3.1.2

Year	Public Library Branches
1994	6,223
1995	6,172
1996	6,205
1997	6,332
1998	6,435

source: Statistical Abstract 2001

Defining variables as

B = The number of public branch libraries in the U.S.

t = Time in years since 1990.

i   Does this data look linear? If not describe its shape. How is it similar to the data in part **a**?

ii   Graph the function $B(t) = 28.7t^2 - 286.2t + 6899.3$
     Describe how well this function fits the data.

iii At what point does this graph change directions? What does this point represent in this context?

iv   According to your model how many branch libraries were there in 1990?

As you can see from the data given in **Concept Investigation 1** not all data has a linear pattern. Both of the given data sets are curved and form a portion of what is called a **parabola**. Parabolas can be described as a "U" shape or an "up-side down U" shape. The point where the parabola turns around and goes in the opposite direction is called the **vertex**. The vertex represents where the lowest/minimum value occurs on the graph if the graph is upward facing and represents the highest/maximum value on the graph if the point is downward facing. Examples of each of these types of graphs are shown in **Graphic 3.1.1** and **Graphic 3.1.2**. Data that shows this type of pattern can be modeled using a **quadratic function.** The graph of a quadratic function is called a parabola.

Graphic 3.1.1

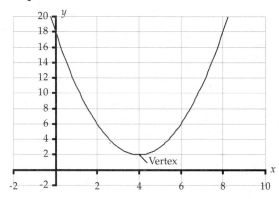

Upward Facing Parabola

Vertex: (4, 2)

Lowest point

Minimum point

Graphic 3.1.2

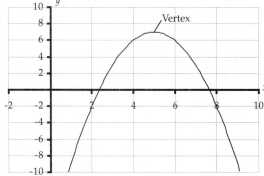

Downward Facing Parabola

Vertex: (5, 7)

Highest point

Maximum point

Definition 3.1.1

Quadratic Function: Is a function that can be written in one of these forms

$$f(x) = ax^2 + bx + c$$

$$f(x) = a(x - h)^2 + k$$

where $a, b, c, h,$ and k are real numbers and.
$$a \neq 0$$
(note: Quadratic Functions will be discussed in more detail in section 3.2)

Parabola: The graph of a quadratic function.
A parabola has a "U" shape and can either face upward or downward.

Vertex: The point on a parabola where the graph changes direction.
The maximum or minimum value occurs at this point on the graph of a parabola.

Example 1

Create scatter plots for the following sets of data. Determine what type of model would best fit the data. If a quadratic function would be a good fit give an estimate for the vertex and determine if it is a maximum or minimum point.

a.

Table 3.1.3

Input	Output
0	19
1	9
2	3
3	1
4	3
5	9
6	19

b.

Table 3.1.4

x	y
-2.3	12.92
-1	12.4
1.2	11.52
2	11.2
3.2	10.72
4.2	10.32
5	10

c.

Table 3.1.5

x	y
-7	-12.5
-6.5	-11.13
-4.3	-8.045
-4	-8
-3	-8.5
-2.6	-8.98

Solution

a.

Graphic 3.1.3

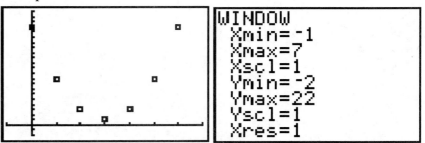

This data has the shape of a parabola and thus a quadratic function would be used to model it. The vertex is the minimum point on the graph and appears to be at about $(3, 1)$.

b.

Graphic 3.1.4

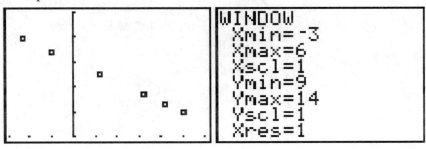

This data has a linear pattern.

c.

Graphic 3.1.5

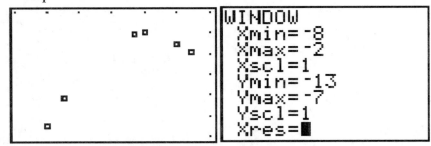

This data has the shape of a parabola and thus a quadratic function would be used to model it. The vertex is the maximum point on the graph and appears to be at about $(-4, -8)$. With this graph you may want to trace the plotted points in order to determine an estimate for the vertex.

Problem 1

Create scatter plots for the following sets of data. If a quadratic function would be a good fit give an estimate for the vertex and determine if it is a maximum or minimum point.

a.

Table 3.1.6

Input	Output
2	10
3	0
4	-6
5	-8
6	-6
7	0
8	10

b.

Table 3.1.7

Input	Output
-4	-2
-3	2.5
-2	4
-1	2.5
0	-2
1	-9.5

Solution   See page 137

In this section you will be given data that may follow a linear or quadratic pattern. If the data is quadratic you will be given any needed models to use in your calculator. You can use the trace feature to estimate the vertex of any given model. In the next few sections you will learn more about quadratic functions and learn a method to model data that follows a quadratic pattern.

Section 3.1 Key Points

- Not all data follows a linear pattern.

- Quadratic Function: A function that can be written in one of these forms
$$f(x) = ax^2 + bx + c \text{ or } f(x) = a(x-h)^2 + k$$
where $a, b, c, h,$ and k are real numbers and $a \neq 0$.

- Parabola: The graph of a quadratic function.
A parabola has a "U" shape and can either face upward or downward.

- Vertex: The point on a parabola where the graph changes direction.
  i   A parabola that faces upward will have a vertex that contains the minimum value on the graph.
  ii A parabola that faces downward will have a vertex that contains the maximum value on the graph.

Section 3.1 Problem Solutions:

Problem 1   Solution

a.

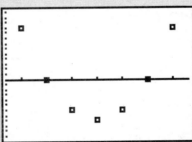

This data appears to be quadratic with the vertex being a minimum point at about $(5, -8)$.

b.

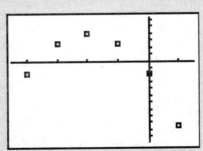

This data appears to be quadratic with maximum point as the vertex. The vertex is at the point $(-2, 4)$.

3.1 Exercises

1. The average number of days each month above 70°F in San Diego, California is given in **Table 3.1.6**

Table 3.1.6

Month	Average Number of Days Above 70°F
May	12
June	21
July	30
August	31
September	29
October	26
November	14
December	8

source: Weatherbase.com

   a. Define variables and create a scatter plot.
   b. Would a linear or quadratic function best model this data?
   c. If a quadratic model would be best estimate the vertex and determine if it is a maximum or minimum point.
   d. Use the scatter plot to estimate in what month the average number of days above 70°F is five or fewer.

2. The number of cassette singles shipped by major recording media manufacturers is given in **Table 3.1.7**

Table 3.1.7

Year	Cassette Singles (in millions)	Year	Cassette Singles (in millions)
1987	5.1	1995	70.7
1988	22.5	1996	59.9
1991	69	1997	42.2
1992	84.6	1998	26.4
1993	85.6	1999	14.2
1994	81.1	2000	1.3

source: Statistical Abstract 2001

   a. Let C be the number of cassette singles in millions shipped t years since 1980. Create a scatter plot for this data on your calculator.
   b. Graph the function C(t) on the same window as your scatter plot.
   $$C(t) = -2.336(t-13)^2 + 85.6$$
   c. How well does this model fit the data?
   d. Estimate a vertex for this model.
   e. Explain what the vertex means in this context.
   f. Use the graph to estimate in what year(s) no cassette singles were shipped.

3. The number of cable television systems in the United States during the 1990's are given in **Table 3.1.8**

Table 3.1.8

Year	Cable TV Systems
1992	11,075
1993	11,217
1994	11,214
1995	11,218
1996	11,119
1997	10,950

source: Statistical Abstract 2001

   a. Let C be the number of cable systems in the United States t years since 1990. Create a scatter plot on your calculator for this data.
   b. Graph the function C(t) on the same window as your scatter plot.
   $$C(t) = -34.625t^2 + 285.482t + 10649.643$$
   c. How well does this model fit the given data?
   d. Estimate a vertex for this model. Is the vertex a maximum or minimum point for this function?
   e. Explain what the vertex means in this context.

4. Use the graph to estimate the following:

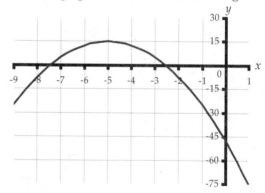

   a. Vertex
   b. Horizontal Intercept(s)
   c. Vertical Intercept

5. Use the graph to estimate the following:

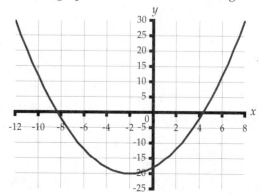

   a. Vertex
   b. x-intercept(s)
   c. y-intercept

6. Use the graph to estimate the following:

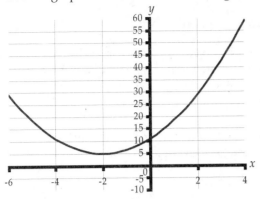

a. Vertex

b. Horizontal Intercept(s)

c. Vertical Intercept

7. Use the graph to estimate the following:

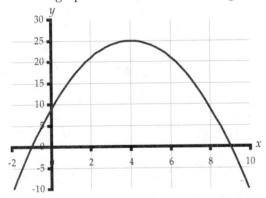

a. Vertex

b. x-intercept(s)

c. y-intercept

For exercises 8 and 9 use the table to find the horizontal intercepts

8.

X	Y1
-4	6
-3	0
-2	-4
-1	-6
0	-6
1	-4
2	0

$Y_1 \blacksquare X^2+X-6$

9.

X	Y1
-.8	16
-.4	0
0	-8
.4	-8
.8	0
1.2	16
1.6	40

$Y_1 \blacksquare 25X^2-10X-8$

For exercises 10 through 16 determine what type of model (linear, quadratic, or other) would best fit the data. If quadratic give an estimate for the vertex and determine if it is a maximum or minimum point.

10.

Table 3.1.9

Input	Output
-7	-8
-5	8
-3	-8
-1	-56
1	-136
2	-188

11.

Table 3.1.10

Input	Output
1	-57
2	-20
4	6
6	8
8	34
9	71

12.

Table 3.1.11

Input	Output
1	12
2	5
4	-3
6	-3
8	5
9	12

13.

Table 3.1.12

Input	Output
-2	-12
-1	-9.5
0	-7
3	0.5
4	3
6	8

14.

Table 3.1.13

Input	Output
-7	42.8
-2	25.8
1	15.6
5	2
9	-11.6
18	-42.2

15.

Table 3.1.14

Input	Output
-5	-48
-3	8
-2	15
-1	8
1	-48
2	-97

16.

Table 3.1.15

Input	Output
-8	17
-5	19
0	22
7	27
16	32
27	37

Section 3.2   Graphing Quadratics in Vertex Form

• Vertex Form • Graphing Quadratics in Vertex Form

In the last section you were given several quadratic functions to use as models for data. We are going to investigate what defines a quadratic function and then look at one form in more detail.

Concept Investigation 1

State what kind of function you think the following functions are; linear, quadratic or other. Then graph the function on your calculator to confirm your answer.

a. $f(t) = 3.5t - 7$

b. $R(t) = 5t^2$

c. $P(u) = 4u^2 + 5u - 8$

d. $Q(m) = 3.5(m - 4) - 9.8$

e. $G(d) = 7(d - 5)^2 + 5$

f. $T(c) = 0.5(c + 4)^3 - 5$

g. $E(w) = 3.5(2)^w$

h. $F(x) = (x + 4)^2$

i. $H(n) = 2n^3 - 5n^2 + n - 15$

j. $K(v) = 5v^2 - 9$

What characteristics do quadratic functions have?

Quadratic functions are most often represented by one of the following two forms.

Standard Form:

$$f(x) = ax^2 + bx + c$$

where a, b, and c are real numbers and a cannot be zero.

Vertex Form

$$f(x) = a(x - h)^2 + k$$

where a, h, and k are real numbers and a cannot be zero.

You should note that in both of these definitions the only constant that cannot be zero is a. This is because if a was zero the squared term would go away and it would no longer be quadratic. All of the other constants, b, c, h, and k, in these forms can be zero and the function will remain a quadratic.

Both of these forms are helpful in their own ways. In this section and the next we are going to consider the vertex form and how it can help us model quadratic data. Later we will also use the standard form and learn to solve both types of quadratics. Because understanding the graph of a function is an important part of the modeling process we are going to take a close look at the vertex form and how the constants a, h, and k affect the graph of the function.

Concept Investigation 2

Consider the vertex form of a quadratic .

$$f(x) = a(x-h)^2 + k$$

We are going to study one part of this function at a time. For each section of this investigation consider how the graph changes as you change one of the constants in the function.

a. Graph the following group of functions on the same calculator window. (Use zoom standard for your window settings.)

    i $f(x) = x^2$ The basic quadratic function.

    ii $f(x) = x^2 + 2$

    iii $f(x) = x^2 + 5$

    iv $f(x) = x^2 + 6$

    v $f(x) = x^2 + 8$

In these functions we are considering how a positive k value changes the graph of a basic quadratic function. In your own words what does a positive k value do to the graph?

b. Graph the following group of functions on the same calculator window.

    i $f(x) = x^2$

    ii $f(x) = x^2 - 2$

    iii $f(x) = x^2 - 5$

    iv $f(x) = x^2 - 6$

    v $f(x) = x^2 - 8$

In these functions we are considering how a negative k value changes the graph of a basic quadratic function. In your own words what does a negative k value do to the graph?

Concept Connection:
Although the vertex form of a quadratic function is convenient to use for graphing and modeling quadratics, many students struggle with the vertex form for one basic reason. Many students cannot understand why the constants a and k look positive when they are positive and negative when they are negative but the constant h always looks the opposite of what it actually is. When using the vertex form

$$f(x) = a(x-h)^2 + k$$

you need to notice that the constant h is being subtracted from the variable x. This creates a situation where the sign of h gets hidden by the subtraction that it is a part of. This is best shown by a few examples. Consider the following situations and how the problem looks once it has been simplified.

CC Example 1:
Consider the expression

$$x - h$$

Now substitute the following values for h and simplify.

$$h = 1, 3, -5, -3$$

$h = 1$

$$x - (1)$$

$$x - 1$$

The positive h value now looks negative.

$h = 3$

$$x - (3)$$

$$x - 3$$

Again the positive h value of 3 now looks like a negative 3.

$h = -5$

$$x - (-5)$$

$$x + 5$$

The negative h value looks like a positive 5.

$h = -3$

$$x - (-3)$$

$$x + 3$$

Now the negative h value of -3 looks like a positive 3.

c. Graph the following group of functions on the same calculator window.

  i $f(x) = x^2$

  ii $f(x) = (x-2)^2$

  iii $f(x) = (x-4)^2$

  iv $f(x) = (x-6)^2$

  v $f(x) = (x-8)^2$

In these functions we are considering how a **positive** h value changes the graph of a basic quadratic function. In your own words what does a **positive** h value do to the graph? (See the Concept Connection.)

d. Graph the following group of functions on the same calculator window.

  i $f(x) = x^2$

  ii $f(x) = (x+2)^2$

  iii $f(x) = (x+4)^2$

  iv $f(x) = (x+6)^2$

  v $f(x) = (x+8)^2$

In these functions we are considering how a **negative** h value changes the graph of a basic quadratic function. In your own words what does a **negative** h value do to the graph? (Remember that h is the only constant in the vertex form that looks the opposite than it is.)

e. Graph the following functions and estimate the vertex of the parabola.

  i $f(x) = x^2$ Vertex $(0, 0)$

  ii $f(x) = (x-2)^2$ Vertex

  iii $f(x) = (x-4)^2 + 3$ Vertex

  iv $f(x) = (x-6)^2 + 6$ Vertex

  v $f(x) = (x-8)^2 - 5$ Vertex

  vi $f(x) = (x+2)^2 - 4$ Vertex

  vii $f(x) = (x+5)^2 + 2$ Vertex

  viii $f(x) = (x+7)^2 + 4.5$ Vertex

  ix $f(x) = (x-2.5)^2 + 3.5$ Vertex

What is the relationship between the vertex form of a quadratic $f(x) = a(x - h)^2 + k$ and the vertex of the parabola?

Be sure to use caution when interpreting the value of h and k. Remember that h will appear to have the opposite sign. Since these two constants control where the vertex of the parabola will be located they will also give you the values for the maximum or minimum point on the graph. When interpreting the vertex be sure to consider whether it is a maximum or minimum point.

Definition 3.2.1

Vertex Form: A quadratic function written in the form
$$f(x) = a(x - h)^2 + k$$
where a, h, and k are real numbers and $a \neq 0$.

Vertex in the Vertex Form: The vertex of a quadratic equation in vertex form can be read directly from the equation.
$$\text{Vertex} = (h, k)$$
Remember to use caution when reading the value of h, The signs look opposite.

To complete our information about the vertex form we still need to investigate what the value of a does to the graph of a parabola.

Concept Investigation 3

a. Graph the following group of functions on the same calculator window. Estimate the vertex.

    i $f(x) = (x + 2)^2 - 5$ (note: $a = 1$)   Vertex

    ii $f(x) = 2(x + 2)^2 - 5$ Vertex

    iii $f(x) = 5(x + 2)^2 - 5$ Vertex

    iv $f(x) = 18.7(x + 2)^2 - 5$ Vertex

In these functions we are considering how a positive a value greater than 1 changes the graph of a quadratic function. Does the value of a affect the vertex of the graph?

In your own words what does a positive a value greater than 1 do to the graph?

b. Graph the following group of functions on the same calculator window.

   i $f(x) = (x-4)^2 + 3$

   ii $f(x) = -2(x-4)^2 + 3$

   iii $f(x) = -5(x-4)^2 + 3$

   iv $f(x) = -6.3(x-4)^2 + 3$

   v $f(x) = -8.7(x-4)^2 + 3$

In these functions we are considering how an a value less than -1 changes the graph of a quadratic function. In your own words what does a negative a value do to the graph?

The value of a controls more than just whether the parabola faces upward or downward. Lets look at some other values of a and see how they can affect the graph.

c. Graph the following group of functions on the same calculator window.

   i $f(x) = x^2$

   ii $f(x) = 0.5x^2$

   iii $f(x) = -0.3x^2$

   iv $f(x) = -\frac{2}{3}x^2$ Use Parentheses around the fractions.

   v $f(x) = \frac{1}{10}x^2$

In these functions we are considering how an a value between -1 and 1 changes the graph of a quadratic function. In your own words how do these values of a change the graph?

If we put all of the information we know about a, h, and k together then we can sketch the graph of a quadratic function by hand. One other characteristic of a parabola that is helpful, is its symmetry about the vertical line going through the vertex. This vertical line is called the axis of symmetry and has the equation $x = h$ where the vertex is (h, k). This basically means that it looks the same on the right side of the axis of symmetry as it does on the left side. This feature of a parabola makes graphing even easier since you only need to have points on one side of the vertex in order to copy them for the other side.

Graphic 3.2.1

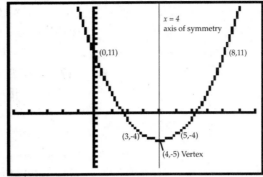

In **Graphic 3.2.1** you can see that if you move one space to the right and left of the vertex you get the points $(3, -4)$ and $(5, -4)$ that are at the same height. Also moving left and right 4 spaces results in two points with the same height. These points are called symmetric points since they are equal distance from the vertex both horizontally and vertically.

Example 1

Sketch the graph of the following quadratic.
$$f(x) = 2.5(x - 6)^2 + 2$$

Solution

Step 1 Determine the vertex.

Since the quadratic is given in vertex form we can easily determine that the vertex is $(6, 2)$.

Step 2 Investigate the value of a.

The value of a is 2.5. Since a is positive the graph will open upward and because it is greater than 1 the graph will be narrow.

Step 3 Find the vertical intercept.

To find the vertical intercept we just need to make the input variable zero.
$$f(x) = 2.5(x - 6)^2 + 2$$
$$f(0) = 2.5(0 - 6)^2 + 2$$
$$f(0) = 2.5(-6)^2 + 2$$
$$f(0) = 2.5(36) + 2$$
$$f(0) = 90 + 2$$
$$f(0) = 92$$

Therefore the vertical intercept is $(0, 92)$.

Step 4 Pick two points on the left or right of the vertex.

The vertex is $(6, 2)$ so we will choose $x = 2$ and 4. Substitute these values into the function to find the outputs for these input values.

$$f(x) = 2.5(x-6)^2 + 2$$
$$f(2) = 2.5(2-6)^2 + 2$$
$$f(2) = 2.5(-4)^2 + 2$$
$$f(2) = 2.5(16) + 2$$
$$f(2) = 40 + 2$$
$$f(2) = 42$$

and

$$f(4) = 2.5(4-6)^2 + 2$$
$$f(4) = 2.5(-2)^2 + 2$$
$$f(4) = 2.5(4) + 2$$
$$f(4) = 10 + 2$$
$$f(4) = 12$$

Remember that another way to evaluate a function for several values is to use the table feature on the calculator.

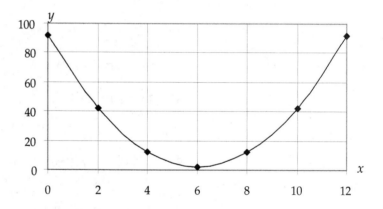

Therefore we have the points (2, 42) and (4, 12).

Step 5 Sketch the vertex, the vertical intercept, the points from step 4 and their symmetric pairs and connect the points with a smooth curve.

Graphic 3.2.2

Problem 1
Sketch the graph of the following quadratic.
$$f(x) = -0.5(x+2)^2 + 4$$

Solution   See page 149

Graphing a Quadratic from the Vertex Form:
1.   Determine the vertex.
2.   Investigate the value of a.
3.   Find the vertical intercept.
4.   Pick two points on the left or right of the vertex.
5.   Sketch the vertex, the vertical intercept, the points from step 4 and their symmetric pairs and connect the points with a smooth curve.

Example 2

The average number of hours per person per year spent watching television during the late 1990's can be modeled by

$$H(t) = 9.5(t-7)^2 + 1544$$

where $H(t)$ represents the average number of hours per person per year spent watching television t years since 1990.

a. How many hours did the average person spend watching television in 1996?

b. Sketch a graph of this model.

c. In what year was the average number of hours spent watching television the least?

d. Use your graph to estimate in what year(s) the average number of hours spent watching television was 1800 hours per person per year.

Solution

a. 1996 would be $t = 6$ so we need to substitute in 6 and solve for H.

$$H(t) = 9.5(t-7)^2 + 1544$$
$$H(6) = 9.5(6-7)^2 + 1544$$
$$H(6) = 9.5(-1)^2 + 1544$$
$$H(6) = 9.5 + 1544$$
$$H(6) = 1553.5$$

Thus in 1996 the average person spent 1553.5 hours per year watching television.

b.

Step 1 Determine the Vertex.

Since the quadratic is given in vertex form we can easily determine that the vertex is $(7, 1544)$.

Step 2 Investigate the value of a.

The value of a is 9.5. Since a is positive the graph will open upward and because it is greater than 1 the graph will be narrow.

Step 3 Find the vertical intercept.

To find the vertical intercept we just need to make the input variable zero.

$$H(t) = 9.5(t-7)^2 + 1544$$
$$H(0) = 9.5(0-7)^2 + 1544$$
$$H(0) = 2009.5$$

Therefore the vertical intercept is $(0, 2009.5)$.

Step 4 Pick two points on the left or right of the vertex.

The vertex is $(7, 1544)$ so we will choose $t = 3$ and 5. Substitute these values into the function to find the outputs for these input values.

$$H(t) = 9.5(t-7)^2 + 1544$$
$$H(3) = 9.5(3-7)^2 + 1544$$
$$H(3) = 1696$$

and

$$H(5) = 9.5(5-7)^2 + 1544$$
$$H(5) = 1582$$

Therefore we have the points $(3, 1696)$ and $(5, 1582)$.

Step 5 Sketch the vertex, the vertical intercept, the points from step 4 and their symmetric pairs and connect the points with a smooth curve.

Since $(3, 1696)$ is a point on the left of the vertex the point $(11, 1696)$ will be its symmetric pair on the right side of the vertex. The same is true for $(5, 1582)$ and $(9, 1582)$, and $(0, 2009.5)$ and $(14, 2009.5)$.

Graphic 3.2.3

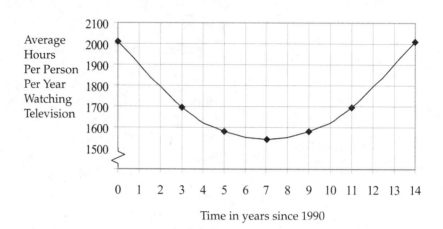

Time in years since 1990

c.   The lowest point on the graph is the vertex at $(7, 1544)$. In 1997 people watched an average of 1544 hours of television per year, this was the least amount of television watched during the late 1990's.

d.   According to the graph the average hours per person per year spent watching television reached 1800 in year 2 and again in year 12. Since time is measured in years since 1990 2 and 12 would be the years 1992 and 2002 respectively.

Problem 2

The number of cellular telephone subscribers, in thousands, can be modeled by

$$C(t) = 833.53(t + 1)^2 + 3200$$

where $C(t)$ represents the number of cellular telephone subscribers, in thousands, t years since 1990.

a.   How many cellular telephone subscribers were there in 2000?

b.   Sketch a graph of this model.

c.   According to this model in what year was the number of cellular telephone subscribers the least?

d.   How many cellular telephone subscribers were there in 1985? Does your answer make sense?

Solution   See page 150

Section 3.2 Key Points

- Vertex Form: A quadratic function written in the form
$$f(x) = a(x-h)^2 + k$$
where a, h, and k are real numbers and $a \neq 0$.

- The values of a, h, and k affect the graph of a parabola.
   - **i** h positive will move the graph to the right h units from the origin.
   - **ii** h negative will move the graph to the left h units form the origin.
   - **iii** k positive will move the graph up k units from the origin.
   - **iv** k negative will move the graph down k units from the origin.
   - **v** a positive makes the graph face upward.
   - **vi** a negative makes the graph face downward.
   - **vii** a between -1 and 1 makes the graph wider. The closer a is to zero the wider the graph gets.
   - **viii** a greater than 1 or less than -1 makes the graph more narrow. The farther a is from zero the more narrow the graph gets.

- Vertex in the Vertex Form: The vertex of a quadratic equation in vertex form can be read directly from the equation.
$$\text{Vertex} = (h, k)$$
Remember to use caution when reading the value of h, the signs look opposite.

- Axis of Symmetry: Is the vertical line going through the vertex of a parabola.

- Parabolas are symmetric: This means that a parabola looks the same on each side of the axis of symmetry. Symmetric points can be used to make graphing a parabola easier.

- Sketching the graph of a quadratic from the vertex form.
   Step 1 Determine the Vertex.
   Step 2 Investigate the value of a.
   Step 3 Find the vertical intercept.
   Step 4 Pick two points on the left or right of the vertex.
   Step 5 Sketch the vertex, the vertical intercept, the points from step 4 and their symmetric pairs and connect the points with a smooth curve.

Section 3.2 Problem Solutions

Problem 1   Solution
$$f(x) = -0.5(x+2)^2 + 4$$

Step 1 Determine the Vertex.

The vertex is $(-2, 4)$.

Step 2 Investigate the value of a.

The value of a is -0.5. Since a is negative the graph will face downward and because it is between -1 and 1 makes the graph wider.

Step 3 Find the vertical intercept.
$$f(0) = -0.5(0+2)^2 + 4$$
$$f(0) = 2$$
Therefore the vertical intercept is $(0, 2)$.

Step 4 Pick two points on the left or right of the vertex.

The vertex is $(-2, 4)$ so we will choose $x = -1$ and 1.

$f(-1) = 3.5$

$f(1) = -0.5$

So the points $(-1, 3.5)$ and $(1, -0.5)$ are on the graph. This means that their symmetric pairs $(-3, 3.5)$ and $(-5, -0.5)$ are also on the graph.

Step 5 Sketch the vertex, the vertical intercept, the points from step 4 and their symmetric pairs and connect the points with a smooth curve.

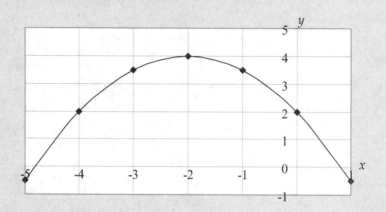

Problem 2   Solution

$$C(t) = 833.53(t + 1)^2 + 3200$$

a. The year 2000 would be represented by $t = 2000$.

$C(10) = 104057$

Therefore there were approximately 104,057 thousand cellular telephone subscribers in 2000. This can also be stated as 104 million cellular telephone subscribers.

b. Note that the vertex is at $(-1, 3200)$.

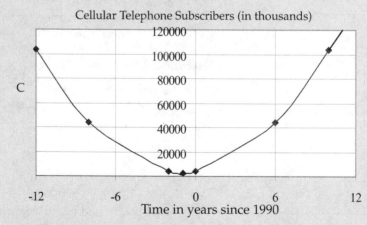

Cellular Telephone Subscribers (in thousands)

Time in years since 1990

c. The vertex is the lowest point so the number of cellular telephone subscribers was the least in 1989.

d.

$C(-5) = 16536$

This answer does not make sense since there were only 3200 thousand in 1989 there would not be more than that in 1985.

3.2 Exercises

For exercises 1 through 7 state how you would change the values of a, h and/or k in the vertex form to make the parabola fit the data better.

1.

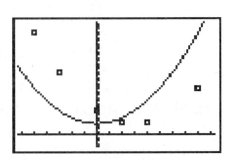

2.

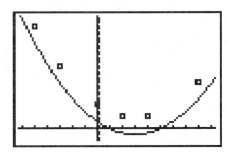

3.

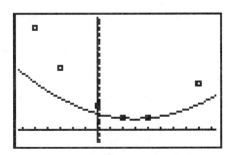

4.

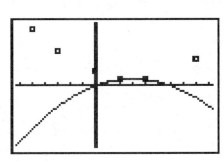

5.

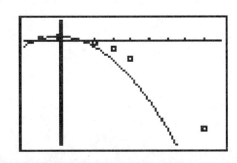

6.

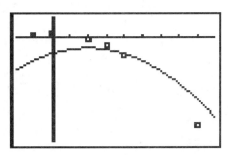

7.

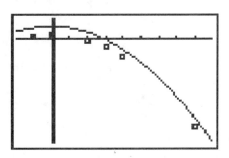

8. The poverty threshold for an individual under 65 years old can be modeled by
$$P(t) = 4.95(t - 57)^2 + 1406$$
where $P(t)$ represents the poverty threshold, in dollars, for an individual in the U.S. under 65 years old t years since 1900.

source: Model based on data from the Statistical Abstract 2001.

a. What was the poverty threshold in 1990?

b. Sketch a graph of this model.

c. According to this model when did the poverty threshold reach a minimum? Does this make sense?

d. Use your graph to estimate when the poverty threshold was $3000.

9. The total number of persons, in thousands, 65 years old and over who were below the poverty level can be modeled by
$$N(t) = -59(t - 12)^2 + 3890$$
where $N(t)$ represents the total number of persons 65 years old and over in the U.S. who were below the poverty level, in thousands, t years since 1980.

source: Model based on data from the Statistical Abstract 2001.

a. How many people 65 years old and over were below the poverty level in 1989?

b. Sketch a graph of this model.

c. Estimate the vertex of this model and explain its meaning in this context.

d. Use your graph to estimate when the number of people 65 years old and over in the U.S. reached 4 million.

10. The amount that personal households and non-profit organizations have invested in time and savings deposits can be modeled by

$$D(t) = 73.6(t - 3.5)^2 + 2176$$

Where $D(t)$ represents the amount in billions of dollars the households and nonprofit organizations have invested in time and savings accounts t years since 1990.

a. Sketch a graph of this model.

b. How much did households and nonprofit organizations have invested in time and savings accounts in 1996?

c. In what year were these deposits at their lowest levels?

d. Use your graph to estimate when the amount households and nonprofit organizations have invested in time and savings accounts reached $3000 billion.

11. The percent of the female population who experience congestive heart failure based on their age in years can be modeled by

$$H(a) = 0.004(a - 26)^2 + 0.007$$

Where $H(a)$ represents the percent, as a whole number, of women a years old who experience congestive heart failure.

source: Heart Disease and Stroke Statistics - 2004 Update, American Heart Association.

a. Sketch the graph of this model.

b. What percent of women experience congestive heart failure at 30 years of age?

c. According to this model at what age do the fewest percentage of women experience congestive heart failure?

d. Use your graph to estimate at what age 5% of women would expect to experience congestive heart failure.

Math Tutorial More practice problems like exercises 12 through 22 can be found in section 3.2 of the CD Tutorial.

For exercises 11 through 20 sketch the graph of the given functions and label the vertex, vertical intercept, and at least one additional symmetric pair.

12. $g(x) = (x - 7)^2 + 9$

13. $f(x) = (x - 5)^2 + 3$

14. $q(a) = (a + 7)^2 + 2$

15. $B(n) = (n - 3)^2 - 4$

16. $T(z) = (z + 6)^2 - 8$

17. $g(m) = 2.4(m + 4)^2 + 20$

18. $h(d) = -4(d + 15)^2 - 8$

19. $s(t) = -0.25(t + 50)^2 + 25$

20. $C(u) = -0.007(u - 400)^2$

21. $p(w) = 123(w - 4)^2 - 2500$

22. $f(x) = 5(x + 13)^2 - 45$

In exercises 23 through 27 answer the following questions:

a. Find the vertex.

b. Is the parabola wide or narrow?

c. Does the parabola face upward or downward?

d. Give a calculator window that will give a good picture of this parabola.
- X Min
- X Max
- Y Min
- Y Max

23. $f(x) = 0.0005(x - 1000)^2$

24. $f(x) = 0.0005(x - 1000)^2 + 1000$

25. $f(x) = -0.0005(x + 10,000)^2 + 5000$

26. $f(x) = -10(x + 25,000)^2 - 10,000$

27. $f(x) = (x - 55.8)^2 - 29.7$

Section 3.3   Finding Quadratic Models

• Finding Quadratic Models • Domain • Range

Now we will use all the information we have about graphing quadratics from the vertex form in order to find models for data that takes the shape of a parabola. We will also look at the domain and range of quadratic functions and what you should be careful of when thinking about model breakdown.

Example 1

The average monthly temperature in Anchorage, Alaska is given in **Table 3.3.1**

Table 3.3.1

Month	Average Temperature (°F)
March	25
April	36
May	47
June	55
July	59
August	57
October	35
November	22

source: Weatherbase.com

a. Will a linear or quadratic model fit this data best? Why?

b. Find a model for this data.

c. Using your model estimate the average temperatures during September and February.

d. The actual average during September is 48 °F and during February is 18 °F. How well does your model predict these values?

e. Give a reasonable domain and range for this model.

Solution

a. A quadratic model will fit this data best because it is shaped like a downward facing parabola.

b.

Step 1 Define the variables

T = Average Temperature in Anchorage Alaska (°F).
m = The month of the year. i.e. $m = 5$ represents May.

Step 2 Adjust the data. (if needed) **Table 3.3.2**

Table 3.3.2

m	T (°F)
3	25
4	36
5	47
6	55
7	59
8	57
10	35
11	22

Step 3 Create a scattergram.

The inputs go from 3 to 11 and the outputs go from 22 to 59 so spreading out some results in **Graphic 3.3.1**

Graphic 3.3.1.

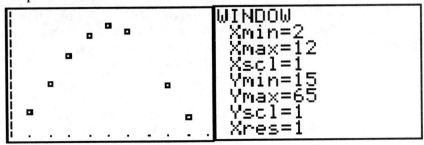

Step 4 Select a model type. (We now have linear and quadratic to choose from.)

Since the data has the shape of a downward facing parabola we should choose a quadratic model.

Step 5 Pick a vertex and substitute it in for h and k in the vertex form.

The highest point on this scattergram looks like a reasonable vertex so we will use it as the vertex.

$$\text{Vertex} = (7, 59)$$
$$T(m) = a(m - 7)^2 + 59$$

Step 6 Pick another point and use it to find a.

We can choose the last point in the data because it is farther away from the vertex and seems to follow a smooth curve.

$$\text{Other Point} = (11, 22)$$

$$T(m) = a(m - 7)^2 + 59$$

Substitute 11 for the month and 22 for the average temperature.

$$22 = a(11 - 7)^2 + 59$$

$$22 = a(4)^2 + 59$$

Solve for a.

$$22 = 16a + 59$$

$$\underline{-59 \qquad\qquad -59}$$

$$-37 = 16a$$

$$\frac{-37}{16} = \frac{16a}{16}$$

$$-2.3125 = a$$

Step 7 Write the model.

You now have a, h and k so you can write the model.

$$T(m) = -2.3(m - 7)^2 + 59$$

Step 8 Check your model by graphing it on the calculator

Graphic 3.3.2.

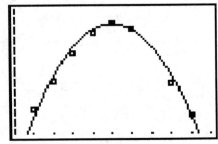

c. September is the 9th month of the year and February is the 2nd month so
$$T(m) = -2.3(m-7)^2 + 59$$
$$T(9) = -2.3(9-7)^2 + 59$$
$$T(9) = 49.8$$
and
$$T(2) = -2.3(2-7)^2 + 59$$
$$T(2) = 1.5$$

The average temperature in Anchorage, Alaska during September is 49.8 °F and during February is 1.5 °F.

d. Our estimate for September is fairly accurate but the estimate for February is not close to the actual value. This estimate probably represents model breakdown in this situation.

e. From what we saw in part d the model will work well within the given data but not so well outside of the data. Therefore we can set the domain to be $[3, 11]$. To find the range for this model we need to look for the lowest and highest points on this model within the chosen domain. The highest point is clearly the vertex of $(7, 59)$. The lowest point is either on the right or left hand side of the domain. To determine what the lowest output is we will substitute the two ends of the domain and find the related output values.
$$T(3) = 22.2$$
$$T(11) = 22.2$$

Since both of these values happen to be the same the lowest output value is 22.2 so our range will be $[22.2, 59]$.

Problem 1

The number of cable television systems in the United States during the 1990's are given in **Table 3.3.3**

Table 3.3.3

Year	Cable Television Systems
1992	11,075
1993	11,217
1995	11,218
1996	11,119
1997	10,950

source: Statistical Abstract 2001

a. Find a model for this data.

b. Explain what the vertex means in this context.

c. How many cable television systems does your model predict there will be in 1999?

d. Give a reasonable domain and range for your model.

e. Find the vertical intercept for your model and explain its meaning in this context.

f. Use a table or graph to estimate when there will only be 10,500 cable television systems.

Solution   See page 164

Concept Connection:
When considering domain and range for a quadratic function without a context your domain will be All Real Numbers and your range will start or end at the output value of the vertex and will go to positive or negative infinity.

CC-Example 1:
Give the domain and range for the function
$f(x) = 2(x-3)^2 + 5$

Solution:
Domain:
   All Real Numbers
   or $(-\infty, \infty)$
This function faces upward so its lowest point is the vertex.
Range:
   $[5, \infty)$
   or $y \geq 5$

CC-Example 2:
Give the domain and range for the function
$f(x) = -0.5(x+1)^2 - 3$

Solution:
Domain:
   All Real Numbers
   or $(-\infty, \infty)$
This function faces downward so its highest point is the vertex.
Range:
   $(-\infty, -3\,]$
   or $y \leq -3$

Modeling Steps For Quadratics:
1. Define the variables (be sure to use units).
2. Adjust the data (if needed).
3. Create a scattergram (on calculator).
4. Select a model type (we now have linear and quadratic models).
5. Pick a vertex and substitute it in for h and k in the vertex form.
6. Pick another point and use it to find a.
7. Write the model.
8. Check your model by graphing it on the calculator.

As you can see from example 1 the modeling process for quadratics is about the same as that for linear equations. It may even be considered easier since you do not have to calculate the slope. If you can pick a reasonable vertex the process is not too difficult. If your model does not fit well you may want to check your calculations from step 6. Students most often make mistakes when solving for the value of a.

Finding a reasonable domain is exactly the same as it was for linear models. Try to expand the domain beyond the given data unless model breakdown occurs. You will want to use more caution with model breakdown since quadratic models usually will not stay reliable very far beyond the given data.

Finding the range is still the lowest to highest output values the function within the set domain. You must be careful not to assume that the lowest and highest outputs of the function will be the outputs from the ends of the domain. Since quadratics have a maximum or minimum point at the vertex the range will typically include this as the highest or lowest value. If the vertex is within the domain values it will be one endpoint of the range and one of the ends of the domain will provide the other range endpoint. Be sure to give the range stating the lowest output followed by the highest output value. Many students want to order them based on what input value they come from, this often causes the range to be presented backwards.

Example 2

The number of public branch libraries in the United States for several years is given in **Table 3.3.4**

Table 3.3.4

Year	Public Library Branches
1994	6,223
1995	6,172
1996	6,205
1997	6,332
1998	6,435

source: Statistical Abstract 2001

a. Find a model for this data.

b. Using your model estimate the number of branch libraries in 2000.

c. Give a reasonable domain and range for this model.

d. Use the graph or table to estimate when there are 6500 branch libraries.

Solution

a.

   Step 1 Define the variables
      B = The number of public branch libraries in the U.S..
      t = Time in years since 1990.

Step 2 Adjust the data. (if needed)

Table 3.3.5

t	B
4	6,223
5	6,172
6	6,205
7	6,332
8	6,435

Step 3 Create a scattergram.

The inputs go from 4 to 8 and the outputs go from 6172 to 6435 so spreading out some results in **Graphic 3.3.3**

Graphic 3.3.3

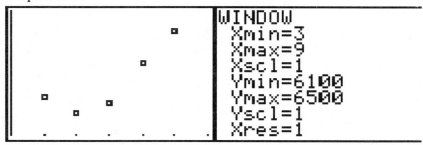

Step 4 Select a model type. (We now have linear and quadratic to choose from.)

Since the data has the shape of a upward facing parabola we should choose a quadratic model.

Step 5 Pick a vertex and substitute it in for h and k in the vertex form.

The lowest point on this scattergram looks like a reasonable vertex so we will use it for the model.

$$\text{Vertex} = (5, 6172)$$

$$B(t) = a(t-5)^2 + 6172$$

Step 6 Pick another point and use it to find a.

We can choose the last point in the data because it is farther away from the vertex and seems to follow a smooth curve.

$$\text{Other Point} = (8, 6435)$$

$$B(t) = a(t-5)^2 + 6172$$
$$6435 = a(8-5)^2 + 6172$$

Substitute 8 for the year and 6435 for the number of public branch libraries.

$$6435 = a(3)^2 + 6172$$

Solve for a.

$$6435 = 9a + 6172$$
$$\underline{-6172 \qquad\qquad -6172}$$
$$263 = 9a$$
$$29.22 = a$$

Step 7 Write the model.

You now have a, h and k so you can write the model.

$$B(t) = 29.22(t-5)^2 + 6172$$

Step 8 Check your model by graphing it on the calculator

Graphic 3.3.4.

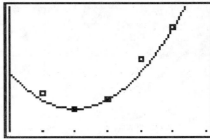

This model fits the data fairly well but the two points it misses are both above the model so moving the model up slightly may make a better fit. We can adjust the model for a better fit by making k bigger. The new model becomes

$$B(t) = 29.22(t-5)^2 + 6180$$

The graph of this adjusted model is overall closer to all the points in the data.

Graphic 3.3.5

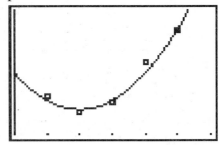

Note that the vertex of our adjusted model is different than the one we picked in step 5.

b. The year 2000 is represented by $t = 10$ so

$$B(10) = 29.22(10-5)^2 + 6180$$

$$B(10) = 6910.5$$

In 2000 there were approximately 6,911 public branch libraries.

c. In this problem it is probably reasonable to assume that there will continue to be more public branch offices as populations continue to grow. Therefore we will spread out the domain to include a few years beyond the given data giving us a domain of $[3, 10]$. The resulting range will have a minimum value at the vertex of 6180 and the maximum appears to be on the right side. Since $B(10) = 6910.5$ the range will be $[6180, 6911]$.

d. Using the table we get an estimate of $t = 2$ or $t = 8$.

X	Y1
1	6647.5
2	6443
3	6296.9
4	6209.2
6	6209.2
7	6296.9
8	6443

Y₁■29.22(X-5)²+...

Therefore there were about 6500 branch libraries in 1992 and again in 1998.

Some data has the same curve to it as a parabola but does not form both sides of the U shape. When this happens you need to use caution when determining the domain and range since model breakdown can occur to the left or right of the vertex.

Example 3

The number of cellular telephone subscribers in the U.S. is given in **Table 3.3.6**

Table 3.3.6

Year	Cellular Telephone Subscribers (in thousands)
1990	5,283
1991	7,557
1992	11,033
1993	16,009
1994	24,134
1996	44,043
1997	55,312
1999	86,047
2000	109,478

source: Statistical Abstract 2001

a. Find a model for this data.

b. Estimate the number of cellular phone subscribers in 1980 and 1995.

c. The actual number of cellular phone subscribers in 1995 was 33,786,000, how does your estimate from part b compare to the actual value?

d. Give a reasonable domain and range for your model.

Solution

a.

Step 1 Define the variables
C = The number of cellular telephone subscribers in the U.S. in thousands.
t = Time in years since 1990.

Step 2 Adjust the data. (if needed)

Table 3.3.7

Year	Cellular Telephone Subscribers (in thousands)
0	5,283
1	7,557
2	11,033
3	16,009
4	24,134
6	44,043
7	55,312
9	86,047
10	109,478

Step 3 Create a scattergram.
The inputs go from 0 to 10 and the outputs go from 5,283 to 109,478 so spreading out some results in **Graphic 3.3.6**

Graphic 3.3.6

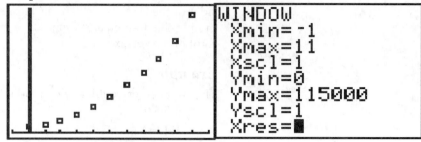

Step 4 Select a model type.

Since the data is curved upward it takes on the shape of the right half of a n upward facing parabola so we should choose a quadratic model.

Step 5 Pick a vertex and substitute it in for h and k in the vertex form.

The lowest point on this scattergram looks like a reasonable vertex so we will use it for the model.

$$\text{Vertex} = (0, 5283)$$

$$C(t) = a(t-0)^2 + 5283$$

$$C(t) = at^2 + 5283 \qquad \text{Simplify the function.}$$

Step 6 Pick another point and use it to find a.

We can choose the seventh point in the data because it is a ways from the vertex and seems to follow a smooth curve that will come close to all the data points.

$$\text{Other Point} = (6, 44043)$$

$$C(t) = at^2 + 5283 \qquad \text{Substitute 6 for the year and 44043 for}$$
$$44043 = a(6)^2 + 5283 \qquad \text{the number of cellular telephone}$$
$$44043 = 36a + 5283 \qquad \text{subscribers.}$$

$$\underline{-5283 \qquad\qquad -5283} \qquad \text{Solve for } a.$$

$$38760 = 36a$$

$$1076.67 = a$$

Step 7 Write the model.

You now have a, h and k so you can write the model.

$$C(t) = 1076.67t^2 + 5283$$

Step 8 Check your model by graphing it on the calculator

Graphic 3.3.7

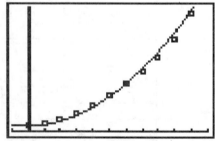

This model is not bad but we may be able to adjust it some by raising the graph and then making it a little wider. This will mean changing the values of a and k.

By playing with several possibilities we can come up with the model
$$C(t) = 1000t^2 + 7000$$
and graph in **Graphic 3.3.8**.

Graphic 3.3.8

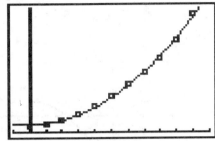

b. 1980 and 1995 are represented by $t = -10$ and $t = 5$ respectively.
$$C(-10) = 107000$$
$$C(5) = 32000$$

Therefore in 1980 there were 107,000,000 cellular telephone subscribers in the U.S.. This does not make sense since that number would not decrease so drastically during the next ten years so we believe this is model breakdown.

In 1995 there were 32,000,000 cellular telephone subscribers.

c. Comparing the actual value in 1995 to our estimate we are off by a little over 1 million subscribers but that is not a very large error considering the size of these numbers. We can be satisfied with this result.

d. Since there were probably fewer cellular telephone subscribers before 1990 we should not believe this model should be used for years to the left of the vertex. It does appear that we could extend the data farther to the right. So we can use the domain $[0, 12]$.

The resulting range will start at the lowest point, the vertex, and go up until it reaches the highest point at the right hand side of the domain.

Vertex $(0, 7000)$

$$C(12) = 151000$$

This gives a range of $[7000, 151000]$.

Problem 2

Find a model for the given data.

Table 3.3.8

x	$f(x)$
−6	−33
−4	−45
−2	−49
0	−45
2	−33
4	−13

Solution   See page 166

Example 4

Give the domain and range of the following functions.

a. $f(x) = 2(x+3)^2 + 17$

b. $g(x) = -1.3(x+5)^2 + 12$

c.

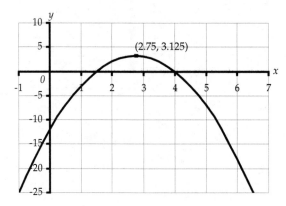

Solution

a. The domain will include all real numbers since there are not real numbers that make this function undefined. From the vertex form we know that the vertex of this quadratic is $(-3, 17)$ and that this quadratic faces upward since a is positive. Therefore the vertex is a minimum point for the graph and the graph extends upward to infinity. With this information we could sketch the graph of this function

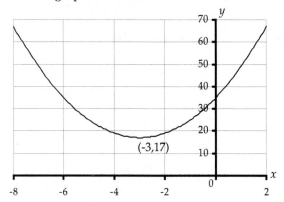

From this we get
Domain: All Real Numbers
Range: $[17, \infty)$
(Note that we use a bracket next to the 17 and an open parenthesis next to the infinity. This is because the function actually takes on the value 17 but cannot actually reach infinity.)

b. Again the domain is all real numbers since no real value of x will make the function undefined. From the vertex form we know the vertex is $(-5, 12)$ and that the graph faces downward since a is negative. This makes the vertex a maximum point and the graph continues downward to negative infinity. Thus we get
Domain: All Real Numbers
Range: $(-\infty, 12]$

c. Looking at the graph we can see that this function is a quadratic so the domain will be all real numbers. The vertex is the maximum point $(2.75, 3.125)$ so it is the highest point in the range. The graph continues down to negative infinity so we get
Domain: All Real Numbers
Range: $(-\infty, 3.125]$

Problem 3

Give the domain and range of the following functions:

a. $f(x) = -5(x-4)^2 - 10$

b. $g(x) = 3(x-7)^2 - 17$

Solution   See page 166

Section 3.3 Key Points

- Vertex Form: A quadratic function written in the form
$$f(x) = a(x-h)^2 + k$$

- Vertex in the Vertex Form: The vertex of a quadratic equation in vertex form can be read directly from the equation.
$$\text{Vertex} = (h, k)$$
  Remember to use caution when reading the value of h, the signs look opposite.

- Modeling Steps For Quadratics:
  Step 1. Define the variables (be sure to use units).
  Step 2   Adjust the data (if needed).
  Step 3   Create a scattergram (on calculator).
  Step 4   Select a model type (we now have linear and quadratic models).
  Step 5   Pick a vertex and substitute it in for h and k in the vertex form.
  Step 6   Pick another point and use it to find a.
  Step 7   Write the model.
  Step 8   Check your model by graphing it on the calculator.

- Domain: Expand on the data set if possible be sure to watch for model breakdown.
  In problems without a context the domain will be All Real Numbers.

- Range: The lowest to highest points within the domain.
  When the vertex is part of the domain it will be one of these points.
  In problems without a context the vertex will start or end the domain and positive or negative infinity will be the other endpoint.
  $(-\infty, k]$ or $[k, \infty)$

Section 3.3 Problem Solutions

Problem 1   Solution

a.

Step 1 Define the variables
C = The number of cable television systems in the U.S..
t = Time in years since 1990.

Step 2 Adjust the data. (if needed)

Table 3.3.9

t	C
2	11,075
3	11,217
5	11,218
6	11,119
7	10,950

Step 3 Create a scattergram.
The inputs go from 2 to 7 and the outputs go from 10,950 to 11,218 so spreading out some results in **Graphic 3.3.9**

Graphic 3.3.9

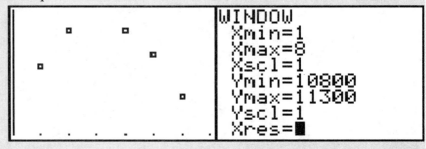

Step 4 Select a model type. (We now have linear and quadratic to choose from.)
Since the data has the shape of a downward facing parabola we should choose a quadratic model.

Step 5 Pick a vertex and substitute it in for h and k in the vertex form. The point where this graph looks like it turns around is not represented by a point in the data. Using the arrow buttons (not trace) on the calculator. we can estimate that the point $(4, 11250)$ will make a good vertex. There will be many other possibilities; we are just choosing something that looks good.

Vertex = $(4, 11250)$

$$C(t) = a(t-4)^2 + 11250$$

Step 6 Pick another point and use it to find a.
We can choose the last point in the data because it is farther away from the vertex and seems to follow a smooth curve.

Other Point = $(7, 10950)$

$$10950 = a(7-4)^2 + 11250$$

$$10950 = 9a + 11250$$

$$-33.3 = a$$

Step 7 Write the model.
You now have a, h and k so you can write the model.
$$C(t) = -33.3(t-4)^2 + 11250$$

Step 8 Check your model by graphing it on the calculator
Graphic 3.3.10

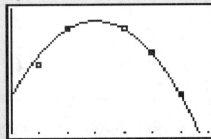

b. The vertex of $(4, 11250)$ represents when the number of cable television systems reached a maximum. Specifically that in 1994 there were the most cable television systems with a total of 11,250 systems.

c. 1999 is represented by $t = 9$ so
$$C(9) = -33.3(9-4)^2 + 11250$$
$$C(9) = 10416.75$$
In 1999 there were approximately 10,417 cable television systems in the U.S..

d. It seems reasonable to expand beyond the data in either direction so the domain is $[0, 10]$. This will result in a range of $[10050, 11250]$. The lowest point was found on the right end of the domain and the highest was represented by the vertex.

e. $t = 0$ represents 1990 so $C(0) = 10717$ is the vertical intercept and represents that in 1990 there were 10,717 cable television systems in the U.S..

f. Making the window larger we can use the trace feature to estimate the solutions.

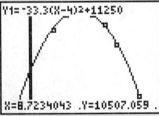

X	Y1	
0	10717	
-1	10418	
-2	10051	
8	10717	
9	10418	
10	10051	

X=

Using trace we get two estimates 8.7 and -0.72.

Using the table we estimate approximately -1 and 9.

Both techniques gives us the years 1989 and 1999 are when there were 10,500 cable television systems in the U.S.

Problem 2   Solution

a.

Create a scattergram.

Graphic 3.3.11

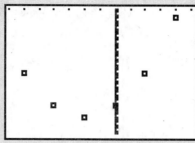

This appears to be a quadratic with a vertex of $(-2, -49)$ so we have
$$f(x) = a(x + 2)^2 - 49$$
Using the point $(4, -13)$ we can find a.
$$f(x) = a(x + 2)^2 - 49$$
$$-13 = a(4 + 2)^2 - 49$$
$$-13 = 36a - 49$$
$$1 = a$$
Therefore we have the model
$$f(x) = (x + 2)^2 - 49$$
We check this model with the graph.

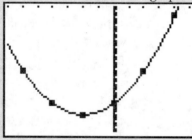

Problem 3   Solution

a.   This parabola faces down and has a vertex of $(4, -10)$ so we have
Domain: All Real Numbers
Range: $(-\infty, -10]$

b.   This parabola faces upward and has a vertex of $(7, -17)$ so we have
Domain: All Real Numbers
Range: $[-17, \infty)$

3.3 Exercises

1. The average monthly low temperatures in Anchorage, Alaska for certain months are given in **Table 3.3.9**

Table 3.3.9

Month	Average Low Temperature (oF)
April	28
May	39
June	47
July	51
August	49
September	41
October	28
November	15

source: Weatherbase.com

a. Find a model for this data.

b. Explain the meaning of the vertex for your model in this context.

c. What does your model predict the average low temperature will be in March?

d. Give a reasonable domain and range for your model.

2. The average poverty threshold for a family of four is given in **Table 3.3.10**

Table 3.3.10

Year	Average Poverty Threshold ($)
1965	3022
1970	3223
1975	3968
1980	5500
1985	8414

source: Statistical Abstract 2001

a. Find a model for this data.

b. Estimate the average poverty threshold for a family of four in 1990.

c. Give a reasonable domain and range for your model.

3. The number of white families below the poverty level in the U.S. for the late 1990's are given in **Table 3.3.11**

Table 3.3.11

Year	Number of Families (in thousands)
1995	4,994
1996	5,059
1997	4,990
1998	4,829
1999	4,377

source: Statistical Abstract 2001

a. Find a model for this data.

b. Estimate the number of families below the poverty level in 2000.

c. Explain the meaning of the vertex in this context.

d. Give a reasonable domain and range for your model.

4. Of the total number of people who own a home computer, the percent of those who use their home computers 6 or 7 days a week varies by age group. Some of these percentages are given in **Table 3.3.12**

Table 3.3.12

Age Group	Percent
20 to 29 yrs old	26.7
30 to 39 yrs old	24.2
40 to 49 yrs old	24.3
50 to 59 yrs old	26.6
60 to 69 yrs old	29.7

source: Statistical Abstract 2001

a. Find a model for this data (you may want to use 25 to represent 20 to 29 year olds).

b. Give a reasonable domain and range for this model.

c. Estimate the percent of teenagers who use their home computers 6 or 7 days a week.

5. The number of hours per year an average person spent using the internet is given in **Table 3.3.13**

Table 3.3.13

Year	Hours Per Year
1995	5
1996	10
1997	34
1998	61
1999	99
2000	135

source: Statistical Abstract 2001

a. Find a model for this data.

b. Determine if model breakdown occurs near the vertex.

c. Give a reasonable domain and range for this model.

d. Estimate the number of hours per year the average person spent on the internet in 2001.

e. Use a table or graph to estimate when the average person will spend 365 hours per year on the internet.

6. Lead used in paint has been decreasing since its peak around 1920. Lead usage in paint for several years is given in **Table 3.3.14**

Table 3.3.14

Year	Lead Usage (thousands of tons)
1940	70
1950	35
1960	10
1970	5
1980	0.01

source: Estimated from information at AmericanScientist.org

  a. Find a model for this data.

  b. Estimate the lead used in paints in 1955.

  c. Estimate the lead used in paints in 2000.

  d. Give a reasonable domain and range for this model.

  e. Use a table or the graph to estimate when 50 thousand tons of lead were used in paints.

For exercises 7 through 11 find a model for the given data. Give the domain and range for the model you found. Hint: These problems do not have a context.

7.

Table 3.3.15

Input	Output
-7	-8
-5	8
-3	-8
-1	-56
1	-136
2	-188

8.

Table 3.3.16

Input	Output
-20	121.2
-10	140.2
4	150.0
15	143.95
30	116.2
50	44.2

9.

Table 3.3.17

Input	Output
1	12
2	5
4	-3
6	-3
8	5
9	12

10.

Table 3.3.18

Input	Output
-2	-12
-1	-9.5
0	-7
3	0.5
4	3
6	8

11.

Table 3.3.19

Input	Output
-100	15300
-80	-1500
-60	-8700
-40	-6300
-30	-1500
-20	5700

For exercises 12 through 17 give the domain and range of the quadratic functions.

12. $f(x) = -2(x+4)^2 + 15$

13. $g(x) = -0.25(x-5)^2 + 17$

14. $f(x) = 5(x+4)^2 - 58$

15. $h(x) = 0.3(x-2.7)^2 + 5$

16.

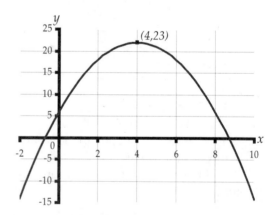

17.

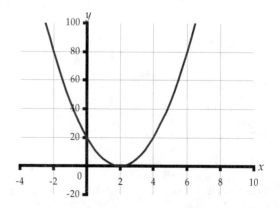

Section 3.4   Solving Quadratic Equations I

• **Solving from Vertex Form** • **Solving by Factoring**

So far in this chapter we have worked mostly with the vertex form of a quadratic and used it to model and graph. In this section we will learn to solve
quadratic equations from both the vertex form and the standard form. We will
learn several tools that can be used to solve these functions. One thing you
need to consider is what each tool helps you do and when to use it effectively
to get the job done.

In the previous sections we have been given values for the input variable
and been asked to solve the function for the output variable. This has not been
hard since it mostly involves simplifying an expression. When you are given a
value for the output variable, solving for the input becomes more difficult. The
reason for this difficulty is that the input variable is squared and thus harder
to isolate.Isoltaing the variable will require removing an exponent of 2. This
cannot be done by addition, subtraction, multiplication or division. Therefore
we need an operation that will undo a squared term. That operation is the
square root, $\sqrt{\ }$.

One caution you need to use is that when you square a real number it will
effectively remove any negative sign. This is fine until you want to undo that
operation.

$$x^2 = 25$$
$$(5)^2 = 25 \qquad (-5)^2 = 25$$
$$x = 5 \qquad x = -5$$

We know that five squared is 25 but
negative 5 squared is also 25.
Both must be given as solutions
to this equation.

$$x^2 = 25$$
$$x = \pm\sqrt{25}$$
$$x = 5 \qquad x = -5$$

When using a square root we must use the
plus/minus symbol to represent both
solutions.

The square root we use in mathematics always results in a positive number. This causes us to lose possible negative results so we must use a plus/mi-
nus, $\pm$, symbol to show that there are two possible solutions. Using the square
root and plus/minus is an example of the **Square Root Property.**

Square Root Property:

If $c \geq 0$ the solutions to the equation
$$x^2 = c$$
are
$$x = \pm\sqrt{c}$$
If c is negative then the equation has no real solutions.

With this property in mind we are going to look at three basic ways to
solve quadratic equations. In this section we will look at the first two methods.
First we will use the square root property to solve quadratics when they are
given in vertex form.

Example 1

In problem 1 of section 3.3 we looked at the number of cable television systems in the U.S. and found the model
$$C(t) = -33.3(t-4)^2 + 11250$$
Where $C(t)$ represents the number of cable systems in the U.S. t years since 1990.

a.   Find when there were 10,000 cable systems.

b.   Find the horizontal intercepts and explain their meaning in this context.

Solution

a.   10,000 cable systems is represented by $C(t) = 10000$ so we need to solve for t.

$$C(t) = -33.3(t-4)^2 + 11250$$
$$10000 = -33.3(t-4)^2 + 11250$$
$$\underline{-11250 -11250}$$

$$-1250 = -33.3(t-4)^2 \qquad \text{Isolate the squared term.}$$
$$\frac{-1250}{-33.3} = \frac{-33.3(t-4)^2}{-33.3}$$
$$37.538 = (t-4)^2 \qquad \text{Use the square root property}$$
$$\pm\sqrt{37.538} = t-4 \qquad \begin{array}{l}\text{being sure to use a plus/minus to}\\ \text{represent both possible solutions.}\end{array}$$
$$\pm 6.127 = t-4$$
$$6.127 = t-4 \quad \text{or} \quad -6.127 = t-4 \quad \text{Rewrite into two equations and}$$
$$10.127 = t \quad \text{or} \quad -2.127 = t \qquad \text{add 4 to both sides.}$$

You can check your answers using the graph and trace.

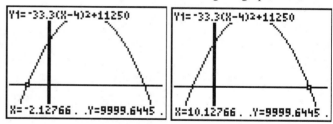

$t = 10.127$ represents about the year 2000 and $t = -2.127$ represents about 1988. The value $t = -2.127$ is not within the domain for this model so we must discard it leaving us with there being about 10,000 cable systems in the year 2000.

b.   To find the horizontal intercepts we need to let the output variable equal zero and solve for t.
$$C(t) = -33.3(t-4)^2 + 11250$$
$$0 = -33.3(t-4)^2 + 11250$$
$$\underline{-11250 -11250} \qquad \text{Isolate the squared term.}$$

$$-11250 = -33.3(t-4)^2$$
$$\frac{-11250}{-33.3} = \frac{-33.3(t-4)^2}{-33.3}$$
$$337.84 = (t-4)^2$$

$$\pm\sqrt{337.84} = t - 4$$

Use the square root property being sure to use a plus/minus to represent both possible solutions.

$$\pm 18.38 = t - 4$$

$$18.38 = t - 4 \ \text{ or } \ -18.38 = t - 4$$

Rewrite into two equations and add 4 to both sides.

$$22.38 = t \ \text{ or } \ -14.38 = t$$

These two solutions represent the years 2012 and 1975, when according to this model there were no cable television systems in the U.S. These solutions are probably model breakdown since these inputs are not in the domain of the model.

Problem 1

In section 3.2 we investigated the average number of hours per person per year spent watching television during the late 1990's. Using the model

$$H(t) = 9.5(t - 7)^2 + 1544$$

where $H(t)$ represents the average number of hours per person per year spent watching television t years since 1990. Determine when the average person will spend 1825 hours per year watching television.

Solution   See page 181

Solving Quadratic Equations in Vertex Form:
1.   Isolate the squared part (this contains the unknown).
2.   Use the square root property to eliminate the exponent of 2. Use $\pm$ on the side away from the variable.
3.   Write two equations and solve.
4.   Check solution(s) in the original equation. Be sure that solutions a within the domain of the model and make sense in the context of the problem.

Example 2
Solve

a. $5x^2 + 10 = 255$

b. $4(2t + 5)^2 - 82 = -62.64$

Solution

a.

$$5x^2 + 10 = 255$$
$$\underline{\quad -10 \quad -10 \quad}$$

Isolate the squared part of the equation.

$$5x^2 = 245$$
$$\frac{5x^2}{5} = \frac{245}{5}$$
$$x^2 = 49$$
$$x = \pm\sqrt{49}$$
$$x = \pm 7$$

Use the square root property being sure to use a plus/minus symbol.

$$5(7)^2 + 10 = 255$$
$$255 = 255$$
$$5(-7)^2 + 10 = 255$$
$$255 = 255$$

Check your answers.

b.

$$4(2t+5)^2 - 82 = -62.64$$

$$4(2t+5)^2 = 19.36 \qquad \text{Isolate the squared part of the equation.}$$

$$(2t+5)^2 = 4.84 \qquad \text{Use the square root property being sure}$$

$$2t+5 = \pm\sqrt{4.84} \qquad \text{to use a plus/minus symbol.}$$

$$2t+5 = \pm 2.2$$

$$\text{Write two equations and solve.}$$

$2t+5 = 2.2$	$2t+5 = -2.2$
$2t = -2.8$	$2t = -7.2$
$t = -1.4$	$t = -3.6$

$$4(2(-1.4)+5)^2 - 82 = -62.64 \qquad \text{Check your answers.}$$

$$-62.64 = -62.64$$

$$4(2(-3.6)+5)^2 - 82 = -62.64$$

$$-62.64 = -62.64$$

Problem 2

Solve

a. $7x^2 + 9 = 121$

b. $-3(4x-7)^2 + 17 = -58$

Solution   See page 181

    In many situations you may be given a model or formula that is a quadratic in standard form $ax^2 + bx + c = 0$. Whenever this happens you will not be able to easily use the method of solving done in example 1. Factoring is one method used to solve some quadratic equations and has several other uses in algebra. The basis of factoring is to take a polynomial and break it into simpler pieces that are multiplied together.

Standard Form	Factored Form
$f(x) = x^2 + 8x + 15$	$f(x) = (x+3)(x+5)$

    The main reason this is helpful is the **Product Property of Zero** which basically says that when you multiply any number by zero the answer is zero.

Product Property of Zero:

    The product of a real number and zero is zero.

Zero Factor Property:

    If $ab = 0$ then $a = 0$, $b = 0$, or both.

    The **Zero Factor Property** follows from the product property of zero and states that if two numbers are multiplied together and the answer is zero then one or both of those factors must be zero. Let's investigate why this is so helpful.

Concept Investigation 1

Solve the following equations.

a. $3x = 0$

b. $-9x = 0$

c. $5(x + 2) = 0$

d. $-13(x - 6) = 0$

All of these problems included multiplication. For each of the following equations list the two factors being multiplied together and say which one must equal zero for the product to equal zero.

a. $3x = 0$ 3 and x so $x = 0$

                                       3 cannot equal zero so x must equal zero.

b. $-9x = 0$

c. $5(x + 2) = 0$ 5 and $(x + 2)$ so $x + 2 = 0$

                                       $5 \neq 0$ so $(x + 2)$ must equal zero.

d. $-13(x - 6) = 0$

In all of the equations given there has been only one factor that could have equaled zero. In the following equations list the factors being multiplied together and state which can equal zero. Then solve.

a. $(x + 5)(x - 9) = 0$ $(x + 5)$ and $(x - 9)$ both can equal zero.
                                       $x + 5 = 0$ or $x - 9 = 0$
                                       $x = -5$ or $x = 9$

b. $(x - 3)(x - 12) = 0$

c. $(x + 17)(x + 2) = 0$

d. $(2x - 5)(x - 4) = 0$

e. $3(x - 7)(x + 15) = 0$

f. $(x + 3)(x - 7)(x + 15) = 0$

As you can see from these problems equations that involve multiplication and equal zero can be solved by looking at each factor one at a time rather than the entire equation at once.

The most basic step in any factoring process will be to factor out the common elements from the terms of an expression.

Example 3

Factor out the common elements.

a. $5x^2 + 20x$

b. $15w^3z - 9w^2z^2$

c. $2x^2 + 6x - 4$

d. $5x(x-8) + 2(x-8)$

e. $3z(z-5) - (z-5)$

Solution

a.   Both terms in this expression have at least one x and also are divisible by 5.
$$5x(x+4)$$

b.   Both of these terms have a w^2, a z and are divisible by 3. Taking $3w^2z$ out.
$$3w^2z(5w - 3z)$$

c.   All of the terms in this quadratic are divisible by 2. Since the last term does not have an x in it that is not a common factor.
$$2(x^2 + 3x - 2)$$

d.   Both terms here have the expression $(x-8)$ in common.
$$(x-8)(5x+2)$$

e.   Both terms in this problem have the expression $(z-5)$ in common. You may notice that it seems nothing would remain after taking $(z-5)$ out of the second term. This is not true since a 1 will remain in its place. This is because $(z-5)$ divided by $(z-5)$ is 1.
$$(z-5)(3z-1)$$

Factoring out what is in common will always be the first step we will try to complete. In many cases there will not be anything in common and we will move on to other steps.

If we can factor a quadratic from standard form we will be able to use the factored form to solve more easily. There are many methods used to factor quadratics but we will concentrate on one called the AC method. When working with a quadratic in standard form this method will provide basic steps that will guide you through the factoring process.

AC Method of Factoring Quadratics:
1.   Take out anything in common.
2.   Multiply a and c together. (Do this step off to the side, in the margin.)
3.   Find factors of ac that add up to b. (Do this off to the side also.)
4.   Rewrite the middle (bx) term using the factors from step 3.
5.   Group and factor out what's in common.

Example 4

Factor

a. $x^2 + 8x + 15$

b. $6x^2 + x - 35$

Solution

a.   This quadratic is in standard form $ax^2 + bx + c$ so we will use the AC method.

Step 1 Take out anything in common.

   The terms in this quadratic have nothing in common.

Step 2 Multiply a and c together. (Do this step off to the side, in the margin.)

   $a = 1$ and $c = 15$ so $ac = 1(15) = 15$

Step 3 Find factors of ac that sum to b. (Do this off to the side also.)

   List the factors of 15.

	15
1	15
3	5
−1	−15
−3	−5

List both the positive and negative factors.

   In this list the factors 3 and 5 will add up to 8.

Step 4 Rewrite the middle (bx) term using the factors from step 3.

   The factors 3 and 5, found in the previous step, will be used to re-write the bx term in the expression.
   $$x^2 + 3x + 5x + 15$$

Step 5 Group and factor out what's in common.

   If we group the first two terms together and the last two terms together we can factor out some common elements.

   $(x^2 + 3x) + (5x + 15)$ Group first and last two terms together.
   $x(x + 3) + 5(x + 3)$ Factor out x from the first group and 5 from the second group.
   $(x + 3)(x + 5)$ Factor out the $(x + 3)$.

b.   This quadratic is in standard form $ax^2 + bx + c$ so we will use the AC method.

Step 1 Take out anything in common.

   The terms in this quadratic have nothing in common.

Step 2 Multiply a and c together. (Do this step off to the side, in the margin.)

   $a = 6$ and $c = -35$ so $ac = 6(-35) = -210$

Step 3 Find factors of ac that sum to b. (Do this off to the side also.)

List the factors of -210.

−210

1	−210	−1	210
2	−105	−2	105
3	−70	−3	70
5	−42	−5	42
6	−35	−6	35
7	−30	−7	30
10	−21	−10	21
14	−15	−14	15

The product must be negative so one factor must be positive and the other must be negative. Be sure to give both lists of positive and negative factors.

In this list the factors -14 and 15 will add up to 1.

Step 4 Rewrite the middle (bx) term using the factors from step 3.

The factors 3 and 5 will replace the b value in the expression.

$$6x^2 - 14x + 15x - 35$$

Step 5 Group and factor out what's in common.

If we group the first two terms together and the last two terms together we can factor out some common elements.

$(6x^2 - 14x) + (15x - 35)$ Group first and last two terms together.

$2x(3x - 7) + 5(3x - 7)$ Factor out $2x$ from the first group and 5 from the second group.

$(3x - 7)(2x + 5)$ Factor out the $(3x - 7)$.

Problem 3

Factor

a. $x^2 - 2x - 48$

b. $10x^2 + 23x + 12$

Solution   See page 182

We can use the factored form to solve an equation only if it is equal to zero. If the quadratic is not equal to zero you must first move everything to one side so that it equals zero and then factor.

Example 5

The profit a local photographer makes from selling n copies of a photograph can be modeled by

$$P(n) = n(40 - 2n)$$

where $P(n)$ represents the amount of profit in dollars from selling n copies of a photograph. Find the number of copies the photographer must sell of a photo to make a profit of $150.

Solution

The $150 is a desired profit so it must take the place of $P(n)$.

$$150 = n(40 - 2n)$$ Substitute 150 for P.

$$150 = 40n - 2n^2$$ Distribute the n.

$$\underline{2n^2 \qquad 2n^2}$$ Get everything to one side and make

$$2n^2 + 150 = 40n$$ it equal to zero.

$$\underline{-40n \qquad -40n}$$

$$2n^2 - 40n + 150 = 0$$ Factor using AC method.

$$2(n^2 - 20n + 75) = 0$$ Step 1

$$\frac{2(n^2 - 20n + 75)}{2} = \frac{0}{2}$$ Because this is an equation we can divide both sides by 2.

$$n^2 - 20n + 75 = 0$$

$$n^2 - 15n - 5n + 75 = 0$$

$$(n^2 - 15n) + (-5n + 75) = 0 \quad \text{Step 4}$$

$$n(n - 15) - 5(n - 15) = 0 \quad \text{Step 5}$$

$$(n - 15)(n - 5) = 0$$

$$n - 15 = 0 \qquad n - 5 = 0$$

$$n = 15 \qquad n = 5$$

1(75)		Step 2
1	75	Step 3
3	25	
5	15	
-1	-75	
-3	-25	
-5	-15	

In order to make a profit of $150 the photographer must sell 5 or 15 photographs. If he sells between 5 and 15 he will make more than $150 in profit.

Problem 4

The average cost for building a small plane at Private Planes 101 depends on the number of planes built in a year. This average cost can be modeled by

$$A(p) = p(31 - 5p) + 194$$

where $A(p)$ represents the average cost in thousands of dollars per plane to build p planes in a year. How many planes does Private Planes 101 need to build in a year to have an average cost per plane of $200,000?

Solution See page 183

Solving Quadratics Using Factoring:
1. Set the quadratic equal to zero. (Move all terms to one side of the equal sign.)
2. Put the quadratic into standard form.
3. Factor the quadratic. (Use AC method.)
4. Set each of the factors equal to zero and solve.
5. Check your answers in the original equation.

Example 6

Solve the following by factoring:

a. $x^2 + 7x - 40 = 20$

b. $2x^2 + 27 = 21x$

c. $x^3 + 8x^2 + 15x = 0$

Solution

a.

$$x^2 + 7x - 40 = 20$$

$$x^2 + 7x - 60 = 0$$

$$x^2 - 5x + 12x - 60 = 0$$

$$(x^2 - 5x) + (12x - 60) = 0$$

$$x(x - 5) + 12(x - 5) = 0$$

$$(x - 5)(x + 12) = 0$$

$$x - 5 = 0 \qquad x + 12 = 0$$

$$x = 5 \qquad x = -12$$

$$(5)^2 + 7(5) - 60 = 0$$

$$0 = 0$$

$$(-12)^2 + 7(12) - 60 = 0$$

$$0 = 0$$

Set the quadratic equal to zero and factor.
Make two equations and finish solving.

$$1(-60) = -60$$

1	−60	−1	60
2	−30	−2	30
3	−20	−3	20
4	−15	−4	15
5	−12	−5	12
6	−10	−6	10

Check your answers.

b.

$$2x^2 + 27 = 21x$$

$$2x^2 - 21x + 27 = 0$$

$$2x^2 - 3x - 18x + 27 = 0$$

$$(2x^2 - 3x) + (-18x + 27) = 0$$

$$x(2x - 3) - 9(2x - 3) = 0$$

$$(2x - 3)(x - 9) = 0$$

$$2x - 3 = 0 \qquad x - 9 = 0$$

$$x = \frac{3}{2} \qquad x = 9$$

$$2\left(\frac{3}{2}\right)^2 + 27 = 21\left(\frac{3}{2}\right)$$

$$31.5 = 31.5$$

$$2(9)^2 + 27 = 21(9)$$

$$189 = 189$$

Set the quadratic equal to zero and factor.
Make two equations and finish solving.

$$2(27) = 54$$

1	54	−1	−54
2	27	−2	−27
3	18	−3	−18
6	9	−6	−9

Check your answers.

c.

$$x^3 + 8x^2 + 15x = 0$$

$$x(x^2 + 8x + 15) = 0$$

$$x(x^2 + 3x + 5x + 15) = 0$$

$$x[(x^2 + 3x) + (5x + 15)] = 0$$

$$x[x(x + 3) + 5(x + 3)] = 0$$

$$x(x + 3)(x + 5) = 0$$

$$x = 0 \qquad x + 3 = 0 \qquad x + 5 = 0$$

$$x = 0 \qquad x = -3 \qquad x = -5$$

$$(0)^3 + 8(0)^2 + 15(0) = 0$$

$$0 = 0$$

$$(-3)^3 + 8(-3)^2 + 15(-3) = 0$$

$$0 = 0$$

$$(-5)^3 + 8(-5)^2 + 15(-5) = 0$$

$$0 = 0$$

Take out the x in common and factor the remaining quadratic.

The factored out x will remain at the front of each step until the factoring is complete.

Now rewrite into three equations

Check your answers.

Problem 5

Solve the following by factoring

a. $x^2 + 13x = -36$

b. $2x^3 + 11x^2 + 21x - 5 = 6x - 5$

Solution   See page 183

The zero factor property can also be used to factor expressions using their graphs. As you solved different equations by factoring you always set the equation equal to zero and then factor. If we set a function equal to zero and solve we are looking for the horizontal intercepts of the function. We can use the connection between the horizontal intercepts and the factors of an expression to factor an expression using it's graph.

Example 7

Use the graph to factor the quadratic.

a.

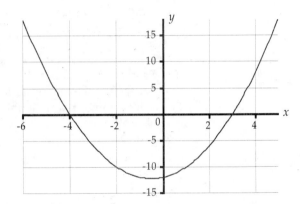

b.

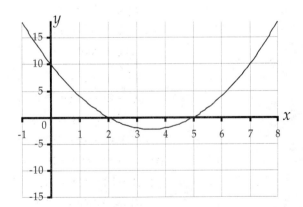

Solution

a.   The horizontal intercepts for this model are located at $(-4, 0)$ and $(3, 0)$ so we know that $x = -4$ and $x = 3$ are solutions to this quadratic equal to zero. Therefore we have the following:

$$x = -4 \qquad x = 3$$
$$x + 4 = 0 \qquad x - 3 = 0$$

This gives us the factors $(x + 4)$ and $(x - 3)$ and the factorization
$$y = (x + 4)(x - 3)$$

If we multiply this factorization out we get $y = x^2 + x - 12$. The y-intercept for this quadratic would be -12 which agrees with the graph so we have the factorization correct.

b. The horizontal intercepts for this graph are $(2, 0)$ and $(5, 0)$. Therefore we get

$$x = 2 \qquad x = 5$$
$$x - 2 = 0 \qquad x - 5 = 0$$
$$y = (x - 2)(x - 5)$$

Again if we multiply this factorization out we get $y = x^2 - 7x + 10$ which has a vertical intercept of 10. This agrees with the graph so we have the factorization correct.

Section 3.4 Key Points

- Solving Quadratics in Vertex Form:
  1. Isolate the squared part.
  2. Use the square root property to eliminate the exponent of 2. Use $\pm$ on one side.
  3. Write two equations and solve.
- Solving Quadratics Using Factoring:
  1. Set the quadratic equal to zero. (Move all terms to one side.)
  2. Put the quadratic into standard form.
  3. Factor the quadratic.
  4. Set each of the factors equal to zero and solve.
  5. Check your answers in the original equation
- Non Real Solutions to Quadratics
  When a negative is under the square root during the solving process we will have no real solutions to that equation.

Section 3.4 Problem Solutions

Problem 1   *Solution*

The 1825 is an average number of hours spent watching television so should be substituted into $H(t)$.

$$H(t) = 9.5(t-7)^2 + 1544$$
$$1825 = 9.5(t-7)^2 + 1544$$
$$-1544 \qquad\qquad\qquad -1544$$

$$281 = 9.5(t-7)^2$$
$$\frac{281}{9.5} = \frac{9.5(t-7)^2}{9.5}$$
$$29.5789 = (t-7)^2$$
$$\pm\sqrt{29.5789} = t-7$$
$$\pm 5.44 = t-7$$

$$5.44 = t-7 \qquad\qquad -5.44 = t-7$$
$$12.44 = t \qquad\qquad 1.56 = t$$

Therefore in about 1992 and 2002 people were spending an average of 1825 hours per year watching television.

We can check this solution using the graph.

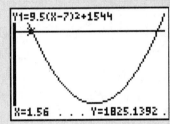 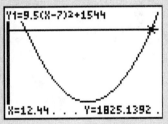

Problem 2   *Solution*

a.

$$7x^2 + 9 = 121$$
$$7x^2 = 112 \qquad\qquad \text{Isolate the squared term.}$$
$$x^2 = 16$$
$$x = \pm\sqrt{16} \qquad\qquad \text{Use the square root property being sure to}$$
$$x = \pm 4 \qquad\qquad\qquad \text{use a plus/minus symbol.}$$
$$7(4)^2 + 9 = 121 \qquad\qquad \text{Check your answers.}$$
$$121 = 121$$
$$7(-4)^2 + 9 = 121$$
$$121 = 121$$

Problem 2   Solution Continued

b.

$$-3(4x-7)^2 + 17 = -58$$

$$-3(4x-7)^2 = -75 \qquad \text{Isolate the squared term.}$$

$$(4x-7)^2 = 25$$

$$4x-7 = \pm\sqrt{25} \qquad \text{Use the square root property being sure to}$$
$$4x-7 = \pm 5 \qquad \text{use a plus/minus symbol.}$$

$$4x-7 = 5 \qquad 4x-7 = -5 \qquad \text{Write two equations and solve.}$$

$$4x = 12 \qquad 4x = 2$$

$$x = 3 \qquad x = \frac{1}{2}$$

$$-3(4(3)-7)^2 + 17 = -58$$
$$-58 = -58 \qquad \text{Check your answers.}$$

$$-3\left(4\left(\frac{1}{2}\right)-7\right)^2 + 17 = -58$$

$$-58 = -58$$

Problem 3   Solution

a.

				Steps 2 and 3 of AC method.

$$x^2 - 2x - 48$$

$$x^2 - 8x + 6x - 48 \qquad \text{Rewrite the } bx \text{ term.} \qquad 1(-48) = -48$$

$(x^2 - 8x) + (6x - 48)$	Group and factor.	1	−48	−1	48
$x(x-8) + 6(x-8)$		2	−24	−2	24
$(x-8)(x+6)$		3	−16	−3	16
		4	−12	−4	12
		6	−8	−6	8

b.

$$10x^2 + 23x + 12 \qquad\qquad\qquad \text{Steps 2 and 3 of AC method.}$$

$$10x^2 + 8x + 15x + 12 \qquad \text{Rewrite the } bx \text{ term.} \qquad 10(12) = 120$$

$(10x^2 + 8x) + (15x + 12)$	Group and factor.	1	120	−1	−120
$2x(5x+4) + 3(5x+4)$		2	60	−2	−60
$(5x+4)(2x+3)$		3	40	−3	−40
		4	30	−4	−30
		5	24	−5	−24
		6	20	−6	−20
		8	15	−8	−15
		10	12	−10	−12

Problem 4   Solution

The \$200,000 is an average cost for building a small plane at Private Planes 101 so 200 should be substituted into $A(p)$.

$$A(p) = p(31 - 5p) + 194$$

Steps 2 and 3 of AC method.

$$200 = p(31 - 5p) + 194$$

$5(6) = 30$

$$200 = 31p - 5p^2 + 194$$

1	30

$$5p^2 - 31p + 6 = 0 \quad \text{Set equal to zero.}$$

2	15

$$5p^2 - 30p - p + 6 = 0 \quad \text{Factor}$$

3	10

$$(5p^2 - 30p) + (-p + 6) = 0$$

5	6

$$5p(p - 6) - 1(p - 6) = 0$$

−1	−30

$$(p - 6)(5p - 1) = 0$$

−2	−15

$$p - 6 = 0 \qquad 5p - 1 = 0$$

−3	−10

$$p = 6 \qquad p = 0.2$$

−5	−6

$p = 0.2$ means $1/5$ of a plane should be produced. This does not make sense in this context so we know that 6 planes need to be produced for the average cost to be \$200,000 per plane.

We can check this solution using a graph.

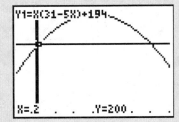 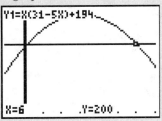

Problem 5   Solution

a.

$$x^2 + 13x = -36$$

$$x^2 + 13x + 36 = 0 \qquad \text{Set equal to zero.}$$

$$x^2 + 9x + 4x + 36 = 0 \qquad \text{Factor}$$

$$(x^2 + 9x) + (4x + 36) = 0$$

$$x(x + 9) + 4(x + 9) = 0$$

$$(x + 9)(x + 4) = 0$$

$$x + 9 = 0 \qquad x + 4 = 0 \qquad \text{Write two equations and solve.}$$

$$x = -9 \qquad x = -4$$

$$(-9)^2 + 13(-9) = -36 \qquad \text{Check your answers.}$$

$$-36 = -36$$

$$(-4)^2 + 13(-4) = -36$$

$$-36 = -36$$

Problem 5   Solution Continued

b.

$$2x^3 + 11x^2 + 21x - 5 = 6x - 5$$

$$2x^3 + 11x^2 + 15x = 0 \qquad \text{Set equal to zero.}$$

$$x(2x^2 + 11x + 15) = 0 \qquad \text{Factor}$$

$$x(2x^2 + 6x + 5x + 15) = 0$$

$$x[(2x^2 + 6x) + (5x + 15)] = 0$$

$$x[2x(x + 3) + 5(x + 3)] = 0$$

$$x(x + 3)(2x + 5) = 0$$

$$x = 0 \qquad x + 3 = 0 \qquad 2x + 5 = 0 \qquad \text{Write three equations and solve.}$$

$$x = 0 \qquad x = -3 \qquad x = \frac{-5}{2}$$

$$2(0)^3 + 11(0)^2 + 21(0) - 5 = 6(0) - 5 \qquad \text{Check your answers.}$$

$$-5 = -5$$

$$2(-3)^3 + 11(-3)^2 + 21(-3) - 5 = 6(-3) - 5$$

$$-23 = -23$$

$$2\left(\frac{-5}{2}\right)^3 + 11\left(\frac{-5}{2}\right)^2 + 21\left(\frac{-5}{2}\right) - 5 = 6\left(\frac{-5}{2}\right) - 5$$

$$-20 = -20$$

3.4 Exercises

1. The number of cassette singles shipped by major recording media manufacturers can be modeled by
$$C(t) = -2.336(t - 13)^2 + 85.6$$
where $C(t)$ is the number of cassette singles in millions shipped t years since 1980.

   source: Model based on data from the Statistical Abstract 2001.

   a. Find how many cassette singles were shipped in 1998.

   b. Find when 50 million cassette singles were shipped.

   c. What is the vertex of this model and what does it represent in this context?

   d. When do you think model breakdown occurs for this model?

2. The poverty threshold for an individual under 65 years old can be modeled by
$$P(t) = 4.95(t - 57)^2 + 1406$$
where $P(t)$ represents the poverty threshold, in dollars, for an individual in the U.S. under 65 years old t years since 1900.

   source: Model based on data from the Statistical Abstract 2001.

   a. What was the poverty threshold in 1995?

   b. When was the poverty threshold $11,500?

   c. When was the poverty threshold $3,000?

   d. What is the vertex of this model and what does it represent in this context?

   e. When do you think model breakdown occurs for this model?

3. The amount that personal households and non-profit organizations have invested in time and savings deposits can be modeled by
$$D(t) = 73.6(t - 3.5)^2 + 2176$$
where $D(t)$ represents the amount in billions of dollars the households and nonprofit organizations have deposited in time and savings accounts t years since 1990.

   a. How much did personal households and non-profit organizations have invested in time and savings deposits in 2000?

   b. Find when personal households and nonprofit organizations had $7500 billion invested in time and savings deposits.

   c. What is the vertex of this model and what does it represent in this context?

4. The total number of persons, in thousands, 65 years old and over who were below the poverty level can be modeled by
$$N(t) = -59(t - 12)^2 + 3890$$
where $N(t)$ represents the total number of persons 65 years old and over in the U.S. who were below the poverty level, in thousands, t years since 1980.

   source: Model based on data from the Statistical Abstract 2001.

   a. How many people 65 years old and over were below the poverty level in 2000?

   b. When were there 1 million people 65 years old and over below the poverty level?

   c. What is the vertex of this model and what does it represent in this context?

5. The average profit made by a local company making custom car parts for racing teams can be modeled by
$$A(p) = p(80 - 4p)$$
where $A(p)$ represents the average profit in dollars per part when p parts are produced. Use factoring to find the following: Check your answers using the table.

   a. Find the number of parts that need to be produced for the company to earn $144 profit per part.

   b. Find the number of parts that need to be produced for the company to earn $300 profit per part.

   c. Find the number of parts that need to be produced for the company to earn $400 profit per part.

6. The average profit for mixing custom paints for a small manufacturing company can be modeled by
$$P(q) = q(105 - 7q)$$
where $P(q)$ represents the average profit in dollars per quart mixed when q quarts are mixed for one order. Use factoring to find the number of quarts that need to be ordered and mixed for the average profit to be $350 per quart. Check your answer with the table.

7. The average cost to manufacture custom tooling machines can be modeled by
$$C(m) = m(108 - 6m)$$
where $C(m)$ represents the average cost in dollars per machine when m machines are made.

   a. When will the average cost per machine be $390? Check your answer with the table.

   b. When will the average cost per machine be $480? Check your answer with a graph.

Math
Tutorial   More practice problems like exercises 8 through 30 can be found in section 3.4 of the CD Tutorial.

In exercises 38 through 41 use the graph to factor the quadratic.

38.

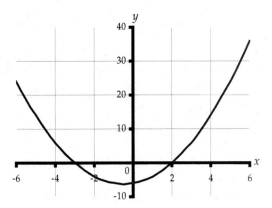

In Exercises 8 through 15 factor.

8. $x^2 - 4x - 21$

9. $x^2 + 9x + 20$

10. $w^2 - 7w - 18$

11. $t^2 - 11t + 28$

12. $2x^2 + 13x + 15$

13. $7m^2 - 25m + 12$

14. $4x^2 - 31x - 45$

39.

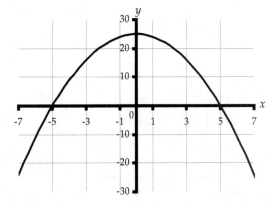

15. $6w^2 + 29w + 28$

16. $10t^2 - 41t - 18$

17. $12x^2 - 43x + 56$

18. $x^3 - 4x^2 - 21x$

19. $w^3 - 7w^2 + 10w$

20. $10x^3 + 35x^2 + 30x$

In Exercises 21 through 30 solve by factoring or the square root property.

21. $x^2 + 6x + 5 = 0$

40.

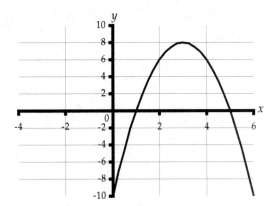

22. $h^2 + 12h + 27 = 0$

23. $5x^2 - 80 = 0$

24. $-3m^2 + 75 = 0$

25. $3t^2 - 7t - 5 = 5$

26. $55 + 55h = 10h^2 - 50$

27. $6w^2 - 15w = 4w - 10$

28. $11x + x^2 = -28$

29. $x^2 + 7x - 9 = 7x + 16$

30. $w^2 - 3x + 8 = 24 - 3x$

41.

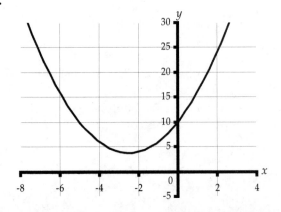

31. $28p^2 + 3p + 60 = 100$

32. $12t^2 - 43t + 40 = -16$

33. $6x^2 + 39x + 45 = 0$

34. $x^3 - 4x^2 - 21x = 0$

35. $w^3 - 3w^2 - 3w + 9 = 7w + 9$

36. $5t^2 - 14 = 0$

37. $-6m^2 + 56 = 0$

Section 3.5   Solving Quadratic Equations II

• Solving by Quadratic Formula • Solving Systems of Equations with Quadratics

In the last section we learned to solve quadratics that were in vertex form and learned to use factoring to solve quadratics in standard form. In this section we will discuss a third method for solving quadratics. Many models that we may encounter do not have numbers that are going to be easy to factor. this leads us to the need for the third method of solving a quadratic, the **Quadratic Formula**.

$$x = \frac{-b \pm \sqrt{b^2 - 4ac}}{2a}$$

This method can be used with any quadratic in standard form as long as it equals zero. This formula comes from solving the standard form of a quadratic for x. If you would like a proof of this formula you can easily find one on the internet by doing a search for the quadratic formula. For now we are going to use it to solve some quadratics that are in standard form.

Example 1

Solve the following quadratics. Round your answers to three decimal places.

a. $3x^2 - 6x - 24 = 0$

b. $4t^2 - 8t + 5 = 50$

c. $3.4x^2 + 4.2x - 7.8 = 0$

Solution

a.

$$3x^2 - 6x - 24 = 0$$

$$a = 3 \qquad b = -6 \qquad c = -24$$

$$x = \frac{-(-6) \pm \sqrt{(-6)^2 - 4(3)(-24)}}{2(3)}$$

The equation is in standard form and equal to zero so use the Quadratic Formula.

$$x = \frac{6 \pm \sqrt{324}}{6}$$

$$x = \frac{6 \pm 18}{6}$$

$$x = \frac{6 + 18}{6} \qquad x = \frac{6 - 18}{6}$$ Separate into two equations.

$$x = \frac{24}{6} \qquad x = \frac{-12}{6}$$ Simplify.

$$x = 4 \qquad x = -2$$

$$3(4)^2 - 6(4) - 24 = 0$$ Check your solutions.

$$48 - 24 - 24 = 0$$

$$0 = 0$$

$$3(-2)^2 - 6(-2) - 24 = 0$$

$$12 + 12 - 24 = 0$$

$$0 = 0$$

b.

$$4t^2 - 8t + 5 = 50$$

$$4t^2 - 8t - 45 = 0$$ Set it equal to zero.

$$a = 4 \qquad b = -8 \qquad c = -45$$ Use the Quadratic Formula.

$$t = \frac{-(-8) \pm \sqrt{(-8)^2 - 4(4)(-45)}}{2(4)}$$

$$t = \frac{8 \pm \sqrt{784}}{8}$$

$$t = \frac{8 \pm 28}{8}$$

$$t = \frac{8 + 28}{8} \qquad t = \frac{8 - 28}{8}$$ Separate into two equations.

$$t = \frac{36}{8} \qquad t = \frac{-20}{8}$$ Simplify.

$$t = \frac{9}{2} \qquad t = \frac{-5}{2}$$

Check your solution using the table.

X	Y1	
4.5	50	
-2.5	50	

X=

c.

$$3.4x^2 + 4.2x - 7.8 = 0$$

$$a = 3.4 \qquad b = 4.2 \qquad c = -7.8$$ Use Quadratic Formula.

$$x = \frac{-(4.2) \pm \sqrt{(4.2)^2 - 4(3.4)(-7.8)}}{2(3.4)}$$

$$x = \frac{-4.2 \pm \sqrt{123.72}}{6.8}$$

$$x \approx \frac{-4.2 \pm 11.1229}{6.8}$$

$$x \approx \frac{-4.2 + 11.1229}{6.8} \qquad x \approx \frac{-4.2 - 11.1229}{6.8}$$ Separate into two equations and simplify.

$$x \approx 1.018 \qquad x \approx -2.253$$ Check your solution using the graph.

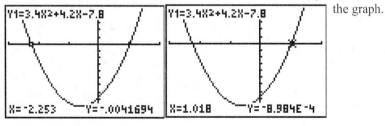

Problem 1

Solve the following quadratics. Round your answers to three decimal places.

a. $2x^2 + 13x + 15 = 0$

b. $1.5x^2 + 2 = -6.5x$

Solution   See page 192

When using the quadratic formula it is important that you be very careful with your calculations. Doing each calculation one step at a time on the calculator will lessen the number of arithmetic errors you make. In the formula itself you should note that it starts with negative b and the plus/minus sign in front of the square root. Another common mistake is to put the $2a$ in the denominator only under the square root and not under the negative b as well. The quadratic formula will find all possible solutions of every quadratic making it a very powerful solving tool.

Example 2

In section 3.1 we considered data for the number of public branch libraries in the U.S. and were given the model
$$B(t) = 28.7t^2 - 286.2t + 6899.3$$

where $B(t)$ represents the number of public branch libraries in the U.S. t years since 1990. When were there 6500 public branch libraries in the U.S.?

Solution

6500 represents a number of branch libraries so it will be substituted into $B(t)$. Since the numbers in this model are large we will use the quadratic formula to solve.

$$6500 = 28.7t^2 - 286.2t + 6899.3$$

$$\underline{-6500 \qquad\qquad\qquad\qquad -6500}$$

$$0 = 28.7t^2 - 286.2t + 399.3 \qquad \text{Set it equal to zero.}$$

$$a = 28.7 \qquad b = -286.2 \qquad c = 399.3$$

$$t = \frac{-b \pm \sqrt{b^2 - 4ac}}{2a} \qquad \text{Use the Quadratic Formula.}$$

$$t = \frac{-(-286.2) \pm \sqrt{(-286.2)^2 - 4(28.7)(399.3)}}{2(28.7)}$$

$$t = \frac{286.2 \pm \sqrt{81910.44 - 45839.64}}{57.4}$$

$$t = \frac{286.2 \pm \sqrt{36070.8}}{57.4}$$

$$t \approx \frac{286.2 \pm 189.92}{57.4} \qquad \text{Separate into two equations and simplify.}$$

$$t \approx \frac{286.2 - 189.92}{57.4} \qquad t \approx \frac{286.2 + 189.92}{57.4}$$

$$t \approx \frac{96.28}{57.4} \qquad t \approx \frac{476.12}{57.4}$$

$$t \approx 1.68 \qquad t \approx 8.29$$

X	Y1	
1.68	6499.5	
8.29	6499.1	
X=		

This means that in about 1992 and 1998 there were approximately 6500 public branch libraries in the U.S..

Problem 2

The number of people unemployed in Hawaii during the 1990's can be modeled by

$$U(t) = -726.25t^2 + 9824.85t + 3763.21$$

where $U(t)$ represents the number of people unemployed in Hawaii t years since 1990. According to this model when were there 30,000 people unemployed in Hawaii?

Solution   See page 193

Solving Quadratics Using The Quadratic Formula:
1.   Set the quadratic equal to zero. (Move all terms to one side of the equal sign.)
2.   Put the quadratic into standard form.
3.   Substitute the values of a, b, and c into the quadratic formula.

$$x = \frac{-b \pm \sqrt{b^2 - 4ac}}{2a}$$

4.   Simplify the quadratic formula.
5.   Check solutions in the original equation.

Now that we can solve quadratics in several ways we will consider systems of equations that contain quadratics. In chapter 2 we learned that we could solve systems using three different methods: graphing, substitution and elimination. When solving systems that contain quadratics substitution is often the best choice.

Example 3

Solve the following systems of equations:

a.
$$y = 4x + 9$$
$$y = x^2 + 5x + 3$$

b.
$$y = 5x^2 + 2x + 7$$
$$y = 2x^2 - 3x + 10$$

Solution

a.

$$y = 4x + 9$$
$$\underline{y = x^2 + 5x + 3}$$

$$4x + 9 = x^2 + 5x + 3 \qquad \text{Substitute for } y.$$

$$0 = x^2 + x - 6 \qquad \text{You are left with a quadratic that can be}$$
$$0 = (x + 3)(x - 2) \qquad \text{solved by factoring.}$$

$$x + 3 = 0 \qquad x - 2 = 0$$
$$x = -3 \qquad x = 2$$

$$y = 4(-3) + 9 \qquad \text{Use the values of } x \text{ to find the corresponding}$$
$$y = -3 \qquad \text{values of } y.$$

$$y = 4(2) + 9$$
$$y = 17$$

$$(-3, -3) \qquad (2, 17) \qquad \text{These two points are the solutions to the system of equations.}$$

These solutions can be checked using either the table or the graph features on your calculator. First you need to put both equations into your Y= screen and then graph them using a window that will include both solutions or by going to the table and inputting both x values to see if the y values are the same. Remember some rounding error may occur if the solutions were not exact.

b.

$$y = 5x^2 + 2x + 7$$
$$y = 2x^2 - 3x + 10$$

$$5x^2 + 2x + 7 = 2x^2 - 3x + 10 \qquad \text{Substitute for } y.$$

$$3x^2 + 5x - 3 = 0$$

$$a = 3 \qquad b = 5 \qquad c = -3$$

You are left with a quadratic that can be solved using the Quadratic Formula.

$$x = \frac{-(5) \pm \sqrt{(5)^2 - 4(3)(-3)}}{2(3)}$$

$$x = \frac{-5 \pm \sqrt{61}}{6}$$

$$x \approx \frac{-5 \pm 7.81}{6}$$

$$x \approx 0.468 \qquad x \approx -2.135$$

$$y = 5(0.468)^2 + 2(0.468) + 7 \qquad \text{Find the corresponding } y \text{ values.}$$

$$y = 9.031$$

$$y = 5(-2.135)^2 + 2(-2.135) + 7$$

$$y = 25.521$$

$$(0.468, 9.031) \qquad (-2.135, 25.521)$$

There are two solutions to this system.
Check the solutions with the table or the graph.

Problem 3

Solve the following system of equations:

a.

$$y = 3x^2 + 5x - 74$$
$$y = 6x^2 + 60x + 126$$

Solution   See page 194

In some cases you may be asked to find a solution of a quadratic that does not exist in the real numbers. This can happen in a problem when you are asked to find a value that the function will never reach. This will occur in an upward facing parabola when the output value you are looking for is below the vertex or in a downward facing parabola when the output value is above the vertex. When using the quadratic formula the value of the **discriminant**, $b^2 - 4ac$,determines if the equation will have real solutions or not. When the discriminant is negative the quadratic will have not real solutions since in the Real Number System we cannot take the square root of negative numbers. For this chapter when we get a negative under the square root we will simply state that there are no real solutions.

Section 3.5 Key Points

- Solving Quadratics Using The Quadratic Formula:
    1. Set the quadratic equal to zero. (Move all terms to one side.)
    2. Put the quadratic into standard form.
    3. Substitute the values of a, b, and c into the quadratic formula.

    $$x = \frac{-b \pm \sqrt{b^2 - 4ac}}{2a}$$

    4. Simplify the quadratic formula.
    5. Check solutions in the original equation.
- The Discriminant is the value of $b^2 - 4ac$ in the quadratic formula.
- Solving Systems of Equations that Contain Quadratics:
    Use the substitution method, if a quadratic remains after simplifying then solve using one of the techniques for solving quadratics.
- Non Real Solutions to Quadratics
    When a negative is under the square root during the solving process we will have no real solutions to that equation.

Section 3.5 Problem Solutions

Problem 1   Solution

a.

$$2x^2 + 13x + 15 = 0$$

$$a = 2 \qquad b = 13 \qquad c = 15$$

$$x = \frac{-(13) \pm \sqrt{(13)^2 - 4(2)(15)}}{2(2)} \qquad \text{Use the Quadratic Formula.}$$

$$x = \frac{-13 \pm \sqrt{49}}{4}$$

$$x = \frac{-13 \pm 7}{4}$$

$$x = \frac{-13 + 7}{4} \qquad x = \frac{-13 - 7}{4} \qquad \text{Write two equations and simplify.}$$

$$x = \frac{-3}{2} \qquad x = -5$$

X	Y₁	
-1.5	0	
-5	0	
X=		

Check your solutions.

Problem 1   Solution Continued

b.

$$1.5x^2 + 2 = -6.5x$$

$$1.5x^2 + 6.5x + 2 = 0$$

$$a = 1.5 \qquad b = 6.5 \qquad c = 2$$

$$x = \frac{-(6.5) \pm \sqrt{(6.5)^2 - 4(1.5)(2)}}{2(1.5)}$$ Use Quadratic Formula.

$$x = \frac{-6.5 \pm \sqrt{30.25}}{3}$$

$$x = \frac{-6.5 \pm 5.5}{3}$$

$$x = \frac{-6.5 + 5.5}{3} \qquad x = \frac{-6.5 - 5.5}{3}$$ Write two equations and simplify.

$$x = \frac{-1}{3} \qquad x = -4$$

Check your solutions.

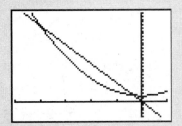

Problem 2   Solution

30,000 represents the number of people unemployed in Hawaii so we can substitute this into $U(t)$.

$$U(t) = -726.25t^2 + 9824.85t + 3763.21$$

$$30000 = -726.25t^2 + 9824.85t + 3763.21$$

$$\underline{-30000 \qquad\qquad\qquad\qquad\qquad -30000}$$

$$0 = -726.25t^2 + 9824.85t - 26236.79$$

$$a = -726.25 \qquad b = 9824.85 \qquad c = -26236.79$$

$$t = \frac{-(9824.85) \pm \sqrt{(9824.85)^2 - 4(-726.25)(-26236.79)}}{2(-726.25)}$$

$$t = \frac{-9824.85 \pm \sqrt{20309802.57}}{-1452.5}$$

$$t \approx 9.87 \qquad t \approx 3.66$$

X	Y1
9.87	29985
3.66	29994

X=9.87

Check the solutions.

In about 1994 and 2000 there were 30,000 people in Hawaii who were unemployed.

Problem 3   Solution

a.

$$y = 3x^2 + 5x - 74$$

$$y = 6x^2 + 60x + 126$$

$$3x^2 + 5x - 74 = 6x^2 + 60x + 126$$

$$0 = 3x^2 + 55x + 200$$

$$a = 3 \qquad b = 55 \qquad c = 200$$

$$x = \frac{-(55) \pm \sqrt{(55)^2 - 4(3)(200)}}{2(3)}$$

$$x = \frac{-55 \pm \sqrt{625}}{6}$$

$$x = \frac{-55 \pm 25}{6}$$

$$x = \frac{-55 + 25}{6} \qquad x = \frac{-55 - 25}{6}$$

$$x = -5 \qquad x = \frac{-40}{3}$$

$$y = 3(-5)^2 + 5(-5) - 74$$

$$y = -24$$

$$y = 3\left(\frac{-40}{3}\right)^2 + 5\left(\frac{-40}{3}\right) - 74$$

$$y \approx 392.67$$

$$(-5, -24) \qquad \left(\frac{-40}{3}, 392.67\right)$$

3.5 Exercises

1. Lead used in paint has been decreasing since its peak around 1920. The amount of lead used in paint can be modeled by

    $$L(t) = 0.0572t^2 - 8.5587t + 320.3243$$

    where $L(t)$ represents lead usage in thousands of tons t years since 1900.

    source: Model based on data from the Statistical Abstract 2001.

    a. How much lead was used in 1955?

    b. When did we use 5,500 tons of lead in paints? (Remember L is measured in thousands of tons)

    c. When did we use 51 thousand tons of lead in paints?

2. The number of Americans a years old that participate in aerobic exercise in thousands can be modeled by

    $$E(a) = -7.5a^2 + 523.1a - 3312.3$$

    where $E(a)$ represents the number of people in thousands who participated in aerobic exercise at age a years old.

    a. Find the number of 20 year old Americans who participate in aerobic exercise.

    b. At what age(s) do 3 million Americans participate in aerobic exercise?

3. During a local rocketry club launch event a competition was held for the highest launch of a model rocket. From the power produced by the motor the height t seconds after launch should be modeled by

    $$h(t) = -16t^2 + 200t + 2$$

    where $h(t)$ represents the height in feet t seconds after the rocket is launched.

    a. Find the height of the rocket 1 second after launch.

    b. When should the rocket first reach a height of 450 feet?

    c. When should the rocket first reach a height of 600 feet?

    d. When should the rocket first reach a height of 700 feet?

4. The height of a ball thrown straight up into the air can be modeled by

    $$h(t) = -16t^2 + 30t + 3.5$$

    where $h(t)$ is the height of the ball in feet t seconds after it is thrown.

    a. What is the height of the ball after 0.5 seconds?

    b. When will the ball be at a height of 15 feet?

    c. Will the ball ever reach a height of 20 feet?

5. The number of hours per year an average person spent using the internet can be modeled by

    $$I(t) = 3.768t^2 - 29.546t + 56.000$$

    where $I(t)$ represents the number of hours per year an average person spent using the internet t years since 1990.

    source: Model based on data from the Statistical Abstract 2001.

    a. How many hours did the average person spend using the internet in 2000?

    b. When will/did the average person spend 100 hours per year on the internet?

    c. When will the average person spend an average of 1 hour per day on the internet?

Math Tutorial   More practice problems like exercises 10 through 25 can be found in section 3.5 of the CD Tutorial.

In Exercises 6 through 15 solve the given quadratics using any of the methods you wish. Round all answers to two decimal places when necessary. Check your solutions graphically or with a table.

6. $a^2 + 2a = 15$

7. $33 = -7(4 - w)^2 + 59$

8. $r^2 + 1.362r - 14.989 = 0$

9. $120 = -28f + 7f^2 - 939$

10. $105 = 5(17 + d)^2 - 20$

11. $2c^2 - 50 = 10c - 2$

12. $9.984x^2 + 57.376x - 134.85 = 0$

13. $(3p - 4)(p + 3) = 15$

14. $4z^2 - 2z + 5 = 2(z - 9) + 8$

15. $23 = -2(s + 9)^2 + 5$

In exercises 16 through 25 solve the system of equations algebraically. Check your solution(s) graphically or with a table.

16. $y = x^2 + 3x - 9$
    $y = 5x - 8$

17. $y = 0.25x^2 + 5x - 3.4$
    $y = -4.5x + 7.5$

18. $y = 3x^2 + 5x - 9$
    $y = -0.5x^2 - 3x + 15$

19. $y = 3x^2 + 4x - 20$
    $y = 2x^2 + 6x + 15$

20.
$$y = x^2 - 4x + 11$$
$$y = -x^2 + 7x - 4$$

21.
$$y = -1.8x^2 - 2.3x + 4.7$$
$$y = 2.48x^2 + 3.4x - 8.47$$

22.
$$y = 4x^2 + 2x - 7$$
$$y = -2x^2 + 5x + 12$$

23.
$$y = -0.3x^2 + 5x - 2.6$$
$$y = 0.5x^2 - 3x - 7.5$$

24.
$$y = 6x^2 + 2x - 9$$
$$y = 9x^2 + 2x - 15$$

25.
$$y = 4x^2 + 9x - 12$$
$$y = -2x^2 + 20x + 23$$

Section 3.6   Graphing from Standard Form

• Graphing from Standard Form • Finding a Vertex from Standard From

Since many functions may be given to you as a quadratic in standard form rather than in vertex form it is important that you learn to graph using the standard form. Since all quadratics have a vertex and vertical intercept these will be the starting points for any graph we make.

A quadratic function in standard form $f(x) = ax^2 + bx + c$ gives us several pieces of information about the graph. The value of a affects the graph of the quadratic the same way as in the vertex form. Therefore if a is positive the parabola will open up and if it is negative it will open down. a will also affect whether the graph is wide or narrow. The value c will also give us information about the graph. When you substitute zero into the input variable for the function the output will be c, which means c will be the vertical intercept for the graph. Using these pieces of information and finding a few more will help us to graph quadratics.

Example 1

Sketch a graph of $f(x) = 2x^2 - 12x + 5$

Solution

Step 1 Determine if the graph faces upward or downward and find the vertical intercept.

Since a is positive in this quadratic we know that the parabola will open up. Since this quadratic is in standard form we know that the vertical intercept is the value of the constant c. In this case the vertical intercept is $(0, 5)$.

Step 2 Find the symmetric pair to the vertical intercept.

To be a symmetric pair the output variable must be the same for both points. therefore we can set the function equal to 5 and solve to find the two inputs that give us an output of 5.

$$f(x) = 2x^2 - 12x + 5$$
$$5 = 2x^2 - 12x + 5 \qquad \text{Set it equal to zero.}$$
$$\underline{-5 \qquad\qquad\qquad -5}$$
$$0 = 2x^2 - 12x$$
$$0 = 2x(x - 6) \qquad \text{Factor out what is in common.}$$
$$2x = 0 \ \text{ or } \ x - 6 = 0 \qquad \text{Make two equations and solve.}$$
$$x = 0 \ \text{ or } \ x = 6$$

Therefore the symmetric points are $(0, 5)$ and $(6, 5)$.

Step 3 Find the vertex.

Using the symmetric pair we know that the vertex must lie on the axis of symmetry in the middle of these two points horizontally. Finding the average of the two input values will give us the axis of symmetry and thus the input value for the vertex.

$$(0, 5) \qquad (6, 5) \qquad \text{Find the average of the input values.}$$
$$x = \frac{0 + 6}{2} = 3$$

Now that we have the input value for the vertex we can substitute it into the function and find the output value for the vertex.

$$f(x) = 2x^2 - 12x + 5$$
$$f(3) = 2(3)^2 - 12(3) + 5$$
$$f(3) = 18 - 36 + 5$$
$$f(3) = -13$$

So the vertex is $(3, -13)$.

Step 4 Find another pair of symmetric points.

Since we know the vertex is at $(3, -13)$ we can easily get another symmetric pair by substituting in numbers to the left or right of the vertex. We will substitute in $x = 1$.

$$f(x) = 2x^2 - 12x + 5$$
$$f(1) = 2(1)^2 - 12(1) + 5$$
$$f(1) = 2 - 12 + 5$$
$$f(1) = -5$$

Since 1 is two units to the left of the vertex its symmetric pair will be two units to the right of the vertex. This gives us the symmetric pair $(1, -5)$ and $(5, -5)$.

Step 5 Plot the points and sketch the graph.

We now have the vertex $(3, -13)$ and two sets of symmetric pairs $(1, -5)$, $(5, -5)$ and $(0, 5)$, $(6, 5)$. Plotting these points and sketching a smooth curve through them gives us **Graphic 3.6.1**.

Graphic 3.6.1

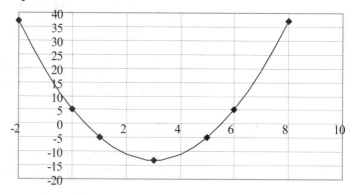

Step 6 Find the horizontal intercepts (if any) and plot them.

Horizontal intercepts will happen when the output variable is equal to zero so substitute zero for the output variable and solve.

$$f(x) = 2x^2 - 12x + 5$$
$$0 = 2x^2 - 12x + 5$$
$$a = 2 \qquad b = -12 \qquad c = 5 \qquad \text{Use the Quadratic Formula}$$
$$x = \frac{-b \pm \sqrt{b^2 - 4ac}}{2a}$$
$$x = \frac{-(-12) \pm \sqrt{(-12)^2 - 4(2)(5)}}{2(2)}$$
$$x = \frac{12 \pm \sqrt{144 - 40}}{4}$$

$$x = \frac{12 \pm \sqrt{104}}{4}$$

$$x = \frac{12 \pm 10.2}{4}$$

$$x = \frac{12 + 10.2}{4} \qquad x = \frac{12 - 10.2}{4}$$

$$x = 5.55 \qquad x = 0.45$$

Graphic 3.6.2

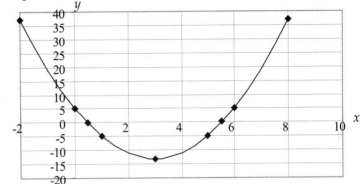

Problem 1

Sketch a graph of $f(x) = 0.25x^2 + 6x - 15$

Solution   See page 206

None of these steps need to be difficult in themselves. You will want to memorize this process and understand what each step is trying to find. In step 2 we find the symmetric point for the vertical intercept because it will be very easy to use. The factoring part of this step will always be to simply take out what is in common. Finding the horizontal intercepts has been saved until the last step since there may be none. If there are no horizontal intercepts there is no reason to go find them. Sketching the graph before looking for these will save you time if you see that there are none.

Graphing Quadratics from Standard Form:
1. Determine if the graph opens up or down and find the vertical intercept.
2. Find the symmetric pair to the vertical intercept.
3. Find the vertex.
4. Find another pair of symmetric points.
5. Plot the points and sketch the graph.
6. Find the horizontal intercepts (if any) and plot them.

Example 2

Sketch a graph of $f(x) = -0.5x^2 + 4x - 10$

Solution
  Step 1 Determine if the graph faces upward or downward and find the vertical intercept.
  Since a is negative in this quadratic we know that the parabola will open down. In this case the vertical intercept is $(0, -10)$.

Step 2 Find the symmetric pair to the vertical intercept.

We set the function equal to -10 and solve to find the two inputs that give us an output of -10.

$$f(x) = -0.5x^2 + 4x - 10$$

$$-10 = -0.5x^2 + 4x - 10 \qquad \text{Set it equal to zero.}$$

$$\underline{10 10}$$

$$0 = -0.5x^2 + 4x$$

$$0 = x(-0.5x + 4) \qquad \text{Factor out what is in common.}$$

$$x = 0 \ \text{ or } \ -0.5x + 4 = 0 \qquad \text{Make two equations and solve.}$$

$$x = 0 \ \text{ or } \ x = 8$$

Therefore the symmetric points are $(0, -10)$ and $(8, -10)$.

Step 3 Find the vertex.

Finding the average of the two input values will give us the input value for the vertex.

$$(0, -10) \qquad (8, -10) \qquad \text{Find the average of the input values.}$$

$$x = \frac{0 + 8}{2} = 4$$

Now that we have the input value for the vertex we can substitute it in and find the output value for the vertex.

$$f(x) = -0.5x^2 + 4x - 10$$

$$f(4) = -0.5(4)^2 + 4(4) - 10$$

$$f(4) = -8 + 16 - 10$$

$$f(4) = -2$$

So the vertex is $(4, -2)$.

Step 4 Find another pair of symmetric points.

Since we know the vertex is at $(4, -2)$ we can easily get another symmetric pair by substituting in numbers to the left or right of the vertex. We will substitute in $x = 2$.

$$f(x) = -0.5x^2 + 4x - 10$$

$$f(2) = -0.5(2)^2 + 4(2) - 10$$

$$f(2) = -2 + 8 - 10$$

$$f(2) = -4$$

Since 2 is two units to the left of the vertex its symmetric pair will be two units to the right of the vertex. This gives us the symmetric pair $(2, -4)$ and $(6, -4)$.

Step 5 Plot the points and sketch the graph.

We now have the vertex $(4, -2)$ and two sets of symmetric pairs $(2, -4)$, $(6, -4)$ and $(0, -10)$, $(8, -10)$. Plotting these points and sketching a smooth curve through them gives us **Graphic 3.6.3**.

SC-Example 1:
Find the vertex and state whether the vertex is a maximum or minimum point for the graph of the function
$$f(x) = 5x^2 + 40x - 62$$

Solution:
The input for the vertex can be found using
$$x = \frac{-b}{2a}$$
so we get
$$x = \frac{-40}{2(5)}$$
$$x = -4$$
Substitute this into the function to find the output value.
$$f(x) = 5x^2 + 40x - 62$$
$$f(-4) = 5(-4)^2 + 40(-4) - 62$$
$$f(-4) = 80 - 160 - 6$$
$$f(-4) = -86$$
This gives a vertex of $(-4, -86)$.
This is a minimum point on the graph of the function since the parabola faces upward.

SC-Example 2:
Find the vertex and state whether the vertex is a maximum or minimum point for the graph of the function
$$f(x) = -0.25x^2 - 3x + 5$$

Solution:
The input for the vertex can be found using
$$x = \frac{-b}{2a}$$
so we get
$$x = \frac{-(-3)}{2(-0.25)}$$
$$x = -6$$
Substitute this into the function to find the output value.
$$f(x) = -0.25x^2 + 3x + 5$$
$$f(-6) = 14$$
This gives a vertex of $(-6, 14)$.
This is a maximum point on the graph of the function since the parabola faces downward.

Graphic 3.6.3

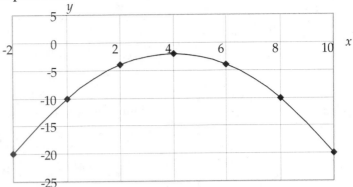

Step 6 Find the horizontal intercepts (if any) and plot them.
As we can see from the sketch the parabola never hits the horizontal axis and so we will not need to find any intercepts.

Problem 2

Sketch a graph of $f(x) = 3x^2 + 6x + 7$

Solution   See page 207

One pattern that can be found for quadratics is the relationship between the vertex and the standard form of a quadratic. There are several ways to see this relationship one being to consider the quadratic formula. The only point on a parabola without a symmetric point is the vertex. With this in mind the only way to have only one solution come from the quadratic formula is to have the square root after the $\pm$ symbol be zero. This way you are not adding or subtracting anything from the remaining parts of the formula. If we consider the square root to be zero we are left with only $x = \frac{-b}{2a}$. This will then represent the one input value that does not have a symmetric pair. Hence the vertex has the input value $\frac{-b}{2a}$. Using this fact we can easily find the vertex of a quadratic in standard form. When graphing the quadratic it is helpful to have the extra symmetric pairs so using the steps given seem to be longer but do serve a purpose.

Example 3

The monthly profit for an amusement park can be modeled by
$$P(t) = -0.181t^2 + 13.767t - 235.63$$

where $P(t)$ represents the monthly profit in millions of dollars when tickets are sold for t dollars each.

a.   What is the amusement parks monthly profit if it sells tickets for $30 each?

b.   How much should the amusement park charge for tickets if it wants a monthly profit of $25 million?

c.   Find the vertex for this model and explain its meaning in this context.

Solution

a. $30 is a ticket price so can be substituted into t.
$$P(t) = -0.181t^2 + 13.767t - 235.63$$
$$P(30) = -0.181(30)^2 + 13.767(30) - 235.63$$
$$P(30) = 14.48$$

Therefore if the amusement park sells tickets for $30 each it will have a monthly profit of about $14.48 million.

b.   The $25 million is a monthly profit so can be substituted into P.
$$P(t) = -0.181t^2 + 13.767t - 235.63$$
$$25 = -0.181t^2 + 13.767t - 235.63$$

$$\underline{-25 \hspace{5cm} -25}$$

Set it equal to zero and use the Quadratic Formula.

$$0 = -0.181t^2 + 13.767t - 260.63$$
$$t \approx 35.51 \qquad t \approx 40.55$$

If the amusement park charges $35.51 or $40.55 per ticket they will have a monthly profit of about $25 million. We hope that they would choose the $35.51 in order to make more people happy.

c.   The vertex will be at an input of
$$t = \frac{-13.767}{2(-0.181)}$$
$$t = 38.03$$

Using a ticket price of $38.03 we get
$$P(t) = -0.181t^2 + 13.767t - 235.63$$
$$P(38.03) = -0.181(38.03)^2 + 13.767(38.03) - 235.63$$
$$P(38.03) = 26.15$$

If the amusement park charges $38.03 per ticket it will make its maximum profit of $26.15 million per month.

Problem 3

The net sales for Gateway Inc. can be modeled by
$$S(t) = 75.85t^2 - 1204.22t + 4725.95$$

where $S(t)$ represents the annual net sales in millions of dollars for Gateway Inc. t years since 1980.

source: Model derived from data found in Gateway Inc. annual reports at Gateway.com.

a.   Using this model estimate the annual net sales for Gateway Inc. in 1995.

b.   When were Gateway's net sales $9,000 million dollars?

c.   Find the vertex for this model and explain its meaning in this context.

Solution   See page 208

The graphs and tables can be used to solve systems of equations that involve things other than lines. When using the graph you look for the place(s) the two graphs intersect. When using a table you need to find input value(s) that make the outputs for both equations equal. When looking for these input value(s) notice when one equation changes from being smaller than the other equation to being larger than the other. The intersection of the two equations must be between these input values.

Example 4

Use the graph or table to estimate the solutions to the systems of equations.

a.

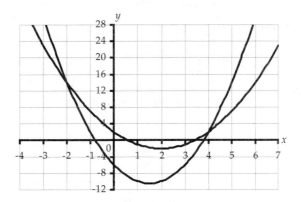

b.

X	Y1	Y2
0	4	⁻6
1	4	0
2	10	10
3	22	24
4	40	42
5	64	64
6	94	90

X=6

c.

X	Y1	Y2
⁻4.4	.36	.24
⁻4.375	.26563	.35938
⁻4.35	.1725	.4775
⁻.13	2.3669	2.5031
⁻.12	2.4144	2.4656
⁻.11	2.4621	2.4279
⁻.1	2.51	2.39

X= ⁻.1

Solution

a. From the graph we can see that the two graphs intersect at about the points $(4, 2)$ and $(-2, 14)$.

b. The table shows that the two equations are equal at the points $(2, 10)$ and $(5, 64)$.

c. This table does not show any exact places where the equations are equal but the equation in Y1 is greater than Y2 at $x = -4.4$ but less than Y2 at $x = -4.375$ so there must be an intersection between these values. One estimate for this intersection could be $(-4.38, 0.3)$. The two equations must also intersect between $x = -0.12$ and $x = -0.11$ so we might estimate this intersection at about $(-0.115, 2.48)$. Remember these are only estimates and many answers could be reasonable.

Graphing quadratic inequalities can be done in the same basic way that graphing linear inequalities were done. First graph the inequality as if it were an equation using a solid curve if there is an equal to part and a dashed curve if it is only less than or greater than but not equal to. Second pick a point not on the graph and check to see if it satisfies the inequality. Finally shade the side of the curve that does satisfy the inequality.

Example 5

Graph the following inequalities:

a. $y < x^2 + 3x - 10$

b. $y \geq -2x^2 + 11x - 12$

Solution

a.   First we will sketch the graph of the quadratic using a dashed curve since there is no equal to part.

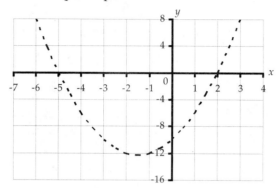

Now if we pick $(0, 0)$ as a test point we find it does not satisfy the inequality so we will shade the other side of the graph.

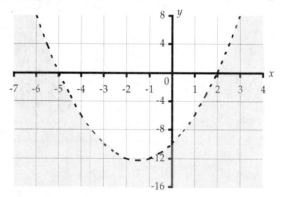

b.   First we will sketch the graph using a solid line since it is a greater than or equal to inequality.

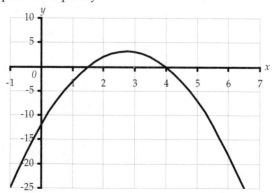

If we pick $(0,0)$ for our test point we find that it does satisfy the inequality so we should shade above the curve.

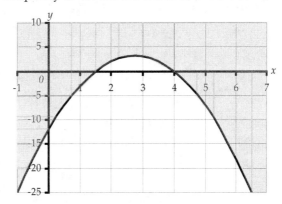

Section 3.6 Key Points

- Graphing Quadratics from Standard Form:
    1. Determine if the graph opens up or down and find the vertical intercept.
    2. Find the symmetric pair to the vertical intercept.
    3. Find the vertex.
    4. Find another pair of symmetric points.
    5. Plot the points and sketch the graph.
    6. Find the horizontal intercepts (if any) and plot them.

- Finding the vertex from the standard form

    The input for the vertex is at $\dfrac{-b}{2a}$ and the output can be found by substituting $\dfrac{-b}{2a}$ into the function.

- To graph a quadratic inequality graph the quadratic as if it were an equation using a solid curve if the equal to part is included and a dashed curve if it is not. Then pick a test point to determine which side of the curve to shade.

Section 3.6 Problem Solutions

Problem 1   Solution

$$f(x) = 0.25x^2 + 6x - 15$$

Step 1 Determine if the graph opens up or down and find the vertical intercept.

This graph opens up since a is positive. The vertical intercept is $(0, -15)$.

Step 2 Find the symmetric pair to the vertical intercept.

$$f(x) = 0.25x^2 + 6x - 15$$
$$-15 = 0.25x^2 + 6x - 15$$
$$0 = 0.25x^2 + 6x$$
$$0 = x(0.25x + 6)$$
$$x = 0 \qquad 0.25x + 6 = 0$$
$$x = 0 \qquad x = -24$$

The symmetric pair is $(0, -15)$ and $(-24, -15)$.

Step 3 Find the vertex.

The vertex is halfway between the symmetric points; $x = -12$

$$f(-12) = 0.25(-12)^2 + 6(-12) - 15$$
$$f(-12) = -51$$

Therefore the vertex is $(-12, -51)$.

Step 4 Find another pair of symmetric points.

Picking points 4 units to the left and right of the vertex gives $(-16, -47)$ and $(-8, -47)$

Step 5 Plot the points and sketch the graph.

Graphic 3.6.4

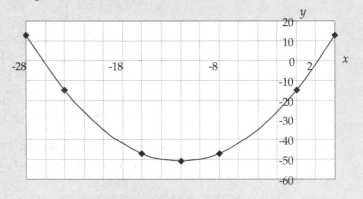

Step 6 Find the horizontal intercepts (if any) and plot them.

$$f(x) = 0.25x^2 + 6x - 15$$

$$0 = 0.25x^2 + 6x - 15 \qquad \text{Use the Quadratic Formula.}$$

$$x = 2.28 \qquad x = -26.28$$

Graphic 3.6.5

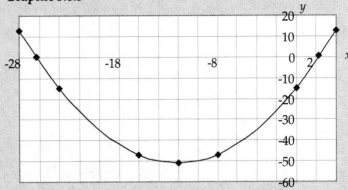

Problem 2   Solution

$$f(x) = 3x^2 + 6x + 7$$

Step 1 Determine if the graph opens up or down and find the vertical intercept.

This graph opens up since a is positive. The vertical intercept is $(0, 7)$.

Step 2 Find the symmetric pair to the vertical intercept.

$$f(x) = 3x^2 + 6x + 7$$

$$7 = 3x^2 + 6x + 7$$

$$0 = 3x^2 + 6x$$

$$0 = 3x(x + 2)$$

$$3x = 0 \qquad x + 2 = 0$$

$$x = 0 \qquad x = -2$$

The symmetric pair is $(0, 7)$ and $(-2, 7)$.

Step 3 Find the vertex.

The vertex is halfway between the symmetric points; $x = -1$

$$f(-1) = 3(-1)^2 + 6(-1) + 7$$

$$f(-1) = 4$$

Therefore the vertex is $(-1, 4)$.

Step 4 Find another pair of symmetric points.

Picking points 3 units to the left and right of the vertex gives $(-4, 31)$ and $(2, 31)$.

Step 5 Plot the points and sketch the graph.

Graphic 3.6.6

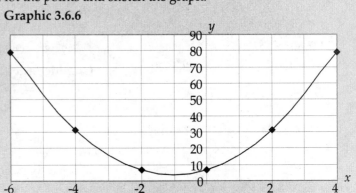

Step 6 Find the horizontal intercepts (if any) and plot them.
From the graph we can see that there are no horizontal intercepts so we are done.

Problem 3   Solution

a. 1995 is represented by $t = 15$ so we get.

$$S(15) = 75.85(15)^2 - 1204.22(15) + 4725.95$$

$$S(15) = 3728.9$$

Therefore Gateway's net sales in 1995 were approximately \$3,728.9 million.

b. \$9,000 million is a annual net sales so we get

$$9000 = 75.85t^2 - 1204.22t + 4725.95$$

$$\underline{-9000 \hphantom{= 75.85t^2 - 1204.22t + 47} -9000}$$

$$0 = 75.85t^2 - 1204.22t - 4274.05 \quad \text{Use the Quadratic Formula}$$

$$t \approx 18.86 \qquad t \approx -2.99$$

Therefore in 1999 Gateway had net sales of about \$9,000 million. At $t = -2.99$ model breakdown occurs since in 1977 they were a new company and could not have made that much in net sales.

c. The vertex can be found at $t = \dfrac{-(-1204.22)}{2(75.85)} = 7.94$. This gives us

$$S(8) = 75.85(8)^2 - 1204.22(8) + 4725.95$$

$$S(8) = -53.41$$

The vertex is $(8, -53.41)$ which represents the lowest net sales for Gateway Inc. The negative net sales represents model breakdown in this context.

3.6 Exercises

1. The cost to produce football uniforms for a school can be modeled by

$$C(u) = \frac{1}{4}u^2 - 25u + 1500$$

where $C(u)$ represents the cost in dollars to produce u football uniforms.

   a. Find the cost to produce 30 uniforms.
   b. Find the vertex and describe its meaning in this context.
   c. How many uniforms can a school get with a budget of $1600?

2. The revenue from selling digital cameras can be modeled by

$$R(c) = -3c^2 + 90c$$

where $R(c)$ represents the revenue in thousands of dollars from selling c thousand digital cameras.

   a. Find the revenue from selling 5000 digital cameras.
   b. How many cameras must the company sell to have a revenue of $600,000?
   c. How many digital cameras must they sell in order to maximize their revenue?

3. The revenue from selling sunglasses can be modeled by

$$R(s) = -1.5s^2 + 30s$$

where $R(s)$ represents the revenue in hundreds of dollars from selling s hundred pairs of sunglasses.

   a. Find the revenue from selling 900 pairs of sunglasses.
   b. How many pairs of sunglasses must the company sell to have a revenue of $10,000?
   c. How many pairs of sunglasses must they sell in order to maximize their revenue?

4. The net sales for Home Depot can be modeled by

$$N(t) = 376.5t^2 + 548.1t + 2318.4$$

where $N(t)$ represents the net sales in millions of dollars for Home Depot t years since 1990.
   source: Model derived from data found in Home Depot annual reports.

   a. Using this model estimate the annual net sales for Home Depot in 1995.
   b. When were Home Depot's net sales 30,000 million dollars?
   c. Find the vertex for this model and explain its meaning in this context.

5. The net income for Dell Corporation can be modeled by

$$I(t) = -145.86t^2 + 3169.342t - 15145.2$$

where $I(t)$ represents the net income in millions of dollars t years since 1990.
   source: Model derived from data found in Dell annual report 2002.

   a. Using this model estimate the net income for Dell in 2000.
   b. When did Dell's net income reach 1,500 million dollars?
   c. Find the vertex for this model and explain its meaning in this context.

6. The net income for Quiksilver can be modeled by

$$I(t) = -1545.5t^2 + 32281.7t - 138849.2$$

where $I(t)$ represents the net income in thousands of dollars t years since 1990.
   source: Model derived from data found in Quiksilver annual report 2001.

   a. Using this model estimate the net income for Quiksilver in 2001.
   b. When did Quiksilver's net income reach 18 million dollars?
   c. Find the vertex for this model and explain its meaning in this context.

7. The average fuel consumption of vehicles driving the roads can be modeled by

$$F(t) = 0.425t^2 - 16.431t + 840.321$$

where $F(t)$ represents the gallons per vehicle per year t years since 1970.

   a. What was the average fuel consumption in 1975?
   b. What was the average fuel consumption in 1985?
   c. Find the vertex for this model and explain its meaning in this context.

8. A baseball is hit so that its height in feet t seconds after it is hit can be represented by

$$h(t) = -16t^2 + 40t + 4$$

   a. What is the height of the ball when it is hit?
   b. When does the ball reach a height of 20 feet?
   c. What is the balls maximum height?

9. A baseball is hit so that its height in feet t seconds after it is hit can be represented by

$$h(t) = -16t^2 + 56t + 4$$

   a. What is the height of the ball when it is hit?
   b. When does the ball reach a height of 25 feet?
   c. What is the ball's maximum height?

10. A baseball is hit so that its height in feet t seconds after it is hit can be represented by
$$h(t) = -16t^2 + 60t + 4$$
   a. What is the height of the ball when it is hit?
   b. When does the ball reach a height of 40 feet?
   c. What is the ball's maximum height?

Math Tutorial   More practice problems like exercises 11 through 20 can be found in section 3.6 of the CD Tutorial.

In Exercises 11 through 20
   a. Sketch a graph of the given quadratic functions.
   b. Label the vertex.
   c. Label the vertical/horizontal intercepts.
   d. Find a symmetric point to the vertical intercept.
   e. State whether the parabola opens up or down.
   f. Give the domain and range of the function.

11. $f(x) = x^2 + 2x - 15$

12. $m(b) = -b^2 + 11b - 24$

13. $D(z) = z^2 - 12z + 43$

14. $g(s) = 2s^2 - 62s + 216$

15. $p(k) = -5k^2 - 17.5k - 12.5$

16. $h(w) = 0.4w^2 - 3.6w - 44.8$

17. $Q(p) = 3p^2 - 30p + 82$

18. $M(a) = -0.25a^2 - 3.5a - 27.5$

19. $W(g) = -0.3(g + 2)^2 + 17$

20. $f(x) = 3(x - 4)^2 - 18$

For exercises 21 through 23 estimate the solutions to the systems using the graphs.

21.

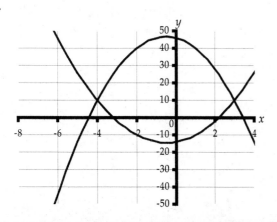

22.

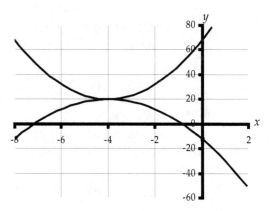

23.

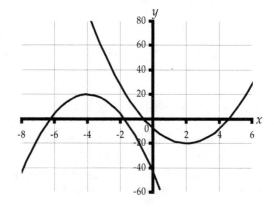

For exercises 24 through 27 estimate the solution(s) to the system using the given tables.

24.

X	Y1	Y2
-6	48	-42
-4	12	12
-2	-8	42
0	-12	48
2	0	30
3	12	12
4	28	-12

$Y_1 = 2X^2 + 2X - 12$

25.

X	Y1	Y2
2.176	17.292	17.797
2.188	17.525	17.499
2.203	17.819	17.125
0	-6	48
-2.735	18.451	18.804
-2.743	18.61	18.609
-2.765	19.051	18.069

$Y_1 = 4X^2 + 2X - 6$

26.

X	Y1	Y2
-3.9	1.41	.1
-3.8	.84	.2
-3.7	.29	.3
-3.6	-.24	.4
2.6	5.96	6.6
2.7	6.69	6.7
2.8	7.44	6.8

$Y_1 = X^2 + 2X - 6$

27.

X	Y1	Y2
2	27	9
3	17	9
4	11	9
5	9	9
6	11	9
7	17	9
8	27	9

$Y_1 = 2(X-5)^2 + 9$

For exercises 28 through 30 graph the inequalities.

28. $y < x^2 + 8x + 15$

29. $y > x^2 - 4x - 21$

30. $y \leq -2(x+3)^2 + 10$

Section 3.7   Polynomial Arithmetic

• **Defining Polynomials** • **Degree** •**Adding and Subtracting Polynomials** • **Multiplying Polynomials**

Up to this point in the course we have worked with linear and quadratic functions. Many models in the world will not fit either of these patterns and thus might be modeled by other types of functions. In this section we will look at a family of functions called polynomials. Both linear and quadratic functions are examples of polynomials. To start we will review some basics that you may know from previous classes.

The most basic component of a polynomial is a **term**. Terms can either be constant, a variable or a combination of constants and variables multiplied together. A **polynomial** is any combination of terms that are added together. The powers of all variables in a polynomial must be positive integers. Basic linear functions usually have two terms and a quadratic in standard form usually has 3 terms.

Definition 3.7.1

Term: A constant, a variable or the product of any number of constants and variables.

$$12 \qquad -3x \qquad 5xy^2$$

Polynomial: Any combination of terms that are added together.

Polynomial	Not a Polynomial
$5x^2y$	$3x^2 + \dfrac{5}{x} - 4$
$3m^2 + 2m - 7$	$3\sqrt{x} + 5$

Example 1

Determine the number of terms in the following polynomial expressions and list terms as either constant or variable.

a. $3x^2 + 5x - 9$

b. $5t + 6$

c. $5m^2 - 3$

d. 104

e. $-98xy^2$

Solution

a. This quadratic has 3 terms. -9 is a constant term and both $3x^2$ and $5x$ are variable terms since they contain at least one variable.

b. This linear expression has 2 terms. 6 is a constant term and $5t$ is a variable term.

c. This quadratic has 2 terms -3 is a constant term and $5m^2$ is a variable term.

d. This is a single constant term.

e. This is a single variable term. Although there are 2 variables involved they are multiplied together and thus part of one term. Terms are always separated by addition.

One way of describing a polynomial is its **degree**. A linear polynomial has a degree one and a quadratic will have degree two. The degree of an individual term is the sum of all the exponents for the variables. The degree of a polynomial is the same as the highest degree term.

Example 2

For the given expressions list the degrees of each term and the entire polynomial.

a. $3x^2 + 5x + 6$

b. $7t - 4$

c. $2x^2y + 5xy - 7y + 2$

d. $4a^3b^4c - 6ab^2c^2$

e. 12

Solution

a. $3x^2$ has degree 2, $5x$ has degree 1, 6 has degree 0, and the polynomial has degree 2.

b. $7t$ has degree 1, -4 has degree 0, and the polynomial has degree 1.

c. $2x^2y$ had degree 3 since x has an exponent of 2 and y has an exponent of 1. $5xy$ has degree 2, $-7y$ has degree 1, 2 has degree 0, and the polynomial has degree 3.

d. $4a^3b^4c$ has degree 8, $-6ab^2c^2$ has degree 5, and the polynomial has degree 8.

e. 12 has degree zero. This is because there are no variables in this term so no variable exponents to sum.

Problem 1

For the given expressions list the degrees of each term and the entire polynomial.

a. $-0.23x^2 + 4x - 3$

b. $8m^3n + 6mn^2 - 2n^3$

c. $-9s^5t^4u^2 - 7s^3t^2u^2$

Solution   See page 216

When working with polynomials you will need to pay close attention to a few details. In order to add or subtract two terms they must be **like terms**. Like terms have the same variables with the same exponents. When multiplying, the terms do not have to be like but you will need to use the distributive property and add exponents for any variables that are the same. The next several examples and problems will show addition, subtraction and multiplying polynomials. You should also read the Skill Connection for additional examples.

SC-Example 1:
Perform the indicated operation and simplify.

a.
$$(x^4 - 3x^2 + 4x) - (3x^3 - 5x + 3)$$

b.
$$(x + 2)(x^2 + 3x - 7)$$

c.
$$(2ab^2 + 5b) + (4a^2b + 3ab^2)$$

d.
$$(x + y)(2x + 3y)$$

Solution:
a. First we need to distribute the negative sign through the second parentheses and then combine like terms.
$$x^4 - 3x^2 + 4x - 3x^3 + 5x - 3$$
$$x^4 - 6x^2 + 9x - 3$$

b. Use the distributive property to multiply the x and then to multiply the 2 through and then combine like terms.
$$(x + 2)(x^2 + 3x - 7)$$
$$x^3 + 3x^2 - 7x + 2x^2 + 6x - 14$$
$$x^3 + 5x^2 - x - 14$$

c. Combine like terms.
$$(2ab^2 + 5b) + (4a^2b + 3ab^2)$$
$$4a^2b + 5ab^2 + 5b$$

d. Use the distributive property to multiply the x and then the y through.
$$(x + y)(2x + 3y)$$
$$2x^2 + 3xy + 2xy + 3y^2$$
$$2x^2 + 5xy + 3y^2$$

When multiplying two binomials the distributive property can be remembered using the acronym F.O.I.L. Multiply the First terms, the Outer terms, the Inner terms and finally the Last terms.

Example 3

The revenue and costs for goods sold by the Dell Computer Corporation can be modeled by the functions
$$R(t) = -1.9t^2 + 41.3t - 188.7$$
$$C(t) = -1.4t^2 + 31.0t - 143.3$$
where $R(t)$ represents the revenue for goods sold in billions of dollars and $C(t)$ represents the costs of selling those goods in billions of dollars t years since 1990.
source: Models derived from data found at CBSMarketWatch.com

a. Find the revenue and cost of Dell in 1999.

b. Find a new function that will give the gross profit of Dell Computer Corporation. (hint: Gross Profit equals Revenue minus Costs.)

c. Use the new profit function to find the profit in 1999.

Solution

a. 1999 is represented by $t = 9$ so we get
$$R(9) = 29.1$$
$$C(9) = 22.3$$
Therefore the Revenue was $29.1 billion and the Costs were $22.3 billion.

b. If we define $P(t)$ to be the gross profit in billions of dollars for the Dell Computer Corporation we get
$$P(t) = R(t) - C(t)$$
$$P(t) = (-1.9t^2 + 41.3t - 188.7) - (-1.4t^2 + 31.0t - 143.3)$$
$$P(t) = -1.9t^2 + 41.3t - 188.7 + 1.4t^2 - 31.0t + 143.3$$
$$P(t) = -0.5t^2 + 10.3t - 45.4$$

c. Again 1999 is represented by $t = 9$ so we get $P(9) = 6.8$. So the gross profit for the Dell Computer Corporation was about $6.8 billion in 1999.

Problem 2

The revenue and profit for state lotteries in the United States can be modeled by
$$R(t) = 1850.24t + 1613$$
$$P(t) = -15.65t^2 + 877.31t + 558.17$$
where $R(t)$ represents the revenue in millions of dollars and $P(t)$ represents the profit in millions of dollars from state lotteries t years since 1980.
source: Models derived from data in the Statistical Abstract 2001.

a. Calculate the revenue and profit gained by state lotteries in 1990.

b. Find a new function for the cost associated with state lotteries.

c. Using the new cost function determine the cost for state lotteries in 2000.

Solution   See page 217

Example 4

The willingness of digital camera producers to produce cameras depends on the price they can sell them for. This can be modeled by

$$S(p) = 0.015p^2 - 1.5p + 80$$

where $S(p)$ represents the supply of digital cameras in thousands when p is the price in dollars and the price is greater than $50.

a. Find the number of digital cameras producers are willing to supply when the price is $100.

b. Find a function for the projected revenue if all the cameras supplied sell at price p.

c. Estimate the projected revenue if digital cameras are sold for $150 each.

Solution

a. The given price of $100 can be substituted into p to get $S(100) = 80$. Therefore the digital camera producers are willing to supply 80 thousand cameras if they will sell for $100 each.

b. Revenue is calculated by taking the number of items sold by the price. In this case the function $S(p)$ represents the number of items sold and p represents the price. Using this we get

$$R(p) = p \cdot S(p)$$
$$R(p) = p(0.015p^2 - 1.5p + 80)$$
$$R(p) = 0.015p^3 - 1.5p^2 + 80p$$

where $R(p)$ represents the revenue in thousands of dollars for selling digital cameras at a price of p dollars.

c. The given price of $150 can be substituted into p to get $R(150) = 28875$. Therefore the digital camera producers will earn $28,875 thousand if cameras sell for $150 each.

Problem 3

The willingness of a car manufacturer to produce SUV's depends on the price they can sell them for. This can be modeled by

$$S(p) = 0.008p^2 - 0.5p + 30$$

where $S(p)$ represents the supply of SUV's in thousands when p is the price in thousands of dollars and the price is greater than $25,000.

a. Find the number of SUV's this car manufacturer is willing to supply when the price is $45,000.

b. Find a function for the projected revenue if all the SUV's supplied sell at price p.

c. Estimate the projected revenue if SUV's are sold for $40,000 each.

Solution   See page 217

Example 5

The area of a Norman window (a rectangle with a semi-circle on top) can be determined by adding the area functions of the rectangle and semi-circle pieces it is made of. If the rectangle part has a height of 99 inches find the following:

a. A function for the total area of the Norman Window.

b. The area of the Norman Window if its width is 48 inches.

Solution

a. The area function will be the sum of the rectangle's area function and the semi-circle's area function. We are missing the width of the window so lets define w as the width of the window in inches. This will result in the following area functions

$$R(w) = 99w \qquad \text{Area of a rectangle is length times width.}$$

$$C(w) = \frac{1}{2}\pi\left(\frac{w}{2}\right)^2 \qquad \begin{array}{l}\text{Half the area of a circle}\\ \text{pi times radius squared.}\end{array}$$

where $R(w)$ represents the area of the rectangle part in square inches and $C(w)$ represents the area of the semi-circle part in square inches. This results in a total area function of

$$N(w) = 99w + \frac{1}{2}\pi\left(\frac{w}{2}\right)^2$$

$$N(w) = \frac{\pi}{8}w^2 + 99w$$

where $N(w)$ represents the total area in square inches of an Norman Window with a height of 99 inches and a width of w inches for the rectangle part.

b. Since the width is given as 48 inches we can substitute 48 for w and find the total area $N(48) = 5656.8$. Therefore a Norman window with these dimensions will have a total area of 5656.8 square inches.

Section 3.7 Key Points

- Terms can consist of constants, variables or both multiplied together.
- Like terms must have the same variables with the same exponents.
- Polynomials are a combination of terms added together.
- The degree of a term is the sum of its variables exponents.
- The degree of a polynomial is the same as the highest degree of its terms.
- Polynomials can be added or subtracted by combining like terms.
- Polynomials can be multiplied together using the distributive property.

Section 3.7 Problem Solutions

Problem 1   Solution

a. $-0.23x^2$ has degree 2, $4x$ has degree 1 and -3 has no degree. The polynomial expression has degree 2.

b. $8m^3n$ has degree 4, $6mn^2$ has degree 3, and $-2n^3$ has degree 3. The polynomial expression has degree 4.

c. $-9s^5t^4u^2$ has degree 11, and $-7s^3t^2u^2$ has degree 7. The polynomial expression has degree 11.

Problem 2   Solution

a. 1990 is represented by $t = 10$ so we get

$$R(10) = 20115$$
$$P(10) = 7766.3$$

Thus in 1990 the states revenue from lotteries was about $20,115 million and their profits were about $7,766.3 million.

b. If we let $C(t)$ be the costs from state lotteries in millions of dollars t years since 1980 we know that $P(t) = R(t) - C(t)$. Solving this for $C(t)$ we get

$$P(t) = R(t) - C(t)$$
$$\underline{-R(t)\ \ -R(t)}$$
$$P(t) - R(t) = -C(t) \qquad \text{Multiply both sides by -1.}$$
$$C(t) = R(t) - P(t)$$

Now we substitute the expressions for revenue and profit and simplify.

$$C(t) = R(t) - P(t)$$
$$C(t) = (1850.24t + 1613) - (-15.65t^2 + 877.31t + 558.17)$$
$$C(t) = 1850.24t + 1613 + 15.65t^2 - 877.31t - 558.17$$
$$C(t) = 15.65t^2 + 972.9t + 1054.83$$

c. The year 2000 is represented by $t = 20$ so we get $C(20) = 26772.83$. Therefore in 2000 the cost of state lotteries in the United States was approximately $26,772.83 million.

Problem 3   Solution

a. A price of $45,000 is represented by $p = 45$ so we get $S(45) = 23.7$. Thus at a selling price of $45,000 this car manufacturer is willing to supply 23,700 SUV's.

b. Revenue is calculated by multiplying the price p by the supply $S(p)$. If we let $R(p)$ represent the revenue in millions of dollars from selling SUV's at a price of p thousand dollars we get

$$R(p) = p \cdot S(p)$$
$$R(p) = p(0.008p^2 - 0.5p + 30)$$
$$R(p) = 0.008p^3 - 0.5p^2 + 30p$$

c. The price of $40,000 is represented by $p = 40$ so we get $R(40) = 912$. Therefore at a price of $40,000 the car manufacturer can expect a revenue of about $912 million.

3.7 Exercises

1. The revenue and costs for goods sold by the International Business Machines, IBM, can be modeled by the functions
$$R(t) = -2.1t^2 + 41.29t - 114.03$$
$$C(t) = -1.87t^2 + 36.45t - 121.35$$
where $R(t)$ represents the revenue for goods sold in billions of dollars and $C(t)$ represents the costs of selling those goods in billions of dollars t years since 1990.
source: Models derived from data found at CBSMarketWatch.com

   a. Find the revenue and cost for IBM in 1998.
   b. Find a new function that will give the gross profit of IBM. (hint: Gross Profit equals Revenue minus Costs.)
   c. Use the new profit function to find the profit in 1998.
   d. Find the vertex of your new profit function and explain its meaning in this context.

2. The revenue and costs for goods sold by NIKE Inc. can be modeled by the functions
$$R(t) = 317.48t^2 - 5394.55t + 31722.7$$
$$C(t) = 238.28t^2 - 4143.83t + 23396.23$$
where $R(t)$ represents the revenue for goods sold in millions of dollars and $C(t)$ represents the costs of selling those goods in millions of dollars t years since 1990.
source: Models derived from data found at CBSMarketWatch.com

   a. Find the revenue and cost for NIKE in 1999.
   b. Find a new function that will give the gross profit of NIKE. (hint: Gross Profit equals Revenue minus Costs.)
   c. Use the new profit function to find the profit in 2000.
   d. Find the vertex of your new profit function and explain its meaning in this context.

3. The revenue and profit for Pearson Publishing Company can be modeled by
$$R(t) = -278.36t^2 + 5944.73t - 27575.11$$
$$P(t) = 36.33t^3 - 1074.5t^2 + 10550.17t - 33971$$
where $R(t)$ represents the revenue in millions of British Pounds and $P(t)$ represents the profit in millions of British Pounds for Pearson t years since 1990.
source: Models derived from data found at Pearson.com.

   a. Calculate the revenue and profit earned by Pearson in 1999.
   b. Find a new function for the costs at Pearson Publishing.

   c. Using the new cost function determine the costs at Pearson Publishing in 2000.

4. The cost and profit for Home Depot Inc. can be modeled by
$$C(t) = -15t^2 + 5526t - 21599.5$$
$$P(t) = -82.25t^2 + 4053.45t - 18523.65$$
where $C(t)$ represents the cost in millions of dollars and $P(t)$ represents the profit in millions of dollars for Home Depot Inc. t years since 1990.
source: Models derived from data found at CBSMarketWatch.com

   a. Calculate the costs and profit of Home Depot in 1999.
   b. Find a new function for the revenue at Home Depot Inc.
   c. Using the new revenue function estimate the revenue at Home Depot in 2001.

5. The willingness of car stereo producers to produce stereos depends on the price they can sell them for. This can be modeled by
$$S(p) = 0.009p^2 - 0.5p + 20$$
where $S(p)$ represents the supply of car stereos in thousands when p is the price in dollars and the price is greater than \$30.

   a. Find the number of car stereos producers are willing to supply when the price is \$100.
   b. Find a function for the projected revenue if all the car stereos supplied sell at price p.
   c. Estimate the projected revenue if car stereos are sold for \$90 each.

6. The willingness of sports equipment producers to produce tennis rackets depends on the price they can sell them for. This can be modeled by
$$S(p) = 0.09p^2 - 4.2p + 51$$
where $S(p)$ represents the supply of tennis rackets in millions when p is the price in dollars and the price is greater than \$25.

   a. Find the number of tennis rackets producers are willing to supply when the price is \$40.
   b. Find a function for the projected revenue if all the tennis rackets supplied sell at price p.
   c. Estimate the projected revenue if tennis rackets are sold for \$75 each.

7. The willingness of car manufacturers to produce Mini-Vans depends on the price they can sell them for. This can be modeled by
$$S(p) = 0.11p^2 - 3.2p + 45$$
where $S(p)$ represents the supply of Mini-Vans in thousands when p is the price in thousands of dollars and the price is greater than \$14,500.

   a. Find the number of Mini-Vans manufacturers are willing to supply when the price is \$25,000.

b. Find a function for the projected revenue if all the Mini-Vans supplied sell at price p.

c. Estimate the projected revenue if Mini-Vans are sold for $31,000 each.

8. The total number of immigrants admitted to the United States as permanent residents under refugee acts t years since 1990 can be represented by

$$I(t) = -17853.5t^2 + 212449.1t - 501783.9$$

Of those admitted under refugee acts the number of them coming from Europe can be represented by

$$E(t) = -6431.5t^2 + 74006.3t - 161816.2$$

source: Models derived from data in the Statistical Abstract 2001.

a. Estimate the total number of immigrants admitted to the U.S. as permanent residents under refugee acts in 1995.

b. Estimate the number of immigrants admitted under refugee acts that were from Europe in 1995.

c. Find a new function to represent the number of non-European immigrants admitted to the U.S. as permanent residents under refugee acts.

d. Use your model to determine the number of non-European immigrants admitted under refugee acts in 1998.

9. The number of men and women in the United States since 1850 can be modeled by

$$M(t) = 2.86t^2 + 97.22t - 137.68$$

$$F(t) = 3.65t^2 - 48.46t + 4883.84$$

where $M(t)$ represents the number of men in thousands and $F(t)$ represents the number of females in thousands in the United States t years since 1800.

source: Models derived from data in the Statistical Abstract 2001.

a. Estimate the number of males and females in the United States in 2000.

b. Find a function for the total population in the U.S..

c. Use the new function to estimate the total population in the U.S. in 2002.

d. Find when the number of men was equal to the number of women in the U.S..

e. Find the vertex of the total population function and explain its meaning in this context.

10. The number of United States residents who are black or of hispanic origin can be modeled by

$$B(t) = 400.99t - 5240.19$$

$$H(t) = 11.51t^2 - 1181.14t + 35414.03$$

where $B(t)$ represents the number of black resi-

dents in thousands and $H(t)$ represents the number of residents of hispanic origin in thousands t years since 1900.

source: Models derived from data in the Statistical Abstract 2001.

a. Find a function that will represent the total number of black and hispanic residents in the U.S..

b. Use this function to determine the number of black and hispanic residents in 2000.

c. Find when the number of residents of hispanic origin was the same as the number of black residents.

11. The number of U.S. residents who are white can be modeled by

$$W(t) = 1.693t + 209.107$$

where $W(t)$ represents the number of U.S. residents who are white in millions t years since 1990.

The number of white residents who are 18 years old or older can be modeled by

$$O(t) = 0.014t^2 + 1.169t + 157.528$$

where $O(t)$ represents the number of white residents 18 years old or older in millions t years since 1990.

source: Models derived from data in the Statistical Abstract 2001.

a. Find a new function for the number of white residents who are under 18 years old.

b. Estimate the number of white residents under 18 years old in 2002.

12. The number of U.S. residents who are white and 65 years old or older can be modeled by

$$R(t) = -0.011t^2 + 0.409t + 28.098$$

where $R(t)$ represents the number of U.S. residents who are white and 65 years old or older in millions t years since 1990.

source: Model derived from data in the Statistical Abstract 2001.

a. Using the function you found in the last exercise for the number of white residents under 18 years old determine when the number of white residents under 18 years old is the same as the number 65 years old or older.

13. The area of a Norman window (a rectangle with a semi-circle on top) can be determined by adding the area functions of the rectangle and semi-circle pieces it is made of. If the rectangle part has a height of 75 inches find the following:

a. A function for the total area of the Norman Window.

b. The area of the Norman Window if its width is 36 inches.

Math Tutorial   More practice problems like exercises 14 through 30 can be found in section 3.7 of the CD Tutorial.

In Exercises 14 through 21 list the degrees of each term and the degree of the entire polynomial.

14. $2x^5 - 7$

15. $3x^2 + 5x - 7$

16. $-14s^3t + 6t^4 - 9$

17. $1.023t + 6.2$

18. $5p^2 + 4p - 87$

19. $4m + 8$

20. $23a^4b^2 - 62a^2b + 9b^3$

21. $0.22w^5x^2y^7z^3 + 0.4wx^3y^4z$

In Exercises 22 through 31 perform the indicated operation and simplify.

22. $(5x^2 - 6x - 12) - (-3x^2 - 10x + 8)$

23. $(2x^2 + 5x - 16) + (3x^2 - 8x + 9)$

24. $(5x^3z^2 - 4x^2z + 6z) - (3x^3z^2 - 17xz + 3z)$

25. $(a^2b + 5ab^2 - 9b) - (3ab^2 + 8b)$

26. $(5ab - 8b)(3a + 4b)$

27. $(2x + 5)(3x^2 - 5x + 7)$

28. $(2x^2 + 3x - 9) + (7x + 2)^2$

29. $(3x + 7y)^2$

30. $7x(3y^2 + 5y - 6) + 8xy$

31. $(7x - 3)(2x + 8) - 9x^2 + 8$

Chapter 3 Review Exercises

1. The population of North Dakota can be modeled by
$$P(t) = -0.89(t-5.6)^2 + 643$$
   where $P(t)$ represents the population in thousands t years since 1990.
   source: Model derived from data in the Statistical Abstract 2001.
   a. Find the population of North Dakota in 1998.
   b. Sketch a graph of this model.
   c. Find the vertex of this model and explain its meaning in this context.
   d. When was the population of North Dakota 640,000?

2. The number of murders, M, in thousands in the United States t years since 1990 can be represented by
$$M(t) = -0.42(t-2.5)^2 + 23$$
   source: Model derived from data in the Statistical Abstract 2001.
   a. Estimate the number of murders in the U.S. in 1996.
   b. Find the vertex of this model and explain its meaning in this context.
   c. In what year were there 14,500 murders in the U.S.?

3. Sketch the graph and label the vertex, vertical intercept, and at least one additional symmetric pair for the following functions.
   a. $f(x) = 3(x-8)^2 + 4$
   b. $g(x) = -0.5(x+7)^2 - 3$

4. The number of juveniles arrested for possession of drugs through the 1990's is given in **Table 3.7.1**

Table 3.7.1

Year	Number of Juveniles (in thousands)
1992	47,901
1994	92,185
1995	115,159
1996	116,225
1997	124,683
1998	118,754
1999	112,640

source: Statistical Abstract 2001.
   a. Find a model for this data.
   b. Give a reasonable domain and range for this model.
   c. Estimate the number of juveniles arrested for possession of drugs in 2000.
   d. If this trend continues in what year will the number of juvenile arrests be at 50,000,000 again?

5. The United States Department of Commerce obligations for research and development for several years is given in **Table 3.7.2**

Table 3.7.2

Year	R & D Obligations (in millions of dollars)
1995	1136
1996	1068
1997	1003
1999	990
2000	1041
2001	1127

source: Statistical Abstract 2001.
   a. Find a model for this data.
   b. Give a reasonable domain and range for this model.
   c. Estimate the research and development obligations for the Department of Commerce in 1998.
   d. Estimate when the research and development obligations for the Department of Commerce will be $1.5 billion.

6. The median sales price in thousands of dollars of new houses in the western United States t years since 1990 can be modeled by
$$P(t) = 1.073t^2 - 5.84t + 144.68$$
   source: Model derived from data in the Statistical Abstract 2001.
   a. Estimate the median price in 1995.
   b. When will the median price of a new home in the west reach $250,000?
   c. Find the vertex of this model and explain its meaning in this context.

7. Solve the following quadratic equations by factoring.
   a. $9x^2 - 24x + 5 = -11$
   b. $3x^2 - x = 2$

8. Sketch the graph. Label the vertex and vertical/horizontal intercepts.
   a. $f(x) = -2.7x^2 + 16.2x - 21.8$
   b. $h(n) = 0.3n^2 + 3n + 14.5$

9. Solve the following systems of equations
   a.
$$y = 2x^2 + 5x + 12$$
$$y = -2x^2 + 7x + 15$$
   b.
$$y = 0.25x^2 + 4x - 7$$
$$y = 0.5x^2 + 3x - 9$$

10. Use the graph to solve the following system of equations.

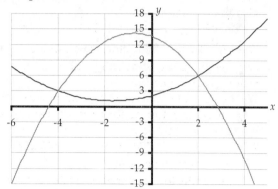

11. Use the table to estimate the solution(s) to the following system.

X	Y₁	Y₂
0	114	-81
1	65	-39
2	30	-9
3	9	9
4	2	15
5	9	9
6	30	-9

X=6

12. John Hopkins University and the University of Washington are the number one and two ranked universities in federal obligations for research and development funds. Their funding can be modeled as

$$J(t) = 16.27t^3 - 321.0t^2 + 2089.32t - 3885.40$$

$$W(t) = 2.89t^3 - 53.94t^2 + 339.66t - 411.82$$

where $J(t)$ represents the federal funding for R & D at John Hopkins University in millions of dollars and $W(t)$ represents the federal funding for R & D at the University of Washington in millions of dollars t years since 1990.

source: Models derived from data in the Statistical Abstract.

a. Find the federal funding for R & D at both universities in 1999.

b. Find a new function for the difference in funding at these top ranked schools.

c. Use your new function to find the difference in federal funding at these universities in 2000.

13. Perform the indicated operation and simplify.

a. $(2x^2y + 5xy - 4y^2) - (7xy + 9y^2)$

b. $(3x + 7)(2x - 9)$

c. $(3x + 4y)(5x - 7y)$

Chapter 3 Test

1. The number of violent crimes in the United States during the late 1900's can be modeled by
$$V(t) = -0.044(t - 11)^2 + 14.5$$
where $V(t)$ represents the number of violent crimes in millions t years since 1980.

    source: Model derived from data in the Statistical Abstract 2001.

    a. Estimate the number of violent crimes in 1995.
    b. Sketch a graph of this function.
    c. Determine the vertex and explain its meaning in this context.
    d. In what year will there be 10 million violent crimes in the United States?

2. Use the graph to solve the system of equations.

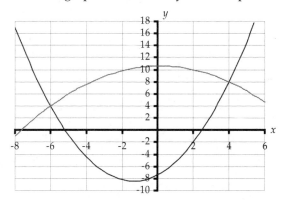

3. Solve the following quadratic equations by factoring.

    a. $3x^2 - 5x + 5 = 33$

    b. $8x^2 - 34x = -35$

4. The total outlays for national defense and veterans benefits by the United States for several years is given in **Table 3.8.1**

    Table 3.8.1

Year	Total Outlays (in billions of dollars)
1993	326.8
1995	310
1997	309.8
1999	320.2
2000	337.4

    source: Statistical Abstract 2001.

    a. Find a model for this data.
    b. Give a reasonable domain and range for this model.
    c. Estimate the total outlays for national defense and veterans benefits in 1998.
    d. When will the total outlays for national defense and veterans benefits reach half a trillion dollars?

5. The total number of graduate science/engineering students in doctoral programs can be modeled by
$$S(t) = 0.504t^3 - 8.596t^2 + 41.766t + 385.022$$
where $S(t)$ represents the total number of science/engineering graduate students in thousands t years since 1990.
The number of female science/engineering graduate students in thousands t years since 1990 can be represented by
$$F(t) = 0.157t^3 - 2.953t^2 + 19.619t + 142.663$$

    source: Statistical Abstract 2001.

    a. Estimate the total number of graduate science/engineering students in doctoral programs in 2000.
    b. Find a new function for the number of male graduate science/engineering students in doctoral programs.
    c. Using this new model estimate the number of male graduate science/engineering students in doctoral programs in 2000.

6. The U.S. commercial space industry revenue for satellite manufacturing for several years is given in **Table 3.8.2**

    Table 3.8.2

Year	Revenues (in billions of dollars)
1996	7.3
1997	10.3
1998	11.8
1999	10.0

    source: Statistical Abstract 2001.

    a. Find a model for this data.
    b. Give a reasonable domain and range for this model.
    c. Estimate the commercial space industries revenues for satellite manufacturing in 2000.
    d. Give the vertex for your model and explain its meaning in this context.

7. Sketch the graph. Label the vertex and vertical/horizontal intercepts.

    a. $f(x) = -1.5x^2 + 12x - 20.5$

    b. $g(m) = 0.4m^2 + 1.6m + 11.6$

8. Solve the system of equations
$$y = 2x^2 + 5x - 9$$
$$y = -7x^2 + 3x + 2$$

9. The number of privately owned single unit hous-
    es started in the late 1990's can be modeled by
    $$H(t) = -52t^2 + 916.2t - 2731.2$$
    where $H(t)$ represents the number of privately
    owned single unit houses started in thousands t
    years since 1990.

    source: Model derived from data in the Statistical Abstract
    2001.

    a. Estimate the number of single unit houses
        started in 2000.

    b. When were there 1000 thousand of these
        homes started?

10. The number of murders, M, in thousands in the
    United States t years since 1990 can be represent-
    ed by
    $$M(t) = -0.42t^2 + 2.1t + 20.375$$
    The percentage, P, of these murders that were
    committed using a handgun can be represented
    by
    $$P(t) = 0.048t^3 - 0.952t^2 + 4.898t + 49.454$$

    source: Models derived from data in the Statistical Abstract
    2001.

    a. Estimate the percentage of murders in 1997
        that were committed using a handgun.

    b. Find a new function that gives the number of
        murders committed by a handgun.

    c. Using your new function estimate the number
        of murders committed by a handgun in 1996.

11. Perform the indicated operation and simplify.

    a. $(4x^2 + 2x - 7) - (3x^2 + 9)$

    b. $(4x^2y + 3xy - 2y^2) + (5x^2y - 7xy + 8)$

    c. $(2x + 8)(3x - 7)$

    d. $(3a - 4b)(2a - 5b)$

12. Use the table to estimate the solution(s) to the
    system of equations.

X	Y₁	Y₂
-9	-15.33	24.667
-8	-4	12
-7	4	4
-6	8.6667	.66667
-5	10	2
-4	8	8
-3	2.6667	18.667

X= -3

Section 4.1   Introduction to Exponentials

• **Growth and Decay** • **Recognizing Exponential Patterns** • **Half -life**

In this chapter we will consider yet another type of function to our list of possible models. So far we have found linear and quadratic models and worked with systems of equations. Now we will discuss another function found in many areas of science and life called an exponential function.

> *"The mathematics of uncontrolled growth are frightening. A single cell of the bacterium E. coli would, under ideal circumstances , divide every twenty minutes . That is not particularly disturbing until you think about it, but the fact is that bacteria multiply geometrically: one become two, two become four, four become eight, and so on. In this way it can be shown that in a single day, one cell of E. coli could produce a super-colony equal in size and weight to the entire planet Earth."*
>
> Michael Crichton (1969) *The Andromeda Strain*, Dell, N.Y. p247

This quote may sound unrealistic; however, with the assumption of "ideal circumstances" the mathematics of this type of situation is amazing. Although Crichton calls this type of growth geometric, today it is more often called exponential growth. Later in this section we will investigate this situation and see just how fast E. coli bacteria grows in "ideal circumstances." First let's consider a simple version of this situation.

Concept Investigation 1

Bacterial growth involves the process of doubling and then doubling again and again. Let's assume that we are doing an experiment in a biology lab starting with a single bacteria cell that in the current environment will split into two new cells every hour.

a. Complete the table below with the number of bacteria, B, after h hours. Remember the bacteria is doubling every hour.

   Table 4.1.1

Hours	Bacteria
0	1
1	2
2	4
3	
4	
5	
6	

b. Create a scatterplot for this data on your calculator. Describe the shape of the graph.

TI - 83 Details:
To enter an exponential function you will need to have a variable in the exponent. This means that you will need to use the [^] key that is just above the division key on the right side of your calculator.

Example:
To enter the exponential function
$$f(x) = 3(2)^x$$
into the Y= screen of your calculator you would use the following key strokes.

[3] [(] [2] [)] [^] [x]

or

[3] [*] [2] [^] [x]

```
Plot1  Plot2  Plot3
\Y1 ▇ 3(2)^X
\Y2 =
\Y3 ▇ 3*2^X
\Y4 =
\Y5 =
\Y6 =
\Y7 =
```

Because of the order of operations the exponent x will be performed first so the parentheses will not be needed. Many students find it safer to put in the parentheses to keep from any confusion.

c. Now rewrite the table from part **a** writing out the calculations not the final results

Table 4.1.2

Hours	Bacteria
0	1
1	$1 \cdot 2$
2	$1 \cdot 2 \cdot 2$
3	
4	
5	
6	

d. As you can see from this last table this situation is calculated using repeated multiplication. Recall that exponents are a shorter way of representing repeated multiplication . Use exponents to re-write this table and find a pattern for a model that will give the number of bacteria after h hours.

Table 4.1.3

Hours	Bacteria
0	1
1	$1(2)$
2	$1(2)^2$
3	$1(2)^3$
4	
5	
6	
h	

e. Graph your model with the data. How well does your model fit the data?

f. Use your model to find the number of bacteria after 12 hours and 24 hours.

An **Exponential Function** is based on a pattern of repeated multiplication that leads to using exponents to simplify the expression. Since the exponent in this type of model is what changes from one input value to the other you end up with a variable in the exponent rather than a constant. It is this variable in the exponent that makes the function exponential rather than a parabola or other type of function.

Definition 4.1.1

Exponential Function: A basic exponential function can be written in the form

$$f(x) = a \cdot b^x$$

where a and b, are real numbers $a \neq 0$, $b > 0$ and $b \neq 1$.

Base: The constant b is called the base of an exponential function.

Finding a model for exponential data can be done in several ways, however using a situation and looking for a pattern is a common approach. This will take practice and in some cases a new way of thinking. Read through the following examples and problems paying close attention to how the final pattern is found leading to a model.

Example 1

A rumor is spreading across a local college campus that there will be no finals for any classes this summer. At 8 a.m. today, 7 people have heard the rumor. Assume that after each hour, 3 times as many students have heard the rumor. For example, 21 people have heard the rumor by 9 a.m. Let $R(t)$ represent the number of people that have heard the rumor t hours after 8 a.m.

a. Find a formula for $R(t)$.

b. How many people have heard the rumor by 8p.m. that night?

c. If the college has about 15,000 students estimate numerically at what time all of them would have heard the rumor.

Solution

a. First we need to define the variables and to create a table.

$R(t)$ = the number of people that have heard the rumor

t = time in hours after 8 a.m.

We are starting with 7 people at 8 a.m. and 3 times as many people each hour have heard the rumor. We can start building the table by writing out the calculations and then simplify later.

Table 4.1.4

t	$R(t)$
0	7
1	$7 \cdot 3$
2	$7 \cdot 3 \cdot 3$
3	$7 \cdot 3 \cdot 3 \cdot 3$
4	$7 \cdot 3 \cdot 3 \cdot 3 \cdot 3$
5	$7 \cdot 3 \cdot 3 \cdot 3 \cdot 3 \cdot 3$
6	$7 \cdot 3 \cdot 3 \cdot 3 \cdot 3 \cdot 3 \cdot 3$

We can see here that we have repeated multiplication by 3 so we can simplify each row by using exponents.

Table 4.1.5

t	$R(t)$
0	7
1	$7(3)$
2	$7(3)^2$
3	$7(3)^3$
4	$7(3)^4$
5	$7(3)^5$
6	$7(3)^6$

When looking at this pattern notice that the 7 and 3 are the same in each expression, after the first. The only part of each expression that is changing is the exponent itself. Note that the input value t has for each row is the same as the exponent in the resulting expression. With this in mind our model can be expressed by, $R(t) = 7(3)^t$.

If we graph this data and our model we get **Graphic 4.1.1**.

Graphic 4.1.1

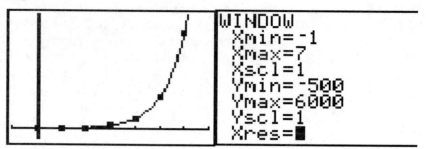

b. 8 p.m. that night is 12 hours after 8 a.m. so we can substitute $t = 12$ into our model.

$$R(12) = 7(3)^{12}$$

$$R(12) = 3720087$$

This means that 3,720,087 people will have heard this rumor by 8 p.m. that night. This is clearly model breakdown since 3.7 million people will not have heard this rumor in 12 hours.

c. Using the table we get.

X	Y1
4	567
5	1701
6	5103
7	15309
8	45927

Y1=7*3^X

The model reaches 15,309 people having heard the rumor when $t = 7$ so by 3 p.m. all of the students at the college should have heard that rumor.

This exponential model is growing so quickly that its domain must be carefully determined so that we avoid obvious model breakdown. We will discuss the domain for an exponential function in section 4.3.

Problem 1

A loan shark lends desperate people money at a very high rate of interest. One loan shark will lend you money but each week the balance you owe will double until it is paid in full. You have found yourself in trouble and need to borrow $5000 to pay your legal bills.

a. Find a model that will give the balance on this loan after w weeks have gone by.

b. Find the balance on this loan if you keep the money for 4 weeks.

c. Estimate numerically after how many weeks the balance of the loan will exceed 1 million dollars.

Solution   See page 237

TI - 83 Details:

If an exponential function has more than a single variable in the exponent you will need to use parenthesis around the entire expression in the exponent.

Example 1:

To enter the exponential function

$$f(x) = 3(2)^{5x}$$

into the Y= screen of your calculator you would use exponents around the entire exponent.

```
Plot1 Plot2 Plot3
\Y1◻3(2)^(5X)
\Y2=
\Y3=
\Y4=
\Y5=
\Y6=
\Y7=
```

Example 2:

Enter the exponential function

$$g(x) = 7\left(\frac{1}{2}\right)^{\frac{x}{3}}$$

```
Plot1 Plot2 Plot3
\Y1◻7(1/2)^(X/3)

\Y2=
\Y3=
\Y4=
\Y5=
\Y6=
```

Now let's look at the E. coli example that we started the section off with.

Example 2

The bacteria E. coli will double every 20 minutes if living under "ideal circumstances". If we assume these conditions and start with one bacterium find the following.

a. Find a model for the number of E. coli bacteria.

b. Use your model to determine the number of bacteria after 12 hours.

c. Use your model to determine the number of bacteria after 24 hours.

Solution   There are several ways you could define your variables and thus get different models for this context. In this problem we will consider two of those options.

Option 1: ($t = 1$ represents one hour)

a. Let's start by defining some variables and creating a table of data. One decision we need to make is what unit of time we should use for this model. The most common time measurement might be hours but since the bacteria doubles every 20 minutes a 20 minute interval may be used as well. We will do this problem both ways and see how the models compare.

E = the number of E. coli bacteria.

t = time in hours since the beginning of the experiment.

Now let's fill in the table, remember that the bacteria are doubling every 20 minutes not every hour. This means that the bacteria will double 3 times each hour.

Table 4.1.6

t (hours)	$E(t)$
0	1
1	$1 \cdot 2 \cdot 2 \cdot 2 = 1(2)^3$
2	$1 \cdot 2 \cdot 2 \cdot 2 \cdot 2 \cdot 2 \cdot 2 = 1(2)^6$
3	$1 \cdot 2 \cdot 2 \cdot 2 \cdot 2 \cdot 2 \cdot 2 \cdot 2 \cdot 2 \cdot 2 = 1(2)^9$
4	$1(2)^{12}$
5	$1(2)^{15}$
6	$1(2)^{18}$

When looking for a pattern be very careful to make sure your model gives you the results you want. In this table we see that the 1 and 2 are the same for each exponential expression. Only the exponent is changing. We need to find a relationship between the input values of t and the exponent that is changing. If you look carefully you should see that the exponent is 3 times as much as the input value. This pattern leads to the model $E(t) = 1(2)^{3t}$. If we check this model by graphing it gives us the expected results.

b. $t = 12$ represents 12 hours later so we substitute 12 into our model and get

$$R(12) = 1(2)^{3(12)}$$
$$R(12) = 1(2)^{36}$$
$$R(12) = 68719476736$$

So after only 12 hours there will be 68.7 billion E. coli bacteria.

c. The time $t = 24$ represents 24 hours later so we substitute 24 into our model and get

$$R(24) = 1(2)^{3(24)}$$

$$R(24) = 1(2)^{72}$$

$R(24) = 4.722 \times 10^{21}$ This answer is given in scientific notation.

This means that there will be 4.7 billion trillion E. coli bacteria after 24 hours. Now that's a lot of bacteria! This could only happen in ideal circumstances and is therefore most likely model breakdown, but the amazingly rapid growth is still true earlier in the process.

Solution   Option 2: ($t = 1$ represents 20 minutes)

a. If we define the time as the number of twenty minute intervals that pass from the beginning of the experiment we would change our table and model accordingly. Let's re-define the variables as

E = the number of E. coli bacteria.

t = the number of twenty minute intervals since the beginning of the experiment.

Now let's fill in the table, remembering that $t = 1$ now represents only 20 minutes so the bacteria will have doubled once. .

Table 4.1.7

t (20 minute periods)	$E(t)$
0	1
1	$1 \cdot 2 = 1(2)$
2	$1 \cdot 2 \cdot 2 = 1(2)^2$
3	$1 \cdot 2 \cdot 2 \cdot 2 = 1(2)^3$
4	$1(2)^4$
5	$1(2)^5$
6	$1(2)^6$

This pattern is the same as the one in the first example we did in this section and results in the model $E(t) = 1(2)^t$. Although this model is the same as the one in example 1 we will have to interpret it very carefully to get the correct results.

b. With the new definition for t, 12 hours will be represented by $t = 36$. This results in

$$E(36) = 1(2)^{36}$$

$$E(36) = 68719476736$$

This is the same result as the previous model that in 12 hours there will be 68.7 billion bacteria.

c. This time $t = 72$ represents 24 hours later so we substitute 72 into our model and get

$$R(24) = 1(2)^{72}$$

$R(24) = 4.722 \times 10^{21}$ This answer is given in scientific notation.

This means that there will be 4.7 billion trillion E. coli bacteria after 24 hours.

As you can see there were two ways to look at this pattern. Most people are comfortable with measuring time in hours but few are comfortable with measuring time in twenty minute intervals. Neither of these models is better than the other but you must use caution when using and interpreting your models. Please note that these are not the only two possibilities but they are two common ones.

Problem 2

Suppose that human beings, under "ideal conditions," could double their population size every 50 years and that there were 6 billion humans on earth in the year 2000.

a.   Find a model for the world population.

b.   Estimate the world population in 2500.

c.   Estimate graphically when the world population would reach 10 billion.

Solution   See page 238

So far we have seen several examples of **Exponential Growth**. The opposite of this type of growth is **Exponential Decay**. Exponential decay plays a large role in sciences such as archeology where scientists use exponential decay of carbon-14 to date historical objects. The exponential decay of radioactive elements is also a large part of the concerns people have with nuclear power plants. The basic concept driving most exponential decay problems is the **half-life** of the object. The half-life is simply a measurement of how long it takes before only half of an initial quantity still remains. The half-life of different elements have large ranges of values, such as radon-222 that has a half-life of only 3.825 days and Rubidium-87 with a half-life of 49 billion years. To get a better idea of how this works let's look at a few examples and problems dealing with exponential decay.

Example 3

Carbon-14 is an isotope found in all living creatures. Once a creature dies and stops taking in new carbon the existing carbon-14 decays and is no longer replaced. Because carbon-14 has a half life of 5700 years we can use the amount of carbon-14 left in an artifact to determine the age of the formerly living thing. Let's assume that an artifact which has been dead for some time started with 100 atoms of carbon-14 at the time of death.

a.   Find a model for the amount of carbon-14 remaining in the artifact.

b.   Estimate the amount of carbon-14 that should be in the artifact if it is 34,200 years old.

Solution

a.   We know that the original amount of carbon-14 was 100 atoms and that half of that amount will be left after 5700 years. With this information we should define variables and create a table to help us find a pattern.

Say What?

There are many words or phrases that imply a situation will be modeled by an exponential function. Here are just a few of them you may see:

- Exponential Growth
- Exponential Decay
- Half-life
- Growth or Decay by a factor of:
    fraction
    percentage
- Double every ...
- Triple every ...
- Repeated multiplication

C = the amount of carbon-14 atoms in the artifact
t = time in years since the artifact died.

Table 4.1.8

t	$C(t)$
0	100
5700	$100\left(\frac{1}{2}\right)$
11400	$100\left(\frac{1}{2}\right)^2$
17100	$100\left(\frac{1}{2}\right)^3$

The years that we chose for the table are based on the fact that half the carbon-14 is left after each 5700 year period has passed. We are repeatedly multiplying by $\frac{1}{2}$ but this pattern is a little harder to find than some of the others we have done. Just as in the previous problems the constant 100 and the base $\frac{1}{2}$ are the same in each row of the table. The only change is in the exponent. This means we need to find the connection between the input values and the exponents. If you look carefully you should note the inputs are multiples of 5700. If you divide each input by 5700 you will get the exponent on that row. If we let t represent the input value and divide it by 5700 we get the model

$$C(t) = 100\left(\frac{1}{2}\right)^{t/5700}$$

b. 34,200 years old can be represented by $t = 34200$ so we get

$$C(34200) = 100\left(\frac{1}{2}\right)^{34200/5700}$$

$$C(34200) = 100\left(\frac{1}{2}\right)^6$$

$$C(34200) = 1.5625$$

This means that after 34,200 years the artifact should have only about 1 or 2 atoms of carbon-14 remaining.

Example 4

The brightness of light is measured with a unit called a lumen. Sharp makes a high end Conference Series XG-P25X LCD Projector that has a brightness of 4000 lumens. Using a series of several mirrors that reflect only $\frac{3}{5}$ of the light that hits it a stage technician is trying to project a series of photos on several walls of a concert stage. The technician is concerned with the brightness of the light that will remain after using several mirrors to place the projected photos in the right places.

a. Find a model that will tell the technician the remaining lumens that will be projected after m mirrors have reflected the image.

b. Use your model to determine the lumens remaining after 5 mirrors.

c. If the technician knows that he needs a minimum of 500 lumens to have a good image use the table to find the maximum number of mirrors he can use with this projector.

Solution

a. The projector will initially project a light with 4000 lumens and after each mirror reflects the light only $\frac{3}{5}$ of that light will remain. Let's define the following variables.
L = the lumens of light remaining.
m = the number of mirrors used to reflect the light.

Table 4.1.9

m	L
0	4000
1	$4000\left(\frac{3}{5}\right)$
2	$4000\left(\frac{3}{5}\right)^2$
3	$4000\left(\frac{3}{5}\right)^3$
m	$4000\left(\frac{3}{5}\right)^m$

This pattern results in the model

$$L(m) = 4000\left(\frac{3}{5}\right)^m$$

b. 5 mirrors is represented by $m = 5$ so we get

$$L(5) = 4000\left(\frac{3}{5}\right)^5$$

$$L(5) = 311.04$$

If the technician uses 5 mirrors to place the photo projection it will only have a brightness of 311.04 lumens.

c. Using the table we get

X	Y1
1	2400
2	1440
3	864
4	518.4
5	311.04
6	186.62
7	111.97

Y1 ◼ 4000(3/5)^X

From this table we see that the technician can only use up to 4 mirrors to have the 500 lumens necessary to project a good image.

Problem 3

Thorium-234 has a half-life of 24.5 days and is a by-product of the decay of Uranium-238.

a. Find a model for the percent of a Thorium-234 sample left after d days.

b. Estimate the percent of Thorium-234 left after 180 days.

c. Estimate numerically after how many days there will be only 40% of the sample left.

Solution   See page 238

Whenever you are given data without a situation to consider you will need to remember the basic concept of an exponential model in order to find a pattern. This fundamental idea is repeated multiplication by the same number, the base. When investigating data look for the initial amount and the base.

Example 5

Use the following tables to find exponential models of the given data.

a.

Table 4.1.10

x	f(x)
0	15
1	60
2	240
3	960
4	3840

b.

Table 4.1.11

x	f(x)
0	16
1	36
2	81
3	182.25
4	410.06

c.

Table 4.1.12

t	h(t)
0	1500
5	300
10	60
15	12
20	2.4

Solution

a. For each of these tables we are given the initial value when the input variable is zero. This initial value is the value of a in the exponential model. We can find the base by dividing each consecutive output value by the previous output value.

Table 4.1.13

x	f(x)	base
0	15	
1	60	$\frac{60}{15} = 4$
2	240	$\frac{240}{60} = 4$
3	960	$\frac{960}{240} = 4$
4	3840	$\frac{3840}{960} = 4$

As you can see from performing these divisions the common multiplier is 4 for each row. If we rewrite each output showing how to calculate it using the base 4 we should see the pattern and therefore the appropriate model.

Table 4.1.14

x	$f(x)$	base
0	15	15
1	60	15(4)
2	240	$15(4)^2$
3	960	$15(4)^3$
4	3840	$15(4)^4$

This leads us to the model $f(x) = 15(4)^x$.

b.

Table 4.1.15

x	$f(x)$	base
0	16	
1	36	$\dfrac{36}{16} = 2.25$
2	81	$\dfrac{81}{36} = 2.25$
3	182.25	$\dfrac{182.25}{81} = 2.25$
4	410.0625	$\dfrac{410.0625}{182.25} = 2.25$

Again by looking for the common multiplier we have found a base. Since the initial value when $x = 0$ is 16 we get the model $f(x) = 16(2.25)^x$

c. We really need to use caution when looking at this example since the inputs are not one unit apart. You need to notice that each input is increasing by 5 units. This will change the pattern we find for this model.

Table 4.1.16

t	$h(t)$	base
0	1500	
5	300	$\dfrac{300}{1500} = 0.2$
10	60	$\dfrac{60}{300} = 0.2$
15	12	$\dfrac{12}{60} = 0.2$
20	2.4	$\dfrac{2.4}{12} = 0.2$

Again by looking for the common multiplier we have found a base. Since the initial value when $t = 0$ is 1500 we know the constant. In order to find a pattern it would be helpful to build another table showing the calculations.

Table 4.1.17

t	$h(t)$
0	1500
5	$1500(0.2)$
10	$1500(0.2)^2$
15	$1500(0.2)^3$
20	$1500(0.2)^4$

As you can see the inputs are not the same as the exponents. We need to find a pattern to show how to relate the input values to the changing exponents. You should be able to see that the exponents are the input values divided by 5. With this fact we get the model $h(t) = 1500(0.2)^{t/5}$.

Problem 4

Use the following tables to find exponential models of the given data.

a.

Table 4.1.18

x	$f(x)$
0	10
1	31
2	96.1
3	297.91
4	923.521

b.

Table 4.1.19

x	$f(x)$
0	16
3	14.4
6	12.96
9	11.664
12	10.4976

Solution   See page 239

Section 4.1 Key Points

- Exponential Function: A basic exponential function can be written in the form

$$f(x) = a \cdot b^x$$

where a and b, are real numbers $a \neq 0$, $b > 0$ and $b \neq 1$.

- Base: The constant b is called the base of an exponential function.
- The constant a is the initial value of the function and is the y-intercept of its graph.
- When finding a pattern it is often best to write out the calculations rather than only showing the results.
- Most often the pattern you most need to pay attention to is the relationship between the input values and the exponents.
- Exponential Growth occurs when a quantity is growing at the same percent per unit of time. Exponential growth occurs in a basic exponential function when a is positive and b is greater than 1.
- Exponential Decay occurs when a quantity is declining at the same percent per unit of time. Exponential decay occurs in a basic exponential function when a is positive and b is less than 1.
- Half-life: The time it takes before only half of an initial quantity still remains is called the half-life of that substance.
- Finding a pattern from a given set of data can be done using division of one output value by the previous output value.
- It is important that when looking for a pattern in data your inputs must be equally spaced so that the correct pattern can be found.

Section 4.1 Problem Solutions

Problem 1   Solution

a. Define the variables.

B = The balance on the loan in dollars.

w = weeks after taking out the loan.

Table 4.1.20

w	$B(w)$
0	5000
1	5000(2)
2	$5000(2)^2$
3	$5000(2)^3$

From this table we can see the pattern that gives us the model

$$B(w) = 5000(2)^w$$

b. Keeping the money for 4 weeks can be represented by $w = 4$ and gives us

$$B(4) = 5000(2)^4$$
$$B(4) = 80000$$

Thus if you keep the $5,000 for 4 weeks you will owe this loan shark $80,000.

c. Using the table we get

From the table we can see that after keeping the money for 8 weeks we would owe the loan shark about 1.28 million dollars.

Problem 2   Solution

a. Define the variables.

P = The world population in billions of people.

t = Time in years after 2000.

Table 4.1.21

t	$P(t)$
0	6
50	6(2)
100	$6(2)^2$
150	$6(2)^3$

From this table we can see a pattern start to develop. The relationship between the inputs and the exponents is one that we divide the inputs by 50 in order to get the necessary exponent. This gives us a model of

$$P(t) = 6(2)^{t/50}$$

b. The year 2500 can be represented by $t = 500$ so we get

$$P(500) = 6(2)^{500/50}$$

$$P(500) = 6144$$

This means that if the world population were to grow in ideal circumstances the population in the year 2500 would be 6,144 billion. This seems to be unrealistic and can be considered model breakdown.

c. Graphing the model and $y = 10$ we get

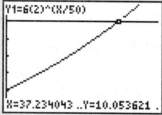

Using trace we find that if this exponential trend continues the world population will reach 10 billion in the year 2037.

Problem 3   Solution

a. Define the variables.

P = The percent of a Thorium-234 sample remaining.

d = Time in days since the sample was taken.

Since we are talking about a percentage of the sample remaining, we must start with 100% at the beginning.

Table 4.1.22

d	$P(d)$
0	100
24.5	$100\left(\dfrac{1}{2}\right)$
49	$100\left(\dfrac{1}{2}\right)^2$
73.5	$100\left(\dfrac{1}{2}\right)^3$

Problem 3   Solution Continued

From this table we can see a pattern start to develop. The relationship between the inputs and the exponents is one that we divide the inputs by 24.5 in order to get the necessary exponent. This gives us a model of

$$P(d) = 100\left(\frac{1}{2}\right)^{d/24.5}$$

b. 180 days can be represented by $d = 180$ so we get

$$P(180) = 100\left(\frac{1}{2}\right)^{180/24.5}$$

$$P(180) = 0.614$$

This means that after 180 days only 0.614% of the Thorium-234 sample will remain.

c. Using the table we get

X	Y1
29	44.023
30	42.795
31	41.601
32	40.441
33	39.313
34	38.216
35	37.15

Y1■100*(1/2)^(X...

Therefore it will take about 32 days for only 40% of the Thorium-234 sample to remain.

Problem 4   Solution

a. Writing out the division so that we can find a base we get.

Table 4.1.23

x	$f(x)$	base
0	10	
1	31	$\frac{31}{10} = 3.1$
2	96.1	$\frac{96.1}{31} = 3.1$
3	297.91	$\frac{297.91}{96.1} = 3.1$
4	923.521	$\frac{923.521}{297.91} = 3.1$

Since the inputs are equally spaced and only one unit apart this pattern is easier to see and results in the model

$$f(x) = 10(3.1)^x$$

Problem 4   Solution Continued

b.   Writing out the division so that we can find a base we get.

Table 4.1.24

x	$f(x)$	base
0	16	
3	14.4	$\dfrac{14.4}{16} = 0.9$
6	12.96	$\dfrac{12.96}{14.4} = 0.9$
9	11.664	$\dfrac{11.664}{12.96} = 0.9$
12	10.4976	$\dfrac{10.4976}{11.664} = 0.9$

The inputs are equally spaced but are 3 units apart so this pattern is harder to see. In order to confirm the pattern and find the relationship between the inputs and the exponents we write out the calculations.

Table 4.1.25

x	$f(x)$
0	16
3	$16(0.9)$
6	$16(0.9)^2$
9	$16(0.9)^3$
12	$16(0.9)^4$

From this table the pattern is easier to see and we get the model
$$f(x) = 16(0.9)^{x/3}$$

4.1 Exercises

1. Under ideal circumstances a certain type of bacteria can double every hour. If a sample of 30 bacteria are allowed to grow in these ideal circumstances answer the following:

   a. Find a model for the number of bacteria after h hours have passed.

   b. Estimate the number of bacteria present after 12 hours.

   c. Estimate the number of bacteria present after 24 hours.

   d. Estimate numerically when the number of bacteria will reach 1 million.

2. Under ideal circumstances a certain type of bacteria can double every 15 minutes. If a sample of 3 bacteria are allowed to grow in ideal circumstances answer the following.

   a. Find a model for the number of bacteria after h hours have passed.

   b. Estimate the number of bacteria present after 5 hours.

   c. Estimate graphically when the number of bacteria will reach 1 million.

3. Under ideal circumstances a certain type of bacteria can double every 15 minutes. If a sample of 5 of these bacteria are allowed to grow in these ideal circumstances answer the following:

   a. Find a model for the number of bacteria after n 15 minute intervals have passed.

   b. Estimate the number of bacteria present after 3 hours.

   c. How do the models you found in exercise 2 and 3 compare?

4. Under ideal circumstances a certain bacteria can triple every 30 minutes. If a sample of 8 of these bacteria are allowed to grow in these ideal circumstances answer the following:

   a. Find a model for the number of bacteria after h hours have passed.

   b. Estimate the number of bacteria present after 3 hours.

5. Under ideal circumstances a certain bacteria can triple every 30 minutes. If a sample of 10 of these bacteria are allowed to grow in these ideal circumstances answer the following:

   a. Find a model for the number of bacteria after n 30 minute intervals have passed.

   b. Estimate the number of bacteria present after 2 hours.

   c. How do the models you found in exercise 4 and 5 compare?

6. The U.S. Census Bureau reported that the number of centenarians, people older than 100, is increasing rapidly. According to the report the number of Hispanic centenarians is doubling about every 7.5 years. In 1990 there were approximately 2072 Hispanic centenarians.
   source: National Institute on Aging Journal June 1999.

   a. If this trend continues find a model that would predict the number of Hispanic centenarians.

   b. Use your model to estimate the number of Hispanic centenarians in 2050.

7. According to the same U.S. Census report discussed in exercise 6 the number of centenarians in general will double every 10 years. In 1990 there were about 37000 centenarians in the U.S..
   source: National Institute on Aging Journal June 1999.

   a. If this trend continues find a model that would predict the number of centenarians.

   b. Use your model to estimate the number of centenarians in 2050.

   c. According to census estimates the number of centenarians in 2050 could be as high as 4.2 million people. How does your estimate compare?

8. In 2000 the population of India broke the 1 billion mark. India's population is thought to be doubling approximately every 33 years. In 1971 India's population was about 560 million people.
   source: CensusIndia.net Census India 2001.

   a. Using this information find a model for the population of India.

   b. Using your model estimate the population of India in 2005.

   c. Estimate graphically when India's population will reach 2 billion.

9. The population of India's Delhi territory has been growing much more rapidly than most other world populations. According to the Census of India the population of the Delhi territory has doubled about every 20 years since 1950.
   source: CensusIndia.net Census India 2001.

   a. Using this information find a model for the population of Delhi, India if in 1950 there were approximately 2.2 million people.

   b. Using your model estimate the population of Delhi, India in 2005.

   c. In 2001 the population of Delhi was about 13.8 million people. How does this compare with your projections for 2005?

10. **Internet Search:** Use the internet to find how long people project it will take the U.S. population to double.

11. Suppose you are given two different options for salary at a temporary job.
Option 1: $2000 each week.
Option 2: You earn 1 penny the first week, 2 pennies the next week, and so on, doubling your salary each week.
The job is going to last for 25 weeks and you want to earn the largest total salary for the 25 weeks.

a. Find the total salary for the 25 weeks if you take Option 1.

b. Before you calculate the total for Option 2 decide which of the two options you would want at this point.

c. Find a model for the salary you will earn in week w of this temporary job under Option 2.

d. Find the total amount of salary you will earn using Option 2. (Note you will need to add up all twenty five weeks salary)

e. Now which salary option would you choose for this job?

f. What option would be best for a 20 week job?

12. Protactinium-234 has a half-life of 269,000 years.
a. Find a model for the percent of a Protactinium-234 sample left after t thousand years.

b. Estimate the percent of Protactinium-234 left after 1 million years.

c. Estimate graphically after how many years will there be only 10% of the sample left.

13. Radon-222 has a half-life of 3.825 days.
a. Find a model for the percent of a Radon-222 sample left after d days.

b. Estimate the percent of Radon-222 left after 30 days.

c. Estimate graphically after how many days will there be only 5% of the Radon-222 sample left.

14. A sample of 300 Polonium-218 atoms is being stored for an experiment that will take place in 2 hours. Polonium-218 has a half life of 3.05 minutes.

a. Find a model for the number of Polonium-218 atoms left after m minutes.

b. Find the number of Polonium-218 atoms remaining at the beginning of the experiment.

c. Estimate numerically when there was 100 Polonium-218 atoms left.

15. Bismuth-210 has a half-life of 5 days.

a. Find a model for the percent of a Bismuth-210 sample left after d days.

b. Estimate the percent of Bismuth-210 left after 15 days.

c. Estimate numerically when there will be only 15% of the Bismuth-210 sample left.

For exercises 16 through 19 use the graphs to answer the questions.

16. Given the graph of $f(x)$

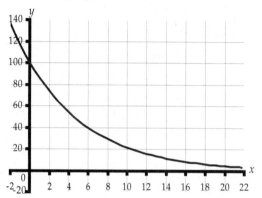

a. Is this an example of exponential growth or exponential decay?

b. Find $f(10)$.

c. Find $f(x) = 40$

d. Estimate the y-intercept.

17. Given the graph of $h(x)$

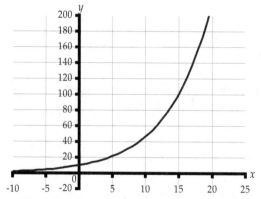

a. Is this an example of exponential growth or exponential decay?

b. Find $h(5)$.

c. Find $h(x) = 100$

d. Estimate the y-intercept.

18. Given the graph of $f(x)$

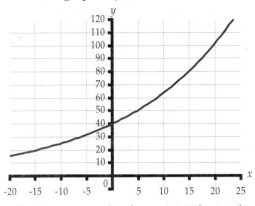

   a. Is this an example of exponential growth or exponential decay?

   b. Find $f(-15)$.

   c. Find $f(x) = 80$

   d. Estimate the vertical intercept.

19. Given the graph of $g(x)$

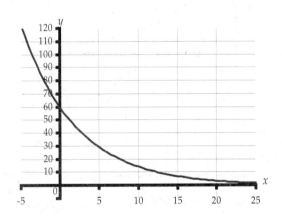

   a. Is this an example of exponential growth or exponential decay?

   b. Find $g(7.5)$.

   c. Find $g(x) = 30$

   d. Estimate the vertical intercept.

For exercises 20 through 26 find exponential models for the given data.

20.

Table 4.1.26

x	$f(x)$
0	25
1	100
2	400
3	1600
4	6400

21.

Table 4.1.27

x	$f(x)$
0	−35
1	−245
2	−1715
3	−12005
4	−84035

22.

Table 4.1.28

x	$f(x)$
0	2000
1	400
2	80
3	16
4	3.2

23.

Table 4.1.29

x	$f(x)$
0	360
1	180
2	90
3	45
4	22.5

24.

Table 4.1.30

x	$f(x)$
0	3
5	12
10	48
15	192
20	768

25.

Table 4.1.31

x	$f(x)$
0	−7
10	−21
20	−63
30	−189
40	−567

26.

Table 4.1.32

x	$f(x)$
2	80
3	320
4	1280
5	5120
6	20480

Section 4.2   Rules for Exponents

• Rules for Exponents • Simplifying Expressions with Exponents • Solving Simple Exponential Equations

In order for us to work with exponential models and problems we need to have a good understanding of the basic rules for exponents and how to use them to solve and simplify problems containing exponents. Many of these rules you already know and have used in previous classes and sections of this textbook. We will use this section as a skill review to prepare us for more applications in the rest of this chapter. In this section we will assume that all variables are not equal to zero. This allows us to ignore the possibility of division by zero which is not defined.

To discuss exponents you need to remember that the basic concept of an exponent is repeated multiplication.

$$2 \cdot 2 \cdot 2 \cdot 2 \cdot 2 \cdot 2 = 2^6 = 64$$

$$xxxxx = x^5$$

$$xxxyy = x^3 y^2$$

$$3 \cdot 3 \cdot 3 \cdot 3 \cdot 7 \cdot 7 \cdot 7 \cdot 7 \cdot 7 \cdot 7 = 3^4 \cdot 7^6 = 81 \cdot 117649 = 9529569$$

As you can see exponents allow us to write a very long expression in a very compact way. When we work with exponents there are two basic parts to an exponential expression, the **base** and the **exponent**. The base is number or variable being raised to a power and the exponent is the power that the base is being raised to. In the expression 5^3, 5 is the base and 3 is the exponent. Using this terminology will help us communicate the rules and properties of exponents.

One of the most common operation we do with exponential expressions is to multiply them together. When we do this any exponential with the same base can be combined into one expression.

$$x^7 x^2 = xxxxxxx \cdot xx = x^9$$

In this example we see that we had 7 x's multiplied by two more x's which gives us a total of 9 x's multiplied together. Therefore we get the final simpler expression of x^9.

Example 1
Simplify the following expressions.

a. $x^5 x^2 x^3$

b. $(3f^4 g^5)(7f^2 g^7)$

c. $(a^2 b^5 c)(a^3 b^4 c^3)$

Solution

a. $x^5 x^2 x^3 = x^{10}$

b. $(3f^4 g^5)(7f^2 g^7) = 21f^6 g^{12}$ When working with the coefficients simply multiply them together.

c. $(a^2 b^5 c)(a^3 b^4 c^3) = a^5 b^9 c^4$

These examples lead us to the **Product Rule for Exponents**.

The Product Rule for Exponents:

$$x^m x^n = x^{m+n}$$

When multiplying exponential expressions that have the same base you add exponents.

$$x^5 x^3 = x^8$$

It is very important with the exponent rules that you notice what operation you are doing to the expression and what operation that this results in for the exponents. Many students will forget that they are working with exponent rules and want to change multiplication into addition.

The next rule is closely related to the Product Rule for Exponents. What should we do with exponents when we are dividing two exponential expressions that have the same base?

$$\frac{x^5}{x^3} = \frac{xxxxx}{xxx} = \frac{xx}{1} = x^2$$

Since multiplication and division are inverse operations we can eliminate any variables that are on both the top and bottom of this fraction. That means that we can cancel 3 x's from the top and bottom leaving us with only 2 x's remaining on the top. When we multiplied exponential expressions with the same base we added exponents; when we divide exponential expressions with the same base we will subtract exponents.

Example 2

Simplify the following expressions.

a. $\dfrac{x^{12}}{x^5}$

b. $\dfrac{a^5 b^3 c^4}{a^3 b^2 c}$

c. $\dfrac{35 m^2 n^4}{7mn}$

Solution

a. $\dfrac{x^{12}}{x^5} = x^7$

b. $\dfrac{a^5 b^3 c^4}{a^3 b^2 c} = a^2 b c^3$

c. $\dfrac{35 m^2 n^4}{7mn} = 5 m n^3$ When working with numbers, reduce the fraction as usual.

These examples lead us to the **Quotient Rule for Exponents**.

The Quotient Rule for Exponents:

$$\frac{x^m}{x^n} = x^{m-n}$$

When dividing exponential expressions that have the same base you subtract exponents.

$$\frac{x^7}{x^3} = x^4$$

The next rule for exponents deals with what to do when an exponential expression is raised to another exponent.

$$(x^3)^2 = (x^3)(x^3) = x^6$$
$$(x^2)^5 = x^2 x^2 x^2 x^2 x^2 = x^{10}$$

Since raising to a power is simply repeated multiplication the **Power Rule for Exponents** follows from the Product Rule for Exponents.

The Power Rule for Exponents:

$$(x^m)^n = x^{mn}$$

When raising an exponential expression to another power you multiply the exponents.

$$(x^4)^7 = x^{28}$$

The rules for **Distributing Exponents** over multiplication or division in an exponential expression are closely related to the Power Rule. When an exponential expression contains more than one variable or a numeric constant that are multiplied or divided the outside power must be distributed to each constant or variable using the Power Rule for Exponents.

Distributing Exponents:

$$(xy)^m = x^m y^m \qquad \left(\frac{x}{y}\right)^m = \frac{x^m}{y^m}$$

When raising an expression to a power that power can distribute over multiplication or division..

$$(xy)^5 = x^5 y^5 \qquad \left(\frac{x}{y}\right)^4 = \frac{x^4}{y^4}$$

Distribution of exponents does **not** work over addition or subtraction

$$(x+y)^2 \neq x^2 + y^2$$
$$(x+y)^2 = x^2 + 2xy + y^2$$

Example 3

Simplify the following expressions.

a. $(w^3)^5$

b. $(a^3b^2c)^3$

c. $(5m^5n^3)^2$

d. $\left(\dfrac{m^2}{n^4}\right)^3$

e. $\left(\dfrac{2xy^2}{3z^5}\right)^4$

Solution

a. $(w^3)^5 = w^{15}$

b. $(a^3b^2c)^3 = (a^3)^3(b^2)^3(c)^3 = a^9b^6c^3$

c. $(5m^5n^3)^2 = (5)^2(m^5)^2(n^3)^2 = 25m^{10}n^6$

d. $\left(\dfrac{m^2}{n^4}\right)^3 = \dfrac{(m^2)^3}{(n^4)^3} = \dfrac{m^6}{n^{12}}$

e. $\left(\dfrac{2xy^2}{3z^5}\right)^4 = \dfrac{(2)^4(x)^4(y^2)^4}{(3)^4(z^5)^4} = \dfrac{16x^4y^8}{81z^{20}}$

Problem 1

Simplify the following expressions. Be sure to follow the order of operations.

a. $(3x^2y^5)(2x^3y)^3$

b. $\dfrac{a^3b^8c}{a^2b^2}$

c. $\dfrac{(2m^2n^3)^4}{10m^5n^{10}}$

d. $\left(\dfrac{m^2n^3}{mn^2}\right)^4\left(\dfrac{m^5}{n^2}\right)$

Solution   See page 257

When using the Quotient Rule for Exponents in some situations you will get negative numbers when you subtract the denominators exponent from the numerators exponent. This leaves us with the need to define how **Negative Exponents** work. To do that lets look at a division problem.

$$\frac{x^3}{x^5} = \frac{xxx}{xxxxx} = \frac{1}{xx} = \frac{1}{x^2} \qquad \text{Using the basic definition of exponents.}$$

$$\frac{x^3}{x^5} = x^{3-5} = x^{-2} \qquad \text{Using the Quotient Rule for Exponents}$$

Since using the basic definition of exponents gives us $\dfrac{1}{x^2}$ and the Quotient Rule for Exponents gives us x^{-2} these two expressions need to be the same for both of these methods to agree and be reliable. Therefore we have that

$$x^{-2} = \frac{1}{x^2}$$

The negative part of the exponent represents a reciprocal of the base. Notice that once you take the reciprocal (flip) the base the exponent becomes positive. The negative exponent only moves the base it does not make that base negative. Remember that a reciprocal of a fraction will flip that fraction over. If an base with a negative exponent is in the denominator of a fraction it will also be a reciprocal and end up in the numerator of the fraction. Answers without negative exponents are usually easier to understand and work with so we will write our answers without them.

Negative Exponents:

$$x^{-1} = \frac{1}{x}$$

When raising a base to a negative exponent you get the reciprocal of that base raised to the absolute value of the exponent.

$$x^{-3} = \frac{1}{x^3} \qquad \left(\frac{1}{2}\right)^{-1} = 2 \qquad \frac{2}{x^{-4}} = 2x^4$$

Example 4

Simplify the following expressions. Write all answers without negative exponents.

a. $x^{-5}y^2$

b. $\dfrac{a^5b}{a^3b^4}$

c. $-2x^{-4}$

d. $\dfrac{21m^3n^{-2}}{7m^{-5}n^3}$

e. $\dfrac{25a^3b^{-7}c^{-2}}{15a^8b^3c^5}$

Solution

a.

$$x^{-5}y^2 = \frac{y^2}{x^5}$$

b.

$\dfrac{a^5b}{a^3b^4}$ First subtract the exponents.

a^2b^{-3} Notice that the result from subtracting exponents is always placed

$\dfrac{a^2}{b^3}$ on top of the fraction and then moved if negative exponents remain. Move any negative exponents to the bottom.

c.

$-2x^{-4} = \dfrac{-2}{x^4}$ The negative exponent moves the x to the bottom.
                    The negative 2 does not move since it is not an exponent.

TI - 83 Details:
Use caution when entering negative numbers into your calculator. Always use the negative key, [(--)] to the left of the [ENTER] key, not the subtraction key.

Also be careful with negative numbers that are being raised to a power. You must use parenthesis in your calculator for it to raise the negative to the power. If you do not use parenthesis the calculator will raise the number to the power and then multiply the result by negative one. This follows the order of operations in a very specific way and may cause errors if you do not use parenthesis.

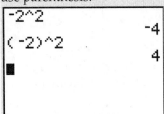

d.

$$\frac{21m^3n^{-2}}{7m^{-5}n^3}$$ First subtract the exponents. Use caution with the negatives.

$3m^8n^{-5}$ Again the results are in the numerator and move to the denominator if they have a negative exponent.

$$\frac{3m^8}{n^5}$$ Move any negative exponents to the bottom.

e.

$$\frac{25a^3b^{-7}c^{-2}}{15a^8b^3c^5}$$

$$\frac{5a^{-5}b^{-10}c^{-7}}{3}$$ Subtract exponents and reduce the constants.

$$\frac{5}{3a^5b^{10}c^7}$$ Move any negative exponents to the bottom.

Concept Investigation 1

a.   Fill in the missing values in the following table.

Table 4.2.1

x	2^x
5	32
4	16
3	
2	
1	
0	
−1	$\frac{1}{2}$
−2	
−3	

b.   When the exponent is reduced by 1 how does the value of the exponential expression change?

c.   What is value of the exponential when the exponent is zero?

d. Create your own table for the exponential expression 5^x. You should include positive, zero and negative values for x.

e. What was the value for 5^0?

f. Pick any base, b, $(b \neq 0)$ you want for an exponential and determine the value of b^0.

g. Make a statement for what you think any base to the power of zero should be.

h. Now make one more table for the an exponential with a base zero. i.e. 0^x.

i. Finally make a statement about the value of any exponential with exponent zero. Check this statement with others in your class or your instructor.

This last statement about exponents equal to zero should lead you to the following property of exponents.

Zero as an Exponent:

$$x^0 = 1 \qquad x \neq 0$$

When raising any exponential expression with a base other than zero to the power of zero the expression will equal 1.

$$25^0 = 1 \qquad (-17.4)^0 = 1$$

$$0^0 \text{ Does Not Exist}$$

The rule for zero as an exponent states that the base must not equal zero. To see why this is necessary look at the following two patterns.

$$4^0 = 1 \qquad 0^4 = 0$$
$$3^0 = 1 \qquad 0^3 = 0$$
$$2^0 = 1 \qquad 0^2 = 0$$
$$1^0 = 1 \qquad 0^1 = 0$$
$$0^0 = 1? \qquad 0^0 = 0?$$

The last line of these two patterns says that 0^0 equals both 1 and 0 which, of course, it can't. This is a conflict and is one demonstration of why 0^0 is undefined.

Example 5

Simplify the following expressions. Write all answer without negative exponents.

a. $(2x^3y^2)^{-2}(3x^{-3}y^6)$

b. $\left(\dfrac{5a^5}{a^3b^4}\right)^{-1}$

c. $\left(\dfrac{18m^2n^{-2}}{9m^{-4}n^5}\right)^{-3}$

Solution

a.

$$(2x^3y^2)^{-2}(3x^{-3}y^6)$$

$(2^{-2}x^{-6}y^{-4})(3x^{-3}y^6)$ Distribute the outside exponents.

$\left(\dfrac{1}{4}x^{-6}y^{-4}\right)(3x^{-3}y^6)$ Take the reciprocal of any numbers with negative exponents.

$\dfrac{3}{4}x^{-9}y^2$ Add exponents when you multiply.

$\dfrac{3y^2}{4x^9}$ Take the reciprocal of any variables with negative exponents.

b.

$$\left(\dfrac{5a^5}{a^3b^4}\right)^{-1}$$

$\dfrac{5^{-1}a^{-5}}{a^{-3}b^{-4}}$ Distribute the outside exponent.

$5^{-1}a^{-2}b^{-4}$ Subtract exponents when you divide.

$\dfrac{1}{5a^2b^4}$ Take the reciprocal of any bases with negative exponents.

c.

$$\left(\dfrac{18m^2n^{-2}}{9m^{-4}n^5}\right)^{-3}$$

$(2m^6n^{-7})^{-3}$ Simplify the inside of the parentheses.

$2^{-3}m^{-18}n^{21}$ Distribute the outside exponent.

$\dfrac{n^{21}}{2^3m^{18}}$ Take the reciprocal of any bases with negative exponents.

$\dfrac{n^{21}}{8m^{18}}$ Multiply out the constant.

Problem 2

Simplify the following expressions. Write all answer without negative exponents.

a. $(5x^2y^{-3})^{-3}(7x^5y^{-4})^2$

b. $\left(\dfrac{3g^4h^{-5}}{6g^{-2}h^5}\right)^3$

c. $\left(\dfrac{4}{3}a^3b^7c\right)^0$

Solution   See page 257

Some simple exponential equations can be solved by inspection or trial and error. Others will require us to use some of the rules for exponents from this section. One property that is very helpful is that if two exponential expressions have the same base and are equal to one another than the exponents must also be equal.

$$3^x = 9 \qquad \text{If possible make the bases the same.}$$

$$3^x = 3^2 \qquad \text{Since the bases are the same the}$$
$$x = 2 \qquad \text{exponents themselves must be equal.}$$

Example 6

Solve the following exponential problems by inspection or trial and error.

a. $2^x = 16$

b. $5(3^t) = 45$

c. $\dfrac{1}{1000} = 10^t$

Solution

a.

$$2^x = 16 \qquad \text{Write 16 as a power of 2.}$$
$$2^x = 2^4 \qquad \text{Since the bases are the same the exponents must be equal.}$$
$$x = 4$$
$$2^4 = 16 \qquad \text{Check your solution.}$$
$$16 = 16$$

b.

$$5(3^t) = 45$$
$$\dfrac{5(3^t)}{5} = \dfrac{45}{5} \quad \text{First isolate the exponential part by dividing by 5.}$$
$$3^t = 9$$
$$3^t = 3^2 \quad \text{Write both sides using the same base.}$$
$$t = 2 \quad \text{Since the bases are the same the exponents must be equal.}$$
$$5(3^2) = 45 \quad \text{Check your solution.}$$
$$5(9) = 45$$
$$45 = 45$$

c.

$$\frac{1}{1000} = 10^t$$ Write both sides using the same base.

$$10^{-3} = 10^t$$ You will need negative exponents in order to get the reciprocal.

$$-3 = t$$

$$\frac{1}{1000} = 10^{-3}$$ Check your solution.

$$\frac{1}{1000} = \frac{1}{1000}$$

Problem 3

Solve the following exponential problems by inspection or trial and error.

a. $-2(5^x) - 74 = -324$

b. $10^x = 100000$

c. $2^x = \frac{1}{4}$

Solution   See page 258

All of the problems we have worked on so far have had integer exponents. There are often fraction exponents used in exponential problems so we will need to know how to work with them. For this chapter we will learn the basic meaning of a rational exponent and use them to do some solving.

A rational exponent is another way of writing a radical such as a square root or cube root.

$$\sqrt{25} = 25^{1/2} = 5 \qquad \sqrt[3]{27} = 27^{1/3} = 3$$

The rational exponent $\frac{1}{2}$ represents a square root where the rational exponent $\frac{1}{3}$ represents a cube root and so on.

Rational Exponents:

$$x^{1/n} = \sqrt[n]{x}$$

Raising a base to a rational exponent with a denominator of n is the same as taking the nth root of the base.

$$8^{1/3} = \sqrt[3]{8} = 2$$

If x is negative n must be odd. If x is positive n can be any whole number greater than or equal to 2.

In this chapter we will use this fact to rewrite some radical expressions into exponent form.

Example 7

Rewrite the following exponents in radical form.

a. $x^{1/5}$

b. $w^{2/3}$

c. $t^{3/7}$

Solution

a. $\sqrt[5]{x}$

b. The denominator of the exponent becomes the radicals index and the numerator stays as the exponent of the variable. Therefore we get

$\sqrt[3]{w^2}$ or $(\sqrt[3]{w})^2$

c. $\sqrt[7]{t^3}$ or $(\sqrt[7]{t})^3$

Example 8

Rewrite the following radicals using rational exponents.

a. $\sqrt{5x}$

b. $\sqrt[3]{w^2}$

c. $(\sqrt[5]{t})^3$

Solution

a. $(5x)^{1/2}$

b. $w^{2/3}$

c. $t^{3/5}$

We will use rational exponents to solve problems that have variables raised to different exponents. Raising both sides of an equation to the reciprocal exponent will help us to eliminate exponents of variables we are trying to solve for.

Example 9

Solve the following equations.

a. $78125 = x^7$

b. $150m^4 = 22509.375$

c. $3t^5 - 17 = 3055$

Solution

a.

$$78125 = x^7 \qquad \text{You need to undo an exponent of 7.}$$
$$(78125)^{1/7} = (x^7)^{1/7} \text{ Raise both sides of the equation to the reciprocal of 7.}$$
$$5 = x$$
$$78125 = 5^7 \qquad \text{Check your solution.}$$
$$78125 = 78125$$

b.

$$150m^4 = 22509.375$$

$$\frac{150m^4}{150} = \frac{22509.375}{150} \qquad \text{Isolate the variable part by dividing by 150.}$$

$$m^4 = 150.0625$$

$$(m^4)^{1/4} = (150.0625)^{1/4} \qquad \begin{array}{l}\text{Raise both sides of the equation to the reciprocal} \\ \text{exponent. Since this is an even root we need the}\end{array}$$

$$m = \pm 3.5 \qquad \text{plus and minus to represent both possible answers.}$$

$$150(3.5)^4 = 22509.375 \qquad \text{Check your solutions.}$$

$$22509.375 = 22509.375$$

$$150(-3.5)^4 = 22509.375$$

$$22509.375 = 22509.375$$

c.

$$3t^5 - 17 = 3055$$

$$3t^5 = 3072 \qquad \text{Isolate the variable part.}$$

$$t^5 = 1024$$

$$(t^5)^{1/5} = (1024)^{1/5} \qquad \begin{array}{l}\text{Raise both sides of the equation to the reciprocal} \\ \text{exponent.}\end{array}$$

$$t = 4$$

$$3(4)^5 - 17 = 3055 \qquad \text{Check your solution.}$$

$$3055 = 3055$$

Problem 4

Solve the following equations.

a. $\quad -6x^9 + 148500 = 30402$

b. $\quad 2m^5 - 61 = 847.70848$

Solution   See page 258

Section 4.2 Key Points

- The Product Rule for Exponents:

$$x^m x^n = x^{m+n}$$

When multiplying exponential expressions that have the same base you add exponents.

- The Quotient Rule for Exponents:

$$\frac{x^m}{x^n} = x^{m-n}$$

When dividing exponential expressions that have the same base you subtract exponents.

- The Power Rule for Exponents:

$$(x^m)^n = x^{mn}$$

When raising an exponential expression to another power you multiply the exponents.

- Distributing Exponents:

$$(xy)^m = x^m y^m \qquad \left(\frac{x}{y}\right)^m = \frac{x^m}{y^m}$$

When raising an expression to a power that power can distribute over multiplication or division. Distribution of exponents does not work over addition or subtraction.

- Negative Exponents:

$$x^{-1} = \frac{1}{x} \qquad x^{-n} = \frac{1}{x^n}$$

When raising a base to a negative exponent you get the reciprocal of that base raised to the absolute value of the exponent.

- Zero as an Exponent:

$$x^0 = 1 \qquad \text{if} \qquad x \neq 0$$

When raising any exponential expression with a base other than zero to the power of zero the expression will equal 1.

- Rational Exponents:

$$x^{1/n} = \sqrt[n]{x}$$

Raising a base to a rational exponent with a denominator of n is the same as taking the nth root of the base.

- Simplifying Expressions with Exponents:
When simplifying expressions that contain exponents be sure to perform any indicated operations such as multiplication or division, combining any exponents of the same base, and eliminate any negative exponents that are left in the result.

Section 4.2 Problem Solutions

Problem 1   *Solution*

a.

$(3x^2y^5)(2x^3y)^3$

$(3x^2y^5)(8x^9y^3)$

$24x^{11}y^8$

b.

$\dfrac{a^3b^8c}{a^2b^2}$

ab^6c

c.

$\dfrac{(2m^2n^3)^4}{10m^5n^{10}}$

$\dfrac{16m^8n^{12}}{10m^5n^{10}}$

$\dfrac{8m^3n^2}{5}$

d.

$\left(\dfrac{m^2n^3}{mn^2}\right)^4\left(\dfrac{m^5}{n^2}\right)$

$(mn)^4\left(\dfrac{m^5}{n^2}\right)$

$m^4n^4\left(\dfrac{m^5}{n^2}\right)$

m^9n^2

Problem 2   *Solution*

a.

$(5x^2y^{-3})^{-3}(7x^5y^{-4})^2$

$(5^{-3}x^{-6}y^9)(7^2x^{10}y^{-8})$

$\left(\dfrac{1}{125}x^{-6}y^9\right)(49x^{10}y^{-8})$

$\dfrac{49}{125}x^4y$

$\dfrac{49x^4y}{125}$

b.

$\left(\dfrac{3g^4h^{-5}}{6g^{-2}h^5}\right)^3$

$\left(\dfrac{1}{2}g^6h^{-10}\right)^3$

$\dfrac{g^{18}}{8h^{30}}$

c.

$\left(\dfrac{4}{3}a^3b^7c\right)^0 = 1$ Remember the variables cannot equal zero.

Problem 3   Solution

a.

$$-2(5^x) - 74 = -324$$

$$-2(5^x) = -250$$ Isolate the exponential part.

$$5^x = 125$$

$$5^x = 5^3$$ Write both sides using the same base.

$$x = 3$$

$$-2(5^3) - 74 = -324$$ Check your solution.

$$-324 = -324$$

b.

$$10^x = 100000$$

$$10^x = 10^5$$ Write both sides using the same base.

$$x = 5$$

$$10^5 = 100000$$ Check your solution.

$$100000 = 100000$$

c.

$$2^x = \frac{1}{4}$$

$$2^x = 2^{-2}$$ Write both sides using the same base.
Remember that a negative exponent gives you
$$x = -2$$ a reciprocal.

$$2^{-2} = \frac{1}{4}$$ Check your solution.

$$\frac{1}{4} = \frac{1}{4}$$

Problem 4   Solution

a.

$$-6x^9 + 148500 = 30402$$

$$-6x^9 = -118098$$ Isolate the term with the exponent.

$$x^9 = 19683$$

$$(x^9)^{1/9} = (19683)^{1/9}$$ Raise both sides to the reciprocal exponent.

$$x = 3$$

$$-6(3)^9 + 148500 = 30402$$ Check your solution.

$$30402 = 30402$$

b.

$$2m^5 - 61 = 847.70848$$ Isolate the term with the exponent.

$$2m^5 = 908.70848$$

$$m^5 = 454.35424$$

$$(m^5)^{1/5} = (454.35424)^{1/5}$$ Raise both sides to the reciprocal exponent.

$$m = 3.4$$

$$2(3.4)^5 - 61 = 847.70848$$ Check your solution.

$$847.70848 = 847.70848$$

4.2 Exercises

Math
Tutorial

More practice problems like exercises 1 through 29 can be found in section 4.2 of the CD Tutorial.

For Exercises 1 through 29 simplify the given expression using the order of operations and exponent rules. Write each answer without negative exponents.

1. $2^5 + 3^4$

2. $2^4(2^5)$

3. $w^2 w^5 w^3$

4. $15g^3 g^7$

5. $\dfrac{7^{23}}{7^{20}}$

6. $\dfrac{z^{12}}{z^8}$

7. $3^{15}(3^{-12})$

8. $s^5(s^{-3})$

9. $\dfrac{3}{b^{-2}}$

10. $\dfrac{5c^{-3}}{d^{-2}}$

11. $\dfrac{x^{-3}y^2}{3x^5 y^{-7}}$

12. $\dfrac{(7x^2 y)^{10}}{(7x^2 y)^8}$

13. $\dfrac{200a^5 bc^3}{25a^2 bc}$

14. $3x^2 y(5x^4 y^3)$

15. $5w^3 z(2w^2 z^3)^4$

16. $\dfrac{(x+9y)^7}{(x+9y)^5}$

17. $(2x^2 y^3)^{-2}$

18. $\left(\dfrac{5w^3 v^7 x^{-4}}{17wx^3}\right)^0$

19. $\left(\dfrac{3}{5}\right)^{-2}$

20. $\left(\dfrac{2}{3}a^3 b^7 c\right)^4$

21. $\left(\dfrac{2x^3 y^{-4}}{5xy^5}\right)\left(\dfrac{15xy^2}{7x^5 y^{-3}}\right)$

22. $\left(\dfrac{2g^{-2}h^{-3}}{5gh^{-6}}\right)^2$

23. $\left(\dfrac{3c^5 d^2}{5c^3 d^2}\right)^{-2}$

24. $(2x^3 y^{-4})^{-3}(3x^2 y^{-6})^2$

25. $\left(\dfrac{1}{5}a^{-2}b^3 c\right)^{-2}\left(\dfrac{2}{3}a^4 b^{-6}c\right)^{-1}$

26. $(8x^3 y^9)^{\frac{1}{3}}$

27. $\left(\dfrac{16m^3 n^6 p}{mn^{-2}p^3}\right)^{\frac{1}{2}}$

28. $(100ab^3 c^2)^{-\frac{1}{2}}(a^6 b^{-2})^{\frac{1}{4}}$

29. $(5x^2 y^7 z)^{\frac{3}{2}}(5x^2 y^7 z)^{\frac{7}{2}}$

Math
Tutorial

More practice problems like exercises 30 through 60 can be found in section 4.2 of the CD Tutorial.

30. Rewrite the following radicals using exponents..
   a. $\sqrt{x}$
   b. $\sqrt[3]{k}$
   c. $\sqrt[5]{m}$

31. Rewrite the following radicals using exponents
   a. $\sqrt{c^3}$
   b. $(\sqrt[3]{t})^2$
   c. $\sqrt[4]{m^3}$

32. Rewrite the following radicals using exponents
   a. $\sqrt{5xy}$
   b. $\sqrt[3]{2x^2 y}$
   c. $\sqrt[7]{4m^3 n^6 p^2}$

33. Rewrite the following exponents in radical form.
   a. $r^{\frac{1}{3}}$
   b. $x^{\frac{1}{2}}$
   c. $n^{\frac{2}{3}}$

34.   Rewrite the following exponents in radical form.

a. $x^{\frac{1}{3}}y^{\frac{1}{3}}$

b. $(mn)^{\frac{1}{5}}$

35.   Rewrite the following exponents in radical form.

a. $r^{\frac{1}{5}}s^{\frac{2}{5}}$

b. $(xy^3z)^{\frac{1}{2}}$

c. $n^{\frac{2}{3}}m^{\frac{1}{3}}p^{\frac{2}{3}}$

For Exercises 36 through 51 solve the following exponential equations using inspection or trial and error.

36. $2^x = 8$ **37.** $5^c = 625$

38. $\dfrac{1}{9} = 3^t$ **39.** $(-2)^d = -32$

40. $\left(\dfrac{1}{2}\right)^x = \dfrac{1}{16}$ **41.** $\left(\dfrac{1}{2}\right)^t = 16$

42. $10^x = 1000$ **43.** $10^c = 10000000$

44. $3^x = 1$ **45.** $(-5)^m = 1$

46. $5(2^x) = 40$ **47.** $3^c + 5 = 32$

48. $-4(5^m) - 9 = -109$ **49.** $(7^t) + 8 = 57$

50. $3(6^x) + 2(6^x) = 180$ **51.** $5(3^x) - 4(3^x) = 81$

For exercises 52through 60 solve the equations.

52. $x^5 = 32$

53. $12w^4 = 7500$

54. $-2.5m^7 = 320$

55. $3x^5 + 94 = 190$

56. $6t^8 + 18 = 393234$

57. $45 - 3.5g^5 = -67$

58. $14 - 7.8x^5 = 1836.5$

59. $\dfrac{4x^3 + 5}{8} = 63.125$

60. $\dfrac{2.4x^6 - 19}{1000} = 282.3386$

Section 4.3   Finding Exponential Models

• **Recognizing Graphs** • **Finding Exponential Models** • **Domain and Range**

In this section we will use the concept of an exponential function and the rules for exponents that we reviewed in the last section to develop a method for finding an exponential model. It is crucial that you can recognize the graph of an exponential model since we always start with a scattergram of data and choose a model from there. With this in mind lets look at a few exponential graphs and describe their basic characteristics.

Recall this definition of a basic exponential function from section 4.1.

Exponential Function: A basic exponential function can be written in the form

$$f(x) = a \cdot b^x$$

where a and b, are real numbers $a \neq 0$, $b > 0$ and $b \neq 1$.

Base: The constant b is called the base of an exponential function.

Concept Investigation 1

Consider the standard form of an exponential function $f(x) = a \cdot b^x$. We are going to investigate one part of this function at a time. For each section of this investigation consider how the graph changes as you change one of the constants in the function.

a.   Graph the following exponential functions on the same calculator window. (use the window Xmin = -7, Xmax = 7, Ymin = -10, and Ymax = 100. Remember to turn statplots off.)

i $f(x) = 2^x$

ii $f(x) = 3^x$

iii $f(x) = 5^x$

iv $f(x) = 10^x$

v $f(x) = 22.5^x$

Describe the basic shape that all of these graphs have.

In these examples we are considering the shape of the graph of a basic exponential function when the value of the base b is greater than 1. In your own words describe how increasing the value of b affects the graph?

b. Graph the following exponential functions on the same calculator window. (use the window Xmin = -7, Xmax = 7, Ymin = -10, and Ymax = 100.)

    i $f(x) = \left(\dfrac{1}{2}\right)^x$

    ii $f(x) = \left(\dfrac{1}{3}\right)^x$

    iii $f(x) = \left(\dfrac{1}{5}\right)^x$

    iv $f(x) = (0.1)^x$

    v $f(x) = (0.025)^x$

In these functions we are considering how a $b < 1$ changes the graph of a basic exponential function. Recall that the base of an exponential function must be positive and cannot equal 1. In your own words what does a value of b less than 1 do to the graph?

c. Graph the following exponential functions on the same calculator window. (use the window Xmin = -7, Xmax = 7, Ymin = -10, and Ymax = 100.)

    i $f(x) = (2)^x$

    ii $f(x) = 5(2)^x$

    iii $f(x) = 10(2)^x$

In these functions we are considering how a positive a value changes the graph of a basic exponential function. In your own words what does a positive a value do to the graph?

d. Graph the following exponential functions on the same calculator window. (use the window Xmin = -7, Xmax = 7, Ymin = -100, and Ymax = 10.)

    i $f(x) = -1(2)^x$

    ii $f(x) = -5(2)^x$

    iii $f(x) = -10(2)^x$

In these functions we are considering how a negative a value changes the graph of a basic exponential function. In your own words what does a negative a value do to the graph?

Using all of the information from this concept investigation should allow us to sketch a graph of a basic exponential function and adjust any models that we are making. You should note that the graph of an exponential of the form $y = ab^x$ never crosses the horizontal axis. The graph does get as close as possible to the horizontal axis but does not touch it. This is because an exponential function of this form can never equal zero. This makes the horizontal axis a **horizontal asymptote** for this graph. A horizontal asymptote is any line that a graph gets very close to but does not touch. Other functions we will study may have horizontal asymptotes along with vertical asymptotes.

Example 1

Sketch the graph of the following functions. Discuss any information you know from the values of a and b.

a. $f(x) = 5(3)^x$

b. $g(t) = 255\left(\dfrac{2}{3}\right)^t$

c. $h(x) = -3(5)^x$

d. $W(m) = -50(0.2)^m$

Solution

a. $a = 5$ so the vertical intercept is $(0, 5)$ and the graph will be above the horizontal axis. The base $b = 3$ so this graph is increasing, showing exponential growth. By trying a few input values we get the points $(1, 15)$, $(2, 45)$, and $(3, 135)$ using these points to plot the graph we get the graph

Graphic 4.3.1

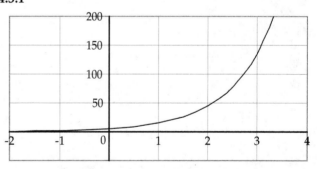

b. $a = 255$ so the vertical intercept is $(0, 255)$ and the graph will be above the horizontal axis. The base $b = \dfrac{2}{3}$ so this graph is decreasing, showing exponential decay. By trying a few input values we get the points $(-2, 573.75)$, $(1, 170)$, and $(2, 113.33)$ using these points we get.

Graphic 4.3.2

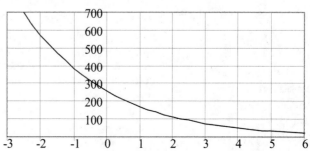

Concept Connection:
Exponential functions like the linear and quadratic functions we have already studied have a pretty standard domain and range when they are not in some real world context.

Consider the basic graph of an exponential function
Graphic 4.3.5

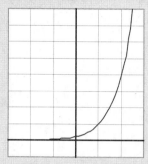

In this graph and the other graphs you see in the examples you should notice that the function is valid for all input values but does not hit all outputs. A basic exponential function cannot equal zero so that cannot be part of the range for the function.

The horizontal axis is a horizontal asymptote.

In general the domain of an exponential function that has no context will be All Real Numbers or $(-\infty, \infty)$. The range for an exponential function will either be all positive or all negative Real Numbers $(-\infty, 0)$ or $(0, \infty)$.

The range will be positive whenever the value of a is positive and negative when the value of a is negative.

Remember that domain and range in a context should take into consideration possible model breakdown in the situation. This will limit the domain and range for most models we find.

c. $a = -3$ so the vertical intercept is $(0, -3)$ and the graph will be below the horizontal axis. The base $b = 5$ so this graph should show exponential growth but it has been flipped under the horizontal axis by the negative a value. By trying a few input values we get the points $(-1, -0.6)$, $(1, -15)$, and $(2, -75)$ using these points we get.
Graphic 4.3.3

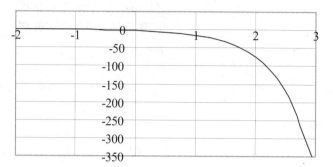

d. $a = -50$ so the vertical intercept is $(0, -50)$ and the graph will be below the horizontal axis. The base $b = 0.2$ so this graph should show exponential decay but it has also been flipped under the horizontal axis by the negative a value. By trying a few input values we get the points $(-1, -250)$, $(1, -10)$, and $(2, -2)$ using these points we get.
Graphic 4.3.4

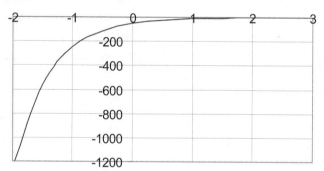

Problem 1

Sketch the graph of the following functions. Discuss any information you know from the values of a and b.

a. $f(x) = -2(2.5)^x$

b. $g(t) = 300(0.5)^t$

Solution   See page 270

When working with exponential models in real world applications the domain and range will again depend on the situation and require us to avoid model breakdown. Since exponential functions grow or decay very quickly the domain will usually be very restricted to values close to the original data. In a context always try and expand the domain beyond the data but be cautious of output values that get to extreme for the context of the problem. The range for an exponential model must come from the domain and since the endpoints of the graph will always be its lowest and highest values the range should always come from the endpoints of the domain just as they did for lines. Remember always be sure to write the domain lowest to highest.

Example 2

The average weekly hits (visits) to the U. S. Small Business Administration web site starting in 1994 are given in **Table 4.3.1**

Table 4.3.1

Year	Average Weekly Hits (in millions)
1994	0.1
1995	0.2
1996	0.5
1997	1.1
1998	2.2
1999	4.6
2000	8.1

source: Data estimated from information found at www.sba.gov

a.   Find a model for this data.

b.   Estimate the average number of weekly hits the SBA web site had in 2001.

c.   What would a reasonable domain and range be for this model?

Solution

a.   Modeling this data will be similar to other models we have done.

Step 1 Define the variables.

H = The average weekly hits in millions for the SBA web site.

t = Time in years since 1990.

Step 2 Adjust the data.

Table 4.3.2

t	H
4	0.1
5	0.2
6	0.5
7	1.1
8	2.2
9	4.6
10	8.1

Step 3 Create a Scattergram.

Graphic 4.3.6

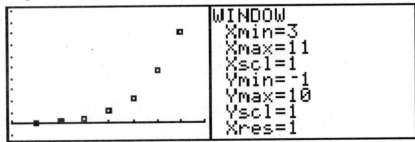

Step 4 Select a model.

As you can see this data is curved up much like a quadratic but seems to be flatter on the left hand side of the data than a quadratic should be. A quadratic model would go up to the left of a vertex and therefore would not be a good choice here. Because of this shape and type of growth we should choose an exponential model.

Step 5 Pick two points.

We can pick the first and next to last points from this data because they appear to fall along the exponential path

$$(4, 0.1) \qquad (9, 4.6)$$

Step 6 Write two equations and solve for b..

$$(4, 0.1) \qquad (9, 4.6)$$

Use the two points to write two equations in standard form.

$$0.1 = a \cdot b^4 \qquad 4.6 = a \cdot b^9$$

$$\frac{4.6}{0.1} = \frac{a \cdot b^9}{a \cdot b^4}$$

Divide the two equations and solve for b.

$$46 = b^5$$

$$(46)^{1/5} = (b^5)^{1/5}$$

Use the Power Rule for Exponents to isolate b.

$$2.15056 = b$$

Step 7 Use b and one equation to find a.

$$0.1 = a(2.15)^4$$

Substitute b into one equation and solve for a.

$$0.1 = 21.3675a$$

$$\frac{0.1}{21.3675} = \frac{21.3675a}{21.3675}$$

$$0.00468 = a$$

Step 8 Write the model.

$$H(t) = 0.00468(2.15)^t$$

Step 9 Check your model for a good fit.

Graphic 4.3.7

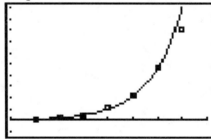

This model fits the data pretty well. It follows the flat pattern on the left side and then grows along with the data as you go to the right.

b. 2001 is represented by $t = 11$ so we can substitute 11 into the model and get

$$H(11) = 0.00468(2.15)^{11}$$

$$H(11) = 21.2$$

Therefore the SBA web site had approximately 21.2 weekly hits in 2001.

c. In this case the web site data probably would be low before 1994 and continue to grow for some time after 2000 so a reasonable domain would probably be $[3, 12]$. In this case the lowest point is on the left endpoint of $t = 3$ and the highest point is on the right endpoint at $t = 12$. Substituting in these values for t gives us a range of $[0.05, 45.7]$. Because this data is growing fairly fast it will most likely not be able to sustain that kind of growth for long. The 45.7 million hits we get for 2002 seems a bit high and perhaps is model breakdown. We should restrict the domain to $[3, 11]$ and that will result in a range of $[0.05, 21.2]$. This range seems more reasonable and we should be satisfied.

With this last example you can see the steps to modeling exponential data. This is one method you can use to model an exponential when you do not have a vertical intercept to take from the data. When you have a vertical intercept to take from the data the modeling process can be shortened. This will be covered in example 3.

Modeling Steps (with no given vertical intercept):
1.   Define the variables. (be sure to use units)
2.   Adjust the data. (if needed)
3.   Create a scattergram. (on calculator)
4.   Select a model type. (we now have linear, quadratic, and exponential)
5.   Pick two points.
6.   Write two equations and solve for b.
7.   Use b and one equation to find a.
8.   Write the model.
9.   Check your model by graphing it on the calculator.

Problem 2

Find a model for the data given in **Table 4.3.3**

Table 4.3.3

x	$f(x)$
2	4.8
3	7.0
5	14.7
6	21.4
8	44.9
10	94.5
12	198.7

Solution   See page 271

Example 3

The invasion of certain weeds can be a devastating problem for an agriculture area. The number of whippleweed plants found on a certain acre of land during a four year period are given in **Table 4.3.4**

Table 4.3.4

Years	Number of Plants
0	1
0.5	3
1	12
1.5	41
2	143
2.5	493
3	1702

a.   Find a model for this data.

b.   Estimate the number of whippleweed plants after 4 years.

c.   Give a reasonable domain and range for this model.

Solution

a.

Step 1 Define the variables.
        P = The number of whippleweed plants on this acre.
        t = The years since the start of the invasion.

Step 2 Adjust the data.

This step is not needed since the data is already reasonable.

Step 3 Create a scattergram.

Graphic 4.3.8

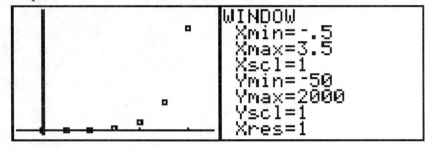

Step 4 Select a model.

This data is again flat on the left side and rises quickly to the right so it seems to be exponential.

Step 5 Pick the vertical intercept and one other point.

The vertical intercept is given as $(0, 1)$ and another point could be the last one at $(3, 1702)$. If you choose two points too close together you may not get a reasonable value for b. In this case one of the last few points in the data should work well.

Step 6 Substitute the vertical intercept into a and use the other point to find b.

$$P = 1 \cdot b^t \qquad \text{Substitute the vertical intercept into } a.$$
$$1702 = b^3 \qquad \text{Substitute the other point in for } P \text{ and } t.$$
$$(1702)^{1/3} = (b^3)^{1/3} \qquad \text{Solve for } b \text{ using the Power Rule for Exponents.}$$
$$11.94 = b$$

Step 7 Write the model.

$$P(t) = 11.94^t$$

Step 8 Check your model for a good fit.

Graphic 4.3.9

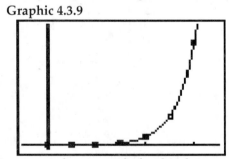

This seems to be a great fit for this data.

b. The fourth year can be represented as $t = 4$ so we get

$$P(4) = 11.94^4$$
$$P(4) = 20324$$

This means that in year 4 there were approximately 20,324 whippleweed plants on the acre of land.

c. It makes sense to start our domain at $t = 0$ since that is the start of the invasion. Since the amount of land and water available to the weeds is limited we should not extend the domain much beyond the data. The answer for part b seems like a possible limit to this situation so we will set the end of the domain to be $t = 4$. Thus for the domain of $[0, 4]$ we get a range of $[1, 20324]$.

Example 3 shows you the second option for finding an exponential model. This method is easier because you already have a value for a in the given vertical intercept so you only need to use one equation to help you find b.

Modeling Steps (with a given vertical intercept):
1. Define the variables. (be sure to use units)
2. Adjust the data. (if needed)
3. Create a scattergram. (on calculator)
4. Select a model type (we now have linear, quadratic, and exponential).
5. Pick the vertical intercept and one other point.
6. Substitute the vertical intercept into a and use the other point to find b.
7. Write the model.
8. Check your model by graphing it on the calculator.

Problem 3
Find a model for the data given in **Table 4.3.5**

Table 4.3.5

x	$f(x)$
0	145
3	74.2
5	47.5
8	24.3
10	14.6
14	6.4
15	5.1

Solution   See page 272

Section 4.3 Key Points

•   An Exponential Function can be written in the form
$$f(x) = a \cdot b^x$$
where a and b, are real numbers $a \neq 0$, $b > 0$ and $b \neq 1$.

•   The constant a controls several parts of the graph of an exponential.
    It represents the vertical intercept.
    A positive a value will result in the function being above the horizontal axis.
    A negative a value will result in the function being below the horizontal axis.

• b is the base of the exponential function and also affects the graph in several ways.
    When $b > 1$ the function will display exponential growth. $(a > 0)$
    When $0 < b < 1$ the function will display exponential decay. $(a > 0)$

•   Modeling Steps For Exponentials (without a given vertical intercept.):
    Step 1. Define the variables.
    Step 2   Adjust the data.
    Step 3   Create a scattergram.
    Step 4   Select a model type.
    Step 5   Pick two points.
    Step 6   Write two equations and solve for b.
    Step 7   Use b and one equation to find a.
    Step 8   Write the model.
    Step 9   Check your model by graphing it on the calculator.

Section 4.3 Key Points (continued)

- When deciding on a domain and range for a model use caution expanding from the data since exponentials grow so quickly your domain will often stay very close to the given data.

- The domain of an exponential function with no context will be All Real Numbers.

- The range of an exponential function with no context will be the positive or negative Real Numbers depending on the sign of a.

- Modeling Steps For Exponentials (with a given vertical intercept.):
  Step 1. Define the variables.
  Step 2   Adjust the data.
  Step 3   Create a scattergram.
  Step 4   Select a model type.
  Step 5   Pick the vertical intercept and one other point.
  Step 6   Substitute the vertical intercept into a and use the other point to find b.
  Step 7   Write the model.
  Step 8   Check your model by graphing it on the calculator.

Section 4.3 Problem Solutions

Problem 1   Solution

a. $f(x) = -2(2.5)^x$

  $a = -2$ so the vertical intercept is $(0, -2)$ and the graph will be below the horizontal axis. $b = 2.5$ so this graph should show exponential growth but it has been flipped under the horizontal axis by the negative a value. By trying a few input values we get the points $(-1, -0.8)$, $(2, -12.5)$, and $(4, -78.13)$ using these points we get

Graphic 4.3.10.

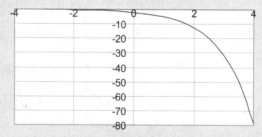

b. $g(t) = 300(0.5)^t$

  $a = 300$ so the vertical intercept is $(0, 300)$ and the graph will be above the horizontal axis. $b = 0.5$ so this graph will show exponential decay. By trying a few input values we get the points $(-1, 600)$, $(1, 150)$, and $(3, 37.5)$ using these points we get

Graphic 4.3.11.

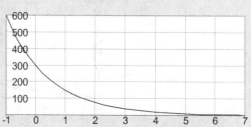

Problem 2   Solution

a. This data is not in a context so we can go right to step 3 creating a scattergram.

    Step 3 Create a scattergram

Graphic 4.3.12.

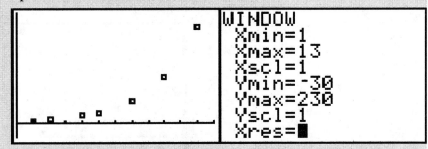

Step 4 Select a model type.

Since this graph is flat on the left side and rises quickly to the right an exponential model is appropriate.

Step 5 Pick two points.

We can choose the first and next to last points since they seem to fall on a smooth curve. $(2, 4.8)$ and $(10, 94.5)$.

Step 6 Write two equations and solve for b.

$$(2, 4.8) \quad\quad (10, 94.5)$$

$$4.8 = a \cdot b^2 \quad\quad 94.5 = a \cdot b^{10}$$

Use the two points to write two equations in standard form.

$$\frac{94.5}{4.8} = \frac{a \cdot b^{10}}{a \cdot b^2}$$

Divide the two equations and solve for b.

$$19.6875 = b^8$$

$$(19.6875)^{1/8} = (b^8)^{1/8}$$

Use the Power Rule for Exponents to get b by itself.

$$1.45 = b$$

Step 7 Use b and one equation to find a.

$$4.8 = a(1.45)^2$$

Substitute b into one equation and solve for a.

$$4.8 = 2.1025a$$

$$\frac{4.8}{2.1025} = \frac{2.1025a}{2.1025}$$

$$2.28 = a$$

Step 8 Write the model.

$$f(x) = 2.28(1.45)^x$$

Step 9 Check your model by graphing it on the calculator.

Graphic 4.3.13

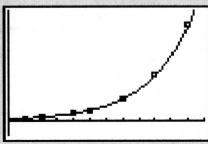

Problem 3   Solution

a. This data is not in a context so we can go right to step 3 creating a scattergram.

    Step 3 Create a scattergram

Graphic 4.3.14.

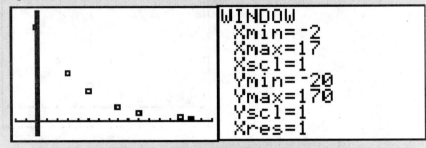

Step 4 Select a model type.
Since this graph is decreasing rapidly and is flat on the right side an exponential model is appropriate.

Step 5 Pick the vertical intercept and one other point.
$(0, 145)$ and $(10, 14.6)$.

Step 6 Substitute the vertical intercept into a and use the other point to find b.

$$f = 145 \cdot b^x \qquad \text{Substitute the vertical intercept for } a.$$

$$14.6 = 145 \cdot b^{10} \qquad \text{Substitute the other point for } f \text{ and } x.$$

$$\frac{14.6}{145} = \frac{145 \cdot b^{10}}{145}$$

$$0.10069 = b^{10}$$

$$(0.10069)^{1/10} = (b^{10})^{1/10} \qquad \begin{array}{l}\text{Solve for } b \text{ using the Power Rule for}\\ \text{Exponents.}\end{array}$$

$$0.795 = b$$

Step 7 Write the model.

$$f(x) = 145(0.795)^x$$

Step 8 Check your model by graphing it on the calculator.

Graphic 4.3.15

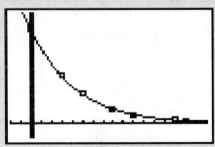

4.3 Exercises

1. While running an experiment in physics class a student was testing the volume of water remaining in a cylinder after a small hole was made in the bottom. The data collected by the student is given in **Table 4.3.1**

Table 4.3.1

Time (seconds)	Volume (liters)	Time (seconds)	Volume (liters)
30	13.24	180	5.32
60	11.45	210	4.34
90	9.96	240	3.59
120	7.79	270	3.20
150	6.10	300	2.66

a. Find a model for the data.

b. Estimate the water remaining after 6 minutes.

c. Give a reasonable domain and range for this model.

d. Estimate numerically how long it took for there to be only 1 liter of water remaining in the cylinder.

2. The growth of the internet has outpaced anything most people had imagined. Data for the number of internet hosts in the early 1990's is given in **Table 4.3.2**

Table 4.3.2

Years Since 1990	Hosts (in millions)
3	1.3
3.5	1.8
4	2.2
4.5	3.2
5	4.9
5.5	6.6
6	9.5

source: Matthew Gray of Massachusetts Institute of Technology

a. Find a model for this data.

b. Estimate the number of internet hosts in 1997.

c. Give a reasonable domain and range for this model.

d. Estimate graphically when the number of internet hosts reached 20 million.

3. The number of nuclear warheads in the U.S. arsenal from 1945 to 1960 was growing at an exponential rate. The number of stockpiled warheads in the U.S. is given in **Table 4.3.6**

Table 4.3.6

Year	Stockpiled Warheads
1945	6
1947	32
1949	235
1951	640
1953	1436
1955	3057
1957	6444
1959	15468

source: Natural Resources Defense Council

a. Find a model for this data.

b. Estimate the number of stockpiled warheads in 1950.

c. Give a reasonable domain and range for this model.

d. Estimate graphically in what year the number of stockpiled warheads surpassed 50,000.

4. In 1959 the U.S. started building Inter-continental Ballistic Missiles to act as a deterrent during the cold war. The number of ICBMs in the U.S. arsenal is given in **Table 4.3.7**

Table 4.3.7

Year	ICBM
1959	6
1960	13
1961	60
1962	213
1963	627

source: Natural Resources Defense Council

a. Find a model for this data.

b. Estimate the number of ICBMs in the U.S. arsenal in 1964.

c. Give a reasonable domain and range for this model.

d. Estimate numerically in what year there would be 2000 ICBMs in the U.S. arsenal.

5. One concern all people should share is the overuse of our natural resources due to larger populations. The amount of organic material in our soils is crucial to the growth of food and other plants. With overuse the percentage of soil that is organic material decreases to dangerous levels. Data demonstrating this loss after years of overuse is given in **Table 4.3.8**

Table 4.3.8

Year	Percent of Organic Material in Soil
0	3
25	2.1
75	0.9
125	0.4
175	0.2

source: Data estimated from information from the University of Wisconsin

  a. Find a model for this data.

  b. Estimate the percent of soil that is organic material after 100 years of overuse.

  c. Give a reasonable domain and range for this model.

For exercises 6 through 10 find a model for the given data and give the domain and range for the model.

6.

Table 4.3.9

x	f(x)
0	268
5	134
9	77
15	33
25	8
40	1

7.

Table 4.3.10

x	f(x)
5	14
7	23
12	76
15	155
18	318
20	512

8.

Table 4.3.11

x	f(x)
4	−23
7	−130
9	−412
11	−1307
13	−4142
15	−13123

9.

Table 4.3.12

x	f(x)
2	7
5	90
7	477
9	2522
11	13339
12	30680

10.

Table 4.3.13

x	f(x)
0	−56
1	−25.2
3	−5.103
5	−1.033
7	−0.2093
9	−0.0424

For exercises 11 through 15 use the graph to give the following information.

  a. Is a positive or negative?

  b. Is b greater than or less than 1?

  c. Domain of the function.

  d. Range of the function.

11.

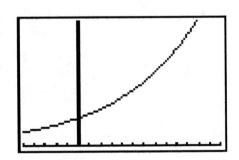

12.

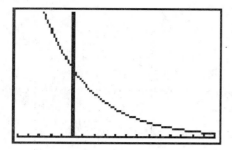

13.

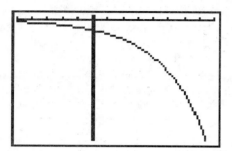

14.

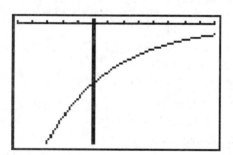

15.

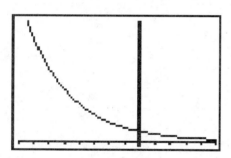

For exercises 16 through 20 sketch the graph of the functions by hand and state any information you know from the values of a and b.

16. $f(x) = 7(2)^x$

17. $g(t) = -3(0.7)^t$

18. $h(m) = 0.5(2.5)^m$

19. $j(w) = -0.5(4)^w$

20. $c(n) = 550(0.75)^n$

Section 4.4   Introduction to Inverses

• Introduction to Inverses • One-to-One Functions • Finding Linear Inverses

So far in this chapter we have investigated exponential functions but have not solved for the input variable because it is in the exponent. In this section we will discuss the concept of an **Inverse Function** and build the basic rules so we can define the inverse for exponential functions in the next section. These will be used throughout the rest of this chapter to solve exponential functions.

Concept Investigation 1

Temperature is measured in different ways around the world. In the United States we commonly measure temperature in degrees Fahrenheit but in most other countries temperature is measured in degrees Celsius. This means that people often have to switch a given temperature from one unit to another. This is especially true for people who live close to the Canadian border and get temperatures in different units. The function

$$C(F) = \frac{5}{9}(F - 32)$$

has the temperature in degrees Fahrenheit as the input value and the temperature in degrees Celsius as the output value.

a. If you know the temperature is 68^0F outside, calculate the temperature in degrees Celsius.

If you were given the temperature in degrees Celsius it would be convenient to have a function that had an input variable that took degrees Celsius and gave you out the value in degrees Fahrenheit. In order to find such a function we can simply solve the above function for F.

b. Solve the function $C = \frac{5}{9}(F - 32)$ for F.

c. Use the function you just found to change 20 degrees Celsius into degrees Fahrenheit.

The function you found in part b undoes the operations that the original given function had done. These functions are an example of what we call inverses. When one function "undoes" the operations of the other function you are looking at an inverse. Finding inverses for linear equations is not a difficult process.

Example 1

In chapter 1 we looked at a cost function to calculate the cost to rent a 10ft truck from U-Haul.

$$U(m) = 0.59m + 19.95$$

where U represented the cost in dollars to rent a 10ft truck from U-haul and drive it m miles.

a.   What are the input and output variables for this function? How would this function be used?

b.   Find the inverse for this function.

c.   What are the input and output variables for the inverse? How would this function be used?

d.   Find the cost to travel 100 miles in this truck.

e.   Find the number of miles you can travel in this truck for a cost of $150.

Solution

a.   In this function m miles is the input variable and U dollars is the output variable. If you wanted to know the cost to drive m miles you would substitute in the number of miles and get out the cost in dollars.

b.   To find the inverse of this function we basically want to make m the output and U the input. To do this it is easiest to not use function notation until the end of the process.

$$U(m) = 0.59m + 19.95$$

$$U = 0.59m + 19.95 \qquad \text{Get out of function notation.}$$

$$U - 19.95 = 0.59m$$

$$\frac{U - 19.95}{0.59} = m \qquad \text{Solve for } m.$$

$$1.695U - 33.81 = m$$

$$m(U) = 1.695U - 33.81 \qquad \text{Re-write in function notation.}$$

c.   For the inverse the input variable is now U dollars and the output is now m miles. This function would be used if you had a cost in mind and wanted to know how many miles you could drive the truck for.

d.   The number of miles is given so it would be best to use the original function.

$$U(m) = 0.59m + 19.95$$

$$U(100) = 0.59(100) + 19.95$$

$$U(100) = 78.95$$

Therefore it cost $78.95 to rent this truck and drive it 100 miles.

e.   The cost is the given quantity so it is easiest to use the inverse function.

$$m(U) = 1.695U - 33.81$$

$$m(150) = 1.695(150) - 33.81$$

$$m(150) = 220.44$$

Therefore you can drive about 220 miles for a rental cost of $150.

Inverses basically take the inputs and outputs of one function and reverse their roles. The input of one function will become the output of the inverse and vise versa. This also means that the domain and range of an inverse is simply the domain and range of the original function only reversed. The domain of one function is the range of its inverse and the range of the function is the domain of the inverse. It is important in a real world problem that you keep the units and definitions of each variable intact so that their meanings do not get lost. The definition of the variables is what will control the meaning of the input and outputs of the function and its inverse.

Finding an Inverse Function in a Real World Problem:
1.   Write without function notation.
2.   Solve for the "other" variable.
      Solve for the original input variable. This will make it the new output
        variable.
3.   Re-write in function notation.

Problem 1

A team of engineers is trying to pump down the pressure in a vacuum chamber. They know the following equation represents the pressure in the chamber.

$$P(s) = 35 - 0.07s$$

where P is the pressure in pounds per square inch (psi) of a vacuum chamber after s seconds.

a.   Find an inverse for this function.

b.   Use your inverse function to estimate the time it will take to pump down this vacuum chamber to 5 psi.

c.   If the original function had a domain of $[0, 500]$ and range of $[0, 35]$ what is the domain and range of the inverse?

Solution   See page 283.

When working with inverses in a real world situation the meanings of the variables play an important role in making the equation apply to the context of the problem. In problems without a context we do not define the variables and so most often x is the input variable for a function and $f(x) = y$ is the output for the function. With this in mind we get some different notation when we work with inverses without a context.

Example 2

Find the inverse for the function $f(x) = 2x - 8$.

Solution
To find the inverse we still want to reverse the roles of the two variables involved. This is most easily done without using function notation and then going back to it at the end of the problem.

   Step 1 Write without function notation by replacing $f(x)$ with y.
$$f(x) = 2x - 8$$
$$y = 2x - 8$$

   Step 2 Solve for x (this will reverse the role of the two variables).
$$y = 2x - 8$$
$$y + 8 = 2x$$
$$\frac{y + 8}{2} = x \qquad \text{Divide both sides by 2.}$$
$$0.5y + 4 = x$$

   Step 3 Interchange the variables x and y. We only do this when there is no context because the input is usually denoted by x.
$$0.5x + 4 = y$$

   Step 4 Re-write in function notation. Use $f^{-1}(x)$ to designate it as the inverse.
$$f^{-1}(x) = 0.5x + 4$$

Finding an Inverse Function in a Problem Without a Context:
1. Write without function notation by replacing $f(x)$ with y
2. Solve for x.
   Solve for the original input variable. This will make it the new output variable.
3. Interchange the variables x and y.
4. Re-write in function notation. Use $f^{-1}(x)$ to designate it as the inverse.
   Note that the -1 in the inverse notation, $f^{-1}(x)$, is not an exponent.

Say What?

Function notation for inverses often causes some confusion for students. The -1 used in the notation to show that the function is an inverse is not an exponent. Recall that a negative exponent would result in a reciprocal of the base. The negative one in the function notation symbolizes the inverse relation not a reciprocal.

If
$$f(x) = 2x + 10$$
then the inverse of $f(x)$ is
$$f^{-1}(x) = \frac{x - 10}{2} = \frac{1}{2}x - 5$$
notice this is not the reciprocal of the original function.
$$\frac{1}{f(x)} = \frac{1}{2x + 10}$$

Always remember
$$f^{-1}(x) \neq \frac{1}{f(x)}$$

Problem 2

Find the inverse for the following functions.

a. $f(x) = -4x + 9$

b. $g(t) = 2.5t - 3.5$

Solution   See page 284

Inverse functions are only possible if each output of an original function can be brought back to a single input value that it came from. This becomes a problem when a single output value comes from two or more different input values. An example would be the function $f(x) = x^2$ has the same output of 4 when $x = 2$ as when $x = -2$ so if you want to go back from an output of 4 to the original input $x = 2$ and $x = -2$ are both options, choosing which one it should be is a problem. Since an inverse should be a function this problem of one input going to two different outputs eliminates the possibility of $f(x) = x^2$ having an inverse function. This problem occurs with many types of functions.

Functions that do not have this problem are called **one-to-one** functions. That is each input goes to exactly one output and each output comes from exactly one input. A one-to-one function is easiest to identify using its graph. If a function is one-to-one it will pass **The Horizontal Line Test** much like a function must pass the vertical line test discussed earlier.

Definition 4.4.1

One-to-One Function: A function where each input corresponds to only one output **and** each output correspond to only one input.

Definition 4.4.2

The Horizontal Line Test for a One-to-One Function: If any horizontal line intersects the graph of a function more than once then that graph does not represent a one-to-one function.

Example 3

Determine if the function is a one-to-one function.

a. $f(x) = -2.4x + 9$

b. $f(x) = 2.5x^2 + 3x - 5$

c. $g(t) = 3.4(1.4^t)$

d. $h(t) = 5$

Solution

Each of these functions can be graphed on a calculator and you can visually use the horizontal line test to determine if they are one-to-one.

a.

Graphic 4.4.1

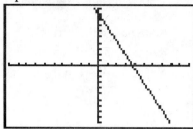

This function passes the horizontal line test since each horizontal line you could draw across this graph would only hit the function once. Therefore this is a one-to-one function.

b.

Graphic 4.4.2

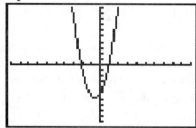

This function fails the horizontal line test since almost any horizontal line you draw through this graph hits the graph more than once. Therefore this is not a one-to-one function.

c.

Graphic 4.4.3

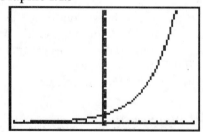

This function passes the horizontal line test since each horizontal line you could draw across this graph would only hit the function once. Therefore this is a one-to-one function.

d.

Graphic 4.4.4

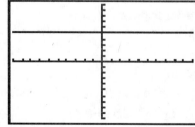

This line is horizontal so when testing it using the horizontal line test it fails to be one-to-one. Horizontal lines are not one-to-one.

Problem 3

Determine if the function is a one-to-one function.

a. $g(t) = \frac{2}{3}t - 7$

b. $h(w) = 0.5w^3 + 3w^2 - 7$

c. $f(x) = -5(0.7)^x$

Solution   see page 284

Functions and their inverses have several special relationships. One of these relationships comes from the fact that an inverse function will take an output from the original function and give back the input you originally started with. This relationship results in an interesting rule for composing a function and its inverse. When you compose a function and its inverse the result will always be the input variable. This is best seen with a few examples.

Example 4

Perform the following compositions and simplify.

a. Let $f(x) = 2x + 6$ and $f^{-1}(x) = \frac{1}{2}x - 3$ find $f(f^{-1}(x))$ and $f^{-1}(f(x))$

b. Let $g(x) = 5x - 20$ and $g^{-1}(x) = \frac{1}{5}x + 4$ find $g(g^{-1}(x))$ and $g^{-1}(g(x))$

Solution

a.

$$f(f^{-1}(x)) = 2\left(\frac{1}{2}x - 3\right) + 6$$

$$f(f^{-1}(x)) = x - 6 + 6$$

$$f(f^{-1}(x)) = x$$

$$f^{-1}(f(x)) = \frac{1}{2}(2x + 6) - 3$$

$$f^{-1}(f(x)) = x + 3 - 3$$

$$f^{-1}(f(x)) = x$$

b.

$$g(g^{-1}(x)) = 5\left(\frac{1}{5}x + 4\right) - 20$$

$$g(g^{-1}(x)) = x + 20 - 20$$

$$g(g^{-1}(x)) = x$$

$$g^{-1}(g(x)) = \frac{1}{5}(5x - 20) + 4$$

$$g^{-1}(g(x)) = x - 4 + 4$$

$$g^{-1}(g(x)) = x$$

The graphs of inverses will also have a simple relationship to the graph of the original function. Since an inverse function basically switches the roles of the input and outputs of the original function the graph of the inverse will do just that. This results in a graph that is a reflection of the original graph over the line $y = x$. To graph an inverse you can use techniques you already know or you can use this reflection property.

Skill Connection:

Recall from Chapter 1 that the composition of functions is the process of making one function the input to the other function.

SC Example 1:
Let:

$$f(x) = 2x + 5$$

$$g(x) = 7x - 9$$

Find $f(g(x))$:

$$f(g(x)) = 2(7x - 9) + 5$$
$$f(g(x)) = 14x - 18 + 5$$
$$f(g(x)) = 14x - 13$$

TI - 83 Details:
When graphing functions on
the calculator you need to be
aware that the screen is a
rectangle and will distort
graphs by stretching them
out along the horizontal axis.
This will happen whenever
the window is not set to the
correct proportions that will
account for the window
being wider than it is tall.
The calculator has a ZOOM
feature called ZSquare that
will take any window and
change it to the correct
proportions to display a
graph correctly.
The following two screens
show the same pair of
perpendicular lines (lines
that cross at a 90 degree
angle).
Standard window:
X min -10, X max 10
Y min -10, Y max 10

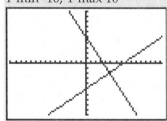

The standard window does
not show these lines as
perpendicular.
Window after ZSquare:
X min -15.161, X max 15.161
Y min -10, Y max 10

The square window does
show these lines correctly as
perpendicular.

Example 5

Graph the following functions and their inverses.

a. $f(x) = 2x + 6$ $f^{-1}(x) = 0.5x - 3$

b. $h(c) = -\dfrac{2}{9}c - 6$ $h^{-1}(c) = -\dfrac{9}{2}c - 27$

c. $g(t) = t^3$ $g^{-1}(t) = \sqrt[3]{t}$

Solution

a. Since both of these functions are linear they can be graphed easily. Putting
    them both on the same axis we get.
    Graphic 4.4.5

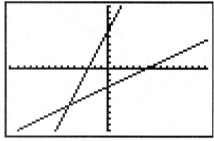

b. Again these functions are both linear so we can graph them easily. This
    time we will put them on the same axis and show the line $y = x$ to help
    show the reflection properties of inverses.
    Graphic 4.4.6

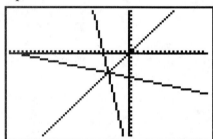

c. These functions are harder to graph so using the reflection properties and
    plotting several points will help get a more accurate graph. When graph-
    ing these on a graphing calculator it is best to use the ZOOM Square fea-
    ture so that the graph will not be distorted by the shape of the calculator
    screen.
    Graphic 4.4.7

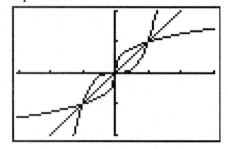

Section 4.4 Key Points

- An Inverse Function will "undo" what the original function did to each input value.
- Finding an Inverse Function in a Real World Problem:
    1. Get out of function notation.
    2. Solve for the "other" variable.
       Solve for the original input variable. This will make it the new output variable.
    3. Re-write in function notation.
- Finding an Inverse Function in a Problem Without a Context:
    1. Take out of function notation by replacing $f(x)$ with y
    2. Solve for x.
       Solve for the original input variable. This will make it the new output variable.
    3. Interchange the variables x and y.
    4. Re-write in function notation. Use $f^{-1}(x)$ to designate it as the inverse.
- One-to-one functions have exactly one input for every output.
- Only functions that are one-to-one will have inverses.
    This means that linear and exponential functions will have inverses but not quadratics.
- The Horizontal Line Test can be used to tell if a function is one-to-one or not.
- The graph of an inverse will be a reflection of the original function over the line $y = x$.

Section 4.4 Problem Solutions

Problem 1   Solution

a. Since this is a real world problem the variables have meaning so we just want to solve for s.

$$P(s) = 35 - 0.07s$$
$$P = 35 - 0.07s$$
$$P - 35 = -0.07s$$
$$\frac{P - 35}{-0.07} = s$$
$$-14.29P + 500 = s(P)$$

b. We are given the desired psi so we can substitute $P = 5$ and solve for s.

$$s(5) = -14.29(5) + 500$$
$$s(5) = 428.55$$

Therefore it will take about 429 seconds to pump the vacuum chamber down to 5psi.

c. The domain and range of the inverse function will be the domain and range of the original function just switched around. The original function had a domain of $[0, 500]$ and range of $[0, 35]$ therefore the domain of the inverse will be $[0, 35]$, and the range will be $[0, 500]$.

Problem 2   Solution

a.

$$f(x) = -4x + 9$$
$$y = -4x + 9$$
$$y - 9 = -4x$$
$$\frac{y-9}{-4} = x$$
$$-0.25y + 2.25 = x$$
$$-0.25x + 2.25 = y$$
$$f^{-1}(x) = -0.25x + 2.25$$

b.

$$g(t) = 2.5t - 3.5$$
$$y = 2.5t - 3.5$$
$$y + 3.5 = 2.5t$$
$$\frac{y + 3.5}{2.5} = t$$
$$0.4y + 1.4 = t$$
$$0.4t + 1.4 = y$$
$$g^{-1}(t) = 0.4t + 1.4$$

Problem 3   Solution

a.

Graphic 4.4.8

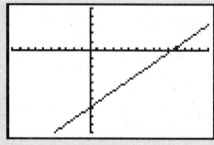

This graph passes the horizontal line test so $g(t)$ is a one-to-one function.

b.

Graphic 4.4.9

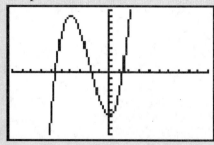

This graph fails the horizontal line test so $h(w)$ is not a one-to-one function.

Problem 3   Solution Continued

c.

Graphic 4.4.10

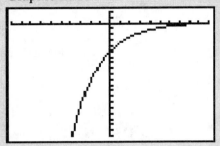

This graph passes the horizontal line test so $f(x)$ is a one-to-one function.

4.4 Exercises

1. The number of homicides, N, of 15-19 year-olds in the U.S. t years after 1990 can be represented by the equation $N = -315.9t + 4809.8$.

   source: Based on data from Statistical Abstract 2001

   a. Find the inverse for this model.

   b. If the model has a domain of $[-1, 12]$ and a range of $[1019, 5125.7]$ give the domain and range for the inverse.

   c. Estimate in what year there were 2000 homicides of 15-19 year olds.

2. $P = 20.5b - 500.5$ represents the profit in dollars from selling b books.

   a. Give a reasonable domain and range for this model.

   b. Find an inverse for this model.

   c. Estimate the profit from selling 100 books.

   d. Estimate the number of books you would need to sell in order to make $500 profit.

   e. Give a reasonable domain and range for the inverse.

3. The population of the United States during the 1990's can be estimated by the equation $P = 2.57t + 249.78$, where P is the population in millions t years since 1990.

   source: Based on data from Statistical Abstract 2001

   a. Find an inverse for this model.

   b. Estimate the year when the U.S. population reached 260 million people.

   c. What are the input and output variables for the inverse?

4. The population of Colorado in millions t years since 1990 can be modeled by.
   $$P(t) = 0.0875t + 3.285$$

   a. Find a model for the inverse function.

   b. Estimate when Colorado's population reached 3.5 million people.

   c. Give a reasonable domain and range for the inverse.

5. The average pounds of fruits and vegetables per person that each American eats can be modeled by:
   $$T(y) = 6.056y + 601.39$$
   pounds per person y years since 1980.

   a. Find an inverse for this model.

   b. Estimate when the average number of pounds of fruits and vegetables per person reached 650.

   c. Give a reasonable domain and range for this inverse.

Math

Tutorial

More practice problems like exercises 6 through 9 can be found in section 4.4 of the CD Tutorial.

For exercises 6 through 9 use the Horizontal Line Test to determine if the function is one-to-one or not.

6.

Graph 4.4.8

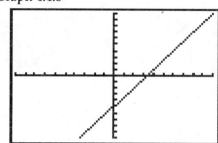

7.

Graph 4.4.9

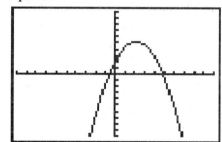

8.

Graph 4.4.10

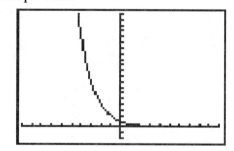

9.

Graph 4.4.11

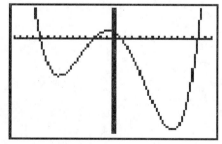

Math
Tutorial

More practice problems like exercises 10 through 15 can be found in section 4.4 of the CD Tutorial.

For exercises 10 through 15 find the inverse of each function

10. $f(x) = 3x + 5$

11. $g(t) = -4t + 8$

12. $h(m) = \frac{2}{3}m - 9$

13. $f(x) = -\frac{5}{7}x + 4$

14. $P(n) = -2.5n - 7.5$

15. $W(a) = 2.4a + 3.7$

For exercises 16 through 20 compose the two given functions and determine if they are inverses.

16. $f(x) = 3x - 9$ and $g(x) = \frac{1}{3}x + 3$

17. $f(x) = 4x + 12$ and $g(x) = 0.25x - 3$

18. $h(x) = 0.6x + 5$ and $g(x) = 0.4x - 2$

19. $f(x) = \frac{1}{7}x + 21$ and $h(x) = 7x + 3$

20. $g(x) = -8x - 12$ and $h(x) = -\frac{1}{8}x - 1\frac{1}{2}$

Section 4.5   Introduction to Logarithms

• Definition of Logarithms • Basic Rules for Logarithms • Change of Base Formula

As we can see from the last example most linear functions have inverses but quadratic functions do not. The exponential function also passes the horizontal line test so it must also have an inverse function.

Graphic 4.5.1

When we try to find the inverse function for an exponential trying to solve for the input variable leads us to a basic problem. There is no way using the arithmetic operations we know to get a variable out of an exponent. This problem leads us to a new type of function that at the most basic level can be defined as the inverse function of an exponential. We use the symbol $\log_b$, read log base b, and call this new function a **logarithm**. A logarithm at its core asks the question "What exponent of the base b gives us what's inside?"

Definition 4.5.1

Logarithmic Function: A basic logarithm function can be written in the form
$$f(x) = \log_b x \text{ read log base } b \text{ of } x.$$
where b is a real number greater than zero and not equal to one. By definition logarithms and exponentials have an inverse relationship.:
$$f(x) = y = b^x \qquad f^{-1}(x) = y = \log_b x$$

Base: The constant b is called the base of the logarithm function If no base is given then that log is assumed to have base 10.

A logarithm asks the basic question:
   "What exponent of the base b gives us what's inside the log?"

Example 1

Evaluate the following logarithms.

a. $\log_5 25$

b. $\log_2 16$

c. $\log 1000$

Solution

a.   With each of these logarithms you will want to ask yourself the basic question, What exponent of 5 will give us 25? In this case we know that $5^2 = 25$ so we know an exponent of 2 will give us 25. Therefore we have $\log_5 25 = 2$.

b.   Ask what exponent of 2 will give me 16? We should know that $2^4 = 16$ so an exponent of 4 will give you 16. Therefore we have that $\log_2 16 = 4$.

c.   In this case no base is written in the logarithm expression. This implies that this is a common logarithm and always has the base 10. Therefore the question becomes, what exponent of 10 will give me 1000? Since $10^3 = 1000$ we know that $\log 1000 = 3$.

As you can see from this example evaluating logarithms is pretty simple if you can recognize the exponent you need. Some logarithms have the same value for any base. In particular when taking the logarithm of 1 no matter what the base is the logarithm will always equal zero.

$$b^0 = 1 \qquad \log_b 1 = 0$$

When working with logarithms if you take the logarithm of the base to a power you will get that power back. These rules are all related directly to the definition of a logarithm and make up some of the most basic rules for logarithms.

Basic Logarithm Rules:

$$\log_b 1 = 0 \text{ Since } b^0 = 1$$

The logarithm of 1 for any base logarithm will always equal zero.

$$\log_b b = 1 \text{ Since } b^1 = b$$

The logarithm of its base is always equal to one.

$$\log_b(b^m) = m \text{ Since } b^m = b^m$$

The logarithm of its base to a power is just that power.

Problem 1

Evaluate the following logarithms.

a. $\log 10^5$

b. $\log_7 7^8$

c. $\log_9 9$

d. $\log_3 1$

Solution   See page 296

Although logarithms can be written with any positive base other than 1 there are two logarithms used the most. The "common" logarithm is base ten and is written as "Log" without a base present. This logarithm is used often in science when very large or small numbers are needed. One other base that is often used in base e. e is a special number that occurs often in nature and science as well in compounding interest situations. Most people will recognize the number pi as approximately 3.14 and that it is actually a number whose decimal expansion is infinite and non repeating. Pi is related to circles and geometry and is used often enough that we have given it a special name and symbol. Well, e is very much the same.

Definition 4.5.2

The Number e: An irrational number represented by the letter e.
$$e \approx 2.718281828$$

We most often approximate it with $e \approx 2.718$. If you look carefully on your calculator you will find a button with e^x on the left side just above a button with LN on it. Remember that e is a number and is only a short way of writing a number that never ends or repeats. If we look at the graph of the following exponential functions you can see that e lies between 2 and 3.

Graphic 4.5.2

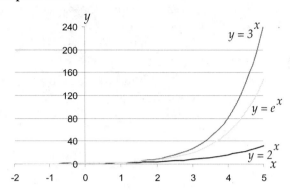

There are many characteristics of the number e that make it very useful but many of these applications are beyond this course. For now you do need to know that it is a frequently used base for a logarithm and that when used the logarithm is written as "Ln" and a base of e is assumed. A logarithm with base e is most often called the **Natural Logarithm**. One of the nicest features of calculators is that the common and natural logarithms can be found with the touch of a button.

Problem 2
Use your calculator to evaluate the following logarithms.

a. $\log 500$

b. $\ln 13.4$

Solution   See page 296

If you want to calculate a logarithm with a base other than 10 or e you can start by trial and error using different exponents of the base or you will need to change the base of the logarithm in order to use a common or natural logarithm calculation on your calculator. The change of base formula is a simple way to change a logarithm from one base to another.

Change of Base Formula for Logarithms:

$$\log_b x = \frac{\log_c x}{\log_c b}$$

To change the base of a logarithm from base b to another base c take the $\log_c$ of the inside and divide by the $\log_c$ of the old base.

Most often we change to base 10 or base e since our calculators can evaluate these bases.

Example 2
Evaluate the following logarithms.

a. $\log_5 114$

b. $\log_2 0.365$

Solution
Since these logarithms are not of base 10 or e we will need to change their base in order to use our calculator to evaluate them. You can change the base to either 10 or e for either of these examples. We change one to base 10 and the other to base e.

a.   Using a base 10 logarithm we get;
$$\log_5 114$$

$$\log_5 114 \;=\; \frac{\log 114}{\log 5}$$

$$\log_5 114 \approx 2.943$$

b.   Using a natural logarithm we get;
$$\log_2 0.365$$

$$\log_2 0.365 \;=\; \frac{\ln 0.365}{\ln 2}$$

$$\log_2 0.365 \approx -1.454$$

Problem 3

Evaluate the following logarithms on your calculator.

a. $\log_3 278$

b. $\log_{17} 11$

Solution   See page 296

The goal of this section is that you start understanding the basic concept of a logarithm and how it relates to exponentials. One of the most important skills you need to learn is to re-write a problem given in exponential form into logarithm form and vise-versa. When working with logarithms and exponentials remember that the bases are related and that the exponent in an exponential is the same as the result from the logarithm.

Logarithm and Exponential forms:
$$\log_b n = m$$
$$n = b^m$$

The base of the logarithm is the same as the base of the related exponential function. The result from the logarithm is the exponent in the exponential function.

When re-writing a logarithm you can think of the base raised to the outside equals the inside.
$$\log_5 125 = 3$$
$$125 = 5^3$$

The domain and range of exponential and logarithmic functions are related since these functions are inverses of one another.

$$f(x) = b^x \qquad f^{-1}(x) = \log_b x$$

Domain: $(-\infty, \infty)$ Domain: $(0, \infty)$
Range: $(0, \infty)$ Range: $(-\infty, \infty)$

Example 3

Re-write each exponential equation into logarithm form.

a. $7^5 = 16807$

b. $4.5^3 = 91.125$

Re-write each logarithm equation into exponential form.

c. $\log_3 243 = 5$

d. $\log_{2.5} 15.625 = 3$

Solution

a. $\log_7 16807 = 5$

b. $\log_{4.5} 91.125 = 3$

c. $243 = 3^5$

d. $15.625 = 2.5^3$

Re-writing exponential functions into logarithmic form and logarithm functions into exponential form is actually writing their inverse functions.

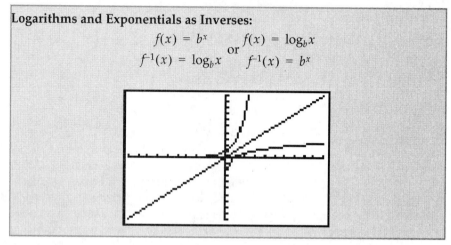

Logarithms and Exponentials as Inverses:

$$f(x) = b^x \qquad f(x) = \log_b x$$
$$\text{or}$$
$$f^{-1}(x) = \log_b x \qquad f^{-1}(x) = b^x$$

Example 4

Find the inverses for the following functions.

a. $f(x) = 3^x$

b. $g(t) = \log t$

c. $h(m) = 5.4^m$

d. $f(x) = e^x$

Solution

We basically need to follow the same steps as finding an inverse in a problem without a context that we learned in section 4.4 but when we solve we will re-write exponentials into logarithmic form and logarithms into exponential form to isolate the variable we want.

a.

$$f(x) = 3^x$$

$y = 3^x$	Take the function out of function notation.
$\log_3 y = x$	Solve for x by writing it in logarithm form.
$\log_3 x = y$	Interchange the variables.
$f^{-1}(x) = \log_3 x$	Write in function notation.

b.

$$g(t) = \log t$$

$y = \log t$	Take the function out of function notation.
$10^y = t$	Solve for t by writing it in exponential form.
$10^t = y$	Interchange the variables.
$g^{-1}(t) = 10^t$	Write in function notation.

c.

$$h(m) = 5.4^m$$
$$y = 5.4^m$$
$$\log_{5.4} y = m$$
$$\log_{5.4} m = y$$
$$h^{-1}(m) = \log_{5.4} m$$

d.

$$f(x) = e^x$$ Since the base here is e the inverse will be the
$$f^{-1}(x) = \ln x$$ Natural Logarithm.

Simple logarithm equations can be solved by re-writing the logarithm into exponential form.

Example 5

Solve each logarithm equation by re-writing it in exponential form.

a. $\log x = 2$

b. $\log_4 x = 5$

Solution

a.

$$\log x = 2$$
$$10^2 = x$$ Re-write as an exponential and calculate.
$$x = 100$$

b.

$$\log_4 x = 5$$
$$4^5 = x$$
$$x = 1024$$

Problem 4

Solve each logarithm equation by re-writing it in exponential form.

a. $\ln x = 4$

b. $\log_2(5x) = 6$

Solution   See page 296

The basic graph of a logarithm function will depend on the base. If the base is greater than 1 it will be an increasing function and grow very quickly for inputs close to zero and then slow to a very gradual increase as the inputs get larger.

Graphic 4.5.3

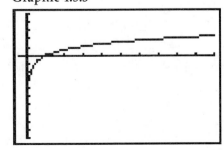

Logarithms with bases less than 1 will be decreasing and again decrease very quickly for input values close to zero but then less once the inputs get larger.

Graphic 4.5.4

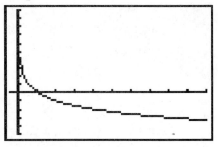

You should notice from these graphs that the domain and range of these logarithm functions have simply reversed from there related exponential functions. The basic domain for a logarithm function will be all positive real numbers or $(0, \infty)$ and the range will be all real numbers or $(-\infty, \infty)$.

Section 4.5 Key Points

- A logarithm can be defined as the inverse for exponential functions.
- Logarithmic Function: A basic logarithm function can be written in the form

$$f(x) = \log_b x$$

  where b is a real number greater than zero and not equal to one.
- Base: The constant b is called the base of the logarithm function.
- A logarithm asks the basic question:
  "What exponent of the base b gives me what's inside?"
- The most basic logarithms are the common logarithm base 10 or the Natural Logarithm base e.
- Basic Logarithm Rules:

$$\log_b 1 = 0$$

  The logarithm of 1 for any base logarithm will always equal zero.

$$\log_b b = 1$$

  The logarithm of its base is always equal to one.

$$\log_b(b^m) = m$$

  The logarithm of its base to a power is just that power.
- Change of Base Formula for Logarithms:

$$\log_b x = \frac{\log_c x}{\log_c b}$$

  To change the base of a logarithm from base b to another base c take the $\log_c$ of the inside and divide by the $\log_c$ of the old base.
- Logarithm and Exponential forms:

$$\log_b n = m$$
$$b^m = n$$

  The base of the logarithm is the same as the base of the related exponential function. The result from the logarithm is the exponent in the exponential function.
- Re-writing a basic exponential function in logarithm form is the same as finding its inverse. Also re-writing a basic logarithm into exponential form is the same as finding its inverse.
- The domain and range of logarithm functions are the same as exponential functions just interchanged.
- The graph of a logarithm will depend on the base. If $b > 1$ then the graph will be increasing and if $b < 1$ then the graph will be decreasing.

Section 4.5 Problem Solutions

Problem 1   Solution

a. $\log 10^5 = 5$

b. $\log_7 7^8 = 8$

c. $\log_9 9 = 1$

d. $\log_3 1 = 0$

Problem 2   Solution

Using the log and ln button on the calculator will give the following approximations.

a. $\log 500 = 2.699$

b. $\ln 13.4 = 2.595$

Problem 3   Solution

a.

$\log_3 278$

$\dfrac{\log 278}{\log 3}$

5.122

b.

$\log_{17} 11$

$\dfrac{\ln 11}{\ln 17}$

0.846

Problem 4   Solution

a.

$\ln x = 4$

$e^4 = x$

$x \approx 54.598$

b.

$\log_2 (5x) = 6$

$2^6 = 5x$

$\dfrac{64}{5} = x$

$x = 12.8$

4.5 Exercises

More practice problems like exercises 1 through 5 can be found in section 4.5 of the CD Tutorial.

For exercises 1 through 5 find the inverse of each function.

1. $f(x) = 3^x$

2. $B(t) = e^t$

3. $h(c) = 10^c$

4. $g(t) = 2^t$

5. $m(r) = 5^r$

More practice problems like exercises 6 through 16 can be found in section 4.5 of the CD Tutorial.

For exercises 6 through 16 evaluate the following logarithms without a calculator.

6. $\log 1000$

7. $\log_2 32$

8. $\log_5\left(\frac{1}{5}\right)$

9. $\log 0.1$

10. $\log_2\left(\frac{1}{16}\right)$

11. $\ln 1$

12. $\ln(e^3)$

13. $\log_7 1$

14. $\log_{19} 19$

15. $\log_7 343$

16. $\log_2 256$

More practice problems like exercises 17 through 20 can be found in section 4.5 of the CD Tutorial.

For exercises 17 through 20 evaluate the following logarithms with a calculator.

17. $\log_7 25$

18. $\log_5 43.2$

19. $\log_2 0.473$

20. $\ln 543$

More practice problems like exercises 21 through 25 can be found in section 4.5 of the CD Tutorial.

For exercises 21 through 25 re-write the following logarithm equations into exponential form.

21. $\log 1000 = 3$

22. $\ln(e^5) = 5$

23. $\log_2(8) = 3$

24. $\log 0.01 = -2$

25. $\log_5\left(\frac{1}{25}\right) = -2$

More practice problems like exercises 26 through 30 can be found in section 4.5 of the CD Tutorial.

For exercises 26 through 30 re-write each exponential equation into logarithm form.

26. $2^{10} = 1024$

27. $3^5 = 243$

28. $3^{2x} = 729$

29. $b^y = c$

30. $\left(\frac{1}{2}\right)^3 = \frac{1}{8}$

Math

Tutorial   More practice problems like exercises 31 through 37 can be found in section 4.5 of the CD Tutorial.

For exercises 31 through 37 solve each logarithm equation by re-writing it in exponential form.

31. $\log x = 3$

32. $\log(2x) = 0.5$

33. $\ln t = 2$

34. $\ln(3x) = 4$

35. $\log_3 t = 5$

36. $\log_7(4x) = 3$

37. $\log_3 w = 2.4$

For exercises 38 through 40 use the given graphs to estimate the answers.

38. Given the graph of $f(x)$

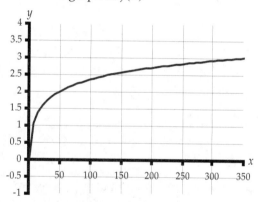

  a. Estimate $f(50)$
  b. Estimate $f(x) = 2.5$

39. Given the graph of $g(x)$

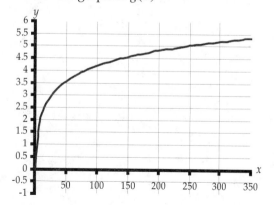

  a. Estimate $g(150)$
  b. Estimate $g(x) = 5$

40. Given the graph of $h(x)$

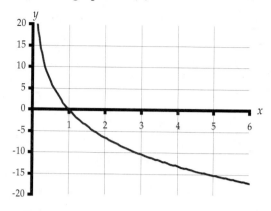

  a. Estimate $h(3)$
  b. Estimate $h(x) = -15$

Section 4.6   Properties of Logarithms

• Properties of Logarithms • Expanding Logarithms • Combining Logarithms

This section will cover the basic properties of logarithms that we will need in the rest of this chapter to solve exponential and logarithm problems.

Because logarithms are inverses of exponential functions the basic rules for exponents we learned in section 4.2 will have their related rules for logarithms. Use the concept investigation to find the related properties of logarithms.

Concept Investigation 1

a. Evaluate the following logarithm expressions on your calculator and compare the results for the expression in the left column to the expression in the right column.

1.	$\ln(7 \cdot 2) =$	**2.**	$\ln 7 + \ln 2 =$
3.	$\log(8 \cdot 3) =$	**4.**	$\log 8 + \log 3 =$
5.	$\ln(5 \cdot 11) =$	**6.**	$\ln 5 + \ln 11 =$
7.	$\log 100 =$	**8.**	$\log 10 + \log 10 =$

Describe in your own words the relationship between these two columns of logarithm expressions.

b. Evaluate the following logarithm expressions on your calculator and compare the results for the expression in the left column to the expression in the right column.

1.	$\log \dfrac{30}{6} =$	**2.**	$\log 30 - \log 6 =$
3.	$\ln \dfrac{45}{5} =$	**4.**	$\ln 45 - \ln 5 =$
5.	$\ln \dfrac{5000}{45} =$	**6.**	$\ln 5000 - \ln 45 =$
7.	$\log \dfrac{1000}{10} =$	**8.**	$\log 1000 - \log 10 =$

Describe in your own words the relationship between these two columns of logarithm expressions.

These two relationships are stated in the **Product Rule for Logarithms** and the **Quotient Rule for Logarithms**.

The Product Rule for Logarithms:

$$\log_b(mn) = \log_b m + \log_b n$$

A logarithm of any base with multiplication inside can be written as two separate logarithms added together.

$$\log_b(5 \cdot 9) = \log_b 5 + \log_b 9$$

The Quotient Rule for Logarithms:

$$\log_b\left(\frac{m}{n}\right) = \log_b m - \log_b n$$

A logarithm of any base with division inside can be written as two separate logarithms subtracted from one another.

$$\log_b\left(\frac{50}{8}\right) = \log_b 50 - \log_b 8$$

These two rules allow us to either take apart a complex logarithm or put two logarithms together into one. In different circumstances we want to do either of these two processes. Most often though we will be putting two logarithms together to become one logarithm so that we can solve a simpler equation.

Example 1

a. Expand the following logarithms as separate simpler logarithms.

   i $\ln(5 \cdot 17)$

   ii $\log\left(\frac{35}{8}\right)$

   iii $\log_4(13xy)$

   iv $\log_5\left(\frac{mn}{9}\right)$

b. Write the following logarithms as a single logarithm.

   i $\log 8 + \log 7$

   ii $\ln 35 - \ln 6$

   iii $\ln(3x) - \ln(5z)$

   iv $\log_7(2m) - \log_7 n$

Solution

a. To separate these logarithms into more simple logarithms we can use the product and quotient rules for logarithms.

   i $\ln 5 + \ln 17$

   ii $\log 35 - \log 8$

   iii $\log_4 13 + \log_4 x + \log_4 y$

   iv $\log_5 m + \log_5 n - \log_5 9$

b. Combining these logarithms will also use the product and quotient rules for logarithms.

   i $\log 56$

   ii $\ln\left(\dfrac{35}{6}\right)$

   iii $\ln\left(\dfrac{3x}{5z}\right)$

   iv $\log_7\left(\dfrac{2m}{n}\right)$

Problem 1

a. Expand the following logarithms as separate simpler logarithms.

   i $\ln(5ab)$

   ii $\log\left(\dfrac{7n}{m}\right)$

b. Write the following logarithms as a single logarithm.

   i $\ln(18s) - \ln(3t)$

   ii $\log_7(5m) + \log_7(3n)$

Solution   See page 304

Concept Investigation 2

a. Evaluate the following logarithm expressions on your calculator and compare the results for the expression in the left column to the expression in the right column.

1.	$\log(7^3) =$	2.	$3\log 7 =$
3.	$\ln(8^5) =$	4.	$5\ln 8 =$
5.	$\log(7^{-2}) =$	6.	$-2\log 7 =$

Describe in your own words the relationship between these two columns of logarithm expressions.

This relationship is one of the most useful rules for logarithms and will be used in a very important role in most exponential and logarithm equations. This rule is stated in the **Power Rule for Logarithms.**

The Power Rule for Logarithms:

$$\log_b(m^n) = n\log_b m$$

A logarithm of any base with a power inside can be written as that logarithm with that power now being multiplied to the front.
$$\log_b(5^4) = 4\log_b 5$$

Using the Power Rule for Exponents together with the Product and Quotient rules allows you to combine or simplify logarithms of all kinds.

Example 2

a. Expand the following logarithms as separate simpler logarithms without any exponents.

   i $\ln(5x^2)$

   ii $\log\left(\dfrac{2x}{5}\right)$

   iii $\log_4(9x^3y^2)$

   iv $\log_5\left(\dfrac{m^2n^5}{2z^3}\right)$

   v $\log(\sqrt{5xy})$

b. Write the following logarithms as a single logarithm with a coefficient of one.

   i $\log 8 + 3\log x + 4\log y$

   ii $\ln 3 + 2\ln a - \ln b$

   iii $\ln x - 5\ln z + 2\ln y$

   iv $\log_7 2 + \log_7 m - 3\log_7 n + \log_7 5$

Solution

a. To separate these logarithms into more simple logarithms we can use the product and quotient rules for logarithms.

   i $\ln 5 + 2\ln x$

   ii $\log 2 + \log x - \log 5$

   iii $\log_4 9 + 3\log_4 x + 2\log_4 y$

   iv $2\log_5 m + 5\log_5 n - \log_5 2 - 3\log_5 z$

v

$$\log\left((5xy)^{\frac{1}{2}}\right)$$

Change the square root into a fraction exponent.

$$\frac{1}{2}\log(5xy)$$

Use the power rule to bring the exponent down to the front of the log.

$$\frac{1}{2}(\log 5 + \log x + \log y)$$

Use the product rule to expand the log.

b. Combining these logarithms will also use the product and quotient rules for logarithms.

i $\log 8x^3y^4$

ii $\ln\left(\dfrac{3a^2}{b}\right)$

iii $\ln\left(\dfrac{xy^2}{z^5}\right)$

iv $\log_7\left(\dfrac{10m}{n^3}\right)$

Problem 2

a. Expand the following logarithms as separate simpler logarithms without any exponents.

i $\log_4(5xy^3)$

ii $\log\left(\dfrac{3m^2}{2n^3}\right)$

iii $\ln(\sqrt{2xy})$

b. Write the following logarithms as a single logarithm with a coefficient of one.

i $2\log_5 m + 3\log_5 n + \log_5 7 - 2\log_5 p$

ii $\log x + \dfrac{1}{2}\log y - 3\log z$

iii $5\ln x + 5\ln z + 5\ln y - 5\ln 2$

Solution   see page 304

These rules for logarithms together with the basic rules discussed in the last section allow us to work with logarithms expanding or simplifying them as needed.

Section 4.6 Key Points

- The Product Rule for Logarithms:
$$\log_b(mn) = \log_b m + \log_b n$$
A logarithm of any base with multiplication inside can be written as two separate logarithms added together.

- The Quotient Rule for Logarithms:
$$\log_b\left(\frac{m}{n}\right) = \log_b m - \log_b n$$
A logarithm of any base with division inside can be written as two separate logarithms subtracted from one another.

- The Power Rule for Logarithms:
$$\log_b(m^n) = n\log_b m$$
A logarithm of any base with a power inside can be written as that logarithm with that power now being multiplied to the front.

Section 4.6 Problem Solutions

Problem 1   Solution

a.

    i $\ln 5 + \ln a + \ln b$

    ii $\log 7 + \log n - \log m$

b. Write the following logarithms as a single logarithm.

    i

$$\ln\left(\frac{18s}{3t}\right)$$

$$\ln\left(\frac{6s}{t}\right)$$

    ii $\log_7(15mn)$

Problem 2   Solution

a. For square roots, remember that they can be represented by a fractional exponent.

    i $\log_4 5 + \log_4 x + 3\log_4 y$

    ii $\log 3 + 2\log m - \log 2 - 3\log n$

    iii $\frac{1}{2}(\ln 2 + \ln x + \ln y)$

b.

    i $\log_5 \dfrac{7m^2 n^3}{p^2}$

    ii $\log \dfrac{x\sqrt{y}}{z^3}$

    iii $\ln\left(\dfrac{x^5 y^5 z^5}{32}\right)$

4.6 Exercises

Math
Tutorial

More practice problems like exercises 1 through 12 can be found in section 4.6 of the CD Tutorial.

For Exercises 1 through 12 Expand the logarithms as separate simpler logarithms with no exponents.

1. $\log(5xy^2)$

2. $\ln(2h^2k^3)$

3. $\log_7(3x^3y^4)$

4. $\log_3\left(\frac{1}{2}ab^2c^3\right)$

5. $\log\left(\frac{2x^2}{y}\right)$

6. $\log\left(\frac{5x^3y}{2z^2}\right)$

7. $\ln\left(\frac{3x^4y^3}{z}\right)$

8. $\log_9(2w^2z^3)$

9. $\log_{15}\left(\frac{\sqrt{3x^4y^3}}{z^5}\right)$

10. $\log_9(\sqrt{2w^5z^3})$

11. $\ln(\sqrt[5]{m^2p^3})$

12. $\log_7(\sqrt[3]{3x^3y^4})$

Math
Tutorial

More practice problems like exercises 13 through 25 can be found in section 4.6 of the CD Tutorial.

For exercises 13 through 25 write the logarithms as a single logarithm with a coefficient of one.

13. $\log 5 + 2\log x + \log y + 3\log z$

14. $\log 3 + 3\log x + 4\log y - \log 7$

15. $\log_3 a + 2\log_3 b - 5\log_3 c$

16. $\ln 5 + 2\ln x + 3\ln z - 4\ln y$

17. $\log_5 7 + \frac{1}{2}\log_5 x + \frac{1}{2}\log_5 y$

18. $\frac{1}{2}\ln 7 + \frac{1}{2}\ln a + \frac{3}{2}\ln b - 4\ln c$

19. $\log_9 5 + \frac{2}{3}\log_9 x + \frac{2}{3}\log_9 y$

20. $5\ln 7 + 2\ln a + 4\ln b - 3\ln c - 2\ln d$

21. $\log 3x + 3\log x - 2\log 7y$

22. $\log_3 a^2 + 2\log_3 bc - 5\log_3 3c$

23. $\ln 5x^3 + 2\ln x + 3\ln z - 4\ln yz$

24. $\log_5 7 + 2\log_5 xy + \log_5 xy$

25. $\frac{1}{2}\ln 7 + \frac{1}{2}\ln 5a + \frac{3}{2}\ln ab - 3\ln c$

Section 4.7   Solving Exponential Equations

• **Solving Exponential Equations** • **Compounding Interest**

In this section we will use the rules for exponentials and logarithms to solve problems involving exponentials. You will find that the Power Rule for Logarithms is one of the most important rules we use in the solving process. Remember that when working with equations what we do to one side of an equation we must also do to the other side of the equation. Since a logarithm is a function, we can take the logarithm of both sides of an equation much like we would square both sides. Remember that when you take the logarithm of both sides you are not multiplying but each side is now the input to the logarithm. In all of these problems we use either Log or Ln since these are logarithms we can calculate on our calculator. Recall the following rules for exponents and logarithms.

Rules for Exponents:.

1.	$x^m \cdot x^n = x^{m+n}$	2.	$(xy)^m = x^m y^m$
3.	$\dfrac{x^m}{x^n} = x^{m-n}$	4.	$\left(\dfrac{x}{y}\right)^m = \dfrac{x^m}{y^m}$
5.	$(x^m)^n = x^{mn}$	6.	$x^0 = 1$
7.	$x^{-1} = \dfrac{1}{x}$	8.	$x^{1/n} = \sqrt[n]{x}$

Rules for Logarithms:.

1.	$\log_b(mn) = \log_b m + \log_b n$	2.	$\log_b(m^n) = n\log_b m$
3.	$\log_b\left(\dfrac{m}{n}\right) = \log_b m - \log_b n$	4.	$\log_b x = \dfrac{\log x}{\log b}$
5.	$\log_b(b) = 1$	6.	$\log_b(1) = 0$

Example 1

As the population ages, more and more people will develop the symptoms of dementia resulting from Alzheimer's disease. According to medical studies shown at www.Brain.com the number of people worldwide who suffer from Alzheimer's disease may double in the next 25 years. Data from past numbers and projections for the future are given in

Table 4.7.1

Year	Number of People with Alzheimer's (in millions)
1993	9
2002	12
2025	22
2050	50

source: Data estimated from information given on www.brain.com

Skill Connection:
When working with exponential equations it is best to use a logarithm base that is convenient to calculate and find approximate values for. The two logarithm functions on your calculator are the most obvious choices for logarithm bases to use when solving.

It is good to note that within any problem you solve you can use any base logarithm you wish but you should stay consistent throughout the problem itself.

Skill Connection:
When working with exponential equations it is best to use a logarithm base that is convenient to calculate and find approximate values for. The two logarithm functions on your calculator are the most obvious choices for logarithm bases to use when solving.

It is good to note that within any problem you solve you can use any base logarithm you wish but you should stay consistent throughout the problem itself.

SC-Example 1: Solve

$$9^x = 62$$

Solution:

Using log.
$$\log(9^x) = \log 62$$
$$x \log 9 = \log 62$$
$$x = \frac{\log 62}{\log 9}$$
$$x \approx 1.878$$

Using ln.
$$\ln(9^x) = \ln 62$$
$$x \ln 9 = \ln 62$$
$$x = \frac{\ln 62}{\ln 9}$$
$$x \approx 1.878$$

In this example
$$x = \frac{\log 62}{\log 9} = \frac{\ln 62}{\ln 9}$$

are exact answers since they have not been rounded during calculation.
$$x \approx 1.878$$

is an approximate solution since it has been rounded after calculation.

In some circumstances it is best to leave an exact answer. In most of our applications the exact answer is difficult to interpret so we use the approximate solution.

a. Find a model for this data.

b. Estimate the number of people with Alzheimer's disease in 2010.

c. Find when there will be 30 million people with Alzheimer's.

Solution

a. First we need to define the variables.

A = The number of people in the world with Alzheimer's disease in millions.

t = Time in years since 1990.

With these definitions we get the following adjusted data.

Table 4.7.2

t	$A(t)$
3	9
12	12
35	22
60	50

This data gives us the following scattergram

Graphic 4.7.1.

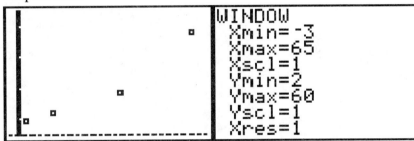

Because of the description given in the problem and the sudden rise in the data we can choose an exponential model. Using the points $(12, 12)$ and $(60, 50)$ we get

$$\begin{array}{cc} (12, 12) & (60, 50) \\ 12 = a \cdot b^{12} & 50 = a \cdot b^{60} \end{array}$$ Use the two points to write two equations in standard form.

$$\frac{50}{12} = \frac{a \cdot b^{60}}{a \cdot b^{12}}$$ Divide the two equations and solve for b.

$$4.167 = b^{48}$$

$$(4.167)^{1/48} = (b^{48})^{1/48}$$ Use the Power Rule for Exponents to isolate b.

$$1.03 = b$$

$$12 = a(1.03)^{12}$$

$$12 = 1.426a$$

$$\frac{12}{1.426} = \frac{1.426a}{1.426}$$

$$8.415 = a$$

$$A(t) = 8.415(1.03)^t$$

This model gives us the graph

Graphic 4.7.2

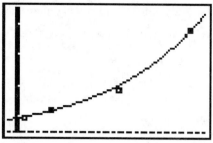

This model seems to fit reasonably so we will use it.

b. 2010 would be represented by $t = 20$ so we get
$$A(20) = 15.198$$
Thus in 2010 there will be approximately 15 million people in the world with Alzheimer's disease.

c. 30 million people with Alzheimer's disease would be represented by $A(t) = 30$ so we get

$$30 = 8.415(1.03)^t$$

$\dfrac{30}{8.415} = \dfrac{8.415(1.03)^t}{8.415}$ Start by isolating the exponential part.

$$3.565 = 1.03^t$$

$\log 3.565 = \log(1.03^t)$ Take the logarithm of both sides.

$\log 3.565 = t \log 1.03$ Use the Power Rule for Logarithms to bring the exponent down.

$\dfrac{\log 3.565}{\log 1.03} = t$ Divide both sides by the constant $\log 1.03$

$$43 \approx t$$

Therefore we find that in 2033 there will be approximately 30 million people worldwide with Alzheimer's disease. This of course assumes that the current trend continues and that no effective cures or treatments are discovered by then.

As you see from this example when the variable you are trying to solve for is in the exponent you will need to bring that variable down in order to isolate it on one side of the equation. This is why the Power Rule for Logarithms is so crucial. By taking the logarithm of both sides of the equation we can use the Power Rule for Logarithms to bring the variable in the exponent down and make it multiplication. It is crucial to first get the exponential part of the equation by itself before you take the logarithm of both sides.

Example 2
Solve the following Exponential equations.

a. $5^{3x} = 5.6$

b. $3^x - 9 = 21$

c. $8^{x-2} = 12$

d. $10^{x^2-2} = 100$

Solution

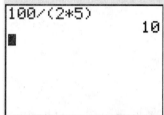
a.

$$5^{3x} = 5.6$$

$$\log(5^{3x}) = \log 5.6 \qquad \text{Take the logarithm of both sides.}$$

$$3x \log 5 = \log 5.6 \qquad \text{Use the Power Rule for Logarithms to bring down the } 3x.$$

$$\frac{3x \log 5}{3 \log 5} = \frac{\log 5.6}{3 \log 5} \qquad \text{Divide both sides by 3 and } \log 5 \text{ to isolate the } x.$$

$$x \approx 0.3568$$

b.

$$3^x - 9 = 21$$

$$\underline{ 9 \qquad 9 } \qquad \text{Isolate the exponential part.}$$

$$3^x = 30$$

$$\ln(3^x) = \ln 30 \qquad \text{Take the logarithm of both sides.}$$

$$x \ln 3 = \ln 30 \qquad \text{Use the Power Rule for Logarithms to bring down the exponent.}$$

$$\frac{x \ln 3}{\ln 3} = \frac{\ln 30}{\ln 3}$$

$$x \approx 3.0959 \qquad \text{Solve for } x.$$

c.

$$8^{x-2} = 12$$

$$\log(8^{x-2}) = \log 12$$

$$(x-2)\log 8 = \log 12 \qquad \text{Be sure to use parentheses around the exponent that you bring down.}$$

$$\frac{(x-2)\log 8}{\log 8} = \frac{\log 12}{\log 8}$$

$$x - 2 = \frac{\log 12}{\log 8}$$

$$\underline{ 2 \qquad 2 }$$

$$x = \frac{\log 12}{\log 8} + 2 \qquad \text{This is the exact solution.}$$

$$x \approx 3.195 \qquad \text{This is an approximate solution.}$$

d.

$$10^{x^2 - 2} = 100$$

$$\log(10^{x^2 - 2}) = \log 100$$

$$(x^2 - 2)\log 10 = \log 100 \qquad \text{Evaluate the logarithms.}$$

$$(x^2 - 2)(1) = 2$$

$$x^2 - 2 = 2 \qquad \text{Solve for } x.$$

$$x^2 = 4$$

$$x = \pm\sqrt{4} \qquad \text{Remember to use the plus/minus symbol when using the square root property.}$$

$$x = \pm 2$$

Problem 1

Solve the following Exponential equations.

a. $\quad 2^{5x} - 12 = 7$

b. $\quad 7^{2x+3} = 81$

Solution   See page 315

Example 3

The California sea otter population from 1914 to 1975 was growing at an exponential rate. The population during these years could be modeled by

$$O(t) = 31.95(1.057)^t$$

where $O(t)$ represents the number of California sea otters t years since 1900.

source: Model derived from data from the National Biological Service

a. Use this model to predict the number of California sea otters in 1960.

b. According to this model when were there 1500 California sea otters?

Solution

a. 1960 is represented by $t = 60$ so we get $O(60) = 889$. Thus in 1960 there were approximately 889 California sea otters.

b. 1500 California sea otters is represented by $O(t) = 1500$ so we get

$$1500 = 31.95(1.057)^t$$

$$\frac{1500}{31.95} = \frac{31.95(1.057)^t}{31.95} \quad \text{Start by isolating the exponential part.}$$

$$46.95 = 1.057^t$$

$$\log 46.95 = \log 1.057^t \quad \text{Take the logarithm of both sides.}$$

$$\log 46.95 = t\log 1.057 \quad \text{Use the Power Rule for Logarithms to bring the exponent down.}$$

$$\frac{\log 46.95}{\log 1.057} = t \qquad \text{Divide both sides by the constant } \log 1.057$$

$$69.4 \approx t$$

So we know that in 1969 there were approximately 1500 California sea otters.

Problem 2

A survey of Boulder Colorado residents asked about the optimal size for growth. The results of this survey stated that most residents thought that a growth in population at a rate of 10% per year was desirable. This type of growth rate would result in a population that can be modeled by

$$P(t) = 96000(1.1)^t$$

where $P(t)$ represents the population of Boulder Colorado t years since 2000.

source: Model derived from data in Census 2000.

a. Estimate the population of Boulder Colorado in 2002.

b. When will the population of Boulder Colorado reach 1 million?

Solution   See page 315

Example 4

An ant colony can grow at a very rapid rate. One such colony studied by Deborah Gordon initially started with about 450 worker ants and grew 79% per year.

source: Information taken from <u>The Development of Organization in an Ant Colony</u> by Deborah M. Gordon, American Scientist, Jan-Feb 1995.

a. Find a model for the number of worker ants in the colony.

b. Estimate the number of worker ants in the colony after 5 years.

c. In the sixth year of the study the colony had about 10,000 worker ants. Does your model predict this many worker ants? Explain possible reasons why or why not.

Solution

a. To find a model we either need two points to work with or we need to see a pattern to follow to build the model. We can start by building a small table of values from the information given. Since the colony grew by 79% each year we can find the size of the colony by calculating the growth and adding that to the original population.

Let's start by defining variables:

A = the number of worker ants in the colony

t = years after the study began

Table 4.7.3

t	Calculation	$A(t)$
0		450
1	$450 + 0.79(450)$	805.5
2	$805.5 + 0.79(805.5)$	1441.8
3	$1441.8 + 0.79(1441.8)$	2580.9

The pattern here may be hard to see so we will use two points and find the model.

$$(0, 450) \qquad (2, 1441.8) \qquad \text{Pick two points}$$
$$450 = ab^0 \qquad 1441.8 = ab^2 \qquad \text{Write two equations}$$
$$a = 450 \qquad 1441.8 = ab^2 \qquad \text{We have the vertical intercept}$$
$$1441.8 = 450b^2$$
$$\frac{1441.8}{450} = \frac{450b^2}{450} \qquad \text{Find } b.$$
$$3.204 = b^2$$
$$\pm\sqrt{3.204} = b$$
$$\pm 1.79 = b$$

Therefore our model will be $A(t) = 450(1.79)^t$.

b. After 5 years $t = 5$ so we get
$$A(5) = 450(1.79)^5$$
$$A(5) = 8269.5$$

Therefore after 5 years there will be about 8270 worker ants in the colony.

c. After 6 years $t = 6$ so we get
$$A(6) = 450(1.79)^6$$
$$A(6) = 14802.4$$

Our model gives a much higher number of ants than the actual study which seems to indicate that the colonies growth slowed. This may have occurred due to a limit in food or space available.

Exponential equations are found in all kinds of science and natural situations as well as a very common business situation, compounding interest. Interest paid to you by a bank for a savings account or certificate of deposit is often compounded daily. Interest that you pay on a loan or credit card balance is also often compounded daily. In the past many banks would compound interest for savings accounts only annually or monthly in order to reduce the amount of interest paid to the customers. Understanding the function used for compounding interest problems is useful when faced with making decisions in many business and financing situations.

For compounding interest problems we use the formula

$$A = P\left(1 + \frac{r}{n}\right)^{nt}$$

where the variables represent the following:

A = The amount in the account.

P = The principal (the amount initially deposited)

r = The annual interest rate written as a decimal.

n = The number of times the interest is compounded in one year.

t = The time the investment is made for, in years.

Using this formula for a typical situation is very simple. You need to identify each quantity and substitute it into the appropriate variable. Then just use caution when calculating the result.

Example 5

If $5000 is invested in a savings account paying 3% annual interest compounded daily what will the account balance be after 4 years?

Solution

First identify each given quantity and decide what you are solving for.

$5000 is the initial deposit so that is represented by $P = 5000$.

3% is the annual interest rate so it is represented by $r = 0.03$.

Compounded daily tells us that there will be 365 compounds in one year so we have $n = 365$.

4 years is the time the investment is made for so it is represented by $t = 4$.

We are asked to find the amount in the account so we need to solve for A. All of this gives us the following equation.

$$A = 5000\left(1 + \frac{0.03}{365}\right)^{365(4)}$$

$$A = 5000(1 + 0.000082192)^{1460}$$

$$A = 5000(1.1275)$$

$$A \approx 5637.46$$

Although we are writing rounded numbers you should always keep the entire number in your calculators memory and use it until the very end and then round to the appropriate place.

Problem 3

An initial deposit of $30,000 is placed in an account that earns 8% interest. Find the amount in the account after 10 years if the interest is compounded;

a.   monthly

b.   weekly

c.   daily

Solution   See page 316

Example 6

JP Manufacturing has $100,000 to invest. They need to double their money in 10 years in order to replace a piece of equipment they rely on for their business. Find the annual interest rate compounded daily that they need in order to double their money in the 10 years.

Solution

In this case we have the following given amounts:

$100,000 is to be invested so that is $P = 100000$

The investment is for 10 years so $t = 10$

They need to double their money so the account balance will need to be $200,000 so $A = 200000$

The interest rate is to compound daily so $n = 365$.

This leaves us to find the interest rate r.

$$200000 = 100000\left(1 + \frac{r}{365}\right)^{365(10)}$$

$$200000 = 100000\left(1 + \frac{r}{365}\right)^{3650}$$

$$\frac{200000}{100000} = \frac{100000\left(1 + \frac{r}{365}\right)^{3650}}{100000}$$

$$2 = \left(1 + \frac{r}{365}\right)^{3650}$$

$$2^{1/3650} = \left(\left(1 + \frac{r}{365}\right)^{3650}\right)^{1/3650}$$

$$1.000189921 = 1 + \frac{r}{365}$$

$$0.000189921 = \frac{r}{365}$$

$$365(0.000189921) = 365\left(\frac{r}{365}\right)$$

$$0.0693 \approx r$$

Therefore JP Manufacturing needs to find an account that will pay them at least 6.93% compounded daily in order to double their initial amount in 10 years.

Example 7

How long will it take an investment of $4000 to double if it is deposited in an account paying 4% interest compounded monthly?

Solution

We know the following values:

$P = 4000$

$A = 8000$

$r = 0.04$

$n = 12$

We need to find the time it takes to double the investment so we need to solve for t.

$$8000 = 4000\left(1 + \frac{0.04}{12}\right)^{12t}$$

$$2 = \left(1 + \frac{0.04}{12}\right)^{12t}$$

$$2 = 1.0033^{12t}$$

$$\log 2 = \log(1.0033^{12t})$$

$$\log 2 = 12t\log 1.0033$$

$$\frac{\log 2}{\log 1.0033} = 12t$$

$$\frac{\frac{\log 2}{\log 1.0033}}{12} = \frac{12t}{12}$$

$$\frac{\frac{\log 2}{\log 1.0033}}{12} = t$$

$$17.5 \approx t$$

So it will take about 17.5 years for the $4000 to double at 4% compounded monthly.

Problem 4
How long will it take for $10,000 to triple if it is invested in an account paying 5% compounded weekly?

Solution   See page 316

One other type of compounding growth is discussed in some areas of business and finance. Continuous compounding is the idea that the interest is always being compounded on itself resulting in a higher return. When dealing with this type of problem the compounding interest equation we have been using will no longer work since n would have to be infinity. The compounding interest equation ends up being transformed into the equation

$$A = Pe^{rt}$$

where A is the account balance after the principal P has invested at a annual rate r compounded continuously for t years. In this equation $e \approx 2.718281828$ and you can use the e^x key on your calculator.

Example 8
If $2000 is invested in a savings account paying 5% annual interest compounded continuously, what will the account balance be after 7 years?

Solution
We know the following values.
   $P = 2000$
   $r = 0.05$
   $t = 7$
   A is the missing quantity that we are being asked to solve for.

$$A = 2000e^{0.05(7)}$$

$$A \approx 2838.14$$

Therefore after 7 years this account will have $2,838.14 in it.

Section 4.7 Key Points

- When solving most exponential equations for the variable in the exponent you can follow these basic steps.
    1. Isolate the exponential part.
    2. Take the logarithm of both sides (use either log or ln).
    3. Use the Power Rule for Logarithms to bring the exponent down.
    4. Solve for the variable.
- Compounding interest problems are based on the equation

$$A = P\left(1 + \frac{r}{n}\right)^{nt}$$

where A is the balance in the account after t years. P is the principal amount deposited at an annual interest rate r, compounded n times a year.

- If interest is compounded continuously we use the equation

$$A = Pe^{rt}$$

where A is the balance in the account after t years. P is the principal amount deposited at an annual interest rate r, compounded continuously.

Section 4.7 Problem Solutions

Problem 1   Solution

a.

$$2^{5x} - 12 = 7$$
$$2^{5x} = 19$$
$$\log(2^{5x}) = \log 19$$
$$5x\log 2 = \log 19$$
$$x = \frac{\log 19}{5\log 2}$$
$$x \approx 0.8496$$

b.

$$7^{2x+3} = 81$$
$$\log(7^{2x+3}) = \log 81$$
$$(2x+3)\log 7 = \log 81$$
$$2x + 3 = \frac{\log 81}{\log 7}$$
$$2x = \frac{\log 81}{\log 7} - 3$$
$$x = \frac{\frac{\log 81}{\log 7} - 3}{2}$$
$$x \approx -0.3708$$

Problem 2   Solution

a. 2002 is represented by $t = 2$ so we get.

$$P(2) = 96000(1.1)^2$$
$$P(2) = 116160$$

Therefore in 2002 Boulder, Colorado would have had approximately 116,160 people if they grew at 10% annually.

Problem 2   Solution Continued

b. A population of 1 million would be represented by $P(t) = 1000000$ so we get

$$1000000 = 96000(1.1)^t$$

$$10.41667 = 1.1^t$$

$$\ln 10.41667 = \ln(1.1^t)$$

$$\ln 10.41667 = t\ln(1.1)$$

$$\frac{\ln 10.41667}{\ln 1.1} = t$$

$$24.587 \approx t$$

If the population of Boulder, Colorado continues to grow at a rate of 10% per year they will reach 1 million people around 2025.

Problem 3   Solution

a. Compounding monthly means $n = 12$ so we get.

$$A = 30000\left(1 + \frac{0.08}{12}\right)^{12(10)}$$

$$A \approx 66589.21$$

$30,000 will grow to $66,589.21 in 10 years if earning 8% annual interest compounded monthly.

b. Compounding weekly means $n = 52$ so we get.

$$A = 30000\left(1 + \frac{0.08}{52}\right)^{52(10)}$$

$$A \approx 66725.20$$

$30,000 will grow to $66,725.20 in 10 years if earning 8% annual interest compounded weekly.

c. Compounding daily means $n = 365$ so we get.

$$A = 30000\left(1 + \frac{0.08}{365}\right)^{365(10)}$$

$$A \approx 66760.38$$

$30,000 will grow to $66,760.38 in 10 years if earning 8% annual interest compounded daily.

Problem 4   Solution

Compounding weekly means $n = 52$ so we get

$$30000 = 10000\left(1 + \frac{0.05}{52}\right)^{52t}$$

$$3 = 1.0009615^{52t}$$

$$\log 3 = \log(1.0009615^{52t})$$

$$\log 3 = 52t\log 1.0009615$$

$$\frac{\log 3}{52\log 1.0009615} = t$$

$$21.98 \approx t$$

Therefore it will take about 22 years for $10,000 to triple if it is in an account that pays 5% compounded weekly.

4.7 Exercises

1. The use of super computers at universities all over the country has been a vital part of research and development for many areas of education. The Cray C90 housed at Rutgers University in New Jersey has seen dramatic increases in its use per year since 1987. The number of hours the Cray C90 has been used per academic year are given in

Table 4.6.1

Academic Year	Cray C90 Hours
1987	32
1988	100
1989	329
1990	831
1991	1,685
1992	2,233
1993	3,084
1994	8,517
1995	15,584
1996	27,399

source: Rutgers University High Performance Computing

  a. Find a model for this data.

  b. Give a reasonable domain and range for this model.

  c. Estimate the number of hours the Cray C90 was used in 1997.

  d. According to your model when will the Cray C90 be used 500,000 hours per year?

2. According to the United Nations records the world population in 1975 was approximately 4 billion. Statistics indicate that the world population since World War II has been growing at a rate of 1.9% per year. Assuming exponential growth the world population can be modeled by
$$P(t) = 4(1.019)^t$$
where $P(t)$ is the world population in billions and t is the time in years since 1975.

  a. Estimate the world population in 2000.

  b. When will the world population reach 10 billion?

3. A 13 year research study found that the humpback whale population off the coast of Australia was increasing at a rate of about 14% per year. In 1981 the study estimated the population to be 350 whales.

  a. Find a model for the humpback whale population.

  b. Give a reasonable domain and range for the model.

  c. Estimate the humpback whale population in 1990.

  d. If this trend continues when will the whale population reach 6000?

4. The white-tailed deer populations in the Northeast United States has been growing since the early 1980's. The population of white-tailed deer can be modeled by
$$W(t) = 1.19(1.08)^t$$
where $W(t)$ represents the number of white-tailed deer in millions in the Northeast t years since 1980.

  source: model derived from data from the National Biological Service.

  a. Estimate the white-tailed deer population in 1990.

  b. When will the white-tailed deer population reach 5 million?

  c. What may cause this population to stop growing at this rate?

5. Dr. Arnd Leike a professor of physics at the University Muenchen in Germany won a 2002 Ig Nobel Prize in Physics for his investigation into the "exponential decay" of a beer's head (the foam on top when poured). After testing several beers for the rate of decay of the head he came to the conclusion that a beer could be identified by its unique head decay rate. The following functions are for three of the beers Dr Leike tested.
$$E(s) = 16.89(0.996)^s$$
$$B(s) = 13.25(0.991)^s$$
$$A(s) = 13.36(0.993)^s$$
where $E(s)$ represents the height of the head of an Erdinger beer, $B(s)$ is the height of the head of a Budweiser Budvar, and $A(s)$ is the head height of an Augustinerbrau. All head heights are in cm s seconds after a pour.

  source: European Journal of Physics Volume 23 2002

  a. Use these models to estimate the height of each head at the end of the pour.

  b. Use these models to estimate the height of each head after 200 seconds.

  c. You may not like drinking a beer until the head has decayed to only 1cm if so how long will it take each of these beers to reach that height?

6. The population of South Africa has been growing at a rate of 1.8% per year. In 1996 the population of South Africa was 41.7 million.

  source: U.S. Dept. of Commerce, Bureau of the Census.

  a. Assuming exponential growth find a model for the population of South Africa.

  b. Estimate South Africa's population in 2002.

  c. How long will it take South Africa's population to double if it continues to grow at this rate?

7. The population of Denmark has been growing at a natural rate of 0.1% per year. In 1996 the population of Denmark was about 5.2 million.
   source: U.S. Dept. of Commerce, Bureau of the Census.

   a. Assuming exponential growth find a model for the population of Denmark.

   b. Estimate Denmark's population in 2005.

   c. How long will it take Denmark's population to double if it continues to grow at this rate?

8. The sandhill crane is a migratory bird in the United States that is being watched for its population trends. The National Biological Service estimates the populations present trend to be a growth of approximately 4.3% per year. In 1996 the estimated population was 500,000.
   source: National Biological Service.

   a. Assuming this trend continues find a model for the sandhill crane population.

   b. Estimate the population in 2002.

   c. If this trend continues when will the population reach 1 million sandhill cranes?

9. An initial deposit of $10,000 is placed in an account that earns 5% interest. Find the amount in the account after 10 years if the interest is compounded

   a. monthly

   b. weekly

   c. daily

10. An initial deposit of $500,000 is placed in an account that earns 9% interest. Find the amount in the account after 10 years if the interest is compounded

    a. monthly

    b. daily

    c. continuously

11. An initial deposit of $100,000 is placed in an account that earns 7% interest. Find the amount in the account after 20 years if the interest is compounded

    a. daily

    b. hourly

    c. continuously

12. An initial deposit of $5,000 is placed in an account that earns 3% interest. Find the amount in the account after 5 years if the interest is compounded

    a. monthly

    b. daily

    c. continuously

13. Cogs R Us has $40,000 to invest. They need to double their money in 8 years in order to replace a piece of equipment they rely on for their business. Find the annual interest rate compounded daily that they need in order to double their money in the 8 years.

14. John and Mary hope to pay for their child's college education. They have $20,000 to invest and believe they will need about 4 times that much money in about 17 years in order to pay for college. Find the annual interest rate compounded daily that they need in order to have the money they need in the 17 years.

15. How long will it take an investment of $5000 to double if it is deposited in an account paying 7% interest compounded monthly?

16. How long will it take an investment of $10,000 to double if it is deposited in an account paying 9% interest compounded continuously?

17. How long will it take an investment of $8000 to triple if it is deposited in an account paying 2% interest compounded daily?

Math   Tutorial   More practice problems like exercises 18 through 30 can be found in section 4.7 of the CD Tutorial.

For exercises 18 through 30 solve the following exponential equations. Round all answers to three decimal digits.

18. $3^w = 125$

19. $4^{x+7} = 3$

20. $5(3.2)^x = 74.2$

21. $4(1.5)^x = 30.375$

22. $2^{2t} - 58 = 6$

23. $3.4^t + 8 = 47.304$

24. $-3(2.5)^m - 89 = -3262$

25. $3(2)^{n+2} = 96$

26. $5(4)^{3x+2} - 830 = 14.5$

27. $2^{x^2+6} = 1024$

28. $10^{x^2-5} = 0.10$

29. $3(4.6)^{2m+7} = 17.3$

30. $5(4.3)^x + 7 = 2(4.3)^x + 89$

In exercises 31 through 35 find the inverse for the given function.

31. $f(x) = 5(3)^x$

32. $g(x) = 3.4(10)^x$

33. $h(x) = -2.4(4.7)^x$

34. $f(x) = 4.2e^x$

35. $g(x) = -3.4e^x$

For exercises 36 through 40 solve the system of equations graphically.

36. $y = 2.5(3)^x$
$y = 150(0.8)^x$

37. $y = 1.5(1.8)^x$
$y = 3x + 15$

38. $y = 105(0.7)^x$
$y = -1.5x^2 + 5x + 50$

39. $y = -5(0.8)^x$
$y = -1.8x - 20$

40. $y = -24(1.2)^x$
$y = 3x^2 + 2x - 75$

Section 4.8   Solving Logarithmic Equations

• **Applications of Logarithms** • **Solving Other Logarithmic Equations**

In this section we will learn to use the rules for both exponentials and logarithms to solve equations involving logarithms. Logarithms are used most often in areas of science that require us to work with very large or extremely small numbers.

One of those areas is the measurement of earthquakes. The size of an earthquake is most often measured by its magnitude. In 1935 Charles Richter defined the magnitude of an earthquake to be

$$M = \log\left(\frac{I}{S}\right)$$

where I is the intensity of the earthquake (measured by the amplitude in centimeters of a seismograph reading taken 100km from the epicenter of the earthquake) and S is the intensity of a "standard earthquake" (whose amplitude is 1 micron = 10^{-4} cm) (a standard earthquake is the smallest measurable earthquake known).

Example 1

If the intensity of an earthquake were 500 times the intensity of a standard earthquake what would its magnitude be?

Solution

The intensity of this earthquake would be $I = 500S$ so we can substitute this into the magnitude formula and calculate the magnitude.

$$M = \log\left(\frac{500S}{S}\right)$$

$$M = \log 500$$

$$M = 2.7$$

Therefore an earthquake that is 500 times the intensity of a standard earthquake has a magnitude of 2.7.

Example 2

What is the intensity of an earthquake of magnitude 6.5?

Solution

Since we know the intensity of a standard earthquake is 10^{-4} we can substitute this for S and 6.5 for M and solve for the intensity of the earthquake.

$$6.5 = \log\left(\frac{I}{10^{-4}}\right)$$

$$10^{6.5} = \frac{I}{10^{-4}} \qquad \text{Re-write the logarithm in exponential form.}$$

$$3162277.66 = \frac{I}{10^{-4}}$$

$$10^{-4}(3162277.66) = \left(\frac{I}{10^{-4}}\right)10^{-4}$$

$$316.23 = I$$

Therefore the intensity of a 6.5 magnitude earthquake is about 316.23cm. A 6.5 magnitude earthquake hit central California in 2003 killing 2 people and destroying several buildings. If this earthquake had hit in a more developed area the destruction could have been much worse.

Problem 1

What is the intensity of an earthquake with magnitude 8?

Solution   See page 325

Another application is the use of common logarithms in chemistry to calculate the pH of a solution. The pH of a solution is a measurement of how acidic or alkaline a solution is. A neutral solution will have a pH value of 7, while an acidic solution like vinegar (pH of about 3) or your stomach (pH of about 1) will have pH values less than 7. Alkaline solutions like lye (pH of about 9), used to make soap, have pH values greater than 7. The pH of a solution can be calculated by taking the negative log of the hydrogen ion concentration.

$$pH = -\log(H^+)$$

The hydrogen ion concentration has the unit M which stands for the molarity of the solution.

Example 3

What is the pH of an aqueous solution when the concentration of hydrogen ion is 5.0×10^{-4} M?

Solution

Since the hydrogen ion concentration is given as 5.0×10^{-4} M we can substitute that in for H^+ and get

$$pH = -\log(5.0 \times 10^{-4})$$
$$pH = 3.30$$

Therefore we an aqueous solution with a hydrogen ion concentration of 5.0×10^{-4} M has a pH of 3.30.

Example 4

Find the hydrogen ion concentration of a solution with pH = 4.7.

Solution

Since we know the pH value we can substitute 4.7 for pH in the formula and solve for H.

$$4.7 = -\log(H^+)$$ Multiply both sides by -1 to isolate the logarithm.
$$-4.7 = \log(H^+)$$

$$10^{-4.7} = H^+$$ Re-write the logarithm in exponential form.

$$1.995 \times 10^{-5} = H^+$$

Therefore a solution with a pH value of 4.7 will have a hydrogen ion concentration of 1.995×10^{-5} M.

Problem 2

Find the hydrogen ion concentration of a solution with pH = 2.3.

Solution   See page 325

Example 5

Solve the following logarithm equations.

a. $\log x = \log 5$

b. $\log(x + 20) = 2$

c. $\ln t = 3$

d. $\log(2x) + 7 = 9$

Solution

a. In this case we have a logarithm equal to another logarithm of the same base so we know that the inside of the logarithms must be equal. Therefore $x = 5$ is the solution to this equation.

b. This equation starts out with a logarithm isolated on the left side of the equation and it is equal to a constant. In this case we can re-write the logarithm in exponential form and then solve.

$$\log(x + 20) = 2$$
$$10^2 = x + 20$$
$$100 = x + 20$$
$$80 = x$$

c. Again we have a single logarithm equal to a constant so we re-write the logarithm into exponential form and solve.

$$\ln t = 3$$
$$e^3 = t$$
$$20.086 \approx t$$

In this case e^3 is the exact answer and is sometimes the required or needed solution. 20.086 is an approximate answer and is suitable for many applications.

d. We must first start by isolating the logarithm on one side of the equation and then we re-write the logarithm into exponential form and solve.

$$\log(2x) + 7 = 9$$

$$\underline{\quad -7 \quad -7 \quad}$$ Isolate the logarithm

$$\log(2x) = 2$$
$$10^2 = 2x$$ Re-write the logarithm into exponential form.
$$100 = 2x$$
$$50 = x$$ Solve for x.

You can see that the relationship between logarithms and exponentials will play a big role in how we solve these equations. In general when trying to solve an equation that has a variable inside a logarithm you will want to isolate the logarithm and then re-write the logarithm in exponential form. This will get the variable out of the logarithm and allow you to solve the equation. If there are more than one logarithm in the equation first combine them into a single log using the rules for logarithms.

Example 6

Solve the following logarithm equations.

a. $\log_6(x) + \log_6(2x) = 2$

b. $\log(2x) + \log(x - 4) = 1$

c. $\log_2(3x^2) - \log_2 x = 5$

d. $\log_2(x + 5) + \log_2(x + 4) = 1$

Solution

a.   First you can combine the logarithms together using the Product Rule for Logarithms and then re-write the logarithm in exponential form so you can solve for x.

$$\log_6(x) + \log_6(2x) = 2$$
$$\log_6(2x^2) = 2$$
$$6^2 = 2x^2$$
$$36 = 2x^2$$
$$18 = x^2$$
$$\pm\sqrt{18} = x \qquad \text{These two answers will need to be checked.}$$
$$\pm 4.24 = x$$

In this case we have two possible solutions but because we cannot evaluate the logarithm of a negative number $x = -4.24$ cannot be a solution. Therefore $x = 4.24$ is our only valid solution.

b.   Again combine the logarithms and then re-write in exponential form.

$$\log(2x) + \log(x - 4) = 1$$
$$\log(2x^2 - 8x) = 1$$
$$10 = 2x^2 - 8x$$
$$0 = 2x^2 - 8x - 10 \qquad \text{We have a quadratic left so we can factor or use the quadratic formula.}$$
$$0 = 2(x - 5)(x + 1)$$
$$x - 5 = 0 \qquad x + 1 = 0 \qquad \text{These two answer will need to be checked.}$$
$$x = 5 \qquad x = -1$$

Again we have two possible solutions but when $x = -1$ is substituted into the logarithm it is impossible to evaluate. Therefore $x = 5$ is our only solution.

c.   In this situation we will need to use the Quotient Rule for Logarithms in order to combine the two logarithms that are subtracted.

$$\log_2(3x^2) - \log_2 x = 5$$
$$\log_2\left(\frac{3x^2}{x}\right) = 5 \qquad \text{Simplify the fraction.}$$
$$\log_2(3x) = 5$$
$$2^5 = 3x \qquad \text{Re-write into exponential form.}$$
$$32 = 3x$$
$$10.67 \approx x$$

d.

$$\log_2(x + 5) + \log_2(x + 4) = 1$$
$$\log_2(x^2 + 9x + 20) = 1 \qquad \text{Combine the logarithms using the product rule and then rewrite in exponential form.}$$
$$x^2 + 9x + 20 = 2^1$$
$$x^2 + 9x + 18 = 0 \qquad \text{Factor.}$$
$$(x + 3)(x + 6) = 0$$
$$x + 3 = 0 \qquad x + 6 = 0$$
$$x = -3 \qquad x = -6$$

Although we found two answers for this problem only $x = -3$ works in this case because when you substitute $x = -6$ into the equation it is undefined. The negative 3 does work because once it is substituted into the logarithms you get a positive value inside each logarithm and can thus evaluate them.

Problem 3

Solve the following logarithm equations.

a. $\log(2x) + \log(3x) = 3$

b. $\ln(3x + 5) = 4$

c. $\log_3(x + 11) + \log_3(x + 5) = 3$

d. $\log_4(3x) + \log_4(2x - 7) = 2$

Solution   See page 326

Section 4.8 Key Points

- When solving logarithm equations with a variable inside the logarithm you can follow these basic steps.
    1.   Isolate the logarithm part; this may include combining logarithms.
    2.   Re-write the logarithm into exponential form.
    3.   Solve for the variable.

- The magnitude of an earthquake can be calculated using the equation

$$M = \log\left(\frac{I}{S}\right)$$

where I is the intensity of the earthquake, S is the intensity of a "standard earthquake" 10^{-4} cm, and M is the magnitude of the earthquake measured on the Richter scale.

- The pH of a solution can be measured using the equation
$$pH = -\log(H^+)$$
where H^+ is the hydrogen ion concentration in the solution.

Section 4.8 Problem Solutions

Problem 1   Solution

Since the magnitude of the earthquake is 8 we can substitute $M = 8$ into the equation and solve for I.

$$8 = \log\left(\frac{I}{10^{-4}}\right)$$

$$10^8 = \frac{I}{10^{-4}}$$

$$100000000 = \frac{I}{10^{-4}}$$

$$10^{-4}(100000000) = \left(\frac{I}{10^{-4}}\right)10^{-4}$$

$$10000 = I$$

Therefore the intensity of an magnitude 8 earthquake would be 10,000 cm.

Problem 2   Solution

We are given the pH of 2.3 so we can substitute that into the equation and solve for H^+.

$$2.3 = -\log(H^+)$$

$$-2.3 = \log(H^+)$$

$$10^{-2.3} = H^+$$

$$0.00501 = H^+$$

Therefore a solution with a pH value of 2.3 has a hydrogen ion concentration of 0.00501M.

Problem 3   *Solution*

a.

$$\log(2x) + \log(3x) = 3$$
$$\log(6x^2) = 3$$
$$6x^2 = 10^3$$
$$6x^2 = 1000$$
$$x^2 = 166.667$$
$$x = \pm\sqrt{166.67}$$
$$x = \pm 12.91$$

In this case we have two possible answers but the -12.91 results in a negative inside the logarithms so we cannot use that solution. Therefore $x = 12.91$ is the only solution.

b.

$$\ln(3x + 5) = 4$$
$$3x + 5 = e^4$$
$$3x = e^4 - 5$$
$$x = \frac{e^4 - 5}{3}$$
$$x = 16.533$$

c.

$$\log_3(x + 11) + \log_3(x + 5) = 3$$
$$\log_3(x^2 + 16x + 55) = 3$$
$$x^2 + 16x + 55 = 27$$
$$x^2 + 16x + 28 = 0$$
$$(x + 2)(x + 14) = 0$$
$$x + 2 = 0 \qquad x + 14 = 0$$
$$x = -2 \qquad x = -14$$

Here we have two possible answers but the $x = -14$ will result in the logarithm of a negative number so it will not work. Therefore we have only $x = -2$ as a solution.

d.

$$\log_4(3x) + \log_4(2x - 7) = 2$$
$$\log_4(6x^2 - 21x) = 2$$
$$6x^2 - 21x = 4^2$$
$$6x^2 - 21x = 16$$
$$6x^2 - 21x - 16 = 0 \qquad \text{Use the Quadratic Formula to solve.}$$
$$x = 4.14 \qquad x = -0.64$$

Here we have two possible answers but the $x = -0.64$ will result in the logarithm of a negative number so it will not work. Therefore we have only $x = 4.14$ as a solution.

4.8 Exercises

1. If the intensity of an earthquake were 2000 times the intensity of a standard earthquake what would its magnitude be?

2. If the intensity of an earthquake were 1,000,000 times the intensity of a standard earthquake what would its magnitude be?

3. If the intensity of an earthquake were 500,000 cm what would its magnitude be?

4. If the intensity of an earthquake were 25,000 cm what would its magnitude be?

5. What is the intensity of an earthquake of magnitude 7.5?

6. What is the intensity of an earthquake of magnitude 9.0?

7. What is the intensity of an earthquake of magnitude 4.3?

8. What is the pH of an aqueous solution when the concentration of hydrogen ion is 2.3×10^{-3} M?

9. What is the pH of an aqueous solution when the concentration of hydrogen ion is 4.0×10^{-7} M?

10. Find the hydrogen ion concentration of a solution with pH = 6.52.

11. Find the hydrogen ion concentration of a solution with pH = 3.1.

12. Find the hydrogen ion concentration of a solution with pH = 5.43.

13. Find the hydrogen ion concentration of a solution with pH = 1.36.

14. Find the hydrogen ion concentration of a solution with pH = 4.28.

Math Tutorial   More practice problems like exercises 15 through 32 can be found in section 4.8 of the CD Tutorial.

For exercises 15 through 32 solve each logarithm equation. Check that all solutions are valid.

15. $\log(5x + 2) = 2$

16. $\ln(3t) + 5 = 3$

17. $\log_5(3x) + \log_5 x = 4$

18. $\log_3(x + 2) + \log_3(x - 3) = 2$

19. $\log_2(2x) + \log_2(5x - 4) = 6$

20. $\log(5x^3) - \log(2x) = 2$

21. $\ln(x + 4) = 2$

22. $\log_4(x - 2) = 2$

23. $\log(2x + 1) = -0.5$

24. $\log(x^2 - 3x) = 1$

25. $\log_5(x) + \log_5(2x + 7) - 3 = 0$

26. $\log_5(x + 12) + \log_5(x + 8) = 1$

27. $\log_4(-2x + 5) + \log_4(x + 21.5) = 4$

28. $3\log_2(2x) + \log_2(16) = 7$

29. $\ln(3x) + \ln(x + 5) = 4$

30. $2\log(3x) + 8 = 2$

31. $\ln(3x^2 + 5x) = 2$

32. $5\log(2x) = 3$

Chapter 4 Review Exercises

1. The population of Africa is estimated to be doubling about every 28 years. The population of Africa in 1996 was about 731.5 million.
    source: U.S. Dept. of Commerce, Bureau of the Census.

    a. Using this information find a model for the population of Africa.

    b. Using your model estimate the population of Africa in 2005.

2. The flu is traveling through a large city at an alarming rate. Every day the number of people who have flu symptoms is 3 times what it was the previous day. Assume one person started this flu epidemic.

    a. Find a model for the number of people with flu symptoms after d days.

    b. Use your model to estimate the number of people with flu symptoms after 2 weeks.

3. Polonium-210 has a half-life of 138 days.

    a. Find a model for the percent of a Polonium-210 sample left after d days.

    b. Estimate the percent of Polonium-210 left after 300 days.

4. Find an exponential model for the data

    Table 4.8.1

x	$f(x)$
0	5000
1	4000
2	3200
3	2560
4	2048

5. Find an exponential model for the data

    Table 4.8.2

x	$f(x)$
0	0.2
1	1.52
2	11.53
3	87.58
4	665.05

For Exercises 6 through 15 simplify the given expression using the order of operations and exponent rules. Write each answer without negative exponents.

6. $(2x^3y^4z)^3(5x^{-3}y^2z)^{-2}$

7. $2^7(2^3)$

8. $\left(\dfrac{225a^5b^3c}{15ab^6c^{-4}}\right)$

9. $\left(\dfrac{31m^5n^4}{a^5c^7}\right)^0$

10. $(3x^2y^5)(5x^2y^2)$

11. $(a^3b^{-5}c^{-2})^{-2}$

12. $(3m^{-1}n^3p^{-2})^2(5m^2n^{-6}p^4)$

13. $\left(\dfrac{a^2b^{-3}c^5}{a^3b^5c^7}\right)$

14. $\left(\dfrac{3a^{-1}b^3c^5}{ab^{-2}c^3}\right)^{-2}$

15. $\left(\dfrac{3x^2y^5z}{5xy^3z}\right)\left(\dfrac{15x^3yz^4}{10xz}\right)$

For exercises 16 and 17 sketch the graph of the function and state any information you know from the values of a and b.

16. $f(x) = 5(1.3)^x$

17. $g(t) = -0.25(0.5)^t$

18. The number of non-strategic nuclear warheads stockpiled by the U.S. during the 1950's is given in **Table 4.8.3**

    Table 4.8.3

Year	Non-Strategic Warheads
1951	91
1952	205
1953	436
1954	563
1955	857
1956	1,618
1957	2,244
1958	4,122
1959	8,462
1960	13,433

    source: Natural Resources Defense Council

    a. Find a model for this data.

    b. Give a reasonable domain and range for your model.

    c. Estimate the number of non-strategic warheads stockpiled by the U.S. in 1965.

19. The following data was collected during an experiment designed to measure the decay of the radioactive material $^{137}\text{Ba}^\text{m}$. Every 60 seconds the number of counts per minute were taken from a Geiger counter. The readings are recorded in **Table 4.8.4** .

Table 4.8.4

Time (in seconds)	Counts per minute
0	3098
60	2270
120	1856
180	1436
240	1220
300	914
360	596

   a. Find an exponential model for this data.

   b. Estimate the number of counts per minute this sample would have after 10 minutes.

   c. Give a reasonable domain and range for this model.

For exercises 20 through 22 determine if the following are graph of one-to-one functions.

20.

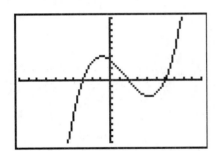

21.

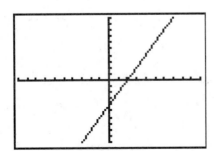

22.

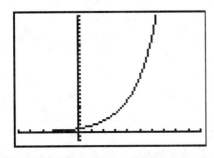

For exercises 23 through 27 find the inverse for each function.

23. $f(x) = 1.4x - 7$

24. $g(t) = -2t + 6$

25. $h(x) = 5^x$

26. $f(x) = 3.5(6)^x$

27. $g(x) = 2e^x$

For Exercises 28 through 30 write the logarithms as separate simpler logarithms with no exponents.

28. $\ln(2x^3y^4)$

29. $\log_3(\sqrt{5ab^2c^3})$

30. $\log\left(\dfrac{3x^3y^5}{z^4}\right)$

For exercises 31 through 34 write the logarithms as a single logarithm with a coefficient of one.

31. $\log 4 + 3\log x + 2\log y + \log z$

32. $\log 2 + 4\log x + 5\log y - 2\log z$

33. $\log_3 a + 3\log_3 b - 2\log_3 c$

34. $\ln 7 + 2\ln x + \ln z - 5\ln y - 3\ln z$

35. The number of Franklin's Gulls in North America has been facing significant declines in the past several years. The population of Franklin's Gulls can be modeled by

$$F(t) = 750(0.9405^t)$$

where $F(t)$ represents the number of Franklin's Gulls in thousands in North America t years since 2000.

   source: model derived from data from the National Biological Service.

   a. Estimate the Franklin's Gull population in 2005.

   b. When will the Franklin's Gull population reach 500,000?

   c. What may cause this population to stop declining at this rate?

36. How long will it take an investment of $7000 to double if it is deposited in an account paying 6% interest compounded monthly?

37. How long will it take an investment of $100,000 to double if it is deposited in an account paying 8.5% interest compounded continuously?

For exercises 38 through 42 solve the following exponential equations.

38. $4^w = 12.5$

39. $7^{x+2} = 47$

40. $17(1.9)^x = 55.4$

41. $3(5)^{3x+2} - 700 = 11$

42. $5^{x^2+4} = 15625(6)$

43.   What is the intensity of an earthquake of magnitude 5.7?

44.   What is the pH of an aqueous solution when the concentration of hydrogen ion is 3.7×10^{-3} M?

45.   Find the hydrogen ion concentration of a solution with pH $= 5.6$.

For exercises 46 through 50 solve each logarithm equation. Check that all solutions are valid.

46. $\log(10x + 20) = 5$

47. $\ln(4.3t) + 7.5 = 3$

48. $\log_5(2x) + \log_5 x = 4$

49. $\log_3(x - 4) + \log_3(x + 1) = 3$

50. $\log(8x^5) - \log(2x) = 3$

Chapter 4 Test

1. At 12 noon there are 5 million bacteria on the bathroom door handle. Under these conditions the number of bacteria on the handle is doubling every hour.
   a. Find a model for the number of bacteria on the bathroom door handle h hours after 12 noon.
   b. Estimate the number of bacteria on the handle at 6pm.
   c. Find a new model for this situation if the bacteria are doubling every 15 minutes.

2. Thallium-210 has a half-life of 1.32 minutes.
   a. Find a model for the percent of a Thallium-210 sample left after m minutes.
   b. Estimate the percent of Thallium-210 left after 15 minutes.

3. How long will it take an investment of $1000 to double if it is deposited in an account paying 3.5% interest compounded monthly?

4. What is the intensity of an earthquake of magnitude 7.0?

For exercises 5 through 8 solve the equation.

5. $\log_{16}(2x+1) = -0.5$

6. $\log_7 x + \log_7 (2x+7) - 3 = 0$

7. $20 = -3 + 4(2^x)$

8. $8 = 3^{7x-1}$

9. Is this the graph of a one-to-one function? Explain why or why not.

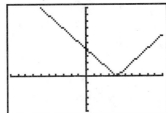

For exercises 10 through 12 simplify the expressions. Write each answer without negative exponents.

10. $(2b^4 c^{-2})^5 (3b^{-3} c^{-4})^{-2}$

11. $\left(\dfrac{16b^{12} c^2}{2b^{-3} c^{-4}}\right)^{-1/3}$

12. $\dfrac{25x^{-9} y^{-8}}{35x^{-10} y^{-3}}$

13. Write as a single logarithm with coefficient 1.
    $$4\log(2a^3) + 5\log(ab^3)$$

14. Write the logarithm as separate simpler logarithms with no exponents.
    $$\log\left(\frac{3xy^5}{\sqrt{z}}\right)$$

15. Use the graph of the exponential to answer the following:

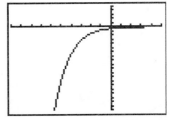

   a. Is the value of a positive or negative?
   b. Is the value of b less than or greater than one?

16. The number of CD singles shipped in the mid 1990's is given in **Table 4.9.1**

Table 4.9.1

Year	CD singles (in millions)
1993	7.8
1994	9.3
1995	21.5
1996	43.2
1997	66.7

source: Statistical Abstract 2001.

   a. Find a model for this data.
   b. Give a reasonable domain and range for this model.
   c. Estimate the number of CD singles shipped in 2000.
   d. When were there only 5 million CD singles shipped?

For exercises 17 through 20 find the inverse of the function.

17. $f(x) = 5x + 2$

18. $g(x) = -2.4x - 7.3$

19. $f(x) = 5^x$

20. $h(x) = 2(7)^x$

For exercises 21 and 22 sketch the graph of the function and state any information you know from the values of a and b.

21. $f(x) = -2(3.1)^x$

22. $g(t) = 40(0.8)^t$

23. Find the hydrogen ion concentration of a solution with pH = 2.58.

Section 5.1   Introduction to Rational Functions

Introduction to Rational Functions•Rational Models•Domain & Range•Direct & Inverse Variation

In this chapter we will study another type of function that is found in many areas of business, physics and other sciences. Rational functions are functions that contain fractions involving polynomials. These functions can be simple or very complex. Rational functions often arise from combining two functions together using division. In this section we will learn some of the basics about different characteristics of rational functions and areas in which they occur.

Concept Investigation 1

Let's start by considering a simple situation involving driving a car.
John is planning on taking a 200 mile driving trip. Let's consider how long this trip will take John if he travels at different average speeds.

a.   Fill in the following table with the times it will take John to travel 200 miles if he drives at an average rate of r miles per hour.

Table 5.1.1

Rate (r) (mph)	Time (t) (hours)
10	20
25	8
40	
50	
80	
100	
200	

What happens to the time it takes to travel the 200 miles as the average speed gets slower?

What happens to the time it takes to travel the 200 miles as the average speed gets faster?

b.   On your graphing calculator create a scattergram of the data in **Table 5.1.1**. Does the scattergram agree with your answers from part a.?

c.   Solve the equation $D = rt$ for time, and use that to write a model for the time it takes John to travel 200 miles. (Verify your model by graphing it with your data.)

d.   What is a reasonable domain and range for the model in this situation?

A function like $t(r) = \dfrac{200}{r}$ is a simple rational function since it has a variable in the denominator of the fraction. Any expression of the form

$$\frac{P(x)}{Q(x)}$$

where $P(x)$ and $Q(x)$ are polynomials and $Q(x) \neq 0$ is called a **rational expression**. Notice that $Q(x)$ cannot equal zero or you would have division by zero and thus it would be undefined. This is always a concern when working with rational expressions. In Concept Investigation 1 you should note that it does not make sense for John to average zero miles per hour or he will never travel the 200 miles.

Definition 5.1.1
Rational Expressions:
An expression of the form

$$\frac{P(x)}{Q(x)}$$

where $P(x)$ and $Q(x)$ are polynomials and $Q(x) \neq 0$ is called a rational expression.

$$\frac{5x+2}{x-6} \qquad \frac{3}{x}$$

are rational expressions.

When in a context the domain of a rational function needs to avoid any values that make the denominator zero or make the situation not make sense. The domain will usually be restricted to a small area of the graph and thus the range will be the lowest to the highest points on the graph within the domain. When working with a situation set the domain depending on what makes sense in the context. Be cautious with any restrictions that may be stated in the problem that would limit the domain in some way.

Example 1

A group of students in the chess club want to rent a bus to take them to the National Chess competition. The bus is going to cost $1500 to rent and can fit up to 60 people.

a. Find a model for the per person cost to rent the bus if s students take the bus and each student pays an equal share.

b. How much would the per person cost be if 30 students take the bus?

c. How much would the per person cost be if 60 students take the bus?

d. What would a reasonable domain and range be for this model?

Solution

a. Let $C(s)$ be the cost per student in dollars for s students to take the bus to the National Chess competition. Since the students are going to each pay an equal amount we might consider a few simple examples:
   If only one student takes the bus that student will need to pay $1500. If two students take the bus they will have to pay $\dfrac{1500}{2} = 750$ dollars each.

   So we are taking the total cost of $1500 and dividing it by the number of students taking the bus. This pattern would continue and we would get the function:

$$C(s) = \frac{1500}{s}$$

b. If 30 students take the bus we can substitute 30 for s and calculate C.

$$C(30) = \frac{1500}{30}$$

$$C(30) = 50$$

Therefore if 30 students take the bus it will cost $50 per person.

c. Substituting in $s = 60$ we get

$$C(60) = \frac{1500}{60}$$

$$C(60) = 25$$

Therefore if 60 students take the bus it will cost $25 per person.

d. Since the bus can only hold up to 60 people we must limit the domain to positive numbers up to 60. This means we could have a possible domain of $[1, 60]$. With this domain the range would be $[25, 1500]$. Of course there are other possible domains and ranges but these would be considered reasonable.

The previous function is an example of **Inverse Variation** and it could be stated that C varies inversely with s. That is, when one value increases the other decreases. In this example the more students that take the bus the less the per student cost will be.

Variation is when two or more variables are related to one another using multiplication and/or division. When two variables are related and both either increase together or decrease together we call it **Direct Variation**. The equation $D = 60t$ is an example of direct variation, when the value of t increases so does the value of D.

Definition 5.1.2

Direct Variation:

The variable y varies directly with x if

$$y = kx$$

Inverse Variation:

The variable y varies inversely with x if

$$y = \frac{k}{x}$$

in both cases k is called the variation constant (or the constant of proportionality).

The form of an equation that represents direct variation is a simple linear equation with a vertical intercept of $(0, 0)$ and the variation constant is the slope of the line. Since we have studied linear equations earlier we will concentrate on problems involving inverse variation. You should note that an equation that represents variables that vary inversely is also a simple kind of rational function.

Example 2

The illumination of a light source is inversely proportional to the square of the distance from the light source. A certain light has an illumination of 60 foot candles at a distance of 5 feet from the light source.

a. Find a model for the illumination of this light.

b. What is the illumination of this light at a distance of 10 feet from the light source?

c. What is the illumination of this light at a distance of 100 feet?

Solution

a. Let I be the illuminance of the light in foot candles and d be the distance from the light source in feet.

   Since we are told that the illumination is inversely proportional to the square of the distance from the light source we get a model of

$$I = \frac{k}{d^2}$$

   We still need to find the variation constant k. Since we are told that at 5 feet from the light source the illumination is 60 foot candles we can substitute these values in and find k.

$$60 = \frac{k}{5^2} \qquad \text{Substitute the given values for } I \text{ and } k.$$

$$60 = \frac{k}{25} \qquad \text{Solve for } k.$$

$$1500 = k$$

   Now that we know $k = 1500$ we can write the model for illumination as

$$I(d) = \frac{1500}{d^2}$$

b. We are given the distance of 10 feet so we can substitute $d = 10$ and calculate the illumination.

$$I(10) = \frac{1500}{10^2}$$

$$I(10) = \frac{1500}{100}$$

$$I(10) = 15$$

   Therefore the illumination at 10 feet from the light source is 15 foot candles.

c. We are given the distance of 100 feet so we can substitute $d = 100$ and calculate the illumination.

$$I(10) = \frac{1500}{100^2}$$

$$I(10) = \frac{1500}{10000}$$

$$I(10) = 0.15$$

   Therefore the illumination at 100 feet from the light source is 0.15 foot candles.

   In any direct or inverse variation problem you need one example of the relationship between the two variables in order to find the variation constant and then you will be able to write the formula for that particular situation. In example 2 the variation constant will change based on the strength of the light source you are working with.

Problem 1

In physics if a fixed force is applied to an object the amount of acceleration a in meters per second squared of that object is inversely proportional to the mass in kilograms of that object. When a fixed amount of force is applied to a 5kg mass it is accelerated at 10mps^2 .(mps^2 is meters per second squared)

a. Find a function for the acceleration a of a mass m when this fixed amount of force is applied.

b. What is the acceleration of a 15kg mass when this force is applied?

Solution   See page 340

Another type of situation that involves rational functions is when we are combining two functions using division. In the next example we will investigate one of these situations.

Example 3

In the state of California the student teacher ratio has been dropping steadily since about 1995. The total number of students in the K-12 public schools in California can be modeled by

$$S(t) = 112.25t + 4930.6$$

where S is the number of students in thousands in the California K-12 public schools and t is time in years since 1990. The number of teachers in California's K-12 public schools can be modeled by

$$T(t) = 11.75t + 175.6$$

where T is the number of teachers in thousands in the California K-12 public schools and t is time in years since 1990.

a. Estimate the number of students in California's K-12 public schools in 1995.

b. Estimate the number of teachers in California's K-12 public schools in 1995.

c. Find a model for the average number of students per teacher in the California K-12 public schools.

d. Estimate the average number of students per teacher there in California's K-12 public schools during the year 2000.

e. Use the graph of your new model to estimate when the number of students per teacher in California's K-12 public schools will be 20.

Solution

a. We are given the year 1995 so we can substitute $t = 5$ and get

$$S(5) = 112.25(5) + 4930.6$$
$$S(5) = 5491.9$$

Therefore in 1995 there were approximately 5,491.9 thousand students in California's K-12 public schools.

b. Again we are given 1995 but this time we need to substitute $t = 5$ into the $T(t)$ function.

$$T(5) = 11.75(5) + 175.6$$
$$T(5) = 234.35$$

Therefore in 1995 there were approximately 234.35 thousand teachers in California's K-12 public schools.

c. We are asked for a model that would give the average number of students per teacher in California's K-12 public schools so we need to take the number of students and divide it by the number of teachers. Let $A(t)$ be the average number of students per teacher in California's K-12 public schools t years since 1990.

$$A(t) = \frac{S(t)}{T(t)} = \frac{112.25t + 4930.6}{11.75t + 175.6}$$

d. We are asked for the average number of students in 2000 so we can substitute $t = 10$ into our new model $A(t)$

$$A(10) = \frac{112.25(10) + 4930.6}{11.75(10) + 175.6}$$
$$A(10) = 20.65$$

Therefore in 2000 there was an average of 20.65 students per teacher in California's K-12 public schools.

e.   Looking at the graph and using trace we get

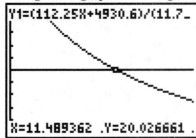

We can estimate that when $t = 11.5$ the number of students per teacher is about 20. Thus according to this model around the year 2002 the average number of students per teacher in California's K-12 public schools will be 20.

When working with problems like those in Example 3 you need to remember the rules for when you can divide two functions. When the functions are in context you need to be sure the units of the input variables are the same and that when the units of the outputs are divided the resulting unit makes since in the context of the problem.

Problem 2

The number of people in the United States enrolled in medicare can be modeled by

$$M(t) = 0.39t + 35.65$$

where $M(t)$ represents the number of people enrolled in medicare in millions t years since 1990. The disbursements by the medicare program can be modeled by

$$D(t) = -3160.64t^2 + 52536.5t - 4548.31$$

where $D(t)$ represents the amount of money medicare disbursed to people in millions of dollars t years since 1990.

a.   Find a model for the average amount disbursed per person enrolled in medicare t years since 1990.

b.   Estimate the average amount disbursed to a medicare recipient in 1999.

c.   Use the graph of your model to estimate the year that the average amount disbursed to medicare recipients reached a maximum.

Solution   See page 341

The domain of a rational function in an abstract math question is mainly concerned with excluding values from the domain that would result in the denominator being zero. The easiest way to determine the domain of a rational function is to set the denominator equal to zero and solve. The domain then becomes all real numbers except those values that make the denominator equal zero. Any place where the denominator is zero would result in a **vertical asymptote**, or a hole with a missing value. Vertical asymptotes are similar to the horizontal asymptotes we saw in the graphs of exponential functions. The graph of a function will not touch a vertical asymptote but will instead will get as close as possible and then jump over it and continue on the other side. A hole will occur, instead of a vertical asymptote, at any input value that make the numerator and denominator both equal to zero. Determining when each of these occurs will be left for a future course but we will look at the graphs of these functions to see them occur.

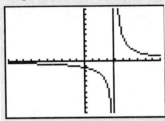
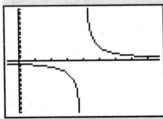
Example 4

Find the domain of the following rational functions:

a. $f(x) = \dfrac{5}{x}$

b. $g(x) = \dfrac{5 + x}{x + 9}$

c. $h(x) = \dfrac{x + 4}{(x + 4)(x - 7)}$

d. $f(x) = \dfrac{3x + 2}{x^2 + 5x + 6}$

e.

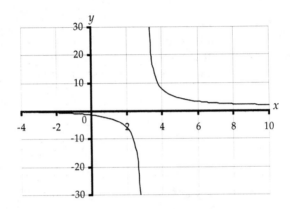

Solution

a. Since the denominator would be zero when $x = 0$ we have a domain of
all real numbers except zero. This can also be written simply as $x \neq 0$.
Looking at the graph of $f(x)$ we can see that the function jumps over the
input value $x = 0$ and there is a vertical asymptote in its place.

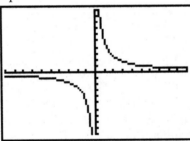

b. The denominator would be zero when $x = -9$ so its domain is all real
numbers such that $x \neq -9$. Looking at this graph again we see a vertical asymptote. Pay attention to the way this function must be entered into the
calculator with parenthesis around the numerator and another set of parenthesis around the denominator of the fraction.

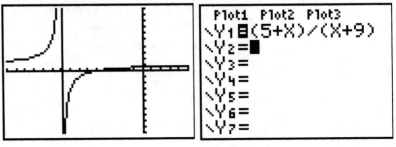

c. Set the denominator equal to zero and you get

$$(x+4)(x-7) = 0$$

$$x + 4 = 0 \qquad x - 7 = 0$$

$$x = -4 \qquad x = 7$$

Therefore the domain is all real numbers except $x \neq -4$ or 7. This graph is shown in two parts so that you can see the hole that appears at $x = -4$ and then the asymptote at $x = 7$. Without doing two windows it is almost impossible to see the hole.

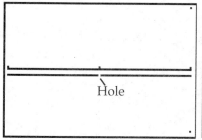
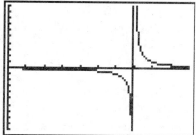

d. Set the denominator equal to zero

$$x^2 + 5x + 6 = 0$$

$$(x+3)(x+2) = 0$$

$$x + 3 = 0 \qquad x + 2 = 0$$

$$x = -3 \qquad x = -2$$

Therefore the domain is all real numbers except $x \neq -3$ or -2 This graph has an interesting shape to it but does have two vertical asymptotes. Again the numerator and denominator of the fraction needs parenthesis around them to create the graph correctly.

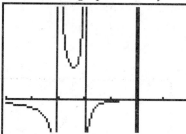
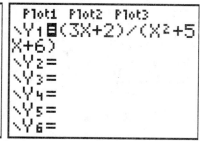

e. The graph of this function shows a vertical intercept at about $x = 3$ so the domain should be All Real Numbers except $x \neq 3$.

Problem 3

Find the domain of the following rational functions:

a. $f(x) = \dfrac{3}{x}$

b. $g(x) = \dfrac{x+2}{x-7}$

c. $h(x) = \dfrac{x+2}{x^2 - 3x - 10}$

Solution   See page 341

Section 5.1 Key Points

- An expression of the form

$$\frac{P(x)}{Q(x)}$$

  where $P(x)$ and $Q(x)$ are polynomials and $Q(x) \neq 0$ is called a rational expression.

- The domain of a rational function is found by setting the denominator equal to zero, the domain will be all real numbers except where the denominator equals zero.

- The variable y varies directly with x if

$$y = kx$$

  k is called the variation constant (or the constant of proportionality). k is also the slope of this linear relationship.

- The variable y varies inversely with x if

$$y = \frac{k}{x}$$

  k is called the variation constant (or the constant of proportionality). Inverse variation is an example of a simple rational function.

Section 5.1 Problem Solutions

Problem 1   Solution

a. Since we are told that a fixed amount of force is applied and that acceleration and mass vary inversely we can set up the basic formula

$$a = \frac{k}{m}$$

We are given one example of the mass and acceleration relationship so using this we can find the variation constant k.

$$10 = \frac{k}{5}$$

$$50 = k$$

This gives us the model

$$a(m) = \frac{50}{m}$$

where a is the acceleration in meters per second squared and m is the mass in kg.

b. We are told we have a 15 kg mass so we can substitute $m = 15$ and get

$$a(15) = \frac{50}{15}$$

$$a(15) = 3.3$$

When this force is applied to a 15kg mass object that object should accelerate at 3.3 mps^2.

Problem 2   *Solution*

a.   Let $P(t)$ be the average dollars disbursed per person by medicare t years since 1990.

$$P(t) = \frac{-3160.64t^2 + 52536.5t - 4548.31}{0.39t + 35.65}$$

b.   Substitute $t = 9$

$$P(9) = \frac{-3160.64(9)^2 + 52536.5(9) - 4548.31}{0.39(9) + 35.65}$$

$$P(9) = 5420.54$$

Therefore in 1999 the United States medicare program disbursed an average of $5,420.54 per person enrolled in medicare.

c.   Using the graph and trace we get

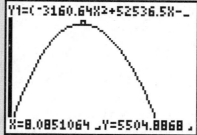

We can see that the maximum on this graph is at about $(8, 5504.89)$. Therefore in 1998 the average disbursements to medicare recipients reached a maximum of about $5,504.89.

Problem 3   *Solution*

a.   Since the denominator would be zero when $x = 0$ we have a domain of all real numbers except zero.

b.   Since the denominator would be zero when $x = 7$ we have a domain of all real numbers except $x \neq 7$.

c.   Set the denominator equal to zero

$$x^2 - 3x - 10 = 0$$

$$(x - 5)(x + 2) = 0$$

$$x - 5 = 0 \qquad x + 2 = 0$$

$$x = 5 \qquad x = -2$$

Therefore the domain is all real numbers except $x \neq 5$ or -2. This functions graph will have an asymptote at $x = 5$ and a hole at $x = -2$.

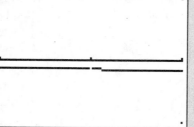
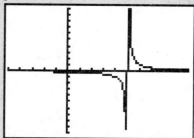

5.1 Exercises

1.   The math club is throwing a graduation party for 5 of its members. They have decided to hire a band for $500 and buy $300 worth of food and drinks for the party. They decided each member of the club that attends the party (excluding the five graduates) should pay an equal amount of the costs.

   a. Find a model for the per person cost for this party if m members of the club attend the party. (m does include the 5 graduates)

   b. Find the per person cost for each non graduating member of the club who attends the party if 45 members attend.

   c. What is a reasonable domain and range for this model?

2.   The Fancy Affair catering company is catering an event for a local charity. Jan the owner of Fancy Affair is donating her time to the cause but needs to charge the charity for the food, decorations and supplies used. If p people attend the charity event Jan has figured her total cost to be modeled by

$$C(p) = 4.55p + 365.00$$

   where C is the total cost in dollars for the food, decorations and supplies when p people attend the charity event.

   a. Find the total cost for 100 people to attend the event.

   b. Find a new function that gives the per person cost for p people to attend the charity event.

   c. Use your new model to find the per person cost for 150 people to attend the event.

   d. If the location of the charity event can only hold up to 250 people what is a reasonable domain and range of the model you found in part b?

3.   A light has an illumination of 25.5 foot candles at a distance of 10 feet from the light source.(See example 2.)

   a. Find a model for the illumination of this light.

   b. What is the illumination of this light at a distance of 5 feet from the light source?

   c. What is the illuminating of this light at a distance of 30 feet from the light source?

   d. Use a graph to estimate at what distance the illumination will be 50 foot candles.

4.

   a. If y varies inversely with x^3 and $y = 405$ when $x = 3$ find an equation to represent this relationship.

   b. Find y if $x = 5$

5.   If a fixed force is applied to an object the amount of acceleration a in meters per second squared of that object is inversely proportional to the mass in kilograms of that object. When a fixed force is applied to a 20kg mass it is accelerated at 0.5mps^2.

   a. Find a function for the acceleration a of a mass m when this fixed amount of force is applied.

   b. What is the acceleration of a 10kg mass when this force is applied?

   c. What is the acceleration of a 5kg mass when this force is applied?

   d. Estimate numerically what size mass this force can accelerate at 0.7mps^2.

6.   The weight of a body varies inversely as the square of its distance from the center of the earth. If the radius of the earth is 4000 miles, how much would a 220pound man weight 2000 miles above the surface of the earth? Hint: the person weighs 220 pounds when 4000 miles from the center of the earth.

7.   The pressure P of a certain amount of gas in a balloon is inversely proportional to the volume of the balloon. If the pressure in a balloon is 5 lb. per square inch when the volume of the balloon is 4 cubic inches what is the pressure in the balloon if the volume is only 2 cubic inches?

8.   The current that flows through an electrical circuit is inversely proportional to the resistance of that circuit. When the resistance R is 200ohms, the current I is 1.2amp. Find the current when the resistance is 130 ohms.

9.   The force needed to balance a 200g weight on a fulcrum is inversely proportional to the square of the distance from the fulcrum the force is applied. 2.25 newtons of force applied 4 units away from the fulcrum is needed to balance the weight.

   a. Find the force needed to balance the 200g weight if it is applied 1 unit away from the fulcrum.

   b. Find the force needed to balance the 200g weight if it is applied 3 units away from the fulcrum.

   c. Find the force needed to balance the 200g weight if it is applied 10 units away from the fulcrum.

10. The pressure of a certain amount of gas in a balloon is inversely proportional to volume of the balloon. For one such balloon we have the function

$$P(v) = \frac{30}{v}$$

where $P(v)$ is the pressure of the gas in the balloon in pounds per square inch when the volume of the balloon is v square inches.

a. Find $P(2)$ and explain its meaning in this context.

b. Find $P(10)$ and explain its meaning in this context.

11. The force needed to lift a boulder using a pry-bar and fulcrum can be modeled by the function

$$F(d) = \frac{1500}{d^2}$$

where $F(d)$ is the force in Newtons needed to lift the boulder when it is applied d inches away from the fulcrum.

a. Find $F(6)$ and explain its meaning in this context.

b. Find $F(24)$ and explain its meaning in this context.

12. The average amount of benefits received by people from the U.S. food stamp program can be modeled by

$$B(t) = \frac{-470001t^2 + 4110992t + 14032612}{-469.4t^2 + 3745t + 19774}$$

where $B(t)$ is the average benefit in dollars per person for people on the U.S. food stamp program t years since 1990.

source: Model derived from data from the Statistical Abstract 2001.

a. Find the average benefit for a person participating in the food stamp program in 1995.

b. Use a graph to estimate when the average benefit for a person participating in the food stamp program was $800.

13. The population of the United States since 1970 can be modeled by

$$P(t) = 0.226t^2 + 1.885t + 204.72$$

where $P(t)$ represents the population of the United States in millions t years since 1970. The national debt of the United States in millions of dollars t years since 1970 can be modeled by

$$D(t) = 8215.1t^2 - 23035.4t + 413525.6$$

where $D(t)$ represents the national debt of the U.S. in millions of dollars t years since 1970.

source: Models derived from data from the U.S. Department of Commerce Bureau of Economic Analysis

a. Find a new model for the average amount of national debt per person in the U.S. t years since 1970.

b. Find the average amount of national debt per person in 2000.

c. Estimate numerically in what year the average amount of national debt per person was $10,000.

14. The state of California's spending per person has increased dramatically since 1950. The states population from 1950 to 2000 can be modeled by

$$P(t) = 0.464t - 12.47$$

where $P(t)$ is California's population in millions of people t years since 1900. The amount California spent in millions of dollars can be modeled by

$$S(t) = 55.125t^2 - 6435.607t + 186914.286$$

where $S(t)$ is the amount California spent in millions of dollars during year t, years since 1900.

source: Models derived from data in the Governor's Budget Summary as printed in the North County Times Feb. 9, 2003.

a. Estimate the population of California in 1980.

b. Estimate the amount California spent in 1990.

c. Find a new function that give the spending per capita (per person) t years since 1900.

d. Estimate the per capita spending in California in 1980.

e. Estimate numerically when the per capita spending in California reached $2500.

15. The average amount of benefits received by people from the U.S. food stamp program can be modeled by

$$B(t) = \frac{-470001t^2 + 4110992t + 14032612}{-469.4t^2 + 3745t + 19774}$$

where $B(t)$ is the average benefit in dollars per person for people on the U.S. food stamp program t years since 1990.

source: Model derived from data from the Statistical Abstract 2001.

a. Estimate the average benefit in 2000.

b. Use a graph to estimate when the average benefit for a person participating in the food stamp program was $700.

For exercises 16 through 22 give the domain of the rational functions.

16. $f(x) = \dfrac{x+5}{x-3}$

17. $p(t) = \dfrac{3x-7}{4x+5}$

18. $h(a) = \dfrac{3a - 1}{(2a + 7)(a - 3)}$

19. $g(x) = \dfrac{2x - 7}{(x + 4)(x - 9)}$

20. $h(m) = \dfrac{4m^2 + 2m - 9}{m^2 + 7m + 12}$

21. $f(x) = \dfrac{3x + 7}{x^2 - 9x + 8}$

22. $f(x) = \dfrac{2x + 1}{x^2 + 3x + 19}$

For exercises 23 and 24 use the graph to answer the questions.

23. Given the graph of $f(x)$

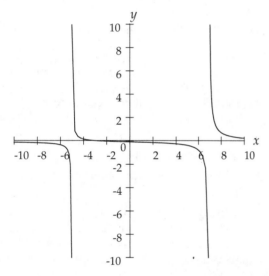

a. Find the domain of $f(x)$

b. Estimate $f(0)$

c. Estimate when $f(x) = 5$

24. Given the graph of $h(x)$

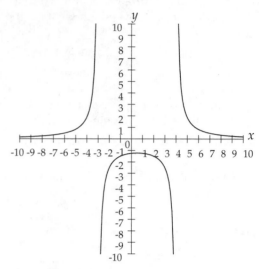

a. Find the domain.

b. Estimate $h(1)$

c. Estimate $h(-4)$

d. Estimate when $h(x) = -2$

For exercises 25 and 26 use the table to give values that are not included in the functions domain.

25.

X	Y1	
-7	1.875	
-6	5	
-5	ERROR	
-4	-15	
-3	ERROR	
-2	5	
-1	1.875	

X= -1

26.

X	Y1	
1	.66667	
2	1.2	
3	3	
4	ERROR	
5	-6	
6	-6	
7	ERROR	

X=7

Section 5.2 Multiplying & Dividing Rational Expressions

•Simplifying Rational Expressions• Multiplying & Dividing Rational Expressions

To prepare us to solve equations involving rational functions we need to develop some basic skills to handle rational expressions. In this section we will study how to multiply and divide rational expressions. In the next section we will study how to add and subtract rational expressions. You should notice in these two sections that working with rational expressions is very much the same as working with fractions. The connection between working with rational expressions and with fractions is clear and can be a good basis for understanding these two sections of this chapter.

We are going to start by learning to simplify rational expressions and then multiplication and division because it is typically easier than adding or subtracting. Simplifying rational expressions is the same as simplifying numeric fractions. The numerator and denominator must both include multiplication in order for a factor to cancel and thus reduce the fraction. When working with numeric fractions we often take this for granted and do the process without thinking about all the steps. In order to work with rational expressions you will need to focus on each step of the process to properly reduce the expression. Let's start with some simple examples with numeric fractions and some simple rational expressions.

Example 1

Simplify the following:

a. $\dfrac{25}{40}$

b. $\dfrac{420}{770}$

c. $\dfrac{5x^2}{10x}$

d. $\dfrac{2(x+7)}{x+7}$

e. $\dfrac{(x+3)(x-5)}{(x-2)(x+3)}$

Solution
a.

$$\frac{25}{40} = \frac{5 \cdot 5}{2 \cdot 2 \cdot 2 \cdot 5}$$ Factor the numerator and denominator.

$$= \frac{5 \cdot \cancel{5}}{2 \cdot 2 \cdot 2 \cdot \cancel{5}}$$ Cancel any common factors.

$$= \frac{5}{2 \cdot 2 \cdot 2}$$

$$= \frac{5}{8}$$ Multiply remaining factors together.

b.

$$\frac{420}{770} = \frac{2 \cdot 2 \cdot 3 \cdot 5 \cdot 7}{2 \cdot 5 \cdot 7 \cdot 11}$$ Factor the numerator and denominator

$$= \frac{2 \cdot \cancel{2} \cdot 3 \cdot \cancel{5} \cdot \cancel{7}}{\cancel{2} \cdot \cancel{5} \cdot \cancel{7} \cdot 11}$$ Cancel the common factors

$$= \frac{2 \cdot 3}{11}$$

$$= \frac{6}{11}$$ Multiply the remaining factors.

c.

$$\frac{5x^2}{10x} = \frac{5 \cdot x \cdot x}{2 \cdot 5 \cdot x}$$ Factor

$$= \frac{\cancel{5} \cdot \cancel{x} \cdot x}{2 \cdot \cancel{5} \cdot \cancel{x}}$$ Cancel the common factors

$$= \frac{x}{2}$$

d.

$$\frac{2(x+7)}{x+7} = \frac{2\cancel{(x+7)}}{\cancel{x+7}}$$ Already factored so cancel out common factors.

$$= \frac{2}{1}$$ When all factors in the numerator or denominator cancel a 1 is left.

$$= 2$$ Reduce.

e.

$$\frac{(x+3)(x-5)}{(x-2)(x+3)} = \frac{\cancel{(x+3)}(x-5)}{(x-2)\cancel{(x+3)}}$$ Cancel common factors.

$$= \frac{x-5}{x-2}$$ Note that the remaining x does not cancel because it is not multiplied but subtracted

You should note that an expression with addition or subtraction involved can be canceled but only if that expression is being multiplied by the remaining factors. Any addition or subtraction that remains separate from the multiplication in the numerator or denominator will stop you from canceling the like factors. The next example will work with some more complicated rational expressions and we will consider a couple of situations where we are not able to reduce the expression.

Example 2
Simplify the following:

a. $\dfrac{x^2 + 8x + 12}{x^2 + 7x + 10}$

b. $\dfrac{6x^2 - 29x + 28}{15x^2 - 41x + 28}$

c. $\dfrac{(x+4)(x-3)}{(x-3)+5}$

d. $\dfrac{18x^2 - 3x - 10}{x^2 - 2x - 3}$

Skill Connection:

The process for simplifying many rational expressions will require you to factor the numerator and denominator. Therefore you may want to review the steps to factoring we went over in section 3.4.

AC Method of Factoring:

1. Take out anything in common.
2. Multiply a and c together. (Do this step off to the side, in the margin.)
3. Find factors of ac that add up to b. (Do this off to the side also.)
4. Rewrite the middle (bx) term using the factors from step 3.
5. Group and factor out what's in common.

SC-Example 1:

Factor $3x^2 - 13x - 10$

Solution:

Step 1: There is nothing in common.

Step 2:
$$a = 3 \qquad c = -10$$
$$ac = -30$$

Step 3:

ac	$= -30$
1	-30
2	-15
3	-10
5	-6
-1	30
-2	15
-3	10
-5	6

$2 \qquad -15$ gives us -13.

Step 4: $3x^2 - 15x + 2x - 10$

Step 5:
$$3x^2 - 15x + 2x - 10$$
$$(3x^2 - 15x) + (2x - 10)$$
$$3x(x - 5) + 2(x - 5)$$
$$(3x + 2)(x - 5)$$

Solution

a.
$$\frac{x^2 + 8x + 12}{x^2 + 7x + 10} = \frac{(x+6)(x+2)}{(x+5)(x+2)} \qquad \text{Factor.}$$
$$= \frac{(x+6)\cancel{(x+2)}}{(x+5)\cancel{(x+2)}} \qquad \text{Cancel common factors.}$$
$$= \frac{x+6}{x+5}$$

b.
$$\frac{6x^2 - 29x + 28}{15x^2 - 41x + 28} = \frac{(2x-7)(3x-4)}{(3x-4)(5x-7)} \qquad \text{Factor}$$
$$= \frac{(2x-7)\cancel{(3x-4)}}{\cancel{(3x-4)}(5x-7)} \qquad \text{Cancel common factors.}$$
$$= \frac{2x-7}{5x-7}$$

c.
$$\frac{(x+4)(x-3)}{(x-3)+5} = \frac{(x+4)(x-3)}{x+2} \qquad \text{The } x\text{-3 cannot cancel because of the addition present in the denominator.}$$

d.
$$\frac{18x^2 - 3x - 10}{x^2 - 2x - 3} = \frac{(3x+2)(6x-5)}{(x-3)(x+1)} \qquad \text{There are no common factors so it is already simplified.}$$

In example 2 part c and d you should note that the lack of common factors keeps us from simplifying the rational expression further. In all of these expressions you can multiply the factors back together as you would with numeric fractions or you can leave them in factored form. This is more of a preference issue for mathematicians than a set rule that must be followed.

Problem 1

Simplify the following:

a. $\dfrac{(x+5)(x+7)}{(x+7)(x-9)}$

b. $\dfrac{x^2 - 5x + 6}{x^2 - 13x + 30}$

c. $\dfrac{x^3 - 5x^2 + 6x}{x^2 + 5x - 14}$

d. $\dfrac{5(x+7)}{10(x+2)+3}$

Solution See page 352

One special case that can occur is when an expression in the numerator is almost the same as an expression in the denominator. Most of the time the expression cannot be canceled but occasionally you will be able to take out a common factor and make the two expressions the same. The most common factor that does need to be taken out is -1.

Say What?
Some phrases we use in mathematics have many meanings depending on the context you are using them in. One of those phrases would be to

"**Cancel Out ...** "

We often use "Cancel out" in place of more specific phrases such as :
• Adds to zero
• Divides to one
• Is the inverse of

This is usually done to simplify the language being used to make something easier to understand or read. Be cautious with this phrase that you realize what operation is being used to "Cancel" something out so that you do not "cancel out" at the wrong time.

The most common place for this to happen is with division and canceling when there is addition involved rather than multiplication.

$$\frac{x+5}{x+2} \neq \frac{5}{2}$$

Here the x's cannot cancel using division because of the addition involved in the numerator and denominator.

$$\frac{5x}{2x} = \frac{5}{2}$$

In this fraction the x's can cancel out because only multiplication is involved making the x's common factors that do divide to one.

Example 3
Simplify the following:

a. $\dfrac{7(x-5)}{3(5-x)}$

b. $\dfrac{2m+6}{5m+15}$

Solution

a.
$$\frac{7(x-5)}{3(5-x)} = \frac{7(x-5)}{-3(x-5)}$$ Factor -1 out of the denominator to make the expressions the same.

$$= \frac{7(x-5)}{-3(x-5)}$$ Cancel out common factors.

$$= -\frac{7}{3}$$ The negative is typically put if front of the fraction or in the numerator.

b.
$$\frac{2m+6}{5(m+3)} = \frac{2(m+3)}{5(m+3)}$$ Factor completely.

$$= \frac{2(m+3)}{5(m+3)}$$ Cancel out common factors.

$$= \frac{2}{5}$$

Simplifying Rational Expressions:
1. Factor the numerator and denominator (if needed).
2. Cancel any common factors.
3. Leave in factored form or multiply remaining factors together.

Caution: Do not cancel unless the expressions to be canceled are being multiplied by the remaining parts of the numerator or denominator. You can cancel factors but you cannot cancel terms.

$$\frac{5(x+2)}{(x+3)(x+2)} \qquad \frac{5+(x+2)}{(x+3)(x+2)}$$
Cancel   Do Not Cancel

Simplifying is a key part of all operations involving rational expressions. When multiplying or dividing you can simplify before the multiplication is performed or after. Many students find it easier to simplify the rational expressions first so that there is less multiplication to be done. Remember to always check the final product for any further simplification that can be made.

When multiplying or dividing fractions you do not need common denominators. This makes it easier to multiply or divide any two rational expressions. Recall that when multiplying fractions you simply multiply the numerators together and multiply the denominators together. Don't forget to simplify your results.

Example 4
Multiply the following:

a. $\dfrac{3}{5} \cdot \dfrac{2}{7}$

b. $\dfrac{20}{18} \cdot \dfrac{6}{10}$

c. $\dfrac{x+5}{x-3} \cdot \dfrac{x+2}{x+7}$

d. $\dfrac{(x+3)(x-4)}{(x-5)(x-4)} \cdot \dfrac{(x+2)(x+7)}{(x+3)(x+7)}$

e. $\dfrac{x^2-3x-18}{x^2+7x+10} \cdot \dfrac{x^2+3x-10}{x^2+7x+12}$

Solution

a.

$$\frac{3}{5} \cdot \frac{2}{7} = \frac{6}{35} \qquad \text{Multiply numerator and denominators together.}$$

b.

$$\frac{20}{18} \cdot \frac{6}{10} = \frac{2 \cdot 2 \cdot 5}{2 \cdot 3 \cdot 3} \cdot \frac{2 \cdot 3}{2 \cdot 5} \qquad \text{Factor the numerator and denominators.}$$

$$= \frac{\cancel{2} \cdot 2 \cdot \cancel{5}}{\cancel{2} \cdot \cancel{3} \cdot 3} \cdot \frac{2 \cdot \cancel{3}}{2 \cdot \cancel{5}} \qquad \text{Cancel out common factors.}$$

$$= \frac{2}{3}$$

c.

$$\frac{x+5}{x-3} \cdot \frac{x+2}{x+7} = \frac{(x+5)(x+2)}{(x-3)(x+7)} \qquad \begin{array}{l}\text{There are no common factors so}\\ \text{multiply together.}\end{array}$$

$$= \frac{x^2+7x+10}{x^2+4x-21} \qquad \text{You may also leave it in factored form.}$$

d.

$$\frac{(x+3)(x-4)}{(x-5)(x-4)} \cdot \frac{(x+2)(x+7)}{(x+3)(x+7)} = \frac{\cancel{(x+3)}\cancel{(x-4)}}{(x-5)\cancel{(x-4)}} \cdot \frac{(x+2)\cancel{(x+7)}}{\cancel{(x+3)}\cancel{(x+7)}}$$

$$= \frac{x+2}{x-5} \qquad \begin{array}{l}\text{Cancel common factors and}\\ \text{multiply.}\end{array}$$

e.

$$\frac{x^2-3x-18}{x^2+7x+10} \cdot \frac{x^2+3x-10}{x^2+7x+12} = \frac{(x+3)(x-6)}{(x+5)(x+2)} \cdot \frac{(x+5)(x-2)}{(x+3)(x+4)} \qquad \text{Factor}$$

$$= \frac{(x+3)(x-6)}{(x+5)(x+2)} \cdot \frac{(x+5)(x-2)}{(x+3)(x+4)} \qquad \text{Reduce}$$

$$= \frac{(x-6)(x-2)}{(x+2)(x+4)} \qquad \text{Multiply}$$

$$= \frac{x^2-8x+12}{x^2+6x+8}$$

Multiplying Rational Expressions:

1. Factor the numerator and denominator of each fraction (if needed).
2. Cancel any common factors.
3. Multiply the numerators together and multiply the denominators together.
4. Leave in factored form or multiply remaining factors together.

Problem 2

Multiply the following:

a. $\dfrac{x+5}{x-3} \cdot \dfrac{x+7}{x+5}$

b. $\dfrac{(x+3)(x+4)}{(x-7)(x+3)} \cdot \dfrac{(x-2)(x-5)}{(x+4)(x-6)}$

c. $\dfrac{x^2-5x-14}{2x^2-x-15} \cdot \dfrac{x^2+2x-15}{3x^2+4x-4}$

Solution   See page 353

Dividing rational expressions is the same as dividing numerical fractions in that you multiply by the reciprocal of the fraction you are dividing by. This means that division will simply be the same as multiplication after you have flipped over the second fraction.

Example 5

Divide the following:

a. $\dfrac{2}{3} \div \dfrac{5}{7}$

b. $\dfrac{\dfrac{7}{10}}{\dfrac{2}{5}}$

c. $\dfrac{x+3}{x-7} \div \dfrac{x-4}{x-7}$

d. $\dfrac{(x+2)(x+5)}{(x-3)(2x+7)} \div \dfrac{(x-3)(x+5)}{(2x+7)(x-9)}$

e. $\dfrac{2x^2+11x+12}{x^2-11x+30} \div \dfrac{2x^2+15x+18}{x^2+2x-35}$

Solution

a.

$$\dfrac{2}{3} \div \dfrac{5}{7} = \dfrac{2}{3} \cdot \dfrac{7}{5}$$ Multiply by the reciprocal of the second fraction.

$$= \dfrac{14}{15}$$

b.

$$\dfrac{\dfrac{7}{10}}{\dfrac{2}{5}} = \dfrac{7}{10} \cdot \dfrac{5}{2}$$ Multiply by the reciprocal of the fraction you are dividing by.

$$= \dfrac{7}{2 \cdot \cancel{5}} \cdot \dfrac{\cancel{5}}{2}$$ Factor and cancel common factors.

$$= \dfrac{7}{4}$$

$$= 1\dfrac{3}{4}$$ Reduce.

c.

$$\frac{x+3}{x-7} \div \frac{x-4}{x-7} = \frac{x+3}{x-7} \cdot \frac{x-7}{x-4}$$

Multiply by the reciprocal of the second fraction.

$$= \frac{x+3}{\cancel{x-7}} \cdot \frac{\cancel{x-7}}{x-4}$$

Cancel common factors.

$$= \frac{x+3}{x-4}$$

Multiply

d.

$$\frac{(x+2)(x+5)}{(x-3)(2x+7)} \div \frac{(x-3)(x+5)}{(2x+7)(x-9)} = \frac{(x+2)(x+5)}{(x-3)(2x+7)} \cdot \frac{(2x+7)(x-9)}{(x-3)(x+5)}$$

$$= \frac{(x+2)(x+5)}{(x-3)(2x+7)} \cdot \frac{(2x+7)(x-9)}{(x-3)(x+5)}$$

$$= \frac{(x+2)(x-9)}{(x-3)(x-3)}$$

Multiply by the reciprocal,

$$= \frac{(x+2)(x-9)}{(x-3)^2}$$

then cancel common factors.

$$= \frac{x^2-7x-18}{x^2-6x+9}$$

Multiply out if desired.

e.

$$\frac{2x^2+11x+12}{x^2-11x+30} \div \frac{2x^2+15x+18}{x^2+2x-35} = \frac{2x^2+11x+12}{x^2-11x+30} \cdot \frac{x^2+2x-35}{2x^2+15x+18}$$

$$= \frac{(x+4)(2x+3)}{(x-5)(x-6)} \cdot \frac{(x-5)(x+7)}{(2x+3)(x+6)}$$

$$= \frac{(x+4)\cancel{(2x+3)}}{\cancel{(x-5)}(x-6)} \cdot \frac{\cancel{(x-5)}(x+7)}{\cancel{(2x+3)}(x+6)}$$

$$= \frac{(x+4)(x+7)}{(x-6)(x+6)}$$

$$= \frac{x^2+11x+28}{x^2-36}$$

Dividing Rational Expressions:
1. Multiply by the reciprocal of the second fraction. (Flip over the fraction you are dividing by and make the division into multiplication.)
2. Factor the numerator and denominator of each fraction (if needed).
3. Cancel any common factors.
4. Multiply the numerators together and multiply the denominators together.
5. Leave in factored form or multiply remaining factors together.

Problem 3

Divide the following:

a. $\dfrac{x+5}{x-9} \div \dfrac{x+5}{x+7}$

b. $\dfrac{(x+2)(x+4)}{(x-3)(x+7)} \div \dfrac{(x+4)(x-8)}{(x+7)(x-5)}$

c. $\dfrac{x^2-4x-21}{2x^2-9x-35} \div \dfrac{x^2+12x+27}{2x^2-3x-20}$

Solution   See page 353

Section 5.2 Key Points

- Simplifying Rational Expressions:
    1. Factor the numerator and denominator (if needed).
    2. Cancel any common factors.
    3. Leave in factored form or multiply remaining factors together.
- Multiply Rational Expressions:
    1. Factor the numerator and denominator of each fraction (if needed).
    2. Cancel any common factors.
    3. Multiply the numerators together and multiply the denominators together.
    4. Leave in factored form or multiply remaining factors together.
- Dividing Rational Expression:
    1. Multiply by the reciprocal of the divisor. (the second fraction)
    2. Factor the numerator and denominator of each fraction (if needed).
    3. Cancel any common factors.
    4. Multiply the numerators together and multiply the denominators together.
    5. Leave in factored form or multiply remaining factors together.

Section 5.2 Problem Solutions

Problem 1   Solution

a.

$$\frac{(x+5)(x+7)}{(x+7)(x-9)} = \frac{(x+5)\cancel{(x+7)}}{\cancel{(x+7)}(x-9)}$$

$$= \frac{x+5}{x-9}$$

b.

$$\frac{x^2-5x+6}{x^2-13x+30} = \frac{(x-2)(x-3)}{(x-3)(x-10)}$$

$$= \frac{(x-2)\cancel{(x-3)}}{\cancel{(x-3)}(x-10)}$$

$$= \frac{x-2}{x-10}$$

c.

$$\frac{x^3-5x^2+6x}{x^2+5x-14} = \frac{x(x-2)(x-3)}{(x+7)(x-2)}$$

$$= \frac{x\cancel{(x-2)}(x-3)}{(x+7)\cancel{(x-2)}}$$

$$= \frac{x(x-3)}{x+7}$$

$$= \frac{x^2-3x}{x+7}$$

d.

$$\frac{5(x+7)}{10(x+2)+3} = \frac{5(x+7)}{10x+23}$$

$$= \frac{5x+35}{10x+23}$$

You cannot cancel because the denominator is not factored and has addition in it.

Problem 2   Solution

a.

$$\frac{x+5}{x-3} \cdot \frac{x+7}{x+5} = \frac{\cancel{x+5}}{x-3} \cdot \frac{x+7}{\cancel{x+5}}$$

$$= \frac{x+7}{x-3}$$

b.

$$\frac{(x+3)(x+4)}{(x-7)(x+3)} \cdot \frac{(x-2)(x-5)}{(x+4)(x-6)} = \frac{\cancel{(x+3)}\cancel{(x+4)}}{(x-7)\cancel{(x+3)}} \cdot \frac{(x-2)(x-5)}{\cancel{(x+4)}(x-6)}$$

$$= \frac{(x-2)(x-5)}{(x-7)(x-6)}$$

$$= \frac{x^2-7x+10}{x^2-13x+42}$$

c.

$$\frac{x^2-5x-14}{2x^2-x-15} \cdot \frac{x^2+2x-15}{3x^2+4x-4} = \frac{(x+2)(x-7)}{(2x+5)(x-3)} \cdot \frac{(x+5)(x-3)}{(3x-2)(x+2)}$$

$$= \frac{\cancel{(x+2)}(x-7)}{(2x+5)\cancel{(x-3)}} \cdot \frac{(x+5)\cancel{(x-3)}}{(3x-2)\cancel{(x+2)}}$$

$$= \frac{(x-7)(x+5)}{(2x+5)(3x-2)}$$

$$= \frac{x^2-2x-35}{6x^2+11x-10}$$

Problem 3   Solution

a.

$$\frac{x+5}{x-9} \div \frac{x+5}{x+7} = \frac{x+5}{x-9} \cdot \frac{x+7}{x+5}$$

$$= \frac{\cancel{x+5}}{x-9} \cdot \frac{x+7}{\cancel{x+5}}$$

$$= \frac{x+7}{x-9}$$

b.

$$\frac{(x+2)(x+4)}{(x-3)(x+7)} \div \frac{(x+4)(x-8)}{(x+7)(x-5)} = \frac{(x+2)(x+4)}{(x-3)(x+7)} \cdot \frac{(x+7)(x-5)}{(x+4)(x-8)}$$

$$= \frac{(x+2)(x+4)}{(x-3)(x+7)} \cdot \frac{(x+7)(x-5)}{(x+4)(x-8)}$$

$$= \frac{(x+2)(x-5)}{(x-3)(x-8)}$$

$$= \frac{x^2-3x-10}{x^2-11x+24}$$

c.

$$\frac{x^2-4x-21}{2x^2-9x-35} \div \frac{x^2+12x+27}{2x^2-3x-20} = \frac{x^2-4x-21}{2x^2-9x-35} \cdot \frac{2x^2-3x-20}{x^2+12x+27}$$

$$= \frac{\cancel{(x-7)}\cancel{(x+3)}}{\cancel{(2x+5)}\cancel{(x-7)}} \cdot \frac{\cancel{(2x+5)}(x-4)}{\cancel{(x+3)}(x+9)}$$

$$= \frac{x-4}{x+9}$$

5.2 Exercises

In exercises 1 through 10 simplify the rational expression.

1. $\dfrac{x+3}{2x+6}$

2. $\dfrac{(x+5)(x-3)}{(x-3)(x-2)}$

3. $\dfrac{x^2+6x+9}{(x+2)(x+3)}$

4. $\dfrac{p-8}{p^2-12p+32}$

5. $\dfrac{t^2+2t-15}{t^2-9t+18}$

6. $\dfrac{x^2+5x-14}{x^2-6x+8}$

7. $\dfrac{w^2-16}{w^2+w-12}$

8. $\dfrac{5(x+7)}{(x+7)+10}$

9. $\dfrac{(x-5)}{2(x-5)+3}$

10. $\dfrac{2x^2-23x-70}{x^2-21x+98}$

For exercises 11 through 20 multiply the rational expressions:

11. $\dfrac{x+3}{x+7}\cdot\dfrac{x+7}{x-5}$

12. $\dfrac{x-8}{x-4}\cdot\dfrac{x-5}{x-8}$

13. $\dfrac{2(x-4)}{3x-12}\cdot\dfrac{3(x+5)}{x-7}$

14. $\dfrac{5(w+7)}{2w+10}\cdot\dfrac{4(w+5)}{w-11}$

15. $\dfrac{(x+3)(x+7)}{(x-2)(x+3)}\cdot\dfrac{(x+7)(x-2)}{(x-3)(x-9)}$

16. $\dfrac{(c-3)(c+6)}{(c-7)(c+2)}\cdot\dfrac{(c-7)(c-11)}{(c+6)(c-3)}$

17. $\dfrac{(k+5)(7-k)}{(k-7)(k-3)}\cdot\dfrac{(k-3)(k+6)}{(k+9)(k+5)}$

18. $\dfrac{(t+7)(t-9)}{(t+3)(t+7)}\cdot\dfrac{(t+3)(t+13)}{(9-t)(t-13)}$

19. $\dfrac{m^2+8m+7}{m^2-2m-3}\cdot\dfrac{m^2-9}{m^2+9m+14}$

20. $\dfrac{x^2-16x+55}{x^2-x-12}\cdot\dfrac{x^2+12x+27}{x^2-9x+20}$

In exercises 21 through 30 divide the rational expressions

21. $\dfrac{x+5}{x-3}\div\dfrac{x-5}{x-7}$

22. $\dfrac{x+15}{x-3}\div\dfrac{x+7}{x-3}$

23. $\dfrac{(x+3)(x+2)}{(x-8)(x-7)}\div\dfrac{(x+2)(x-5)}{(x-7)(x-5)}$

24. $\dfrac{(m+7)(m-5)}{(m+2)(m+7)}\div\dfrac{(m-5)(m-12)}{(m+2)(m+6)}$

25. $\dfrac{w^2+8w+15}{w^2+12w+35}\div\dfrac{w^2-5w-24}{w^2+3w-28}$

26. $\dfrac{k^2+k-20}{k^2+10k+21}\div\dfrac{k^2-10k+24}{k^2-13k+42}$

27. $\dfrac{c^2-c-20}{c^2+6c+8}\div\dfrac{2c^2+11c+12}{3c^2+c-10}$

28. $\dfrac{3k^2+19k+20}{k^2+6k+5}\div\dfrac{2k^2+2k-40}{k^2-2k-3}$

29. $\dfrac{6t^2+t-35}{10t^2+17t-20}\div\dfrac{12t^2-t-63}{20t^2+29t-36}$

30. $\dfrac{2x^2-5x-12}{x^2-3x-28}\div\dfrac{6x^2-7x-24}{3x^2+13x-56}$

Section 5.3 Adding & Subtracting Rational Expressions

• Adding & Subtracting Rational Expressions

Now that we have studied simplifying, multiplying and dividing rational expressions we are going to learn how to add and subtract them. Adding and subtracting fractions requires us to have common denominators. This has always been a condition to add or subtract fractions and requires a little more work than multiplying and dividing in which we do not need common denominators. Being able to add or subtract rational expressions will allow us to simplify situations where several expressions are used.

Finding a common denominator for a rational expression will be the same process as finding one for a numeric fraction but once again we will need to focus more carefully on each step of the process. When finding the least common denominator (LCD) of a fraction you need to factor each denominator and compare them so that you can choose the right combination of factors that will make up the least common denominator. In some cases you may be able to figure out the LCD without doing all of these steps but with rational expressions it is going to take a little more patience.

Example 1

Find the Least Common Denominator for each of the following sets of fractions and write each fraction in terms of the LCD.

a. $\dfrac{12}{35}$ $\dfrac{8}{165}$

b. $\dfrac{3}{140}$ $\dfrac{2}{1575}$

c. $\dfrac{2}{5x}$ $\dfrac{3}{10x^2}$

Solution

a.

$$\dfrac{12}{35} \qquad \dfrac{8}{165}$$

$$\dfrac{12}{5 \cdot 7} \qquad \dfrac{8}{3 \cdot 5 \cdot 11} \qquad \text{Factor both denominators.}$$

$$LCD = 3 \cdot 5 \cdot 7 \cdot 11$$

$$LCD = 1155 \qquad \text{Take a copy of each factor for the LCD.}$$

$$\dfrac{3 \cdot 11}{3 \cdot 11} \cdot \dfrac{12}{5 \cdot 7} \qquad \dfrac{8}{3 \cdot 5 \cdot 11} \cdot \dfrac{7}{7} \qquad \begin{array}{l} \text{Multiply each fraction by the factors} \\ \text{that it's denominator is missing.} \end{array}$$

$$\dfrac{396}{1155} \qquad \dfrac{56}{1155}$$

b.

$$\frac{3}{140} \qquad \frac{2}{1575}$$

$$\frac{3}{2^2 \cdot 5 \cdot 7} \qquad \frac{2}{3^2 \cdot 5^2 \cdot 7} \qquad \text{Factor both denominators.}$$

$$LCD = 2^2 \cdot 3^2 \cdot 5^2 \cdot 7 \qquad \text{Take the highest power of each}$$

$$LCD = 6300 \qquad\qquad \text{factor for the LCD.}$$

$$\frac{3^2 \cdot 5}{3^2 \cdot 5} \cdot \frac{3}{2^2 \cdot 5 \cdot 7} \qquad \frac{2}{3^2 \cdot 5^2 \cdot 7} \cdot \frac{2^2}{2^2} \qquad \text{Multiply each fraction by the}$$

$$\qquad\qquad\qquad\qquad\qquad\qquad\qquad\qquad \text{factors it's denominator is missing.}$$

$$\frac{135}{6300} \qquad \frac{8}{6300}$$

c.

$$\frac{2}{5x} \qquad \frac{3}{10x^2}$$

$$\frac{2}{5 \cdot x} \qquad \frac{3}{2 \cdot 5 \cdot x^2}$$

$$LCD = 2 \cdot 5 \cdot x^2$$

$$LCD = 10x^2$$

$$\frac{2 \cdot x}{2 \cdot x} \cdot \frac{2}{5 \cdot x} \qquad \frac{3}{2 \cdot 5 \cdot x^2}$$

$$\frac{4x}{10x^2} \qquad \frac{3}{10x^2}$$

With simple denominators it is easier to find the factors you need to make up the LCD. Note that you want to take the highest power of each factor present to be a part of the LCD. When you are working with more complicated denominators you will find situations in which the denominators look very similar but cannot be changed easily. Let's find the LCD for the two fractions:

$$\frac{1}{x+2} \qquad \frac{1}{x+4}$$

It seems like you could either add 2 to $x+2$ or multiply $x+2$ by 2 and get $x+4$. The problem with these ideas is that multiplying by 2 will give you $2x+4$ not $x+4$ and adding 2 to the denominator is not possible since that would change the value of the fraction you are working on. The only way to get a LCD from these two denominators is to use both of them as factors in the new denominator giving you $(x+4)(x+2)$ as the LCD.

$$\frac{(x+4)}{(x+4)} \cdot \frac{1}{(x+2)} \qquad \frac{1}{(x+4)} \cdot \frac{(x+2)}{(x+2)}$$

$$\frac{x+4}{(x+4)(x+2)} \qquad \frac{x+2}{(x+4)(x+2)}$$

Example 2

Find the Least Common Denominator for each of the following sets of fractions and write each fraction in terms of the LCD.

a. $\quad \dfrac{x+5}{x-6} \qquad \dfrac{x+2}{x+7}$

b. $\quad \dfrac{x+3}{(x-5)(x+4)} \qquad \dfrac{x-7}{(x-5)(x+2)}$

c. $\quad \dfrac{5x+7}{x^2+5x+6} \qquad \dfrac{3x-8}{2x^2+9x+9}$

Solution

a.

$$\frac{x+5}{x-6} \qquad \frac{x+2}{x+7}$$

$$LCD = (x-6)(x+7)$$

$$LCD = x^2 + x - 42$$

The denominators are already factored so we take a copy of each factor for the LCD.

$$\frac{(x+7)}{(x+7)} \cdot \frac{(x+5)}{(x-6)} \qquad \frac{(x+2)}{(x+7)} \cdot \frac{(x-6)}{(x-6)}$$

$$\frac{(x+7)(x+5)}{(x-6)(x+7)} \qquad \frac{(x+2)(x-6)}{(x-6)(x+7)}$$

It is sometimes easier to leave the fractions in this factored form.

$$\frac{x^2 + 12x + 35}{x^2 + x - 42} \qquad \frac{x^2 - 4x - 12}{x^2 + x - 42}$$

b.

$$\frac{x+3}{(x-5)(x+4)} \qquad \frac{x-7}{(x-5)(x+2)}$$

$$LCD = (x-5)(x+4)(x+2)$$

$$LCD = x^3 + x^2 - 22x - 40$$

Since each denominator only has one copy of $(x-5)$ we will only need one copy in the LCD.

$$\frac{(x+2)}{(x+2)} \cdot \frac{(x+3)}{(x-5)(x+4)} \qquad \frac{(x-7)}{(x-5)(x+2)} \cdot \frac{(x+4)}{(x+4)}$$

$$\frac{(x+2)(x+3)}{(x-5)(x+4)(x+2)} \qquad \frac{(x-7)(x+4)}{(x-5)(x+4)(x+2)}$$

$$\frac{x^2 + 5x + 6}{x^3 + x^2 - 22x - 40} \qquad \frac{x^2 - 3x - 28}{x^3 + x^2 - 22x - 40}$$

c.

$$\frac{5x+7}{x^2 + 5x + 6} \qquad \frac{3x-8}{2x^2 + 9x + 9}$$

Factor the denominators.

$$\frac{5x+7}{(x+3)(x+2)} \qquad \frac{3x-8}{(2x+3)(x+3)}$$

$$LCD = (x+3)(x+2)(2x+3)$$

$$LCD = 2x^3 + 13x^2 + 27x + 18$$

$$\frac{(2x+3)}{(2x+3)} \cdot \frac{(5x+7)}{(x+3)(x+2)} \qquad \frac{(3x-8)}{(2x+3)(x+3)} \cdot \frac{(x+2)}{(x+2)}$$

$$\frac{(2x+3)(5x+7)}{(x+3)(x+2)(2x+3)} \qquad \frac{(3x-8)(x+2)}{(x+3)(x+2)(2x+3)}$$

$$\frac{10x^2 + 29x + 21}{2x^3 + 13x^2 + 27x + 18} \qquad \frac{3x^2 - 2x - 16}{2x^3 + 13x^2 + 27x + 18}$$

Finding the Least Common Denominator for Rational Expressions:
1.   Factor the denominators (if needed).
2.   Take the highest power of each factor for the LCD.
3.   Leave in factored form or multiply the factors together.
      We generally leave polynomials factored but multiply out single terms.

To Write a fraction in terms of the LCD.
1.   Find the least common denominator.
2.   Determine what factors of the LCD the fractions denominator is missing.
3.   Multiply the numerator and denominator of the fraction by the missing factors.

Problem 1

Find the Least Common Denominator for each of the following sets of fractions and write each fraction in terms of the LCD.

a. $\dfrac{7}{24m}$ $\dfrac{11}{45m^3n}$

b. $\dfrac{x+3}{x+8}$ $\dfrac{x+5}{x+9}$

c. $\dfrac{x+2}{(x-4)(x-7)}$ $\dfrac{x+4}{(x-7)(x+8)}$

d. $\dfrac{3x+2}{6x^2-7x-20}$ $\dfrac{4x-9}{2x^2-19x+35}$

Solution   See page 361

Getting the common denominator is the hardest part of adding and subtracting rational expressions. Once you have the common denominator you can just add or subtract the numerators and the LCD remains the denominator of the sum.

Example 3

Add the following rational expressions:

a. $\dfrac{5}{7x^2}+\dfrac{12}{5x}$

b. $\dfrac{x+2}{x-3}+\dfrac{x-7}{x-3}$

c. $\dfrac{x+2}{(x+3)(x+5)}+\dfrac{x-7}{x+5}$

d. $\dfrac{x+5}{x^2+5x-24}+\dfrac{x-9}{x^2+12x+32}$

Solution

a.

$$\dfrac{5}{7x^2}+\dfrac{12}{5x}=\dfrac{5}{5}\cdot\dfrac{5}{7x^2}+\dfrac{12}{5x}\cdot\dfrac{7x}{7x}$$ Get a common denominator and rewrite each fraction over the LCD.

$$=\dfrac{25}{35x^2}+\dfrac{84x}{35x^2}$$ Add the numerators. In this case they are not like terms so you can only write them with

$$=\dfrac{84x+25}{35x^2}$$ addition between them in one fraction.

b.

$$\dfrac{x+2}{x-3}+\dfrac{x-7}{x-3}=\dfrac{2x-5}{x-3}$$ Since the denominators are already the same we can simply add the numerators together.

c.

$$\frac{x+2}{(x+3)(x+5)} + \frac{x-7}{x+5} = \frac{x+2}{(x+3)(x+5)} + \frac{x-7}{x+5} \cdot \frac{(x+3)}{(x+3)} \quad \text{Get a common denominator.}$$

$$= \frac{x+2}{(x+3)(x+5)} + \frac{(x-7)(x+3)}{(x+5)(x+3)}$$

$$= \frac{x+2}{(x+3)(x+5)} + \frac{x^2-4x-21}{(x+3)(x+5)} \quad \begin{array}{l}\text{Multiply the} \\ \text{numerator out.}\end{array}$$

$$= \frac{x^2-3x-19}{(x+3)(x+5)} \quad \begin{array}{l}\text{Add the} \\ \text{numerators} \\ \text{together.}\end{array}$$

$$= \frac{x^2-3x-19}{x^2+8x+15}$$

d.

$$\frac{x+5}{x^2+5x-24} + \frac{x-9}{x^2+12x+32} = \frac{x+5}{(x-3)(x+8)} + \frac{x-9}{(x+8)(x+4)}$$

$$= \frac{(x+4)}{(x+4)} \cdot \frac{x+5}{(x-3)(x+8)} + \frac{x-9}{(x+8)(x+4)} \cdot \frac{(x-3)}{(x-3)}$$

$$= \frac{(x+4)(x+5)}{(x-3)(x+8)(x+4)} + \frac{(x-9)(x-3)}{(x-3)(x+8)(x+4)}$$

$$= \frac{x^2+9x+20}{(x-3)(x+8)(x+4)} + \frac{x^2-12x+27}{(x-3)(x+8)(x+4)}$$

$$= \frac{2x^2-3x+47}{(x-3)(x+8)(x+4)}$$

$$= \frac{2x^2-3x+47}{x^3+9x^2-4x-96}$$

Subtraction is the same process as addition but with one warning; be sure to subtract the entire numerator of the second fraction. The most common error students make is to forget to distribute the subtraction over the numerator of the second fraction.

Example 4

Subtract the following rational expressions:

a. $\dfrac{x+5}{x+8} - \dfrac{x-9}{x+8}$

b. $\dfrac{x-7}{(x+2)(x-4)} - \dfrac{x+5}{(x+6)(x+2)}$

c. $\dfrac{3x+2}{x^2-3x-10} - \dfrac{2x+7}{x^2-2x-15}$

Solution

a.

$$\frac{x+5}{x+8} - \frac{x-9}{x+8} = \frac{x+5-x+9}{x+8}$$

$$= \frac{14}{x+8}$$

b.

$$\frac{x-7}{(x+2)(x-4)} - \frac{x+5}{(x+6)(x+2)} =$$

$$= \frac{(x+6)}{(x+6)} \cdot \frac{(x-7)}{(x+2)(x-4)} - \frac{(x+5)}{(x+6)(x+2)} \cdot \frac{(x-4)}{(x-4)}$$

$$= \frac{(x+6)(x-7)}{(x+6)(x+2)(x-4)} - \frac{(x+5)(x-4)}{(x+6)(x+2)(x-4)}$$

$$= \frac{x^2 - x - 42}{(x+6)(x+2)(x-4)} - \frac{x^2 + x - 20}{(x+6)(x+2)(x-4)}$$

$$= \frac{-2x - 22}{(x+6)(x+2)(x-4)}$$

$$= \frac{-2x - 22}{x^3 + 4x^2 - 20x - 48}$$

c.

$$\frac{3x+2}{x^2 - 3x - 10} - \frac{2x+7}{x^2 - 2x - 15} = \frac{3x+2}{(x-5)(x+2)} - \frac{2x+7}{(x-5)(x+3)}$$

$$= \frac{(x+3)}{(x+3)} \cdot \frac{(3x+2)}{(x-5)(x+2)} - \frac{(2x+7)}{(x-5)(x+3)} \cdot \frac{(x+2)}{(x+2)}$$

$$= \frac{3x^2 + 11x + 6}{(x+3)(x-5)(x+2)} - \frac{2x^2 + 11x + 14}{(x+3)(x-5)(x+2)}$$

$$= \frac{x^2 - 8}{(x+3)(x-5)(x+2)}$$

$$= \frac{x^2 - 8}{x^3 - 19x - 30}$$

Adding or Subtracting Rational Expressions:
1.   Write all fractions with a common denominator.
2.   Add or subtract the numerators and keep the denominator the same.
3.   Factor the numerator and reduce (if possible).

Caution: when subtracting rational expressions;
   Be sure to distribute the subtraction to the entire numerator of the second fraction.

Problem 2

Add or subtract the following rational expressions:

a. $\dfrac{5x-4}{(x+5)(x+6)} - \dfrac{3x-16}{(x+5)(x+6)}$

b. $\dfrac{2x+5}{(x+3)(x-4)} + \dfrac{3x+7}{(x+3)(x+7)}$

c. $\dfrac{3x-7}{x^2 - 4x - 45} - \dfrac{2x+3}{x^2 - 5x - 36}$

Solution   See page 362

Section 5.3 Key Points

- Finding a Least Common Denominator:
  1. Factor the denominators (if needed).
  2. Take the highest power of each factor for the LCD.
  3. Leave in factored form or multiply the factors together.

- To Write a fraction in terms of the LCD.
  1. Find the Least Common Denominator.
  2. Determine what factors of the LCD the fraction's denominator is missing.
  3. Multiply the numerator and denominator of the fraction by the missing factors.

- Adding or Subtracting Rational Expressions:
  1. Write all fractions with a common denominator.
  2. Add or subtract the numerators and keep the denominator the same.
  3. Factor the numerator and reduce (if possible).

- Caution: when subtracting rational expressions;
  Be sure to distribute the subtraction to the entire numerator of the second fraction.

Section 5.3 Problem Solutions

Problem 1   Solution

a.

$$\frac{7}{24m} \qquad \frac{11}{45m^3n}$$

$$\frac{7}{2^3 \cdot 3 \cdot m} \qquad \frac{11}{3^2 \cdot 5 \cdot m^3 \cdot n}$$

$$LCD = 2^3 \cdot 3^2 \cdot 5 \cdot m^3 \cdot n$$

$$LCD = 360m^3n$$

$$\frac{3 \cdot 5 \cdot m^2 \cdot n}{3 \cdot 5 \cdot m^2 \cdot n} \cdot \frac{7}{2^3 \cdot 3 \cdot m} \qquad \frac{11}{3^2 \cdot 5 \cdot m^3 \cdot n} \cdot \frac{2^3}{2^3}$$

$$\frac{105m^2n}{360m^3n} \qquad \frac{88}{360m^3n}$$

b.

$$\frac{x+3}{x+8} \qquad \frac{x+5}{x+9}$$

$$LCD = (x+8)(x+9)$$

$$LCD = x^2 + 17x + 72$$

$$\frac{(x+9)}{(x+9)} \cdot \frac{(x+3)}{(x+8)} \qquad \frac{(x+5)}{(x+9)} \cdot \frac{(x+8)}{(x+8)}$$

$$\frac{(x+9)(x+3)}{(x+8)(x+9)} \qquad \frac{(x+5)(x+8)}{(x+8)(x+9)}$$

$$\frac{x^2 + 12x + 27}{x^2 + 17x + 72} \qquad \frac{x^2 + 13x + 40}{x^2 + 17x + 72}$$

Problem 1   Solution Continued

c.

$$\frac{x+2}{(x-4)(x-7)} \qquad \frac{x+4}{(x-7)(x+8)}$$

$$LCD = (x-4)(x-7)(x+8)$$

$$LCD = x^3 - 3x^2 - 60x + 224$$

$$\frac{(x+8)}{(x+8)} \cdot \frac{(x+2)}{(x-4)(x-7)} \qquad \frac{(x+4)}{(x-7)(x+8)} \cdot \frac{(x-4)}{(x-4)}$$

$$\frac{(x+8)(x+2)}{(x-4)(x-7)(x+8)} \qquad \frac{(x+4)(x-4)}{(x-4)(x-7)(x+8)}$$

$$\frac{x^2 + 10x + 16}{x^3 - 3x^2 - 60x + 224} \qquad \frac{x^2 - 16}{x^3 - 3x^2 - 60x + 224}$$

d.

$$\frac{3x+2}{6x^2 - 7x - 20} \qquad \frac{4x-9}{2x^2 - 19x + 35}$$

$$\frac{3x+2}{(2x-5)(3x+4)} \qquad \frac{4x-9}{(2x-5)(x-7)}$$

$$LCD = (2x-5)(3x+4)(x-7)$$

$$LCD = 6x^3 - 49x^2 + 29x + 140$$

$$\frac{(x-7)}{(x-7)} \cdot \frac{(3x+2)}{(2x-5)(3x+4)} \qquad \frac{(4x-9)}{(2x-5)(x-7)} \cdot \frac{(3x+4)}{(3x+4)}$$

$$\frac{(x-7)(3x+2)}{(2x-5)(3x+4)(x-7)} \qquad \frac{(4x-9)(3x^+4)}{(2x-5)(3x+4)(x-7)}$$

$$\frac{3x^2 - 19x - 14}{6x^3 - 49x^2 + 29x + 140} \qquad \frac{12x^2 - 11x - 36}{6x^3 - 49x^2 + 29x + 140}$$

Problem 2   Solution

a.

$$\frac{5x-4}{(x+5)(x+6)} - \frac{3x-16}{(x+5)(x+6)} = \frac{2x+12}{(x+5)(x+6)}$$

$$= \frac{2(x+6)}{(x+5)(x+6)} \qquad \text{Factor the numerator}$$
$$\text{and reduce.}$$

$$= \frac{2\cancel{(x+6)}}{(x+5)\cancel{(x+6)}}$$

$$= \frac{2}{x+5}$$

b.

$$\frac{2x+5}{(x+3)(x-4)} + \frac{3x+7}{(x+3)(x+7)}$$

$$= \frac{(x+7)}{(x+7)} \cdot \frac{(2x+5)}{(x+3)(x-4)} + \frac{(3x+7)}{(x+3)(x+7)} \cdot \frac{(x-4)}{(x-4)}$$

$$= \frac{2x^2 + 19x + 35}{(x+7)(x+3)(x-4)} + \frac{3x^2 - 5x - 28}{(x+7)(x+3)(x-4)}$$

$$= \frac{5x^2 + 14x + 7}{(x+7)(x+3)(x-4)}$$

$$= \frac{5x^2 + 14x + 7}{x^3 + 6x^2 - 19x - 84}$$

Problem 2   Solution Continued

c.

$$\frac{3x-7}{x^2-4x-45} - \frac{2x+3}{x^2-5x-36} = \frac{3x-7}{(x+5)(x-9)} - \frac{2x+3}{(x+4)(x-9)}$$

$$= \frac{(x+4)}{(x+4)} \cdot \frac{(3x-7)}{(x+5)(x-9)} - \frac{(2x+3)}{(x+4)(x-9)} \cdot \frac{(x+5)}{(x+5)}$$

$$= \frac{3x^2+5x-28}{(x+4)(x+5)(x-9)} - \frac{2x^2+13x+15}{(x+4)(x+5)(x-9)}$$

$$= \frac{x^2-8x-43}{(x+4)(x+5)(x-9)}$$

$$= \frac{x^2-8x-43}{x^3-61x-180}$$

5.3 Exercises

For exercises 1 through 13 find the least common denominator for each of the following sets of rational expressions and write each expression in terms of the LCD.

1. $\dfrac{7}{12x^2y}$ $\dfrac{3}{28xy}$

2. $\dfrac{11a}{15b^2c}$ $\dfrac{14b}{25ac^3}$

3. $\dfrac{7m}{1980n^2p}$ $\dfrac{4n}{1575p}$

4. $\dfrac{16xz}{315y^4}$ $\dfrac{9}{84x^2y^2z}$

5. $\dfrac{x+2}{x+8}$ $\dfrac{x-4}{x+7}$

6. $\dfrac{x+9}{x-4}$ $\dfrac{x+7}{x+3}$

7. $\dfrac{x-5}{x+6}$ $\dfrac{x-5}{x+5}$

8. $\dfrac{x+2}{(x+3)(x+7)}$ $\dfrac{x-4}{(x+3)(x+5)}$

9. $\dfrac{x-2}{(x+9)(x-3)}$ $\dfrac{x+7}{(x+4)(x-3)}$

10. $\dfrac{x+1}{(x-7)(x-2)}$ $\dfrac{x+2}{(x-8)(x-2)}$

11. $\dfrac{x+2}{x^2+5x+6}$ $\dfrac{x-4}{x^2-2x-8}$

12. $\dfrac{x+3}{x^2-2x-35}$ $\dfrac{x-7}{x^2+x-20}$

13. $\dfrac{x-5}{2x^2-9x-35}$ $\dfrac{x+6}{2x^2+11x+15}$

For Exercises 14 through 34 add or subtract the rational expressions.

14. $\dfrac{x+2}{x+7}+\dfrac{x+8}{x+7}$

15. $\dfrac{x-3}{x-9}+\dfrac{x-15}{x-9}$

16. $\dfrac{x+7}{x+5}-\dfrac{4x+22}{x+5}$

17. $\dfrac{x+7}{x-2}-\dfrac{x-6}{x-2}$

18. $\dfrac{x+5}{x+3}+\dfrac{x-2}{x+7}$

19. $\dfrac{x-4}{x+6}+\dfrac{x+3}{x-5}$

20. $\dfrac{x+2}{x+3}-\dfrac{x+4}{x+7}$

21. $\dfrac{x-7}{x+2}-\dfrac{x+3}{x+4}$

22. $\dfrac{x+2}{(x+5)(x+3)}+\dfrac{x+4}{(x+5)(x+3)}$

23. $\dfrac{3x-6}{(2x+7)(x+3)}-\dfrac{7x+8}{(2x+7)(x+3)}$

24. $\dfrac{x+1}{(x-7)(x-2)}+\dfrac{x+2}{(x-8)(x-2)}$

25. $\dfrac{2x+5}{(x-11)(x+3)}+\dfrac{x-3}{(x-11)(x-4)}$

26. $\dfrac{x-2}{(x+4)(x-6)}+\dfrac{3x+1}{(x+3)(x-6)}$

27. $\dfrac{x+3}{x^2-9x+14}-\dfrac{x-4}{x^2-10x+16}$

28. $\dfrac{x+2}{x^2+10x+21}-\dfrac{x-4}{x^2+8x+15}$

29. $\dfrac{x-2}{x^2+6x-27}+\dfrac{x+7}{x^2+x-12}$

30. $\dfrac{x-5}{2x^2-9x-35}+\dfrac{x+6}{2x^2+11x+15}$

31. $\dfrac{x+2}{2x^2+7x+3}+\dfrac{x-4}{4x^2+7x-15}$

32. $\dfrac{x+2}{6x^2-29x+28}-\dfrac{x-5}{2x^2-13x+42}$

33. $\dfrac{5x+43}{x^2+6x-55}-\dfrac{2x+10}{x^2+6x-55}$

34. $\dfrac{3x}{3x^2+24x+36}+\dfrac{x^2}{2x^2+16x+24}$

Section 5.4   Solving Rational Equations

• **Solving Rational Equations**

In this section we will learn to solve rational equations. Most often you will want to eliminate all the fractions by multiplying both sides of the equation by the common denominator. This will allow you to solve the remaining equation using the techniques you have already learned in earlier chapters. When solving rational equations you will need to be aware that some solutions will not be valid. When variables are in the denominator of a fraction we must be very careful not to allow division by zero to take place. To avoid this always check your solutions in the original equation to be sure that no invalid solutions are kept.

Example 1

The math club on campus is planning a ski trip to a local mountain resort. The students want to keep the costs for each person down as low as possible so they plan to rent a van and split the costs evenly between them. They have decided that the person driving the van should not have to pay. If the van is going to cost $130 to rent and can fit up to 15 people how many people need to go in the van to keep the transportation costs per person $12?

Solution

Let p be the number of people going on the ski trip in the rented van, and C be the cost per person going on the trip in dollars per person.

Since the driver will not be paying for the van expenses we need to subtract him from the total number of people p. If we take the total cost for the van and divide it by the number of people paying we get the cost per person. This leads us to the equation:

$$C(p) = \frac{130}{p-1}$$

Since we want the average cost to be $12 per person we can replace $C(p)$ with 12 and solve. To solve this equation we need to get the variable p out of the denominator of the fraction. We can do this by multiplying both sides of the equation by the denominator $p-1$.

$$\frac{130}{p-1} = 12$$

$$(p-1)\left(\frac{130}{p-1}\right) = 12(p-1) \quad \text{Multiply both sides by the denominator.}$$

$$130 = 12p - 12 \quad \text{Solve for } p.$$

$$142 = 12p$$

$$\frac{142}{12} = p$$

$$11.83 = p$$

Therefore the math club needs to have at least 12 people go in the van to keep the transportation cost at $12 per person or less. Note that we needed to round this answer up or the cost would have been more than $12 per person. In this type of situation you would always want to round up to the next whole person.

Problem 1

In section 5.1 we found the model $a(m) = \dfrac{50}{m}$ for the acceleration a in mps^2 a fixed force would give when applied to a mass of m kg.

a. If an object has an acceleration of 4 mps^2 when this force is applied what is the object's mass?

b. What size mass can be accelerated at 0.5 mps^2 using the given fixed amount of force?

Solution   See page 371

For rational functions that arise from dividing two functions the technique of multiplying both sides of the equation by the denominator quickly clears the fraction and allows you to solve the remaining equation. Although some of these equations may look very messy the use of a graphing calculator can help manage the solution process.

Example 2

In section 5.1 we found a model for the average disbursements made by the United States Medicare program.

$$P(t) = \frac{-3160.64t^2 + 52536.5t - 4548.31}{0.39t + 35.65}$$

where $P(t)$ represents the average dollars disbursed per person by medicare t years since 1990.

a. In what year did the average dollars disbursed hit \$5500?

Solution

a. We are given an average disbursement so we can substitute $P(t) = 5500$

$$5500 = \frac{-3160.64t^2 + 52536.5t - 4548.31}{0.39t + 35.65}$$

$$(0.39t + 35.65)(5500) = \frac{-3160.64t^2 + 52536.5t - 4548.31}{-0.39t + 35.65} \cdot \overline{(0.39t + 35.65)}$$

$$2145t + 196075 = -3160.64t^2 + 52536.5t - 4548.31$$

$$0 = -3160.64t^2 + 50391.5t - 200623.31$$

$$t = 7.7 \qquad t = 8.24 \qquad \text{Quadratic Formula}$$

Since both $t = 7.7$ and $t = 8.24$ represent the year 1998 we have that in 1998 the average disbursements per person made by medicare was about \$5500. We can check these solutions using the graph or table.

X	Y1	Y2
7.7	5499.9	5500
8.24	5500.1	5500
X=		

Once you have multiplied by the denominator you can combine all the like terms and in the case of example 2 you were left with a quadratic equation and thus can use the quadratic formula or factoring to solve. In general, multiplying by the common denominator will allow you to solve most equations involving rational expressions.

Example 3

Solve the following rational equations:

a. $\dfrac{3}{x+2} = 12$

b. $\dfrac{10}{x-8} = 5$

c. $\dfrac{5}{x+1} = 3 - \dfrac{7}{x+1}$

Solution

a.

$$\dfrac{3}{x+2} = 12$$

$$(\cancel{x+2})\left(\dfrac{3}{\cancel{x+2}}\right) = 12(x+2)$$ Multiply both sides of the equation by the denominator.

$$3 = 12x + 24$$ Solve for x.

$$-21 = 12x$$

$$-\dfrac{21}{12} = x$$

$$-\dfrac{7}{4} = x$$

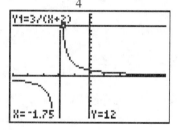

Check the solution using a graph and trace.

b.

$$\dfrac{10}{x-8} = 5$$

$$(\cancel{x-8})\left(\dfrac{10}{\cancel{x-8}}\right) = 5(x-8)$$ Multiply both sides of the equation by the denominator.

$$10 = 5x - 40$$ Solve for x.

$$50 = 5x$$

$$10 = x$$

X	Y1	Y2
10	5	5

Y₁ ▣ 10/(X-8)

Check the solution using the table.

c.

$$\frac{5}{x+1} = 3 - \frac{7}{x+1}$$

$$(x+1)\left(\frac{5}{x+1}\right) = \left(3 - \frac{7}{x+1}\right)(x+1)$$ Multiply both sides by the common denominator.

$$5 = 3(x+1) - \left(\frac{7}{x+1}\right)(x+1)$$ Use the distributive property.

$$5 = 3x + 3 - 7$$

$$5 = 3x - 4$$ Solve for x.

$$9 = 3x$$

$$x = 3$$

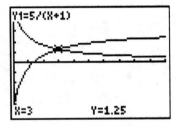

Check the solution.

Problem 2

Solve the following rational equations:

a. $\dfrac{7}{x-4} = 14$

b. $\dfrac{35}{x+3} = 4 + \dfrac{15}{x+3}$

Solution   See page 371

This solving technique can be used with rational functions of all types. When there is more than one denominator it is quickest if you first find a common denominator for all fractions in the equation. When you multiply by the common denominator you will eliminate all of the fractions and you should then be able to solve the remaining equation. Remember to check your solutions for values that may not be valid.

Solving Rational Equations:
1.   Multiply both sides by the common denominator.
2.   Solve the remaining equation.
3.   Check the solution(s) (watch for division by zero).

Example 4

Solve the following rational equations and check your solution(s):

a. $\dfrac{12}{x+3} = \dfrac{7}{x-5}$

b. $\dfrac{4}{x-4} = \dfrac{3}{x+7}$

c. $\dfrac{7}{x+5} + \dfrac{3x}{x-2} = \dfrac{42}{x^2+3x-10}$

d. $\dfrac{2}{x+3} + \dfrac{7}{x+4} = \dfrac{4x-11}{x^2+7x+12}$

Solution

a.

$$\frac{12}{x+3} = \frac{7}{x-5}$$

$$(x+3)(x-5)\left(\frac{12}{x+3}\right) = \left(\frac{7}{x-5}\right)(x+3)(x-5)$$

Multiply both sides by the common denominator.

$$(x-5)12 = 7(x+3)$$

Cancel denominators and distribute the multiplication.

$$12x - 60 = 7x + 21$$

$$5x = 81$$

Solve for x.

$$x = \frac{81}{5}$$

$$x = 16.2$$

$$\frac{12}{(16.2)+3} = \frac{7}{(16.2)-5}$$

Check the solution.

$$0.625 = 0.625$$

b.

$$\frac{4}{x-4} = \frac{3}{x+7}$$

$$(x-4)(x+7)\left(\frac{4}{x-4}\right) = \left(\frac{3}{x+7}\right)(x-4)(x+7)$$

Multiply both sides by the common denominator.

$$(x+7)(4) = (3)(x-4)$$

Solve for x.

$$4x + 28 = 3x - 12$$

$$x = -40$$

$$\frac{4}{(-40)-4} = \frac{3}{(-40)+7}$$

Check the solution.

$$-0.091 = -0.091$$

c.

$$\frac{7}{x+5} + \frac{3x}{x-2} = \frac{42}{x^2+3x-10}$$

$$\frac{7}{x+5} + \frac{3x}{x-2} = \frac{42}{(x+5)(x-2)}$$

$$(x+5)(x-2)\left(\frac{7}{x+5} + \frac{3x}{x-2}\right) = \left(\frac{42}{(x+5)(x-2)}\right) \cdot (x+5)(x-2)$$

$$(x+5)(x-2)\left(\frac{7}{x+5}\right) + (x+5)(x-2)\left(\frac{3x}{x-2}\right) = 42$$

$$7(x-2) + 3x(x+5) = 42$$

Note you cannot cancel on the left side until you distribute.

$$7x - 14 + 3x^2 + 15x = 42$$

$$3x^2 + 22x - 56 = 0$$

$$x = 2 \qquad x = -\frac{28}{3}$$

Check the solutions. Since 2 results in division by zero it is not a valid solution.

X	Y₁	Y₂
2	ERROR	ERROR
-9.333	.8552	.8552
X=		

Because $x = 2$ causes some of the fractions to have division by zero we must eliminate that solution and thus we have only $x = -\dfrac{28}{3}$ as a solution.

d.

$$\frac{2}{x+3} + \frac{7}{x+4} = \frac{4x-11}{x^2+7x+12}$$ Factor to find the common denominator.

$$\frac{2}{x+3} + \frac{7}{x+4} = \frac{4x-11}{(x+3)(x+4)}$$

$$(x+3)(x+4)\left(\frac{2}{x+3} + \frac{7}{x+4}\right) = \left(\frac{4x-11}{(x+3)(x+4)}\right)(x+3)(x+4)$$

$$(x+3)(x+4)\left(\frac{2}{x+3}\right) + (x+3)(x+4)\left(\frac{7}{x+4}\right) = 4x-11$$

$$(x+4)(2) + (x+3)(7) = 4x-11$$

$$2x + 8 + 7x + 21 = 4x - 11$$

$$9x + 29 = 4x - 11$$

$$5x = -40$$

$$x = -8$$ Check the solution.

$$\frac{2}{(-8)+3} + \frac{7}{(-8)+4} = \frac{4(-8)-11}{(-8)^2 + 7(-8) + 12}$$

$$-2.15 = -2.15$$

Problem 3

Solve the following rational equations:

a. $\dfrac{5}{x+2} = 8 - \dfrac{52}{x+7}$

b. $\dfrac{3}{x+2} = \dfrac{6}{x+9}$

c. $\dfrac{5x}{x-4} + \dfrac{3}{x+2} = \dfrac{-18}{x^2-2x-8}$

Solution   See page 371

Section 5.4 Key Points

- Solving Rational Equations:
    - **i**   Multiply both sides by the common denominator.
    - **ii**   Solve the remaining equation.
    - **iii** Check your solution(s) (watch for division by zero).

Section 5.4 Problem Solutions

Problem 1   *Solution*

a. We are given an acceleration of $4\,\text{mps}^2$ so we can substitute $a(m) = 4$ and get

$$4 = \frac{50}{m}$$

$$4m = 50$$

$$m = \frac{50}{4}$$

$$m = 12.5$$

An object with a mass of 12.5kg will accelerate at $4\,\text{mps}^2$ when this force is applied.

b. We are given an acceleration of $0.5\,\text{mps}^2$ so we get.

$$0.5 = \frac{50}{m}$$

$$0.5m = 50$$

$$m = 100$$

A 100kg object will accelerate at only $0.5\,\text{mps}^2$ when this force is applied.

Problem 2   *Solution*

a.

$$\frac{7}{x-4} = 14$$

$$(x-4)\left(\frac{7}{x-4}\right) = 14(x-4) \qquad \text{Multiply both sides by the denominator.}$$

$$7 = 14x - 56 \qquad \text{Solve for } x.$$

$$63 = 14x$$

$$4.5 = x$$

$$\frac{7}{4.5-4} = 14 \qquad \text{Check your solution.}$$

$$\frac{7}{0.5} = 14$$

$$14 = 14$$

b.

$$\frac{35}{x+3} = 4 + \frac{15}{x+3}$$

$$\qquad\qquad\qquad \text{Multiply by the denominator.}$$

$$(x+3)\left(\frac{35}{x+3}\right) = \left(4 + \frac{15}{x+3}\right)(x+3)$$

$$35 = 4(x+3) + \left(\frac{15}{x+3}\right)(x+3) \qquad \text{Distribute both sides.}$$

$$\qquad\qquad\qquad\qquad\qquad\qquad \text{Check your solutions using the table.}$$

$$35 = 4x + 12 + 15$$

$$35 = 4x + 27$$

$$8 = 4x$$

$$2 = x$$

X	Y₁	Y₂
2	7	7
X=		

Problem 3   ***Solution***

a.

$$\frac{5}{x+2} = 8 - \frac{52}{x+7}$$

$$(x+7)(x+2)\left(\frac{5}{x+2}\right) = \left(8 - \frac{52}{x+7}\right)(x+7)(x+2)$$
Multiply by the denominator.

$$5(x+7) = 8(x+7)(x+2) - \left(\frac{52}{x+7}\right)(x+7)(x+2)$$
Distribute on both sides.

$$5x+35 = 8(x^2+9x+14) - 52(x+2)$$

$$5x+35 = 8x^2 + 72x + 112 - 52x - 104$$

$$0 = 8x^2 + 15x - 27$$
Use the distributive property to multiply the two binomials and then distribute the 8.

$$x = -3 \qquad x = \frac{9}{8}$$
Use Quadratic Formula.

X	Y₁	Y₂
-3	-5	-5
1.125	1.6	1.6

X=

Check your Solutions.

b.

$$\frac{3}{x+2} = \frac{6}{x+9}$$

$$(x+9)(x+2)\left(\frac{3}{x+2}\right) = \left(\frac{6}{x+9}\right)(x+9)(x+2)$$

$$3(x+9) = 6(x+2)$$

$$3x+27 = 6x+12$$

$$15 = 3x$$

$$5 = x$$

$$\frac{3}{5+2} = \frac{6}{5+9}$$
Check your solutions.

$$\frac{3}{7} = \frac{3}{7}$$

Problem 3   *Solution Continued*

c.

$$\frac{5x}{x-4} + \frac{3}{x+2} = \frac{-18}{x^2 - 2x - 8}$$

$$\frac{5x}{x-4} + \frac{3}{x+2} = \frac{-18}{(x-4)(x+2)}$$

$$(x-4)(x+2)\left(\frac{5x}{x-4} + \frac{3}{x+2}\right) = \left(\frac{-18}{(x-4)(x+2)}\right)(x-4)(x+2)$$

$$(x-4)(x+2)\left(\frac{5x}{x-4}\right) + (x-4)(x+2)\left(\frac{3}{x+2}\right) = -18$$

$$5x(x+2) + 3(x-4) = -18$$

$$5x^2 + 10x + 3x - 12 = -18$$

$$5x^2 + 13x + 6 = 0$$

$$x = -2 \qquad x = -\frac{3}{5}$$

Check your solutions in the table.

X	Y1	Y2
-2	ERROR	ERROR
-.6	2.795	2.795
X=		

$x = -2$ is an invalid solution since it makes some of the denominators equal zero. Thus only $x = -\frac{3}{5}$ is a solution.

5.4 Exercises

1. The state of California's spending per person has increased dramatically since 1950. The states population from 1950 to 2000 can be modeled by
$$P(t) = 0.464t - 12.47$$
    where $P(t)$ is California's population in millions of people t years since 1900. The amount California spent in millions of dollars can be modeled by
$$S(t) = 55.125t^2 - 6435.607t + 186914.286$$
    where $S(t)$ is the amount California spent in millions of dollars during year t, years since 1900.
    source: Models derived from data in the Governor's Budget Summary as printed in the North County Times Feb. .

    a. Find a new function that gives the spending per capita (per person) t years since 1900.
    b. Find the per capita spending in California in 1995.
    c. Find in what year the per capita spending in California reached $3000 per person.

2. The percent of housing units in Colorado that were vacant in the 1990's can be modeled by
$$P(t) = \frac{216.89t^2 - 2129.2t + 19114.9}{33.67t + 1444.29}$$
    where $P(t)$ is the percent of housing units in Colorado that were vacant t years since 1990.
    source: Model derived from data from the U.S. Department of Commerce Bureau of Economic Analysis

    a. Find the percent of housing units vacant in 1995.
    b. Find when there was an 11.5% vacancy rate for housing units in Colorado.

3. The per capita personal spending in the United States can be modeled by
$$s(t) = \frac{248158.9t + 186907.6}{0.0226t^2 + 1.885t + 204.72}$$
    where $s(t)$ represents the per capita personal spending in dollars in the United States t years since 1970.
    source: Model derived from data from the U.S. Department of Commerce Bureau of Economic Analysis

    a. Find the per capita personal spending in the United States in 1995.
    b. In what year did the per capita personal spending in the United States reach $25,000.

4. The population of the United States since 1970 can be modeled by
$$P(t) = 0.226t^2 + 1.885t + 204.72$$
    where $P(t)$ represents the population of the United States in millions t years since 1970. The national debt of the United States in millions of dollars t years since 1970 can be modeled by
$$D(t) = 8215.1t^2 - 23035.4t + 413525.6$$
    where $D(t)$ represents the national debt of the U.S. in millions of dollars t years since 1970.
    source: Models derived from data from the U.S. Department of Commerce Bureau of Economic Analysis

    a. Find a new model for the average amount of national debt per person in the U.S. t years since 1970.
    b. Find the average amount of national debt per person in 1990.
    c. Find when the average amount of national debt per person will reach $18,000 per person.

5. The average amount of benefits received by people from the U.S. food stamp program can be modeled by
$$B(t) = \frac{-470001t^2 + 4110992t + 14032612}{-469.4t^2 + 3745t + 19774}$$
    where $B(t)$ is the average benefit in dollars per person for people on the U.S. food stamp program t years since 1990.
    source: Model derived from data from the Statistical Abstract 2001.
    Find when the average benefit was $800 per person.

6. The weight of a body varies inversely as the square of its distance from the center of the earth. If the radius of the earth is 4000 miles, how far from the earths surface must a 220 pound man be to weigh only 80 pounds

7. The current that flows through an electrical circuit is inversely proportional to the resistance of that circuit. When the resistance R is 200ohms, the current I is 1.2amp. Find the resistance when the current is 0.9 amp?

8. The illumination of a light source is inversely proportional to the square of the distance from the light source. If a light has an illumination of 25.5 foot candles at a distance of 10 feet from the light source.

    a. Find a model for the illumination of this light.
    b. What is the illumination of this light at a distance of 10 feet from the light source?
    c. How far away from this light source would you need to be for the illumination to be 50 foot candles?

9. The Fancy Affair catering company is catering an event for a local charity. Jan the owner of Fancy Affair is donating her time to the cause but needs to charge the charity for the food, decorations and supplies used. If p people attend the charity event Jan has figured her total cost to be modeled by

$$C(p) = 4.55p + 365.00$$

where C is the total cost in dollars for the food, decorations and supplies when p people attend the charity event.

   a. Find a new function that gives the per person cost for p people to attend the charity event.

   b. Use your new model to find how many people need to attend to keep the per person costs down to $7.50 each.

10.

   a. If y varies inversely with the cube of x and $y = 11$ when $x = 5$ find an equation to represent this relationship.

   b. Find x if $y = 4$

11.

   a. If m varies inversely with n^5 and $m = 25$ when $n = 2$ find an equation to represent this relationship.

   b. Find m if $n = 4$.

   c. Find n if $m = 50$

12.

   a. If W varies inversely with p^4 and $W = 135$ when $p = 3$ find an equation to represent this relationship.

   b. Find W when $p = 10$

   c. Find p when $W = 400$

For Exercises 13 through 39 solve and check with a table or graph.

13. $2 - \dfrac{6}{x} = \dfrac{4}{x}$

14. $3 + \dfrac{5}{2x} = \dfrac{4}{x}$

15. $5 = \dfrac{4}{2w + 3}$

16. $2t = \dfrac{8}{t - 3}$

17. $5x = \dfrac{-10}{3x - 7}$

18. $3m = \dfrac{-9}{m + 4}$

19. $\dfrac{x + 5}{3x - 6} = \dfrac{2}{3}$

20. $\dfrac{2t - 3}{5t + 6} = \dfrac{11}{17}$

21. $\dfrac{x^2}{x + 5} = \dfrac{25}{x + 5}$

22. $\dfrac{x^2}{x + 6} = \dfrac{36}{x + 6}$

23. $\dfrac{w^2}{w - 3} = \dfrac{9}{w - 3}$

24. $\dfrac{8}{k + 3} + 5 = \dfrac{-21}{k - 4}$

25. $\dfrac{12}{x + 5} - 2 = \dfrac{-10}{x + 3}$

26. $\dfrac{n - 8}{n - 5} = \dfrac{n + 9}{n - 2}$

27. $\dfrac{v + 6}{v - 2} = \dfrac{v - 1}{v - 8}$

28. $\dfrac{x + 9}{x - 3} = \dfrac{x + 4}{x - 6}$

29. $\dfrac{d + 3}{d + 5} = \dfrac{d + 8}{d + 2}$

30. $\dfrac{x}{x - 14} + \dfrac{9}{x - 7} = \dfrac{x^2}{x^2 - 21x + 98}$

31. $\dfrac{m + 4}{m + 1} = \dfrac{30}{m^2 - 2m - 3}$

32. $\dfrac{k - 2}{k + 1} = \dfrac{7k + 22}{k^2 + 6k + 5}$

33. $\dfrac{p}{p - 8} + \dfrac{6}{p - 4} = \dfrac{p^2}{p^2 - 12p + 32}$

34. $\dfrac{2x + 5}{x - 7} = \dfrac{x - 2}{x + 3}$

35. $\dfrac{3c - 7}{c + 5} = \dfrac{2c + 3}{c - 8}$

36. $\dfrac{t}{t - 6} + \dfrac{5}{t - 3} = \dfrac{t^2}{t^2 - 9t + 18}$

37. $\dfrac{x}{x - 4} + \dfrac{4}{x - 2} = \dfrac{x^2}{x^2 - 6x + 8}$

38. $\dfrac{25}{w^2 + w - 12} = \dfrac{w + 4}{w - 3}$

39. $\dfrac{c - 3}{c + 4} = \dfrac{14}{c^2 + 6c + 8}$

Chapter 5 Review Exercises

1. The illumination of a light source is inversely proportional to the square of the distance from the light source. A certain light has an illumination of 40 foot candles at a distance of 30 feet from the light source.

    a. Find a model for the illumination of this light.

    b. What is the illumination of this light at a distance of 40 feet from the light source?

    c. At what distance would the illumination of this light be 50 foot candles?

2.

    a. If y varies inversely with x^5 and $y = 7$ when $x = 2$ find a n equation to represent this relationship.

    b. Find y if $x = 4$.

3. Math R Us, MRU, is having a math competition and want to have a total of $500 in prize money. To run the competition they will need to have the prize money plus $7.5 per person competing in the competition. They want to set an entrance fee for each competitor that will cover their costs. MRU plan to give 10 scholarships to those who cannot afford to pay.

    a. Find a model that gives the entrance fee MRU should charge if they have p people compete. (p includes the 10 people who are on scholarship and thus will not pay an entrance fee.)

    b. Use your model to estimate the entrance fee they should charge if 100 people compete.

    c. If MRU wants to have an entrance fee of $10 how many people do they need to participate in this competition?

4. The per capita amount of cheese consumed by Americans can be modeled by

    $$C(t) = \frac{637.325t + 7428.649}{0.226t^2 + 10.925t + 332.82}$$

    where $C(t)$ represents the per capita amount of cheese consumed by Americans in pounds per person t years since 1990.
    source: models derived from data in the statistical abstract 2001.

    a. Estimate the per capita amount of cheese consumed by Americans in 1995.

    b. Estimate when the per capita amount of cheese consumed by Americans will reach 30 pounds per person.

For exercises 5 through 9 find the domain of the given rational function.

5. $f(x) = \dfrac{3x + 2}{x - 9}$

6. $g(x) = \dfrac{x + 5}{(x + 5)(x - 3)}$

7. $h(x) = \dfrac{5x + 2}{2x^2 - 7x - 15}$

8.

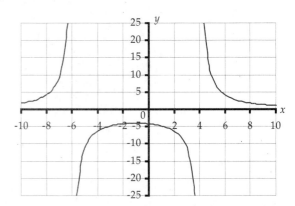

9.

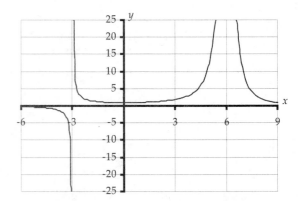

For exercises 10 through 19 perform the indicated operation and simplify the rational expressions:

10. $\dfrac{x + 3}{x - 15} \cdot \dfrac{x - 15}{x - 2}$

11. $\dfrac{4}{x + 3} \cdot \dfrac{x + 9}{x - 7}$

12. $\dfrac{x + 2}{x - 3} \div \dfrac{x + 7}{x - 3}$

13. $\dfrac{(x + 4)(x + 5)}{(x - 5)(x + 2)} \div \dfrac{(x + 5)(x - 7)}{(x + 2)(x - 7)}$

14. $\dfrac{2n + 6}{n^2 + 8n + 15} \cdot \dfrac{3n + 15}{n^2 + 11x + 28}$

15. $\dfrac{v+5}{v^2-6v-55} \div \dfrac{v-8}{v^2-4v-77}$

16. $\dfrac{12}{x+6} + \dfrac{4x+3}{x+6}$

17. $\dfrac{3}{x-5} - \dfrac{7}{x+2}$

18. $\dfrac{x+2}{(x+3)(x+5)} + \dfrac{6}{(x+3)(x-7)}$

19. $\dfrac{2x-7}{x^2-5x-14} + \dfrac{x+5}{x^2-4x-21}$

For exercises 20 through 27 solve the rational equations: Check your answers with a table or graph.

20. $\dfrac{5}{x-3} = \dfrac{2}{x+7}$

21. $\dfrac{4x}{x+3} = \dfrac{2x}{x-9}$

22. $\dfrac{2}{x+5} + 6 = \dfrac{-5}{x-3}$

23. $\dfrac{x}{x+5} + \dfrac{7}{x-3} = \dfrac{56}{(x+5)(x-3)}$

24. $\dfrac{w}{w-7} - \dfrac{3}{w-4} = \dfrac{9}{(w-7)(w-4)}$

25. $\dfrac{5x+3}{x^2+7x-9} = \dfrac{10x-12}{x^2+7x-9}$

26. $\dfrac{3k}{k+2} + \dfrac{2}{k+5} = \dfrac{50}{k^2+7k+10}$

27. $\dfrac{5}{x^2+3x-28} = \dfrac{3x}{x^2-8x+16}$

Chapter 5 Test

1.   The illumination of a light source is inversely proportional to the square of the distance from the light source. A certain light has an illumination of 30 foot candles at a distance of 12 feet from the light source.

   a. Find a model for the illumination of this light.

   b. What is the illumination of this light at a distance of 7 feet from the light source?

   c. At what distance would the illumination of this light be 20 foot candles?

For exercises 2 through 8 perform the indicated operation and simplify the rational expressions:

2. $\dfrac{2x}{x+7} \cdot \dfrac{x+3}{x-4}$

3. $\dfrac{(x+3)(x+5)}{(x-7)(x+3)} \div \dfrac{(x+5)(x+2)}{(x+4)(x-7)}$

4. $\dfrac{5w+3}{w^2-4w-21} \cdot \dfrac{2w-14}{5w^2-17w-12}$

5. $\dfrac{2m+4}{m^2-m-20} \div \dfrac{m+2}{m^2-4m-5}$

6. $\dfrac{5x}{2x-7} + \dfrac{3x-8}{2x-7}$

7. $\dfrac{x+5}{x-3} - \dfrac{x-2}{x+4}$

8. $\dfrac{5x+2}{x^2+5x+6} + \dfrac{x-4}{x^2+9x+14}$

9.   Find the domain for the rational functions

   a. $h(x) = \dfrac{3x-7}{x^2+6x-27}$

   b.

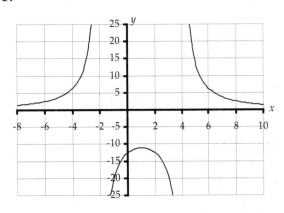

10.   The total labor force in the state of Florida can be modeled by
$$L(t) = 141.5t + 7826.8$$
where $L(t)$ represents the labor force in thousands in the state of Florida t years since 2000. The number of people unemployed in Florida can be modeled by
$$E(t) = 80.5t + 287.5$$
where $E(t)$ represents the number of people in the workforce who are unemployed in thousands in the state of Florida. The unemployment rate is the percentage of people in the labor force that are not employed.

source: models derived from data obtained from the Florida Research and Economic Database 2003.

   a. Find a model for the unemployment rate for the state of Florida.

   b. Estimate the unemployment rate in Florida during 2003.

   c. Estimate when the unemployment rate in Florida will reach 8%.

For exercises 11 through 15 solve the rational equations: Check your answers with a table or graph.

11. $\dfrac{2x+5}{x-7} = \dfrac{3x-12}{x-7}$

12. $\dfrac{5}{x+6} = \dfrac{3}{x-4}$

13. $\dfrac{5}{x+2} + 7 = \dfrac{-16}{x-5}$

14. $\dfrac{x^2}{(x+2)(x+3)} + \dfrac{5}{x+3} = \dfrac{4}{x+2}$

15. $\dfrac{5.6}{x^2-3x-10} = \dfrac{2x}{x^2+9x+14}$

Section 6.1   Introduction to Radical Functions

• **Modeling Data with Radical Functions** • **Graphs of Radical Functions**

In this chapter we will investigate and work with a new type of function that involves using square roots and other higher roots. We will start by looking at some situations and data that are best modeled using square roots or other powers that result in radical expressions. The name **Radical** is given to the symbol $\sqrt{}$ and the expression inside of the radical is called the **Radicand**. The word radical is also used to describe any function that uses a radical with variables in the radicand. When we want to represent a root other than a square root we indicate that by using an **index** in the nook of the radical symbol. Whenever the index is higher than 2 the radical is considered a higher root.

Definition 6.1.1

Radical Expression:

$$\sqrt{x} \qquad \sqrt[n]{x}$$

A square root or nth root is called a radical expression. In these examples x is called the radicand and n is the index. Square roots have an index of 2 but are not written in the nook of the radical.

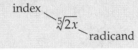

We will give the formal definitions of square roots and higher roots in section 6.2. To start our investigation of radical functions let's consider the following data.

Concept Investigation 1

a.   Fill in the missing parts to this table of data.

Table 6.1.1

x	$f(x)$
0	0
1	1
4	2
9	3
16	4
25	5
36	
49	
100	
144	
196	

b.   Create a scattergram for this data and describe its shape compared to other model types you have learned.

c. Try the following models and describe their fit to this data.
$$y = 0.0666x + 2.305$$

$$y = -0.0003139x^2 + 0.1233x + 1.4236$$

d. Graph $f(x) = \sqrt{x}$ with the data. How well does this fit the data?

e. Change the window to Xmin = −50 , Xmax = 250 , Ymin = −5 , Ymax = 20 . Does this model exist for negative values of x? Why or why not?

f. Does this model have negative output values? Why or why not?

Now that we have explored a radical model lets consider the following applications of some different types of radicals.

Example 1

Allometry is the study of how some aspect of the physiology of a certain species of animal changes in proportion with a change in body size. For example a study of neotropical butterflies at the Department of Zoology, University of Texas Austin, studied the relationship of the airspeeds during natural free flight and several characteristics of the butterflies. One relationship they studied was between the body mass (in grams) of the butterfly with its mean forward airspeed (in meters per second). A sample of the data collected is given in the table.

Table 6.1.2

Body Mass (g)	Velocity (m/s)
0.1	2.75
0.13	3.14
0.16	3.46
0.21	3.99
0.25	4.36
0.3	4.77
0.4	5.49
0.63	6.91

source: The Journal of Experimental Biology 191, 125-139 (1994) as found at jeb.biologist.org

a.   Create a scattergram of the data in table 6.1.1.

b.   An estimated model for this data is given by the following:
     Let $V(m)$ be the mean forward airspeed in meters per second for neotropical butterflies and m be the body mass of the butterfly in grams.
     $$V(m) = 8.7\sqrt{m}$$
   i   Graph this model with the given data.
   ii   How well does it fit the data?
   iii   Describe the general shape of the graph.

c.   Estimate the airspeed of a butterfly with a body mass of 0.5 grams.

d.   Give a reasonable domain and range for this model.

e.   Use the graph to estimate the body mass of a butterfly that has an airspeed of 5 meters per second.

Solution

a.

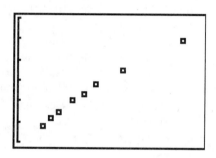

b.

i

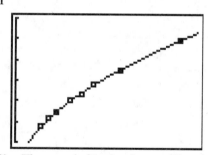

   ii   The graph fits the data well and seems to follow the pattern the data is in.

   iii   This graph is increasing and is slightly curved and thus not linear.

c.   We are given the body mass of the butterfly so we can let $m = 0.5$ and we get

$$V(0.5) = 8.7\sqrt{0.5}$$
$$V(0.5) = 6.15$$

Therefore a butterfly with a body mass of 0.5 grams would have a mean forward airspeed of 6.15 meters per second.

d.   Since the input variable represents the body mass of a butterfly we should choose only small positive numbers. Therefore one possible domain could be $[0.08, 0.75]$. Since the range will be the lowest to highest point within the domain we would get a range of $[2.46, 7.53]$.

e. Using the graph and trace we get

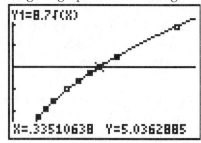

Therefore a butterfly with a body mass of about 0.34 kg will have an airspeed of about 5 meters per second.

The model in the last example is a radical function which contains a square root and can be easily evaluated in your calculator. The basic shape of this type of data is an increasing function that is slightly curved. You may note that it is shaped very similarly to a logarithm's graph, the main difference being that it grows more quickly than a log would and does not go into negative output values. In the situation of the butterfly's velocity (air speed) the outputs would only be positive.

The domain of a radical function used in a context can be found the same way that we have done throughout the text. Start by trying to expand the domain beyond the given data avoiding model breakdown and any restrictions that the problem states. The range will then be the lowest to highest output values within that domain. The range of a radical function will again have its output values come from the endpoints of the domain. Let's look at another example that uses a higher root as part of the radical function.

Example 2

Pediatricians often use growth charts to compare a child's height and weight to the average child of the same age. This helps doctors gauge the growth and development of their patients compared to what is expected in general. The Internet provides parents with several samples of growth charts with heights and weights for girls and boys. Data from one of these charts for girls is given in table 6.1.2.

Table 6.1.3

Age (months)	Height (ft)
4.5	2.0
10.5	2.1667
12	2.4167
24	2.6667
36	2.9167
48	3.1667
60	3.3333

source: aarogya.com "The Wellness Site"

a. Create a scattergram for this data.

b. Let $H(a)$ be the average height of a girl in feet at age a months old.

   i   Graph the function $H(a) = 1.44 \sqrt[5]{a}$ with your data.

   ii How well does this function fit this data?

c. Estimate the average height of girls who are 18 months old.

d. Estimate the average height of girls who are $2\frac{1}{2}$ years old.

e. What would be a reasonable starting value for the domain of this function?

f. Estimate numerically at what age the average height of a girl would be 2.5 feet.

Solution

a.

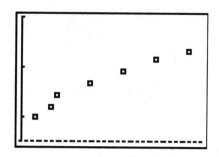

b.

    i   Note the radical was put into the equation editor using fraction exponents.

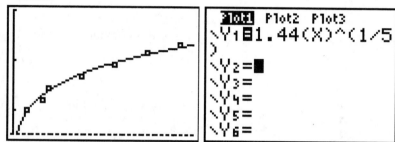

    ii   This function fits the data well and follows the pattern in the data.

c.   We are given the age of the girls so we can substitute $a = 18$ and get

$$H(18) = 1.44 \sqrt[5]{18}$$
$$H(18) = 2.5669$$

    If we convert the 0.5669 to inches by multiplying by 12 we get $0.5669 \cdot 12 = 6.8$ inches. Therefore the average height of an 18 month old girls is about 2 feet 7 inches.

d.   We are told that the girls are $2\frac{1}{2}$ years old so we can substitute $a = 30$ months and get

$$H(30) = 1.44 \sqrt[5]{30}$$
$$H(30) = 2.8431$$

    If we convert the 0.8431 into inches we get $0.8431 \cdot 12 = 10.1$ inches. Therefore the average height of $2\frac{1}{2}$ year old girls is about 2 feet 10 inches.

e.   Since we are talking about the average height of girls at age a the domain will be the ages of girls in months. Therefore negative values would not make sense and $a = 0$ would result in an average height of zero feet so that also is model breakdown. We should probably start this domain at about 3 months of age. This gives us a reasonable height of about 21.5 inches.

f.   Using the table and starting at 12 months we get

X	Y1	
12	2.367	
13	2.4052	
14	2.4411	
15	2.475	
16	2.5072	
17	2.5378	

X=

Therefore the average height of 16 month old girls is 2.5 feet.

Both of these examples require you to evaluate the function for a given value of the input variable which is easily done on the calculator. We have also solved these functions using a graph or table but for us to solve these types of models algebraically for a missing value of the input variable we will need several other skills that we will be learning in the next few sections. In a later section of this chapter we will come back to some of these examples and solve them algebraically for the input variables.

Problem 1

a.   Given the function $f(x) = 7.2\sqrt[3]{x}$ find the following:

   i $f(20)$

   ii   Estimate numerically when $f(x) = 34$

b.   Given the graph of the function $h(x)$ find the following:

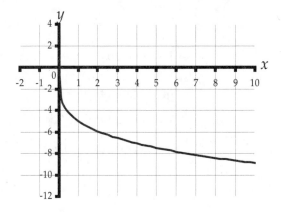

   i   Estimate $h(2)$

   ii   Estimate $h(x) = -8$

Solution   See page 389

Lets look at the graphs of several radical functions and consider the domain and range of those functions in problems without a context.

Concept Investigation 2

Set your graphing calculator's window to Xmin = −10, Xmax = 10, Ymin = −3.5, Ymax = 3.5

a. Graph the following functions on your graphing calculator:

   i $f(x) = \sqrt{x}$

   ii $g(x) = \sqrt[4]{x}$ Remember you need to enter this with fraction exponents.

   iii $h(x) = \sqrt[6]{x}$

   Describe the shape of these graphs.

   How does the graph change as you take higher roots?

   What appears to be the domain and range for these functions?

b. Graph the following functions on your graphing calculator:

   i $f(x) = \sqrt[3]{x}$

   ii $g(x) = \sqrt[5]{x}$

   iii $h(x) = \sqrt[7]{x}$

   Describe the shape of these graphs.

   How does the graph change as you get higher roots?

   What appears to be the domain and range for these functions?

   What is the difference between the radical functions in part a and the radical functions in part b?

As you can see from this concept investigation whether the root is odd or even makes a difference in the shape of the graph and what its domain and range are. You should note that even roots cannot have negative numbers under the radical and thus have only values that make the radicand non-negative as part of their domain. Odd roots do not have this restriction since negatives are possible under an odd root and thus typically have all real numbers as a domain. We will study what happens when negatives are under a square root in the last section of this chapter.

Example 3

Give the domain and range of the following radical functions.

a. $f(x) = \sqrt{x+3}$

b. $g(x) = \sqrt{x-9}$

c.

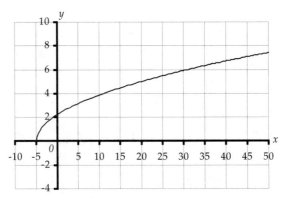

d. $f(x) = \sqrt[3]{x-7}$

e.

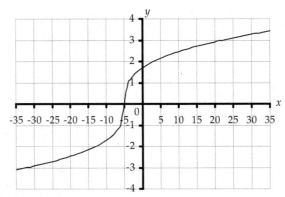

f. $h(x) = \sqrt{-x}$

g.

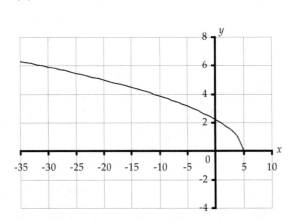

Solution

a.   The domain can only include values that make the radicand non-negative so we need to solve the following inequality

$$x + 3 \geq 0$$

$$x \geq -3$$

Therefore the domain of this function is $x \geq -3$. The lowest point on the graph is zero and the graph continues upward to infinity so we get a range of $[0, \infty)$. We can confirm this domain and range by looking at its graph on the calculator.

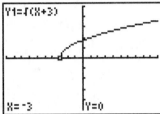

b.   The domain can only include values that make the radicand non-negative so we need to solve the following inequality

$$x - 9 \geq 0$$

$$x \geq 9$$

Therefore the domain of this function is $x \geq 9$. The lowest point on the graph of this function is $(9, 0)$ so the range will start at zero and it continues up to infinity so we get a range of $[0, \infty)$. We can confirm this domain and range by looking at its graph on the calculator.

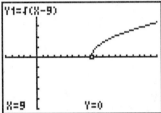

c.   By looking at this graph we can see that the input values being used by this function start at $x = -5$. Therefore the domain of this function should be $x \geq -5$. The range will start at zero and go up to infinity giving us a range of $[0, \infty)$.

d.   This is a cubic function and is thus an odd root so the radicand may be either positive or negative so the domain would include all real numbers. The range will also be all real numbers since the graph goes down to negative infinity and up to positive infinity. Looking at the graph of this function confirms this.

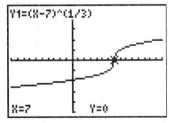

e.   This graph uses all the input values and appears to be an odd root so the domain of this function will be all real numbers. The range is also all real numbers since the graph goes down to negative infinity and up to positive infinity.

f.   Since this is an even root the radicand must be non-negative. Although the radicand looks negative if x is a negative number than $-x$ will be a positive number. We need to solve the following inequality

$$-x \geq 0$$ To isolate x we divide both sides by negative one.

$$\frac{-x}{-1} \leq \frac{0}{-1}$$ Remember we need to flip the inequality symbol whenever we multiply or divide both sides by a

$$x \leq 0$$ negative number.

Therefore the domain of this function is $x \leq 0$. The lowest point on the graph of this function is $(0,0)$ so the range will start at zero and it continues up to infinity so we get a range of $[0, \infty)$. We can confirm this domain and range by looking at its graph on the calculator.

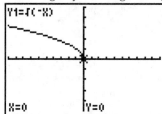

g.   From this graph we can see that only input values less than or equal to 5 are being used so the domain will be $x \leq 5$. The range will be $[0, \infty)$.

Problem 2

Give the domain and range of the following radical functions.

a. $f(x) = \sqrt{x + 8}$

b. $g(x) = \sqrt{-x + 3}$

c. $h(x) = \sqrt[5]{x - 9}$

d.

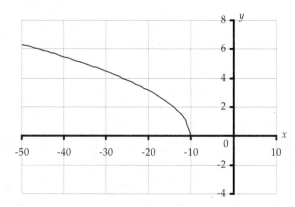

Solution   See page 389

Section 6.1 Key Points

- A radical expression is a square root or higher root:

$$\sqrt{x} \qquad \sqrt[n]{x}$$

- The symbol $\sqrt{}$ is called a radical.
- The radicand is the expression inside the radical.
- The index is the number inside the nook of the radical.
- In a square root the index is assumed to be 2.
- When calculating higher roots in the calculator use rational exponents to represent the radicals. Be sure to use parentheses around all fraction exponents.
- The domain of even roots is restricted to values that make the radicand non-negative.
- The domain of odd roots is typically all real numbers.

Section 6.1 Problem Solutions

Problem 1   Solution

a.

  i $f(20) = 19.544$

  ii Looking at the table we get

Therefore $f(x) = 34$ when $x \approx 105$.

b.

  i   Looking at the graph we can estimate $h(2) = -6$

  ii Looking at the graph we can estimate that $h(x) = -8$ when $x = 6.5$

Problem 2   Solution

a. This is an even root so the radicand must be non-negative.

$$x + 8 \geq 0$$
$$x \geq -8$$

Therefor the domain is $x \geq -8$. The lowest point on the graph is at zero and it extends upward to infinity so the range will be $[0, \infty)$.

b. This is an even root so the radicand must be non-negative.

$$-x + 3 \geq 0$$
$$-x \geq -3 \qquad$$ Solve for x. Remember to flip the inequality when dividing both sides by negative one.
$$x \leq 3$$

Therefor the domain is $x \leq 3$. The lowest point on the graph is at zero and it extends upward to infinity so the range will be $[0, \infty)$.

c. This is an odd root so the domain and range will both be all real numbers.

d. This graph appears to use x values less than or equal to -10 so the domain will be $x \leq -10$ and the range will be $[0, \infty)$.

6.1 Exercises

1. Jim Bob's Heat Source manufactures h hundred thousand space heaters per month. Jim Bob invested $2.3 million in capital towards machinery and computer technology to run the plant and has a fixed cost of $5.4 million. The following data has been collected on the cost of various numbers of heaters produced per month.

Table 6.1.3

Heaters (in 100,000 units)	Cost (in millions of $)
0	3.2
1	5.5
2	6.45
3	7.18
4	7.8
5	8.34
6	8.83
7	9.29
8	9.71
9	10.1
10	10.4

a. Create a scattergram for this data. Does a radical function seem appropriate for this model?

b. Let $C(h)$ be the cost in millions of dollars to produce h hundred thousand heaters per month.

Graph the following function with the data.
$$C(h) = 2.29\sqrt{h} + 3.2$$
How well does this model fit the data?

c. Use the model to estimate the cost to produce 550,000 heaters per month.

d. Use the model to estimate the cost to produce 1,500,000 heaters per month.

e. Give a reasonable domain and range for this model.

2. The physics department is doing an experiment testing the time it takes for an object to fall from different heights. One group collected the following data.

Table 6.1.4

Height (ft)	Drop Time (sec.)
4	0.49
6	0.6
11.5	0.82
18.5	1.05
23	1.17
37	1.48
54.5	1.8

a. Let $T(h)$ be the drop time in seconds for an object dropped from h feet. Plot the data and the model
$$T(h) = 0.243\sqrt{h}$$

b. Use the model to determine the drop time for an object dropped from 15 feet.

c. Use the model to determine the drop time for an object dropped from 100 feet.

d. Determine a reasonable domain and range for this model.

e. Estimate numerically what height an object must be dropped from to have a drop time of 2 seconds.

3. In a study of Basilisk lizards a biologist found that there were several allometric relationships between the body mass of a lizard and different characteristics of its body. One such relationship is demonstrated by the following data and model.

Table 6.1.5

Body Mass (g)	Leg Length (m)
2.5	0.022
15	0.041
34.9	0.054
41.7	0.057
72.1	0.069
90.3	0.074
140.6	0.086
164.2	0.09

source: Data and model derived from Size-Dependence of Water Running Ability in Basilisk Lizards by Blasheen and McMahon

Let $L(M)$ represent the leg length in meters of a Basilisk lizard with a body mass of M grams.
$$L(M) = 0.0165\sqrt[3]{M}$$

a. How well does this model fit the data given?

b. Estimate the leg length of a Basilisk lizard that has a body mass of 50 grams.

c. Estimate the leg length of a Basilisk lizard that has a body mass of 100 grams.

d. Estimate graphically the body mass of a Basilisk lizard that has a leg length of 0.1 meters.

4. Dr. Marina Silva in the Journal of Mammalogy (1998) gives approximately the following formula for the body length of mammals based on the mammal's body mass.
$$L(M) = 0.330\sqrt[3]{M}$$
where $L(M)$ represents the body length in meters of a mammal with a body mass of M kilograms.

a. Use this model to estimate the body length of a mammal with a body mass of 4.6 kg.

b. Use this model to estimate the body length of a mammal with a body mass of 25 kg.

c. If this model is valid for mammals with body masses between 0.01 and 250 kg what is this models range?

d. Estimate numerically the body mass of a mammal with a body length of 1 meter.

5. The butterfly study from Example 1 also developed the following formula for the relationship between the thoracic (middle body portion) mass of the butterfly and its mean forward airspeed

$$V(m) = 17.6 \sqrt[5]{m^3}$$

where $V(m)$ represents the mean forward airspeed in meters per second of a butterfly with a thoracic mass of m grams.

a. Use the model to estimate the airspeed of a butterfly with a thoracic mass of 0.05 grams.

b. Use the model to estimate the airspeed of a butterfly with a thoracic mass of 0.12 grams.

c. If this model is valid for butterflies with a thoracic mass between 0.001 and 0.6 grams determine the range of this model.

6. The average height of boys for various ages is given in the table

Table 6.1.6

Age (months)	Height (ft)
4.5	2.05
10.5	2.3
12	2.45
24	2.75
36	2.95
48	3.2

source: aarogya.com "The Wellness Site"

a. Let $H(a)$ be the average height in feet of boys at a months old. The height can be modeled by

$$H(a) = 1.46 \sqrt[5]{a}$$

Graph the data and the model together. How well does this model fit the data?

b. Estimate the average height for boys who are 18 months old.

c. Estimate the average height for boys who are $2\frac{1}{2}$ years old.

d. How do your answers in parts b and c compare to the average heights of girls found in Example 2?

e. Give a reasonable domain and range for this model.

7.

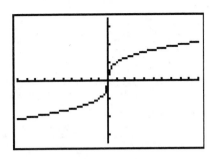

a. Is this the graph of an odd or even root?

b. Give the domain of this function.

c. Give the range of this function.

8.

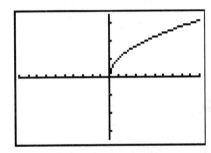

a. Is this the graph of an odd or even root?

b. Give the domain of this function.

c. Give the range of this function.

9.

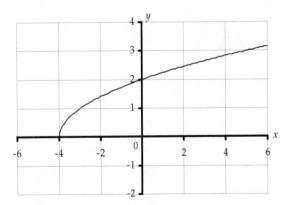

a. Is this the graph of an odd or even root?

b. Give the domain of this function.

c. Give the range of this function.

10.

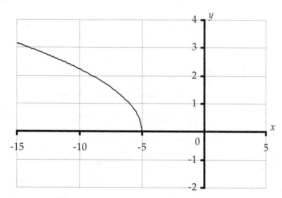

a. Is this the graph of an odd or even root?

b. Give the domain of this function.

c. Give the range of this function.

11.

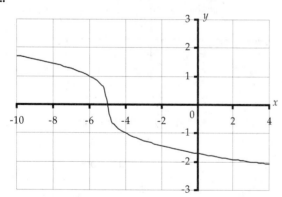

a. Is this the graph of an odd or even root?

b. Give the domain of this function.

c. Give the range of this function.

12.

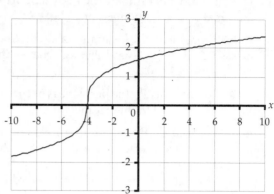

a. Is this the graph of an odd or even root?

b. Give the domain of this function.

c. Give the range of this function.

13.

a. Is this the graph of an odd or even root?

b. Give the domain of this function.

c. Give the range of this function.

14. Give the domain and range of the following functions:

a. $f(x) = 4\sqrt[3]{x}$

b. $g(m) = -3\sqrt[5]{m}$

c. $h(x) = 0.7\sqrt[9]{x}$

d. $f(x) = -\dfrac{5}{8}\sqrt[7]{x}$

15. Give the domain and range of the following functions:

a. $f(x) = 5\sqrt{x}$

b. $g(x) = -7\sqrt{x}$

c. $h(x) = 0.24\sqrt[4]{x}$

d. $f(x) = -\dfrac{2}{3}\sqrt[8]{x}$

16. Give the domain and range of the following functions:

a. $f(x) = \sqrt{x + 12}$

b. $g(x) = \sqrt{x - 6}$

c. $h(x) = \sqrt{-x + 3}$

17. Give the domain and range of the following functions:

a. $f(x) = \sqrt{x + 8}$

b. $g(x) = \sqrt{-x + 10}$

c. $h(x) = \sqrt{-x - 11}$

18. Give the domain and range of the following functions:

a. $f(x) = \sqrt[3]{x + 15}$

b. $g(x) = \sqrt[3]{-x + 12}$

Section 6.2   Simplifying, Adding & Subtracting Radicals

• Square Roots • Higher Roots • Simplifying Radicals • Adding and Subtracting Radicals

Radicals include square roots and other higher roots such as cube roots, and fourth roots. In order to solve problems that involve radicals you will need to know some basic rules for doing arithmetic operations. In this section you will learn to simplify radical expressions and perform basic operations with radicals.

Let's start with a basic definition of a square root.

Definition of a square root:

b is the square root of a if $b^2 = a$.

$$\sqrt{a} = b$$

Using rational exponents we get:

$$\sqrt{a} = \sqrt{b^2} = (b^2)^{\frac{1}{2}} = b$$

$$\sqrt{25} = \sqrt{5^2} = (5^2)^{\frac{1}{2}} = 5$$

Although you are probably more familiar with square roots, higher roots actually have a very similar definition and are defined in much the same way.

Definition of the nth root:

b is the nth root of a if $b^n = a$.

$$\sqrt[n]{a} = b$$

n is called the index of the radical, a is called the radicand and b is called the root.
Using rational exponents we get:

$$\sqrt[n]{a} = \sqrt[n]{b^n} = (b^n)^{\frac{1}{n}} = b$$

$$\sqrt[3]{8} = \sqrt[3]{2^3} = (2^3)^{\frac{1}{3}} = 2$$

$$\sqrt[4]{81} = \sqrt[4]{3^4} = (3^4)^{\frac{1}{4}} = 3$$

$$\sqrt[3]{-125} = \sqrt[3]{(-5)^3} = ((-5)^3)^{\frac{1}{3}} = -5$$

When working with radicals you may notice that square roots always seem to be positive. This is true only by the choice of mathematicians. In general the square root would have both a positive and negative answer.

$$\sqrt{25} = \begin{cases} \sqrt{5^2} = 5 \\ \sqrt{(-5)^2} = -5 \end{cases}$$

$$x^{\frac{1}{2}} = \sqrt{x}$$

$$x^{\frac{1}{n}} = \sqrt[n]{x}$$

If you think of radicals as rational exponents you can perform operations on radicals using the rules for exponents. The most important rules for exponents to remember are:

Product Rule for Exponents:

$$x^m x^n = x^{m+n}$$

$$x^{\frac{1}{5}} x^{\frac{2}{3}} = x^{\frac{2}{15}}$$

Quotient Rule for Exponents:

$$\frac{x^m}{x^n} = x^{m-n}$$

$$\frac{x^4}{x^{3\frac{1}{3}}} = x^{\frac{2}{3}}$$

Power Rule for Exponents:

$$(x^m)^n = x^{mn}$$

$$(x^4)^7 = x^{28}$$

Distributing Exponents:

$$(xy)^m = x^m y^m \qquad \left(\frac{x}{y}\right)^m = \frac{x^m}{y^m}$$

$$(xy)^5 = x^5 y^5 \qquad \left(\frac{x}{y}\right)^4 = \frac{x^4}{y^4}$$

Using these rules is one option to simplify and perform most operations on radicals. Some students find it easiest to change radicals to rational exponents and then use these rules to simplify the problem. When a problem is completed you should change the answers back into radical form.

Since having two possible answers will cause many problems with consistency mathematicians agree to use the **principal root** which is the positive root only. If a negative root is needed than we use a negative sign outside of the square root to designate the negative root.

$$-\sqrt{100} = -10 \text{ but } \sqrt{100} = 10$$

You should note that a root with an odd index can have a negative radicand and thus will have a negative root. If a root with an even index has a negative radicand the root will not be a real number. We will study square roots with negative radicands in the last section of this chapter.

Example 1
Evaluate the following radicals:

a. $\sqrt{36}$

b. $\sqrt[3]{8}$

c. $\sqrt[3]{-27}$

d. $\sqrt[4]{625}$

Solution

a. $\sqrt{36} = \sqrt{6^2} = 6$

b. $\sqrt[3]{8} = \sqrt[3]{2^3} = 2$

c. $\sqrt[3]{-27} = \sqrt[3]{(-3)^3} = -3$

d. $\sqrt[4]{625} = \sqrt[4]{5^4} = 5$

Problem 1
Evaluate the following radicals.

a. $\sqrt{49}$

b. $\sqrt{144}$

c. $\sqrt[3]{-512}$

d. $\sqrt[4]{10000}$

Solution   See page 398

When simplifying radical expressions you are looking for any factors of the radicand that can be pulled out of the radical. Anything that cannot come out of the radical can be left inside as a new reduced radicand. Some radicals will contain variables and thus will only be able to be simplified when the value of those variables is known. Whenever we are given a radical with a variable in the radicand we will assume that the variable represents only non-negative values. This will allow us to not worry about inputs not in the domain. When working with variables in a radicand using the rules for exponents will simplify the process.

Example 2

Simplify the following radicals:

a. $\sqrt{25x^2}$

b. $\sqrt[3]{8m^3n^6}$

c. $\sqrt{15x^3y^6}$

d. $\sqrt[5]{96a^2b^8c^{10}}$

Solution

a.

$$\sqrt{25x^2}$$

$\sqrt{5^2}\sqrt{x^2}$ Break the radicand into factors that are squared.

$5x$ Reduce.

b.

$\sqrt[3]{8m^3n^6}$ Since this is a cube root we will look for factors that are cubed.

$\sqrt[3]{2^3}\sqrt[3]{m^3}\sqrt[3]{n^3}\sqrt[3]{n^3}$ Break the radicand into factors that are cubed.

$2mnn$ Reduce.

$2mn^2$ Simplify.

c.   We will do this problem two ways. First in a similar way as in parts a and b.

$$\sqrt{15x^3y^6}$$

$\sqrt{x^2}\sqrt{y^2}\sqrt{y^2}\sqrt{y^2}\sqrt{3}\sqrt{5}\sqrt{x}$ Break the radicand into factors that are squared.

$xyyy\sqrt{3}\sqrt{5}\sqrt{x}$ Reduce and group together remaining radicals.

$xy^3\sqrt{15x}$ Simplify.

Now we will do it again using the rules for exponents.

$\sqrt{15x^3y^6} = (15x^3y^6)^{\frac{1}{2}}$ Rewrite in exponential form.

$= (3 \cdot 5x^3y^6)^{\frac{1}{2}}$ Factor the constant.

$= 3^{\frac{1}{2}} \cdot 5^{\frac{1}{2}}x^{\frac{3}{2}}y^3$ Distribute the exponents.

$= 3^{\frac{1}{2}} \cdot 5^{\frac{1}{2}}x^{1\frac{1}{2}}y^3$ Write exponents as mixed numbers if needed.

$= xy^3\sqrt{15x}$ Separate the whole and fraction exponent parts and rewrite in radical form. Multiply the constants together.

d.   We will do this problem using the rules for exponents.

$\sqrt[5]{96a^2b^8c^{10}} = (96a^2b^8c^{10})^{\frac{1}{5}}$ Rewrite in exponential form.

$= (2^5 \cdot 3a^2b^8c^{10})^{\frac{1}{5}}$ Factor the constant.

$= 2 \cdot 3^{\frac{1}{5}}a^{\frac{2}{5}}b^{\frac{8}{5}}c^2$ Distribute the exponents.

$= 2 \cdot 3^{\frac{1}{5}}a^{\frac{2}{5}}b^{1\frac{3}{5}}c^2$ Write exponents as mixed numbers. Separate the whole and fraction exponent parts and rewrite in radical form.

$= 2bc^2\sqrt[5]{3a^2b^3}$

You should note that all of these problems could be reduced using either method. It is often best if you find which of these methods you like and use that method consistently. As you simplify more radicals you may find that you do not need to write out all these steps but you should use caution when working with fraction exponents so that you do not make mistakes.

Steps to simplify a radical expression:
1.   Break the radicand into factors that are raised to the same power as the index of the radical.
2.   Reduce the radicals.
3.   Simplify by multiplying any remaining radicands together and multiplying anything that has been taken out of the radicals

Steps to simplify a radical expression using the rules for exponents:
1.   Rewrite the radical in exponential form.
2.   Factor the constant.
3.   Distribute the exponent.
4.   Write exponents as mixed numbers. (if needed)
5.   Separate the whole and fraction exponent parts and rewrite in radical form.
6.   Multiply any remaining constant parts together.

Problem 2
Simplify the following radicals:

a. $\sqrt{16a^2b^4}$

b. $\sqrt{180x^2y^3}$

c. $\sqrt[3]{108m^5n^6}$

d. $\sqrt[9]{x^{36}y^{18}z^{11}}$

Solution   See page 399

Adding and subtracting radical expressions is basically the same as adding and subtracting like terms in a polynomial. You can only add or subtract two radical expressions that have the same variables and exponents outside the radical and the same radicand inside. This can also be looked at a form of factoring.

$$5\sqrt{3x} + 7\sqrt{3x}$$
$$\sqrt{3x}(5+7)$$ Factor out the $\sqrt{3x}$ from both terms.
$$12\sqrt{3x}$$ Combine the constants and you have combined like terms.

Example 3
Add or subtract the following expressions:

a. $3\sqrt{5} + 7\sqrt{5}$

b. $2x\sqrt{10} - 5x\sqrt{10}$

c. $\sqrt{25x^3yz^5} + 2x\sqrt{xyz^5}$

d. $5\sqrt{x} + 2\sqrt{3x} + 4\sqrt{x} - 7\sqrt{3x}$

Solution

a.

$$3\sqrt{5} + 7\sqrt{5} = 10\sqrt{5} \qquad \text{Combine like terms}$$

b.

$$2x\sqrt{10} - 5x\sqrt{10} = -3x\sqrt{10} \quad \text{Combine like terms}$$

c.

$$\sqrt{25x^3yz^5} + 2x\sqrt{xyz^5} = 5xz^2\sqrt{xyz} + 2xz^2\sqrt{xyz} \quad \text{Simplify each radical}$$
$$= 7xz^2\sqrt{xyz} \qquad\qquad \text{Combine like terms}$$

d.

$$5\sqrt{x} + 2\sqrt{3x} + 4\sqrt{x} - 7\sqrt{3x} = 9\sqrt{x} - 5\sqrt{3x} \qquad \text{Combine like terms}$$

Problem 3

Simplify the following by adding or subtracting the like expressions:

a. $2\sqrt{3} - 7\sqrt{3}$

b. $4\sqrt{50} + 7\sqrt{2}$

c. $3x\sqrt{5y^3} + 2xy\sqrt{5y}$

d. $\sqrt{5x} + 2\sqrt{2x} - 6\sqrt{2x} + 4\sqrt{5x}$

Solution   See page 399

When combining radical expressions you need to remember to only combine like expressions. This will include only combining similar radicals. For instance you should not add or subtract a square root with a cube root or any other higher root.

Example 4

Simplify the following by adding or subtracting the like expressions:

a. $5\sqrt{x} + 2\sqrt[3]{x} - 2\sqrt{x} + 3\sqrt[3]{x}$

b. $\sqrt[3]{8x^5y^2} + 5x\sqrt[4]{x^2y^2} + 7x\sqrt[3]{x^2y^2}$

Solution

a.

$$5\sqrt{x} + 2\sqrt[3]{x} - 2\sqrt{x} + 3\sqrt[3]{x} = 3\sqrt{x} + 5\sqrt[3]{x} \qquad \text{Combine like expressions}$$

b.

$$\sqrt[3]{8x^5y^2} + 5x\sqrt[4]{x^2y^2} + 7x\sqrt[3]{x^2y^2} = 2x\sqrt[3]{x^2y^2} + 5x\sqrt[4]{x^2y^2} + 7x\sqrt[3]{x^2y^2}$$
$$= 9x\sqrt[3]{x^2y^2} + 5x\sqrt[4]{x^2y^2}$$

Problem 4

Simplify the following by adding or subtracting the like expressions:

a. $12\sqrt{2m} + 5\sqrt[3]{7m} - 4\sqrt{2m} + 3\sqrt[3]{7m}$

b. $\sqrt[5]{32x^3y} + 5\sqrt[4]{xy^2} + 6\sqrt[5]{x^3y}$

Solution   See page 399

Section 6.2 Key Points

- Definition of a square root:

  b is the square root of a if $b^2 = a$.
- Definition of higher roots:

  b is the nth root of a if $b^n = a$.
- The principal square root is the positive root of a square root.
- To get a negative root we put a negative sign outside the square root.
- Negative radicands result in non real solutions when the index is even.
- Negative radicands result in negative roots when the index is odd.
- Steps to simplify a radical expression:
    1   Break the radicand into factors that are raised to the same power as the index of the radical.
    2. Reduce the radicals.
    3. Simplify by multiplying any remaining radicands together and multiplying anything that has been taken out of the radicals
- Steps to simplify a radical expression using the rules for exponents:
    1. Rewrite the radical in exponential form.
    2. Factor the constant.
    3. Distribute the exponent.
    4. Write exponents as mixed numbers. (if needed)
    5. Separate the whole and fraction exponent parts and rewrite in radical form.
    6. Multiply any remaining constant parts together.
- Adding and subtracting radicals is similar to adding and subtracting like terms.
- Simplify radical expressions before you add or subtract them.
- Only add or subtract radicals with the same index and same radicand.

Section 6.2 Problem Solutions

Problem 1   Solution

a.

$$\sqrt{49} = \sqrt{7^2} = 7$$

b.

$$\sqrt{144} = \sqrt{12^2} = 12$$

c.

$$\sqrt[3]{-512} = \sqrt[3]{(-2)^9} = (-2)^3 = -8$$

or

$$\sqrt[3]{-512} = \sqrt[3]{(-8)^3} = -8$$

This can be done either way depending on what factorization you see first.

d.

$$\sqrt[4]{10000} = \sqrt[4]{2^4 \cdot 5^4} = 2 \cdot 5 = 10$$

or

$$\sqrt[4]{10000} = \sqrt[4]{10^4} = 10$$

This can be done either way depending on what factorization you see first.

Problem 2   Solution

a.

$$\sqrt{16a^2b^4}$$

$$\sqrt{4^2}\sqrt{a^2}\sqrt{b^2}\sqrt{b^2}$$

$$4ab^2$$

b.

$$\sqrt{180x^2y^3}$$

$$\sqrt{2^2}\sqrt{3^2}\sqrt{5}\sqrt{x^2}\sqrt{y^2}\sqrt{y}$$

$$2\cdot 3\cdot x\cdot y\cdot \sqrt{5}\sqrt{y}$$

$$6xy\sqrt{5y}$$

c.

$$\sqrt[3]{108m^5n^6} = (108m^5n^6)^{\frac{1}{3}}$$

$$= (2^2\cdot 3^3 m^5 n^6)^{\frac{1}{3}}$$

$$= 2^{\frac{2}{3}}\cdot 3m^{\frac{5}{3}}n^2$$

$$= 2^{\frac{2}{3}}\cdot 3m^{1\frac{2}{3}}n^2$$

$$= 3mn^2\sqrt[3]{4m^2}$$

d.

$$\sqrt[9]{x^{36}y^{18}z^{11}}$$

$$\sqrt[9]{x^9}\sqrt[9]{x^9}\sqrt[9]{x^9}\sqrt[9]{x^9}\sqrt[9]{y^9}\sqrt[9]{y^9}\sqrt[9]{z^9}\sqrt[9]{z^2}$$

$$xxxxyyz\sqrt[9]{z^2}$$

$$x^4y^2z\sqrt[9]{z^2}$$

Problem 3   Solution

a.

$$2\sqrt{3}-7\sqrt{3} = -5\sqrt{3}$$

b.

$$4\sqrt{50}+7\sqrt{2} = 20\sqrt{2}+7\sqrt{2}$$

$$= 27\sqrt{2}$$

c.

$$3x\sqrt{5y^3}+2xy\sqrt{5y} = 3xy\sqrt{5y}+2xy\sqrt{5y}$$

$$= 5xy\sqrt{5y}$$

d.

$$\sqrt{5x}+2\sqrt{2x}-6\sqrt{2x}+4\sqrt{5x} = 5\sqrt{5x}-4\sqrt{2x}$$

Problem 4   Solution

a.

$$12\sqrt{2m}+5\sqrt[3]{7m}-4\sqrt{2m}+3\sqrt[3]{7m} = 8\sqrt{2m}+8\sqrt[3]{7m}$$

b.

$$\sqrt[5]{32x^3y}+5\sqrt[4]{xy^2}+6\sqrt[5]{x^3y} = 2\sqrt[5]{x^3y}+5\sqrt[4]{xy^2}+6\sqrt[5]{x^3y}$$

$$= 8\sqrt[5]{x^3y}+5\sqrt[4]{xy^2}$$

6.2 Exercises

For Exercises 1 through 20 simplify the given radical expression.

1. $\sqrt{100}$

2. $\sqrt{49x^2}$

3. $\sqrt[3]{125y^6}$

4. $\sqrt[4]{16a^4b^{12}}$

5. $\sqrt[3]{-8}$

6. $\sqrt[5]{-32c^5d^{10}}$

7. $\sqrt{196m^4n^2}$

8. $\sqrt{50x^2y}$

9. $\sqrt{36a^3}$

10. $\sqrt{24w^4z^5}$

11. $\sqrt{1296a^5b^8c^{15}}$

12. $\sqrt{6480x^3y^5z^8}$

13. $\sqrt[3]{8x^3y^6}$

14. $\sqrt[3]{40a^3b^5}$

15. $\sqrt[4]{48a^3b^8c^{21}}$

16. $\sqrt[5]{32m^5n^{10}}$

17. $\sqrt[5]{243s^3t^5u^{10}}$

18. $\sqrt[3]{3888x^3y^5z^8}$

19. $\sqrt[3]{-27a^3b^6}$

20. $\sqrt[3]{-960m^3n^4p^5}$

For exercises 21 through 38 perform the indicated operation and simplify.

21. $\sqrt{5x} + 3\sqrt{5x}$

22. $2x\sqrt{3} + 7x\sqrt{3} + 4x\sqrt{3}$

23. $2\sqrt{4x^2y} - 3x\sqrt{y}$

24. $5\sqrt{49m^2n^5} - 3m\sqrt{16n^5}$

25. $\sqrt[3]{8a} + 4\sqrt[3]{a}$

26. $3\sqrt[5]{64a^5b^{10}c^3} - 10ab\sqrt[5]{2b^5c^3}$

27. $\sqrt[5]{10m^3n^5} + 4n\sqrt[5]{10m^3}$

28. $\sqrt[4]{16x^5y^8} + 7xy^2\sqrt[4]{81x}$

29. $7\sqrt[3]{125x^6y^9z^2} - 9x^2y\sqrt[3]{216y^3z^2}$

30. $2\sqrt[3]{1080a^3b^6c^9} - 8abc\sqrt[3]{625b^3c^6}$

31. $5\sqrt{2x} + 7x\sqrt{2} - 12\sqrt{2x} + 3x\sqrt{2}$

32. $4\sqrt{18} + 5\sqrt{2} - 8\sqrt{75} + 3\sqrt{48}$

33. $3xy\sqrt{9z^5} + 7xz^2\sqrt{yz} - 2xyz^2\sqrt{z}$

34. $5m^2n\sqrt{12mn^2} + 7mn^2\sqrt{3mn} - 10\sqrt{243m^5n^4}$

35. $5\sqrt{2x} + 4\sqrt[3]{2x} + 7\sqrt{2x}$

36. $5x\sqrt{14mn} + 2x\sqrt[4]{14mn} - 7x\sqrt[4]{14mn}$

37. $\sqrt[3]{7xy} + \sqrt[5]{7xy} - \sqrt[3]{448xy} + \sqrt[5]{224xy}$

38. $\sqrt{27x^5y^3} + \sqrt[3]{27x^5y^3} - 3xy\sqrt[3]{x^2} + xy\sqrt{3x^3y}$

Section 6.3   Multiplying & Dividing Radicals

• **Multiplying Radicals** • **Dividing Radicals** • **Rationalize the Denominator**

Multiplying radical expressions is not a difficult process. Multiplying radicals is done using the exponent rules. When you multiply two radical expressions with the same index you multiply the radicands (insides) together. After you multiply the radicands you should simplify the result if possible. Remember you do not need like expressions to multiply, unlike addition and subtraction.

Example 1

Multiply the following and simplify the result:

a. $\sqrt{5} \cdot \sqrt{2}$

b. $\sqrt{2x} \cdot \sqrt{10y}$

c. $\sqrt{2a} \cdot \sqrt{18a}$

d. $\sqrt[3]{4m^2} \cdot \sqrt[3]{5m}$

Solution

a.
$$\sqrt{5} \cdot \sqrt{2} = \sqrt{5 \cdot 2}$$
$$= \sqrt{10}$$

b.
$$\sqrt{2x} \cdot \sqrt{10y} = \sqrt{20xy}$$
$$= 2\sqrt{5xy} \qquad \text{Simplify}$$

c.
$$\sqrt{2a} \cdot \sqrt{18a} = \sqrt{36a^2}$$
$$= 6a \qquad \text{Simplify}$$

d.
$$\sqrt[3]{4m^2} \cdot \sqrt[3]{5m} = \sqrt[3]{20m^3} = m\sqrt[3]{20}$$

Multiplying Radicals:
$$\sqrt[n]{a} \cdot \sqrt[n]{b} = \sqrt[n]{ab}$$
Using exponent rules:
$$\sqrt[n]{a} \cdot \sqrt[n]{b} = a^{\frac{1}{n}} \cdot b^{\frac{1}{n}} = (ab)^{\frac{1}{n}} = \sqrt[n]{ab}$$
When multiplying radicals multiply the radicands together. The indices of each radical must be the same.
$$\sqrt{3} \cdot \sqrt{7} = \sqrt{21}$$
$$\sqrt[4]{5x} \cdot \sqrt[4]{6xy} = \sqrt[4]{30x^2y}$$

Problem 1

Multiply the following and simplify the result:

a. $\sqrt{3a} \cdot \sqrt{5bc}$

b. $\sqrt{5m} \cdot \sqrt{20m^3}$

c. $\sqrt{3y} \cdot \sqrt{12y}$

Solution   See page 410

If the expressions are more complicated you will multiply the constants and variables outside of the radicals together and multiply the constants and variables inside the radicals together. Once you have multiplied each of these together you should simplify the result. Some students find it easiest to simply each radical first then multiply them together and simplify again if necessary.

Example 2

Multiply the following and simplify the result:

a. $5\sqrt{2x} \cdot 3\sqrt{7}$

b. $2x\sqrt{3y} \cdot 5\sqrt{12y}$

c. $5a^2b\sqrt{3ab^3} \cdot 2ab^2\sqrt{21a^2b}$

d. $2mn^2\sqrt[4]{m^2n} \cdot 5mn^3\sqrt[4]{mn^9}$

Solution

a.
$$5\sqrt{2x} \cdot 3\sqrt{7} = 15\sqrt{14x}$$

b.
$$2x\sqrt{3y} \cdot 5\sqrt{12y} = 10x\sqrt{36y^2} \qquad \text{Multiply the insides and outsides.}$$
$$= 10x \cdot 6y \qquad \text{Simplify the radical.}$$
$$= 60xy$$

c.
$$5a^2b\sqrt{3ab^3} \cdot 2ab^2\sqrt{21a^2b} = 10a^3b^3\sqrt{63a^3b^4} \qquad \text{Multiply insides and outsides.}$$
$$= 10a^3b^3(3^2 \cdot 7a^3b^4)^{\frac{1}{2}} \qquad \text{Simplify the radical.}$$
$$= 10a^3b^3 \cdot 3 \cdot 7^{\frac{1}{2}}a^{1\frac{1}{2}}b^2$$
$$= 10 \cdot 3 \cdot 7^{\frac{1}{2}}a^{4\frac{1}{2}}b^5 \qquad \text{Separate the whole parts and fraction exponents.}$$
$$= 30a^4b^5\sqrt{7a} \qquad \text{Rewrite in radical form.}$$

d.

$$2mn^2 \sqrt[4]{m^2n} \cdot 5mn^3 \sqrt[4]{mn^9} = 10m^2n^5 \sqrt[4]{m^3n^{10}}$$

$$= 10m^2n^5(m^3n^{10})^{\frac{1}{4}}$$

$$= 10m^2n^5 m^{\frac{3}{4}} n^{2\frac{2}{4}}$$

$$= 10m^{2\frac{3}{4}} n^{7\frac{2}{4}}$$

$$= 10m^2n^7 \sqrt[4]{m^3n^2}$$

Problem 2

Multiply the following and simplify the result:

a. $4\sqrt{3a} \cdot 6\sqrt{5b}$

b. $3m\sqrt{14n} \cdot 5\sqrt{21mn}$

c. $7x^2y^3 \sqrt[3]{x^2y^5} \cdot 4xy \sqrt[3]{xy^2}$

Solution   See page 411

Example 3

Multiply the following expressions together and simplify:

a. $(5+\sqrt{7})(5-\sqrt{7})$

b. $(2-\sqrt{3x})(2+\sqrt{3x})$

c. $(6+\sqrt{2a})(6-\sqrt{2a})$

Solution

a.

$$(5+\sqrt{7})(5-\sqrt{7}) = 25 - 5\sqrt{7} + 5\sqrt{7} - \sqrt{49}$$
$$= 25 - \sqrt{49}$$
$$= 25 - 7$$
$$= 18$$

Use the distributive property to multiply.
The middle terms cancel.
Reduce the radical and simplify.

b.

$$(2-\sqrt{3x})(2+\sqrt{3x}) = 4 + 2\sqrt{3x} - 2\sqrt{3x} - \sqrt{9x^2}$$
$$= 4 - \sqrt{9x^2}$$
$$= 4 - 3x$$

Use the distributive property to multiply.
The middle terms cancel.
Reduce the radical.

c.

$$(6+\sqrt{2a})(6-\sqrt{2a}) = 36 - 6\sqrt{2a} + 6\sqrt{2a} - \sqrt{4a^2}$$
$$= 36 - \sqrt{4a^2}$$
$$= 36 - 2a$$

You should be seeing a pattern here that when you multiply these expressions together the result has no radicals remaining. These expressions are special in that they are basically the same except for the sign between the two terms. These expressions are called **conjugates** of one another. We will use conjugates later in this section and again in later sections of this chapter.

Definition 6.3.1

Conjugates:

$$a + b \quad \text{and} \quad a - b$$

These expressions are called conjugates of one another. They are simply the sum and difference of the same two terms.

$$5 + x \qquad 5 - x$$

$$2 + \sqrt{3x} \qquad 2 - \sqrt{3x}$$

$$-17 + 4\sqrt{5m} \qquad -17 - 4\sqrt{5m}$$

Division inside a radical can be simplified in the same way that a fraction would be reduced if it were by itself. This follows from the rules for distributing exponents.

$$\sqrt{\frac{50}{2}} = \sqrt{25} = 5$$

$$\sqrt{\frac{50}{2}} = \left(\frac{50}{2}\right)^{\frac{1}{2}} = 25^{\frac{1}{2}} = 5$$

We can use these rules to simplify some radical expressions that have fractions in them. Please note that you can only simplify fractions that are both inside a radical or both outside the radical. You cannot cancel something that is inside the radical with something that is outside of a radical.

Radicals with Fractions:

$$\sqrt[n]{\frac{a}{b}} = \frac{\sqrt[n]{a}}{\sqrt[n]{b}}$$

Using exponent rules:

$$\sqrt[n]{\frac{a}{b}} = \left(\frac{a}{b}\right)^{\frac{1}{n}} = \frac{a^{\frac{1}{n}}}{b^{\frac{1}{n}}} = \frac{\sqrt[n]{a}}{\sqrt[n]{b}}$$

A fraction inside a radical can be made into a fraction with separate radicals in the numerator and denominator of the fraction. This rule is often used in both directions.

Be careful to avoid the common mistake of not taking the root of both the numerator and denominator of a fraction that is inside the radical.

$$\sqrt{\frac{16}{9}} = \frac{\sqrt{16}}{\sqrt{9}} = \frac{4}{3}$$

$$\sqrt{\frac{16}{9}} \neq \frac{\sqrt{16}}{9} = \frac{4}{9} \qquad \text{Avoid the common error of only taking the square root of the numerator.}$$

Example 4

Simplify the following radicals:

a. $\sqrt{\dfrac{100}{25}}$

b. $\sqrt{\dfrac{49}{36}}$

c. $\sqrt{\dfrac{400x^3y}{4xy^5}}$

d. $\sqrt[3]{\dfrac{a^5b^2}{a^2b}}$

Solution

a.

$$\sqrt{\dfrac{100}{25}} = \sqrt{4}$$

$$= 2$$

b.

$$\sqrt{\dfrac{49}{36}} = \dfrac{\sqrt{49}}{\sqrt{36}}$$

$$= \dfrac{7}{6}$$

c.

$$\sqrt{\dfrac{400x^3y}{4xy^5}} = \sqrt{\dfrac{100x^2}{y^4}} \qquad \text{Reduce the fraction.}$$

$$= \dfrac{\sqrt{100x^2}}{\sqrt{y^4}} \qquad \text{Separate the radical and reduce.}$$

$$= \dfrac{10x}{y^2}$$

d.

$$\sqrt[3]{\dfrac{a^5b^2}{a^2b}} = \sqrt[3]{a^3b} \qquad \text{Reduce the fraction.}$$

$$= a\sqrt[3]{b} \qquad \text{Reduce the radical.}$$

Problem 3

Simplify the following radicals:

a. $\sqrt{\dfrac{42}{7}}$

b. $\sqrt{\dfrac{50}{18}}$

c. $\sqrt[4]{\dfrac{144m^5n^3}{mn^7}}$

Solution   See page 411

   In the previous example and problem all of the denominators reduced to where no radicals remain. This will not always happen, but as mathematicians we often like to have no radicals in the denominator of a fraction. Clearing any remaining radicals from the denominator of a fraction is called **rationalizing the denominator**. This process uses multiplication on the top and bottom of the fraction in order to force any radicals in the denominator to reduce completely.

The key to rationalizing the denominator of a fraction is to multiply both the numerator and denominator of the fraction with the right radical expression that will allow the resulting denominator to reduce and be without any remaining radicals. With a single square root this is usually accomplished by multiplying the numerator and denominator by the denominator itself.

Example 5

Simplify the following radical expressions:

a. $\sqrt{\dfrac{3}{5}}$

b. $\sqrt{\dfrac{5y}{2x}}$

c. $\dfrac{2\sqrt{3n}}{5\sqrt{6m}}$

Solution

a.

$$\sqrt{\dfrac{3}{5}} = \dfrac{\sqrt{3}}{\sqrt{5}}$$ Separate into two radicals.

$$= \dfrac{\sqrt{3}}{\sqrt{5}} \cdot \dfrac{\sqrt{5}}{\sqrt{5}}$$ Multiply the numerator and denominator by the denominator. This is the same as multiplying by 1.

$$= \dfrac{\sqrt{15}}{\sqrt{25}}$$

$$= \dfrac{\sqrt{15}}{5}$$ Reduce the radicals.

b.

$$\sqrt{\dfrac{5y}{2x}} = \dfrac{\sqrt{5y}}{\sqrt{2x}}$$

$$= \dfrac{\sqrt{5y}}{\sqrt{2x}} \cdot \dfrac{\sqrt{2x}}{\sqrt{2x}}$$

$$= \dfrac{\sqrt{10xy}}{\sqrt{4x^2}}$$

$$= \dfrac{\sqrt{10xy}}{2x}$$

c.

$$\dfrac{2\sqrt{3n}}{5\sqrt{6m}} = \dfrac{2\sqrt{n}}{5\sqrt{2m}}$$

$$= \dfrac{2\sqrt{n}}{5\sqrt{2m}} \cdot \dfrac{\sqrt{2m}}{\sqrt{2m}}$$

$$= \dfrac{2\sqrt{2mn}}{5\sqrt{4m^2}}$$

$$= \dfrac{2\sqrt{2mn}}{10m}$$ Reduce the radicals.

$$= \dfrac{\sqrt{2mn}}{5m}$$ Reduce the fraction.

If the denominator contains a higher root it will take more thought to choose an appropriate expression to multiply by. If you factor the radicand in the denominator you can then determine what factors are needed to allow the radical to reduce completely. Remember that you want each factor to be repeated enough times that the index of the radical will divide into that factors exponent evenly. If you are working with a cube root you will want each factors exponent to be a multiple of 3. This will allow the $\frac{1}{3}$ exponent from the radical to multiply each factors exponent and get a whole number thus eliminating the radical from the denominator.

$$\frac{1}{\sqrt[3]{x}} = \frac{1}{\sqrt[3]{x}} \cdot \frac{\sqrt[3]{x^2}}{\sqrt[3]{x^2}}$$

Multiplying by $\sqrt[3]{x^2}$ gives you x^3 so the cube root will undo it.

$$= \frac{\sqrt[3]{x^2}}{\sqrt[3]{x^3}}$$

$$= \frac{\sqrt[3]{x^2}}{x}$$

The denominator is clear of radicals and thus rationalized.

Example 6

Simplify the following radical expressions:

a. $\sqrt[3]{\dfrac{5xy}{10x^2}}$

b. $\dfrac{2a}{\sqrt[4]{9a^3b^6}}$

c. $\dfrac{\sqrt[3]{2m}}{\sqrt[3]{8np^2}}$

Solution

a.

$$\sqrt[3]{\frac{5xy}{10x^2}} = \sqrt[3]{\frac{y}{2x}}$$

Reduce the fraction.

$$= \frac{\sqrt[3]{y}}{\sqrt[3]{2x}}$$

Separate the radical.

$$= \frac{\sqrt[3]{y}}{\sqrt[3]{2x}} \cdot \frac{\sqrt[3]{2^2x^2}}{\sqrt[3]{2^2x^2}}$$

Multiply by the necessary number of factors to clear the denominator. In this case we need two more 2's and 2 more x's to get the radical to reduce. Note a cube root will undo a power of 3.

$$= \frac{\sqrt[3]{4x^2y}}{\sqrt[3]{2^3x^3}}$$

$$= \frac{\sqrt[3]{4x^2y}}{2x}$$

Reduce the radicals.

b.

$$\frac{2a}{\sqrt[4]{9a^3b^6}} = \frac{2a}{\sqrt[4]{3^2a^3b^6}}$$ Factor the radicand.

$$= \frac{2a}{\sqrt[4]{3^2a^3b^6}} \cdot \frac{\sqrt[4]{3^2ab^2}}{\sqrt[4]{3^2ab^2}}$$ Multiply by the needed factors. We need two more 3's, one more a and two more b's. Note we need eight b's to get an exponent on b that is divisible by 4 (the root).

$$= \frac{2a\sqrt[4]{3^2ab^2}}{\sqrt[4]{3^4a^4b^8}}$$

$$= \frac{2a\sqrt[4]{3^2ab^2}}{3ab^2}$$ Reduce the radical.

$$= \frac{2\sqrt[4]{3^2ab^2}}{3b^2}$$ Reduce the fraction.

c.

$$\frac{\sqrt[3]{2m}}{\sqrt[3]{8np^2}} = \frac{\sqrt[3]{m}}{\sqrt[3]{4np^2}}$$ Reduce the fraction.

$$= \frac{\sqrt[3]{m}}{\sqrt[3]{2^2np^2}}$$ Factor the radicand.

$$= \frac{\sqrt[3]{m}}{\sqrt[3]{2^2np^2}} \cdot \frac{\sqrt[3]{2n^2p}}{\sqrt[3]{2n^2p}}$$ Multiply by the needed factors.

$$= \frac{\sqrt[3]{2mn^2p}}{\sqrt[3]{2^3n^3p^3}}$$

$$= \frac{\sqrt[3]{2mn^2p}}{2np}$$ Reduce the radical.

Problem 4

Simplify the following radical expressions:

a. $\sqrt[3]{\dfrac{24m^2}{15mn^2}}$

b. $\dfrac{7x^2}{\sqrt[5]{27xy^7}}$

c. $\dfrac{\sqrt[3]{5a^2}}{\sqrt[3]{20ab}}$

Solution   See page 412

Rationalizing the denominator of a fraction simplifies the fraction so that calculations are easier. Often fractions will have radicals in the denominator with another term. This requires us to use a different approach to rationalizing the denominator. If there are two terms we will multiply by the conjugate of the denominator in order to clear all of the radicals in the denominator which is the goal of rationalizing the denominator.

Example 7

Rationalize the following:

a. $\dfrac{5}{2+\sqrt{7}}$

b. $\dfrac{2+3\sqrt{5}}{8+\sqrt{10}}$

c. $\dfrac{2+\sqrt{x}}{3-5\sqrt{x}}$

Solution

a.

$$\frac{5}{2+\sqrt{7}} = \frac{5}{(2+\sqrt{7})} \cdot \frac{(2-\sqrt{7})}{(2-\sqrt{7})} \quad \text{Multiply the top and bottom by the conjugate of the denominator.}$$

$$= \frac{10-5\sqrt{7}}{4-7}$$

$$= \frac{10-5\sqrt{7}}{-3}$$

b.

$$\frac{2+3\sqrt{5}}{8+\sqrt{10}} = \frac{(2+3\sqrt{5})}{(8+\sqrt{10})} \cdot \frac{(8-\sqrt{10})}{(8-\sqrt{10})} \quad \text{Multiply by the conjugate.}$$

$$= \frac{16-2\sqrt{10}+24\sqrt{5}-3\sqrt{50}}{64-10} \quad \text{Use the distributive property.}$$

$$= \frac{16-2\sqrt{10}+24\sqrt{5}-15\sqrt{2}}{54} \quad \text{Reduce the radicals.}$$

c.

$$\frac{2+\sqrt{x}}{3-5\sqrt{x}} = \frac{(2+\sqrt{x})}{(3-5\sqrt{x})} \cdot \frac{(3+5\sqrt{x})}{(3+5\sqrt{x})} \quad \text{Multiply by the conjugate.}$$

$$= \frac{6+10\sqrt{x}+3\sqrt{x}+5\sqrt{x^2}}{9-25x} \quad \text{Use the distributive property.}$$

$$= \frac{6+5x+13\sqrt{x}}{9-25x} \quad \text{Reduce the radicals and combine like terms.}$$

Problem 5

Rationalize the following:

a. $\dfrac{7}{4+\sqrt{13}}$

b. $\dfrac{4+5\sqrt{3}}{7+\sqrt{15}}$

c. $\dfrac{3+\sqrt{a}}{5-7\sqrt{ab}}$

Solution   See page 413

Simplifying radical expressions completely requires you to rationalize all denominators and reduce each radical. There should be no fractions remaining inside a radical and no factors left inside a radical that can be pulled out of the radical.

Section 6.3 Key Points

- Multiplying radicals.

$$\sqrt[n]{a} \cdot \sqrt[n]{b} = \sqrt[n]{ab}$$

When multiplying radicals with the same index you simply multiply the insides and outsides of each radical together and then simplify the result.

- Conjugates

$$a + b \qquad a - b$$

Two expressions that are simply the sum and difference of the same two terms are called conjugates.

- Radicals with fractions

$$\sqrt[n]{\frac{a}{b}} = \frac{\sqrt[n]{a}}{\sqrt[n]{b}}$$

Radicals with fractions can be reduced or separated into two radicals and then reduced.

- Rationalizing denominators
    - i   Fractions with radicals in the denominator need to be rationalized.
    - ii When a single square root is in the denominator you simply multiply both the numerator and denominator by the original radical in the denominator.
    - iii When higher roots are in the denominator you multiply by the root with the same index with the needed factors to make the radical reduce completely.
    - iv If two terms with a radical are in the denominator you will need to use conjugates to eliminate the radical.

Section 6.3 Problem Solutions

Problem 1   Solution

a.

$$\sqrt{3a} \cdot \sqrt{5bc} = \sqrt{15abc}$$

b.

$$\sqrt{5m} \cdot \sqrt{20m^3} = \sqrt{100m^4}$$
$$= 10m^2$$

c.

$$\sqrt{3y} \cdot \sqrt{12y} = \sqrt{36y^2}$$
$$= 6y$$

Problem 2   Solution

a.

$$4\sqrt{3a} \cdot 6\sqrt{5b} = 24\sqrt{15ab}$$

b.

$$3m\sqrt{14n} \cdot 5\sqrt{21mn} = 15m\sqrt{294mn^2}$$
$$= 15m\sqrt{2 \cdot 3 \cdot 7^2mn^2}$$
$$= 105mn\sqrt{6m}$$

c.

$$7x^2y^3\sqrt[3]{x^2y^5} \cdot 4xy\sqrt[3]{xy^2} = 28x^3y^4\sqrt[3]{x^3y^7} \qquad \text{Multiply insides and outsides.}$$
$$= 28x^3y^4(x^3y^7)^{\frac{1}{3}} \qquad \text{Write in exponent form.}$$
$$= 28x^3y^4xy^{2\frac{1}{3}} \qquad \text{Add exponents to simplify.}$$
$$= 28x^4y^{6\frac{1}{3}}$$
$$= 28x^4y^6\sqrt[3]{y} \qquad \begin{array}{l}\text{Separate whole and fraction}\\\text{exponents and write as a radical.}\end{array}$$

Problem 3   Solution

a.

$$\sqrt{\frac{42}{7}} = \sqrt{6}$$

b.

$$\sqrt{\frac{50}{18}} = \sqrt{\frac{25}{9}}$$
$$= \frac{\sqrt{25}}{\sqrt{9}}$$
$$= \frac{5}{3}$$

c.

$$\sqrt[4]{\frac{144m^5n^3}{mn^7}} = \sqrt[4]{\frac{144m^4}{n^4}}$$
$$= \frac{\sqrt[4]{144m^4}}{\sqrt[4]{n^4}}$$
$$= \frac{(2^4 \cdot 3^2m^4)^{\frac{1}{4}}}{n}$$
$$= \frac{2 \cdot 3^{\frac{2}{4}}m}{n}$$
$$= \frac{2m\sqrt[4]{9}}{n}$$

Problem 4   Solution

a.

$$\sqrt[3]{\frac{24m^2}{15mn^2}} = \sqrt[3]{\frac{8m}{5n^2}}$$

$$= \frac{\sqrt[3]{8m}}{\sqrt[3]{5n^2}}$$

$$= \frac{\sqrt[3]{8m}}{\sqrt[3]{5n^2}} \cdot \frac{\sqrt[3]{5^2n}}{\sqrt[3]{5^2n}}$$

$$= \frac{\sqrt[3]{2^3 \cdot 5^2 mn}}{\sqrt[3]{5^3 n^3}}$$

$$= \frac{2\sqrt[3]{25mn}}{5n}$$

b.

$$\frac{7x^2}{\sqrt[5]{27xy^7}} = \frac{7x^2}{\sqrt[5]{27xy^7}}$$

$$= \frac{7x^2}{\sqrt[5]{3^3xy^7}}$$

$$= \frac{7x^2}{\sqrt[5]{3^3xy^7}} \cdot \frac{\sqrt[5]{3^2x^4y^3}}{\sqrt[5]{3^2x^4y^3}}$$

$$= \frac{7x^2\sqrt[5]{3^2x^4y^3}}{\sqrt[5]{3^5x^5y^{10}}}$$

$$= \frac{7x^2\sqrt[5]{9x^4y^3}}{3xy^2}$$

$$= \frac{7x\sqrt[5]{9x^4y^3}}{3y^2}$$

c.

$$\frac{\sqrt[3]{5a^2}}{\sqrt[3]{20ab}} = \frac{\sqrt[3]{a}}{\sqrt[3]{4b}}$$

$$= \frac{\sqrt[3]{a}}{\sqrt[3]{2^2b}}$$

$$= \frac{\sqrt[3]{a}}{\sqrt[3]{2^2b}} \cdot \frac{\sqrt[3]{2b^2}}{\sqrt[3]{2b^2}}$$

$$= \frac{\sqrt[3]{2ab^2}}{\sqrt[3]{2^3b^3}}$$

$$= \frac{\sqrt[3]{2ab^2}}{2b}$$

Problem 5   Solution

a.

$$\frac{7}{4+\sqrt{13}} = \frac{7}{(4+\sqrt{13})} \cdot \frac{(4-\sqrt{13})}{(4-\sqrt{13})}$$

$$= \frac{28-7\sqrt{13}}{16-13}$$

$$= \frac{28-7\sqrt{13}}{3}$$

b.

$$\frac{4+5\sqrt{3}}{7+\sqrt{15}} = \frac{(4+5\sqrt{3})}{(7+\sqrt{15})} \cdot \frac{(7-\sqrt{15})}{(7-\sqrt{15})}$$

$$= \frac{28-4\sqrt{15}+35\sqrt{5}-5\sqrt{45}}{49-15}$$

$$= \frac{28-4\sqrt{15}+35\sqrt{5}-15\sqrt{5}}{34}$$

$$= \frac{28-4\sqrt{15}+20\sqrt{5}}{34}$$

c.

$$\frac{3+\sqrt{a}}{5-7\sqrt{ab}} = \frac{(3+\sqrt{a})}{(5-7\sqrt{ab})} \cdot \frac{(5+7\sqrt{ab})}{(5+7\sqrt{ab})}$$

$$= \frac{15+21\sqrt{ab}+5\sqrt{a}+7\sqrt{a^2 b}}{25-49ab}$$

$$= \frac{15+21\sqrt{ab}+5\sqrt{a}+7a\sqrt{b}}{25-49ab}$$

6.3 Exercises

For Exercises 1 through 20 multiply the given radical expressions and simplify the result.

1. $\sqrt{7} \cdot \sqrt{3}$

2. $\sqrt{6} \cdot \sqrt{10}$

3. $\sqrt{5y} \cdot \sqrt{10x}$

4. $\sqrt{8a} \cdot \sqrt{50a}$

5. $\sqrt[3]{4x} \cdot \sqrt[3]{2x^2}$

6. $\sqrt{7m} \cdot \sqrt{14mn}$

7. $\sqrt{3xy} \cdot \sqrt{4y}$

8. $\sqrt{12a^3b} \cdot \sqrt{15a^2b^5}$

9. $\sqrt{18m^5} \cdot \sqrt{2m}$

10. $5\sqrt{3xy} \cdot 7x\sqrt{2y}$

11. $8m\sqrt{14mn} \cdot 2p\sqrt{50m}$

12. $5n^3\sqrt[4]{m^2n^2} \cdot 7m^2n\sqrt[4]{m^3n^7}$

13. $2x^2\sqrt[3]{5x^2y} \cdot 7y\sqrt[3]{4xy}$

14. $2ab\sqrt[3]{a^5b^2} \cdot 7a\sqrt[3]{ab^2}$

15. $12x^2y\sqrt[5]{7x^3y^4} \cdot 3xy^3\sqrt[5]{98x^4y^6}$

16. $8mn\sqrt[5]{2mn^2p} \cdot 5mp\sqrt[5]{16m^3n^3}$

17. $(3 + \sqrt{7})(3 - \sqrt{7})$

18. $(4 - \sqrt{2x})(4 + \sqrt{2x})$

19. $(8 + 5\sqrt{7ab})(8 - 5\sqrt{7ab})$

20. $(2\sqrt{3} + 5\sqrt{7})(2\sqrt{3} - 5\sqrt{7})$

In exercises 21 through 35 simplify the given radical expressions.

21. $\sqrt{\dfrac{20}{5}}$

22. $\sqrt{\dfrac{432}{75}}$

23. $\sqrt{\dfrac{5x^3}{45xy^2}}$

24. $\sqrt{\dfrac{3a}{4a^3}}$

25. $\sqrt{\dfrac{7cd^2}{3c}}$

26. $\dfrac{5}{\sqrt{3x}}$

27. $\dfrac{5\sqrt{2x}}{3\sqrt{7y}}$

28. $\dfrac{12\sqrt{3ab}}{\sqrt{6a}}$

29. $\sqrt[3]{\dfrac{5x}{7x^2y^2}}$

30. $\sqrt[4]{\dfrac{5ab}{8a^3b^6}}$

31. $\dfrac{5m^2}{\sqrt[3]{2m^4n}}$

32. $\dfrac{\sqrt[3]{4ab^2}}{\sqrt[3]{6a}}$

33. $\dfrac{\sqrt[3]{9x^2y^2}}{7x\sqrt[3]{2xy^3}}$

34. $\dfrac{5ab}{\sqrt[5]{2a^3b^7}}$

35. $\dfrac{8\sqrt[5]{4xy}}{\sqrt[5]{144xy^3z^2}}$

In exercises 36 through 45 rationalize the denominator of each fraction.

36. $\dfrac{5}{2 + \sqrt{3}}$

37. $\dfrac{7}{8 - \sqrt{6}}$

38. $\dfrac{2 + \sqrt{3}}{5 - \sqrt{7}}$

39. $\dfrac{5}{3 + \sqrt{2x}}$

40. $\dfrac{4 + \sqrt{5}}{7 - 5\sqrt{3}}$

41. $\dfrac{4 + 2\sqrt{7x}}{2 - 3\sqrt{12x}}$

42. $\dfrac{2 + \sqrt{15}}{3 + 4\sqrt{30m}}$

43. $\dfrac{2 + 5\sqrt{m}}{3 - \sqrt{mn}}$

44. $\dfrac{7 - 6\sqrt{ab}}{3 + 5\sqrt{ab}}$

45. $\dfrac{4 + 8\sqrt{5x}}{2 + \sqrt{30x}}$

Section 6.4   Solving Radical Equations

• Solving Radical Equations

So far we have simplified radical expressions and done arithmetic operations involving radicals. We have also evaluated radicals for different values. Many applications in physics and other sciences use formulas that contain radicals. Often these formulas need to be solved for a variable that is inside the radical itself. We will use the relationship between radicals and rational exponents that we learned in section 4.2 to help us solve equations involving radicals.

Example 1

Many older clocks use pendulums to keep time. The period T (time to go back-and-forth) of a simple pendulum for a small amplitude is given by the function:

$$T(L) = 2\pi\sqrt{\frac{L}{32}}$$

where T is the period in seconds and L is the length of the pendulum in feet. Use this formula to find the following:

a.   The period of a pendulum if its length is 2ft.

b.   How long a pendulum needs to be if you want the period to be 3 seconds.

Solution

a.   Since the length of the pendulum is 2ft we know that $L = 2$ so we get

$$T(L) = 2\pi\sqrt{\frac{L}{32}}$$

$$T(2) = 2\pi\sqrt{\frac{2}{32}}$$

$$T(2) = 1.57$$

Therefore a 2ft pendulum will have a period of about 1.57 seconds.

b.   We know that $T = 3$ so we get

$$T(L) = 2\pi\sqrt{\frac{L}{32}}$$

$$3 = 2\pi\sqrt{\frac{L}{32}}$$

$$\frac{3}{2\pi} = \frac{2\pi\sqrt{\frac{L}{32}}}{2\pi}$$ Isolate the radical on one side of the equation.

$$\frac{3}{2\pi} = \sqrt{\frac{L}{32}}$$

$$\left(\frac{3}{2\pi}\right)^2 = \left(\sqrt{\frac{L}{32}}\right)^2$$ Square both sides of the equation to eliminate the radical.

$$\frac{9}{4\pi^2} = \frac{L}{32}$$

$$32\left(\frac{9}{4\pi^2}\right) = 32\left(\frac{L}{32}\right)$$ Solve for L.

$$\frac{72}{\pi^2} = L$$

$$7.295 = L$$

We can check this solution with the table.

X	Y₁	
7.295	3	
X=		

To have a period of 3 seconds you will need a pendulum about 7.3 feet long.

You should note that this basic formula also works for the period of a child or adult in a swing; you might want to try it.

As you can see isolating the square root and then squaring both sides will eliminate the radical and allow you to solve for the missing variable.

Example 2

At sea level the speed of sound through air can be calculated using the formula

$$c = 340.3 \sqrt{\frac{T + 273.15}{288.15}}$$

where c is the speed of sound in meters per second and T is the temperature in degrees Celsius. Use this formula to find the following:

a.   The speed of sound when the temperature is $30°C$.

b.   The temperature if the speed of sound is $330 m/s$.

Solution

a. $T = 30$ so we get

$$c = 340.3 \sqrt{\frac{T + 273.15}{288.15}}$$

$$c = 340.3 \sqrt{\frac{30 + 273.15}{288.15}}$$

$$c = 349.05$$

At sea level if the temperature is $30°C$ then the speed of sound will be about 349.05 m/s.

b. $c = 330$ so we get

$$c = 340.3\sqrt{\frac{T + 273.15}{288.15}}$$

$$330 = 340.3\sqrt{\frac{T + 273.15}{288.15}}$$

$$\frac{330}{340.3} = \frac{340.3\sqrt{\dfrac{T + 273.15}{288.15}}}{340.3}$$
    Isolate the square root.

$$0.9697 = \sqrt{\frac{T + 273.15}{288.15}}$$

$$(0.9697)^2 = \left(\sqrt{\frac{T + 273.15}{288.15}}\right)^2$$
    Square both sides to eliminate the square root.

$$0.94038 = \frac{T + 273.15}{288.15}$$

$$288.15(0.94038) = 288.15\left(\frac{T + 273.15}{288.15}\right)$$
    Solve for T.

$$270.9709 = T + 273.15$$

$$-2.179 = T$$

We can check this solution using the graph and trace.

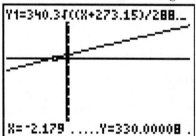

At sea level if the speed of sound through air is 330m/s then the temperature must be about $-2.18°C$.

Problem 1
Solve the following equations:

a. $\sqrt{x + 5} = 7$

b. $2\sqrt{3x + 4} - 15 = -7$

Solution   See page 422
The first step to solving any equation with a square root is to first get the radical by itself on one side of the equation and then eliminate the radical by squaring both sides. Some equations may have more than one radical involved and will require more work to solve. You will want to first isolate one of the radicals so that squaring both sides will eliminate that radical and then work on the remaining problem. If you have patience, these problems can be done.

Example 3
Solve the following:

a. $\sqrt{x + 1} = \sqrt{2x}$

b. $\sqrt{x + 10} = 3 + \sqrt{x}$

Solution

a.

$$\sqrt{x+1} = \sqrt{2x}$$

$$(\sqrt{x+1})^2 = (\sqrt{2x})^2 \qquad \text{Square both sides to eliminate the radical.}$$

$$x+1 = 2x$$

$$\begin{aligned} x+1 &= 2x \\ -x \qquad &-x \end{aligned} \qquad \text{Solve for } x.$$

$$1 = x$$

$$\sqrt{(1)+1} = \sqrt{2(1)} \qquad \text{Check the solution.}$$

$$\sqrt{2} = \sqrt{2}$$

b.

$$\sqrt{x+10} = 3 + \sqrt{x}$$

$$(\sqrt{x+10})^2 = (3+\sqrt{x})^2 \qquad \text{Square both sides to eliminate one of the radicals.}$$

$$x+10 = (3+\sqrt{x})(3+\sqrt{x})$$

$$x+10 = 9 + 3\sqrt{x} + 3\sqrt{x} + x \qquad \text{Be sure to use the distributive property.}$$

$$x+10 = 9 + 6\sqrt{x} + x$$

$$\begin{aligned} -x \qquad\qquad &-x \end{aligned} \qquad \text{Isolate the remaining radical.}$$

$$10 = 9 + 6\sqrt{x}$$

$$\begin{aligned} 10 &= 9 + 6\sqrt{x} \\ -9 \quad &-9 \end{aligned}$$

$$1 = 6\sqrt{x}$$

$$\frac{1}{6} = \frac{6\sqrt{x}}{6}$$

$$\frac{1}{6} = \sqrt{x}$$

$$\left(\frac{1}{6}\right)^2 = (\sqrt{x})^2 \qquad \text{Square both sides again to eliminate the remaining radical.}$$

$$\frac{1}{36} = x$$

X	Y1	Y2
.02778	3.1667	3.1667
X=		

Check the solution.

Problem 2

Solve the following:

a. $\sqrt{x+3} = \sqrt{2x-8}$

b. $\sqrt{3x+5} = 2 - \sqrt{3x+2}$

Solution   See page 422

Equations involving radicals can be more complicated and require you to do more solving after eliminating the radicals. After you have eliminated the radicals use the tools you have learned in other chapters to solve the remaining equation. If a radical other than a square root is found in an equation remember to use the appropriate reciprocal exponent to eliminate the radical.

Example 4

Solve the following:

a. $\sqrt{3x + 1} = 3 + \sqrt{x - 4}$

b. $\sqrt{x - 5} + 7 = 4$

c. $\sqrt[3]{2x} = 5$

d. $\sqrt[5]{4x - 9} = 2$

Solution

a.

$$\sqrt{3x + 1} = 3 + \sqrt{x - 4}$$

$$(\sqrt{3x + 1})^2 = (3 + \sqrt{x - 4})^2 \qquad \text{Square both sides to eliminate one radical.}$$

$$3x + 1 = (3 + \sqrt{x - 4})(3 + \sqrt{x - 4}) \qquad \text{Use the distributive property.}$$

$$3x + 1 = 9 + 3\sqrt{x - 4} + 3\sqrt{x - 4} + (x - 4)$$

$$3x + 1 = 5 + x + 6\sqrt{x - 4} \qquad \text{Get the remaining radical by itself.}$$

$$2x - 4 = 6\sqrt{x - 4}$$

$$(2x - 4)^2 = (6\sqrt{x - 4})^2 \qquad \text{Square both sides to eliminate the remaining radical.}$$

$$(2x - 4)(2x - 4) = 36(x - 4) \qquad \text{Use the distributive property again.}$$

$$4x^2 - 16x + 16 = 36x - 144$$

$$4x^2 - 52x + 160 = 0 \qquad \text{Use the Quadratic Formula to solve for } x.$$

$$x = 5 \qquad x = 8$$

$$\sqrt{3(5) + 1} = 3 + \sqrt{(5) - 4} \qquad \text{Check the solutions.}$$

$$4 = 4$$

$$\sqrt{3(8) + 1} = 3 + \sqrt{(8) - 4}$$

$$5 = 5$$

b.

$$\sqrt{x - 5} + 7 = 4$$

$$\sqrt{x - 5} = -3 \qquad \text{Isolate the radical.}$$

$$(\sqrt{x - 5})^2 = (-3)^2 \qquad \text{Square both sides.}$$

$$x - 5 = 9$$

$$x = 14$$

$$\sqrt{(14) - 5} + 7 = 4 \qquad \text{Check the solution.}$$

$$10 \neq 4 \qquad \text{This solution does not work.}$$

This solution does not work so there are no solutions to this equation. $x = 14$ is an extraneous solution. You should notice that in the second step the square root was equal to a negative number. Since this is not possible there will be no solution.

c.

$$\sqrt[3]{2x} = 5$$

Since this is a cube root we will raise both sides to the third power.

$$(\sqrt[3]{2x})^3 = 5^3$$

$$2x = 125$$

$$\frac{2x}{2} = \frac{125}{2}$$

$$x = 62.5$$

$$\sqrt[3]{2(62.5)} = 5$$ Check the solution.

$$5 = 5$$

d.

$$\sqrt[5]{4x - 9} = 2$$

Since this is a fifth root we will raise both sides to the power of 5.

$$(\sqrt[5]{4x - 9})^5 = 2^5$$

$$4x - 9 = 32$$

$$4x = 41$$

$$x = 10.25$$

$$\sqrt[5]{4(10.25) - 9} = 2$$ Check the solution.

$$2 = 2$$

Problem 3

Solve the following:

a. $\sqrt[4]{2x + 9} = 3$

b. $\sqrt{4x + 1} = 3 + \sqrt{x - 2}$

Solution   See page 423

Section 6.4 Key Points

- When solving equations with square roots use the following steps:
    1. Isolate the radical on one side of the equation.
    2. Square both sides of the equation to eliminate the radical.
    3. Isolate any remaining radical if needed and square both sides again.
    4. Solve the equation.
    5. Check your answer.

- If the radical is not a square root then raise both sides to the same power as the index of the radical. This will eliminate the radical and allow you to finish solving.

Section 6.4 Problem Solutions

Problem 1   Solution

a.

$$\sqrt{x+5} = 7$$

$$\left(\sqrt{x+5}\right)^2 = 7^2 \qquad \text{Square both sides of the equation.}$$

$$x+5 = 49 \qquad \text{Solve.}$$

$$x = 44$$

$$\sqrt{44+5} = 7 \qquad \text{Check your solution.}$$

$$\sqrt{49} = 7$$

$$7 = 7$$

b.

$$2\sqrt{3x+4} - 15 = -7 \qquad \text{Isolate the radical.}$$

$$2\sqrt{3x+4} = 8$$

$$\sqrt{3x+4} = 4$$

$$\left(\sqrt{3x+4}\right)^2 = 4^2 \qquad \text{Square both sides.}$$

$$3x+4 = 16 \qquad \text{Solve.}$$

$$3x = 12$$

$$x = 4$$

$$2\sqrt{3(4)+4} - 15 = -7 \qquad \text{Check the solution.}$$

$$2\sqrt{16} - 15 = -7$$

$$2(4) - 15 = -7$$

$$-7 = -7$$

Problem 2   Solution

a.

$$\sqrt{x+3} = \sqrt{2x-8}$$

$$\left(\sqrt{x+3}\right)^2 = \left(\sqrt{2x-8}\right)^2$$

$$x+3 = 2x-8$$

$$11 = x$$

$$\sqrt{(11)+3} = \sqrt{2(11)-8} \qquad \text{Check the solution.}$$

$$\sqrt{14} = \sqrt{14}$$

b.

$$\sqrt{3x+5} = 2 - \sqrt{3x+2}$$

$$(\sqrt{3x+5})^2 = (2 - \sqrt{3x+2})^2 \qquad \text{Square both sides.}$$

$$3x+5 = (2 - \sqrt{3x+2})(2 - \sqrt{3x+2}) \qquad \text{Use the distributive property.}$$

$$3x+5 = 4 - 2\sqrt{3x+2} - 2\sqrt{3x+2} + (3x+2)$$

$$3x+5 = 4 - 4\sqrt{3x+2} + 3x + 2 \qquad \text{Simplify}$$

$$3x+5 = 6 + 3x - 4\sqrt{3x+2}$$

$$-1 = -4\sqrt{3x+2} \qquad \text{Isolate the radical}$$

$$\frac{1}{4} = \sqrt{3x+2}$$

$$\left(\frac{1}{4}\right)^2 = (\sqrt{3x+2})^2 \qquad \text{Square both sides.}$$

$$\frac{1}{16} = 3x + 2 \qquad \text{Solve}$$

$$-\frac{31}{16} = 3x$$

$$-\frac{31}{48} = x \qquad \text{Check the solution.}$$

X	Y₁	Y₂
-.6458	1.75	1.75

X=

Problem 3   Solution

a.

$$\sqrt[4]{2x+9} = 3$$

$$(\sqrt[4]{2x+9})^4 = 3^4$$

$$2x+9 = 81$$

$$2x = 72$$

$$x = 36$$

$$\sqrt[4]{2(36)+9} = 3 \qquad \text{Check the solution.}$$

$$\sqrt[4]{81} = 3$$

$$3 = 3$$

Problem 3   Solution Continued

b.

$$\sqrt{4x+1} = 3 + \sqrt{x-2}$$

$$(\sqrt{4x+1})^2 = (3 + \sqrt{x-2})^2 \qquad \text{Square both sides.}$$

$$4x+1 = (3 + \sqrt{x-2})(3 + \sqrt{x-2})$$

$$4x+1 = 9 + 3\sqrt{x-2} + 3\sqrt{x-2} + (x-2) \qquad \text{Use the distributive property.}$$

$$4x+1 = 9 + 6\sqrt{x-2} + x - 2 \qquad \text{Simplify.}$$

$$4x+1 = 7 + x + 6\sqrt{x-2}$$

$$3x-6 = 6\sqrt{x-2}$$

$$(3x-6)^2 = (6\sqrt{x-2})^2 \qquad \text{Square both sides.}$$

$$(3x-6)(3x-6) = 36(x-2)$$

$$9x^2 - 18x - 18x + 36 = 36x - 72 \qquad \text{Solve.}$$

$$9x^2 - 36x + 36 = 36x - 72$$

$$9x^2 - 72x + 108 = 0$$

$$x = 6 \qquad x = 2$$

$$\sqrt{4(6)+1} = 3 + \sqrt{(6)-2} \qquad \text{Check the solutions.}$$

$$\sqrt{25} = 3 + \sqrt{4}$$

$$5 = 5$$

$$\sqrt{4(2)+1} = 3 + \sqrt{(2)-2}$$

$$\sqrt{9} = 3$$

$$3 = 3$$

6.4 Exercises

For exercises 1 through 4 use the following information.

Police investigating traffic accidents use the fact that the speed, in miles per hour, of a car traveling on a asphalt road can be determined by the length of the skid marks left by the car after sudden braking. The speed can be modeled by

$$s = \sqrt{30fd}$$

where s is the speed of the car in miles per hour, f is the coefficient of friction for the road and d is the length in feet of the skid marks.

1. Find the speed of a car if it leaves skid marks 150 ft long on a dry asphalt road that has a coefficient of friction equal to 1.

2. Find the speed of a car if it leaves skid marks 120 ft long on an asphalt road with a coefficient of friction equal to 0.444.

3. Find the coefficient of friction of a road if a car traveling 55 mph leaves skid marks 115 ft long after sudden braking. (round to 3 decimal places)

4. Find the length of skid marks a police officer would expect to find if a person traveling 25 mph suddenly breaks on a road with a coefficient of friction equal to 1.

5. Find the period of a pendulum if its length is 3 ft. See example 1.

6. Find the period of a pendulum if its length is 10 ft.

7. If you want a clock's pendulum to have a period of 1 second what must its length be?

8. If you want a clock's pendulum to have a period of 2 seconds what must its length be?

9. When an object is dropped from a height of h feet the time it will take to hit the ground can be approximated by the formula

$$t = \sqrt{\frac{2h}{32}}$$

where t is the time in seconds for the object to fall h feet.

   a. Find how long it will take an object to fall 100 feet.

   b. Find how long it will take an object to fall 50 feet.

   c. If you want an object to fall for 10 seconds at what height should the object be dropped from?

10. Find the speed of sound at sea level when the temperature is $28°C$. See example 2.

11. Find the temperature at sea level if the speed of sound is 345m/s.

12. In section 6.1 we used the function
$$C(h) = 2.29\sqrt{h} + 3.2$$

   to calculate the monthly cost in millions of dollars to produce h hundred thousand space heaters at Jim Bob's Heater Source.

   a. How many heaters can Jim Bob's make in a month if they have a budget of $15 million?

   b. How many heaters can they make if they have a budget cut and can only spend $12 million?

13. In section 6.1 we used the function
$$L(M) = 0.0165\sqrt[3]{M}$$

   to determine the leg length in meters of a Basilisk lizard with a body mass of M grams.

   a. Use this model to estimate the live body mass of a museum specimen that has a leg length of 0.1 meters.

   b. Use the model to estimate the live body mass of a specimen that has a leg length of 0.075 meters.

14. In section 6.1 we used the function
$$L(M) = 0.330\sqrt[3]{M}$$

   where $L(M)$ represents the body length in meters of a mammal with a body mass of M kilograms.

   a. Use this model to estimate the body mass of a mammal whose body length is 1 meter.

   b. Use this model to estimate the body mass of a mammal whose body length is 2.4 meters.

15. In section 6.1 we were given the following formula for the relationship between the Thoracic mass of the butterfly and its mean forward airspeed.

$$V(m) = 17.6\sqrt[5]{m^3}$$

   where $V(m)$ represents the mean forward airspeed in meters per second of a butterfly with a thoracic mass of m grams.

   a. Use the model to estimate the thoracic mass of a butterfly that can fly at 5 meters per second.

   b. Use the model to estimate the thoracic mass of a butterfly that can fly at 6.2 meters per second.

For exercises 16 through 49 solve each equation. Check your solutions with a table or graph.

16. $\sqrt{x} = 3$

17. $\sqrt{x+2} = 5$

18. $\sqrt{w-7} = 10$

19. $5\sqrt{2x} = 40$

20. $\sqrt{3x+4} = 15$

21. $\sqrt{-2t+4} = 7$

22. $\sqrt{-4m-9} = 6$

23. $3\sqrt{2x+5} + 12 = 24$

24. $-2\sqrt{3x-7} - 11 = -19$

25. $-0.25\sqrt{2.3w} = -14$

26. $2.4\sqrt{2.5g+4} - 7.5 = 4.6$

27. $\sqrt{2x+5} = \sqrt{3x-4}$

28. $\sqrt{p+6} = \sqrt{3p+2}$

29. $\sqrt{4+2z} = \sqrt{3-7z}$

30. $\sqrt{x-7} - \sqrt{x} = -1$

31. $\sqrt{x-11} - \sqrt{x} = -1$

32. $\sqrt{2x+3} = 1 - \sqrt{x+5}$

33. $\sqrt{4x^2+9x+5} = 5 + x$

34. $\sqrt{w+2} = 4 - w$

35. $\sqrt{-m+2} = m - 2$

36. $\sqrt{6x+1} - \sqrt{9x} = -1$

37. $\sqrt{2x+11} + \sqrt{2x+7} + 4 = 0$

38. $\sqrt{6x+5} + \sqrt{3x+2} = 5$

39. $\sqrt{3x-5} - \sqrt{3x+3} = 4$

40. $\sqrt{8x+8} - \sqrt{8x-4} = -2$

41. $\sqrt{2x+3} = 1 + \sqrt{x+1}$

42. $\sqrt{2x+5} - 3 = \sqrt{x-2}$

43. $\sqrt[3]{2x+5} = 6$

44. $\sqrt[5]{x-8} = 4$

45. $\sqrt[4]{5x-9} = 2$

46. $\sqrt[7]{145x} = 6$

47. $\sqrt[3]{5x+2} + 7 = 12$

48. $\sqrt[5]{2x-15} + 9 = 4$

49. $\sqrt[3]{-4x+3} = -5$

Section 6.5   Complex Numbers

• Definition of Imaginary and Complex Numbers • Operations with Complex Numbers
• Solving Equations with Complex Solutions

Throughout our work with radicals we have noted that the square root of a negative number is not a real number. We saw this in the chapter on quadratics when we found no real solutions to some problems. $\sqrt{-4}$ is considered a non real number and is called an **Imaginary Number**. Imaginary numbers got their name because when they were first discovered many mathematicians did not believe they existed. Later they were proven to exist and have been shown to be very applicable in different fields of mathematics and science. Although imaginary numbers were proven to exist their name has stuck by then so we must remember that the name imaginary does not mean these numbers do not exist. In mathematics the number $\sqrt{-1}$ is the **imaginary unit** and is usually represented by the letter i. Using the letter i we can represent imaginary numbers without showing a negative under a square root.

Example 1

Simplify the following using the imaginary number i.

a. $\sqrt{-25}$

b. $\sqrt{-100}$

c. $\sqrt{-30}$

d. $-\sqrt{16}$

Solution

a.
$$\sqrt{-25} = \sqrt{-1 \cdot 25} \qquad \text{Factor out the negative 1.}$$
$$= \sqrt{-1} \cdot \sqrt{25}$$
$$= i \cdot 5$$
$$= 5i$$

b. $10i$

c. $i\sqrt{30} \approx 5.477i$

d. -4 This is not an imaginary number since the negative is not inside the square root.

Definition 6.5.1

Imaginary Unit:
$$\sqrt{-1} = i$$

Imaginary Numbers can be combined with the Real Numbers into what are called **Complex Numbers**. Any number that can be written in the form of $a + bi$ is a complex number. a is considered the real part of a complex number and b is considered the imaginary part. Since a and/or b can be zero all real numbers as well as all imaginary numbers are themselves considered complex numbers. Complex numbers are used in many advanced areas of mathematics and many physics and engineering fields. The shape of airplane wings are developed and studied using complex numbers. Many areas of algebra, such as fractals and chaos theory, can be studied when working in the complex number system.

Example 2

For each complex number name the real part and the imaginary part.

a. $5 + 4i$

b. $-3 + 7i$

c. $5i$

d. 9

Solution

a. Real Part = 5 ; Imaginary Part = 4

b. Real Part = –3 ; Imaginary Part = 7

c. Real Part = 0 ; Imaginary Part = 5

d. Real Part = 9 ; Imaginary Part = 0

Definition 6.5.2

> **Complex Number:** Any number that can be written in the form
> $$a + bi$$
> where a and b are real numbers.

Complex numbers can be added and subtracted easily by just adding or subtracting the real parts together and then adding or subtracting the imaginary parts together. This is very similar to combining like terms with variables.

Example 3

Add or subtract the following complex numbers.

a. $(2 + 8i) + (6 + 7i)$

b. $(5 - 4i) + (7 + 6i)$

c. $(6 + 3i) - (4 + 8i)$

d. $(2.5 + 3.8i) - (4.6 - 7.2i)$

Solution

a.
$$\begin{aligned}
(2 + 8i) + (6 + 7i) &= 2 + 6 + 8i + 7i && \text{Add the real parts} \\
&= (2 + 6) + (8i + 7i) && \text{Add the imaginary parts.} \\
&= 8 + 15i
\end{aligned}$$

b. $12 + 2i$

c.
$$\begin{aligned}
(6 + 3i) - (4 + 8i) &= 6 + 3i - 4 - 8i && \text{Distribute the negative.} \\
&= (6 - 4) + (3i - 8i) && \text{Subtract the real parts.} \\
&= 2 - 5i && \text{Subtract the imaginary parts.}
\end{aligned}$$

d. $-2.1 + 11i$ Be sure to watch your negative signs.

Problem 1

Add or subtract the following complex numbers.

a. $(2+6i)+(-3+5i)$

b. $(3.4-7.5i)-(-4.2-5.9i)$

c. $(-7+6i)+(-3-4i)$

d. $(-3+5i)-(4+9i)$

Solution   See page 436

Adding Complex Numbers:
$$(a+bi)+(c+di)$$
$$(a+c)+(b+d)i$$
When adding complex numbers add the real parts together and then add the imaginary parts.

Subtracting Complex Numbers:
$$(a+bi)-(c+di)$$
$$(a-c)+(b-d)i$$
When subtracting complex numbers subtract the real parts and then subtract the imaginary parts.

Since $i=\sqrt{-1}$ we can calculate other powers of i by considering the following pattern.

$$i=\sqrt{-1}$$
$$i^2=(\sqrt{-1})^2=-1$$
$$i^3=-1(\sqrt{-1})=-\sqrt{-1}=-i$$
$$i^4=i^2i^2=(-1)(-1)=1$$
$$i^5=1i=i$$

This pattern will continue to repeat as you have higher and higher powers of i. If you note that $i^4=1$ then you can basically reduce any powers of i by a multiple of 4 without changing the resulting value. For example

$i^5=i^{5-4}=i$ Reduce the exponent by 4

$i^{10}=i^{10-8}=i^2=-1$ Reduce the exponent by 8 and simplify.

In most problems we will deal with the most important power of i that you should know and use is $i^2=-1$ when multiplying complex numbers using this fact will help you to reduce the answers to complex form. Whenever you have a i^2 in a calculation you should replace it with a -1 and continue to combine like terms and simplify.

Example 4

Multiply the following complex numbers.

a. $3(4+9i)$

b. $2i(7-3i)$

c. $(2+5i)(4+8i)$

d. $(3+2i)(5-6i)$

Solution

In all of these problems you will use the distributive property and simplify where possible.

a. $12 + 27i$

b.

$2i(7 - 3i)$	
$14i - 6i^2$	Distribute
$14i - 6(-1)$	Replace i^2 with -1
$14i + 6$	Simplify
$6 + 14i$	Put in complex form

c.

$(2 + 5i)(4 + 8i)$	
$8 + 16i + 20i + 40i^2$	Use the distributive property.
$8 + 36i + 40i^2$	Combine like terms
$8 + 36i + 40(-1)$	Replace i^2 with -1
$8 + 36i - 40$	Simplify
$-32 + 36i$	

d.

$$(3 + 2i)(5 - 6i)$$
$$15 - 18i + 10i - 12i^2$$
$$15 - 8i - 12i^2$$
$$15 - 8i - 12(-1)$$
$$15 - 8i + 12$$
$$27 - 8i$$

Problem 2

Multiply the following complex numbers.

a. $3i(4 + 8i)$

b. $(2 + 7i)(3 + 5i)$

c. $(4 - 2i)(7 + 9i)$

d. $(2 + 5i)(2 - 5i)$

Solution   See page 437

Problem 2d above is an example of multiplying two complex numbers that have a very special relationship. These two complex numbers are what is called complex conjugates of one another. When complex conjugates are multiplied together you should note that the product is a real number and thus has no imaginary part remaining.

Definition 6.5.3

Complex Conjugates:

$$a + bi \text{ and } a - bi$$

are conjugates of one another. The conjugate of a complex number is that complex number with the sign of the imaginary number changed.

$$5 - 3i \text{ and } 5 + 3i$$

are complex conjugates of one another.

Example 5

Write the complex conjugate of the following:

a. $2 + 9i$

b. $4 - 6i$

c. $3.4i$

d. 10

Solution

a. $2 - 9i$

b. $4 + 6i$

c. $-3.4i$

d. 10 Since the imaginary part is zero there is no other complex conjugate.

Example 6

Multiply the following complex numbers by their conjugates.

a. $2 + 9i$

b. $4 - 6i$

c. $3.4i$

Solution

a.
$$(2 + 9i)(2 - 9i)$$
$$4 - 18i + 18i - 81i^2$$
$$4 - 81i^2$$
$$4 - 81(-1)$$
$$4 + 81$$
$$85$$

b.
$$(4 - 6i)(4 + 6i)$$
$$16 + 24i - 24i - 36i^2$$
$$16 - 36i^2$$
$$16 - 36(-1)$$
$$16 + 36$$
$$52$$

c.
$$3.4i(-3.4i)$$
$$-11.56i^2$$
$$-11.56(-1)$$
$$11.56$$

As you can see from this last example when complex conjugates are multiplied together the imaginary parts cancel out and you are left with a real number. This is a very helpful attribute of conjugates when complex numbers are involved in a division problem. When dealing with division or fractions it is standard practice to only allow a denominator with real numbers. Imaginary numbers need to be eliminated from any denominator. This can be done by multiplying both the numerator and denominator by the conjugate of the denominator (similar to what you did to rationalize denominators). This will not change the value of the fraction but will change the denominator into a real number. The resulting fraction can then be written in standard complex form.

Example 7

Divide the following: Put all answers in standard complex form.

a. $\dfrac{10 + 8i}{2}$

b. $\dfrac{4 + 7i}{5 + 3i}$

c. $\dfrac{2 - 9i}{4 + 3i}$

d. $\dfrac{6 - 7i}{5i}$

Solution

a.

$$\dfrac{10 + 8i}{2} = \dfrac{10}{2} + \dfrac{8}{2}i \qquad \text{Reduce the fraction and put into the standard form of a complex number.}$$

$$= 5 + 4i \qquad \text{Simplify}$$

b.

$$\dfrac{4 + 7i}{5 + 3i}$$

$$\dfrac{(4 + 7i)}{(5 + 3i)} \cdot \dfrac{(5 - 3i)}{(5 - 3i)} \qquad \text{Multiply the numerator and denominator by the conjugate of the denominator.}$$

$$\dfrac{20 - 12i + 35i - 21i^2}{25 - 15i + 15i - 9i^2}$$

$$\dfrac{20 + 23i - 21(-1)}{25 - 9(-1)}$$

$$\dfrac{20 + 23i + 21}{25 + 9}$$

$$\dfrac{41 + 23i}{34}$$

$$\dfrac{41}{34} + \dfrac{23}{34}i \qquad \text{Write in the standard form of a complex number.}$$

c.

$$\frac{2-9i}{4+3i}$$

$$\frac{(2-9i)}{(4+3i)} \cdot \frac{(4-3i)}{(4-3i)}$$ Multiply the numerator and denominator by the conjugate of the denominator.

$$\frac{8-6i-36i+27^2}{16-12i+12i-9i^2}$$

$$\frac{8-42i-27}{16+9}$$

$$\frac{-19-42i}{25}$$

$$-\frac{19}{25}-\frac{42}{25}i$$ Write in the standard form of a complex number.

d.

$$\frac{6-7i}{5i}$$

$$\frac{(6-7i)}{5i} \cdot \frac{-5i}{-5i}$$

$$\frac{-30i+35i^2}{-25i^2}$$

$$\frac{-35-30i}{25}$$

$$-\frac{7}{5}-\frac{6}{5}i$$

Problem 3
Divide the following: Put all answers in standard complex form.

a. $\dfrac{14+8i}{2}$

b. $\dfrac{4-7i}{3i}$

c. $\dfrac{4+2i}{3-7i}$

d. $\dfrac{7.2+3.4i}{1.4+5.6i}$

Solution   See page 438

Multiplying Complex Numbers:
When multiplying complex numbers use the distributive property and replace any i^2 in the result with -1. Write the final product in standard form for complex numbers.

Dividing Complex Numbers:

$$\frac{a+bi}{c+di}$$

$$\frac{(a+bi)}{(c+di)} \cdot \frac{(c-di)}{(c-di)}$$

When dividing complex numbers you must clear all denominators of imaginary numbers. This is done by multiplying both the denominator and numerator by the conjugate of the denominator. Remember to reduce the final answer and write it in the standard form for complex numbers.

Many equations will have complex solutions. The most common place we will see these types of solutions is when working with quadratics. The quadratic formula is a great tool to find both real and complex solutions to any quadratic equation. Now when discriminant is a negative number we can write our solutions using complex numbers instead of just saying that there are no real solutions. This results in a more complete answer to the equation. You will notice that if a complex number is a solution to a polynomial, the complex conjugate will also be a solution to that equation. In most applications we are only interested in the real solutions to an equation but in some contexts such as electrical engineering complex solutions are of interest.

Example 8
Solve the following equations. Give answers in the standard form of a complex number.

a. $t^2 + 2t + 5 = 0$

b. $x^2 = -25$

c. $x^2 + 4x = -30$

d. $x^3 - 10x^2 + 29x = 0$

Solution

a.

$$t^2 + 2t + 5 = 0$$

$$t = \frac{-2 \pm \sqrt{2^2 - 4(1)(5)}}{2(1)}$$ Use the Quadratic Formula.

$$t = \frac{-2 \pm \sqrt{-16}}{2}$$ The discriminant is -16 so the answer will be a complex number.

$$t = \frac{-2 \pm 4i}{2}$$

$$t = -1 + 2i \qquad t = -1 - 2i$$ Write in standard form.

b.

$$x^2 = -25$$

$$\sqrt{x^2} = \pm\sqrt{-25}$$

$$x = \pm 5i$$

c.

$$x^2 + 4x = -30$$

$$x^2 + 4x + 30 = 0$$

$$x = \frac{-4 \pm \sqrt{4^2 - 4(1)(30)}}{2(1)}$$

$$x = \frac{-4 \pm \sqrt{-104}}{2}$$

$$x \approx \frac{-4 \pm 10.2i}{2}$$

$$x \approx -2 + 5.1i \qquad x \approx -2 - 5.1i$$

d.

$$x^3 - 10x^2 + 29x = 0$$

$$x(x^2 - 10x + 29) = 0$$

Factor the common term out.

$$x = 0 \qquad x^2 - 10x + 29 = 0$$

Set each factor equal to zero and continue to solve.

$$x = 0 \qquad x = \frac{-(-10) \pm \sqrt{(-10)^2 - 4(1)(29)}}{2(1)}$$

$$x = 0 \qquad x = \frac{10 \pm \sqrt{100 - 116}}{2}$$

$$x = 0 \qquad x = \frac{10 \pm \sqrt{-16}}{2}$$

$$x = 0 \qquad x = \frac{10 \pm 4i}{2}$$

$$x = 0 \qquad x = 5 + 2i \qquad x = 5 - 2i$$

Problem 4

Solve the following equations. Give answers in the standard form of a complex number.

a. $w^2 + 6w + 18 = 0$

b. $x^2 = -81$

c. $x^2 + 8x = -18$

d. $x^3 - 4x^2 + 13x = 0$

Solution   See page 439

Section 6.5 Key Points

- An imaginary number occurs when a negative number is under a square root.
- The imaginary unit:
$$i = \sqrt{-1}$$
- The standard form of a complex number:
$$a + bi$$
- Complex conjugates are found by changing the sign of the imaginary part of complex number.
$$a + bi \text{ and } a - bi$$
- Add and Subtract complex numbers by combining the real parts together and then combine the imaginary parts together.
- Multiply complex numbers using the distributive property. Replace any occurrences of i^2 with -1.
- When dividing complex numbers eliminate any imaginary numbers in the denominator by multiplying the numerator and denominator by the conjugate of the denominator.
- Use the quadratic formula to find any possible complex solutions to quadratic equations.

Section 6.5 Problem Solutions

Problem 1   Solution

a.
$$(2 + 6i) + (-3 + 5i)$$
$$(2 - 3) + (6 + 5)i$$
$$-1 + 11i$$

b.
$$(3.4 - 7.5i) - (-4.2 - 5.9i)$$
$$7.6 - 1.6i$$

c.
$$(-7 + 6i) + (-3 - 4i)$$
$$-10 + 2i$$

d.
$$(-3 + 5i) - (4 + 9i)$$
$$-7 - 4i$$

Problem 2 Solution

a.

$$3i(4 + 8i)$$
$$12i + 24i^2$$
$$12i + 24(-1)$$
$$-24 + 12i$$

b.

$$(2 + 7i)(3 + 5i)$$
$$6 + 10i + 21i + 35i^2$$
$$6 + 31i + 35(-1)$$
$$6 + 31i - 35$$
$$-29 + 31i$$

c.

$$(4 - 2i)(7 + 9i)$$
$$28 + 36i - 14i - 18i^2$$
$$28 + 22i - 18(-1)$$
$$28 + 22i + 18$$
$$46 + 22i$$

d.

$$(2 + 5i)(2 - 5i)$$
$$4 - 10i + 10i - 25i^2$$
$$4 - 25(-1)$$
$$4 + 25$$
$$29$$

Problem 3 Solution

a.

$$\frac{14 + 8i}{2}$$
$$7 + 4i$$

b.

$$\frac{4 - 7i}{3i}$$
$$\frac{(4 - 7i)}{3i} \cdot \frac{-3i}{-3i}$$
$$\frac{-12i + 21i^2}{-9i^2}$$
$$\frac{-12i + 21(-1)}{-9(-1)}$$
$$\frac{-21 - 12i}{9}$$
$$-\frac{21}{9} - \frac{12}{9}i$$

Problem 3   *Solution Continued*

c.

$$\frac{4+2i}{3-7i}$$

$$\frac{(4+2i)}{(3-7i)} \cdot \frac{(3+7i)}{(3+7i)}$$

$$\frac{12+28i+6i+14i^2}{9-21i+21i-49i^2}$$

$$\frac{12+34i+14(-1)}{9-49(-1)}$$

$$\frac{-2+34i}{58}$$

$$-\frac{1}{29}+\frac{17}{29}i$$

d.

$$\frac{7.2+3.4i}{1.4+5.6i}$$

$$\frac{(7.2+3.4i)}{(1.4+5.6i)} \cdot \frac{(1.4-5.6i)}{(1.4-5.6i)}$$

$$\frac{10.08-40.32i+4.76i-19.04i^2}{1.96-31.36i^2}$$

$$\frac{10.08-35.56i-19.04(-1)}{1.96-31.36(-1)}$$

$$0.8739-1.067i$$

Problem 4   *Solution*

a.

$$w^2+6w+18 = 0$$

$$w = \frac{-6 \pm \sqrt{6^2-4(1)(18)}}{2(1)}$$

$$w = \frac{-6 \pm \sqrt{-36}}{2}$$

$$w = \frac{-6 \pm 6i}{2}$$

$$w = -3+3i \qquad w = -3-3i$$

b.

$$x^2 = -81$$

$$\sqrt{x^2} = \pm\sqrt{-81}$$

$$x = \pm 9i$$

Problem 4   Solution Continued

c.

$$x^2 + 8x = -18$$

$$x^2 + 8x + 18 = 0$$

$$x = \frac{-8 \pm \sqrt{8^2 - 4(1)(18)}}{2(1)}$$

$$x = \frac{-8 \pm \sqrt{-8}}{2}$$

$$x = \frac{-8 \pm 2i\sqrt{2}}{2}$$

$$x = -4 + i\sqrt{2} \qquad x = -4 - i\sqrt{2}$$

d.

$$x^3 - 4x^2 + 13x = 0$$

$$x(x^2 - 4x + 13) = 0$$

Factor out the common term.

$$x = 0 \qquad x^2 - 4x + 13 = 0$$

Set each factor equal to zero and continue to solve.

$$x = 0 \qquad x = \frac{-(-4) \pm \sqrt{(-4)^2 - 4(1)(13)}}{2(1)}$$

$$x = 0 \qquad x = \frac{4 \pm \sqrt{-36}}{2}$$

$$x = 0 \qquad x = \frac{4 \pm 6i}{2}$$

$$x = 0 \qquad x = 2 + 3i \qquad x = 2 - 3i$$

6.5 Exercises

For Exercises 1 through 10 simplify the given expression and write your answer in terms of i.

1. $\sqrt{-100}$

2. $5 + \sqrt{-36}$

3. $\sqrt{-49} + \sqrt{-25}$

4. $\sqrt{9} + \sqrt{-16}$

5. $\sqrt{4} - \sqrt{-16}$

6. $\sqrt{-200}$

7. $\sqrt{-3} + \sqrt{-5.6}$

8. $\sqrt{2}(5 + \sqrt{-8})$

9. $\sqrt{-7}(\sqrt{28} + \sqrt{-63})$

10. $(2 + \sqrt{5})(3 - \sqrt{-7})$

For Exercises 11 through 45 simplify the given expression and write your answer in the standard form for a complex number.

11. $(2 + 5i) + (6 + 4i)$

12. $(3 - 8i) + (2 + 6i)$

13. $(5.6 + 3.2i) + (2.3 - 4.9i)$

14. $(3 + 2i) - (5 + 8i)$

15. $(5i) + (3 - 9i)$

16. $(2 - 7i) - (5 - 6i)$

17. $(5 + 7i) - 10$

18. $(3 - 8i) - (10 - 12i)$

19. $(3 + 5i) - (7 + 8i)$

20. $(-4 - 6i) - (3 - 9i)$

21. $(4.7 - 3.5i) + (1.8 - 5.7i)$

22. $(2.4 - 9.6i) - (3.5 + 8.6i)$

23. $(2 + 8i) + (3 - 8i)$

24. $(4 - 7i) - (4 - 7i)$

25. $(2 + 3i)(4 - 7i)$

26. $(2 - 4i)(3 - 5i)$

27. $(2.4 - 3.5i)(4.1 - 2.6i)$

28. $(5 + 4i)(3 + 2i)$

29. $(2.4 + 8.1i)(1.3 + 4.5i)$

30. $(5 + 2i)(5 + 2i)$

31. $(3 - 7i)(3 + 7i)$

32. $(2.3 + 4.5i)(2.3 - 4.5i)$

33. $(2 + 9i)(2 + 9i)$

34. $(3.3 - 4.4i)(3.3 - 4.4i)$

35. $\dfrac{12 + 9i}{3}$

36. $\dfrac{45 - 15i}{5}$

37. $\dfrac{3.45 + 8.29i}{2.47}$

38. $\dfrac{2.4 + 3.78i}{7.2i}$

39. $\dfrac{5 + 8i}{3i}$

40. $\dfrac{4 + 7i}{2i}$

41. $\dfrac{5 + 2i}{2 + 3i}$

42. $\dfrac{4 + 6i}{2 - 7i}$

43. $\dfrac{2.3 - 4.1i}{3.4 - 7.3i}$

44. $\dfrac{3.5 + 7.2i}{2.3 + 4.1i}$

45. $\dfrac{-8.3 - 4.5i}{-2 + 4.7i}$

46. $\dfrac{-7.2 - 8.6i}{-3.5 - 5.73i}$

47. $\dfrac{-12 - 73i}{-5 - 14i}$

For exercises 48 through 59 solve each equation and write any complex solutions in standard form.

48. $x^2 + 9 = 0$

49. $w^2 + 25 = 0$

50. $3t^2 + 45 = -3$

51. $2x^2 - 18 = 0$

52. $3(x-8)^2 + 12 = 4$

53. $-0.25(t+3.4)^2 + 9 = 15$

54. $2x^2 + 5x + 4 = -4$

55. $5x^3 + 2x^2 - 7x = 0$

56. $0.25x^3 - 3.5x^2 + 16.25x = 0$

57. $3x^3 + 24x^2 + 53x = 0$

58. $2x^2 - 28x + 45 = -54$

59. $-3w^2 + 12w - 26 = 0$

Chapter 6 Review Exercises

1. The profit at Big Jim's Mart the first year it was open can be modeled by
$$P(m) = 10.3 + 2\sqrt{m}$$
where $P(m)$ represents the profit in thousands of dollars for Big Jim's Mart during the mth month of the year.

    a. Find the profit for Big Jim's Mart in the 3rd month of the year.

    b. Find the profit for Big Jim's Mart during August.

2. The weight of an Alpaca, a grazing animal found mostly in the Andes, can be modeled by
$$W(a) = 22.37\sqrt[5]{a^3}$$
where $W(a)$ represents the body weight in kilograms of an alpaca who is a years old.
    source: Model derived from data given in the Alpaca Registry Journal Volume II Summer-Fall 1997.

    a. Find the body weight of a 4 year old alpaca.

    b. Estimate the age of an alpaca who weighs 60 kilograms.

3. Give the domain and range of the following functions:

    a. $f(x) = -5\sqrt{x}$

    b. $h(x) = 5\sqrt{x}$

    c. $k(a) = 3\sqrt[4]{a}$

    d. $M(p) = -2.3\sqrt[6]{p}$

    e. $g(x) = 3.4\sqrt[5]{x}$

    f. $f(x) = -2\sqrt[3]{x}$

    g.

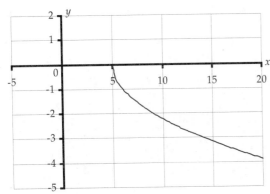

4. Simplify the following radical expressions:

    a. $\sqrt{144x^2y^4}$

    b. $\sqrt{100a^3b}$

    c. $\sqrt{180m^4n^5}$

    d. $\sqrt[3]{64x^3y^5}$

    e. $\sqrt[5]{32a^5b^{10}c^{30}}$

    f. $\sqrt[4]{25m^3n^{11}}$

    g. $\sqrt[3]{-8x^3y^7}$

    h. $\sqrt[5]{-40a^7b^3c^5}$

5. Perform the indicated operation and simplify

    a. $5\sqrt{3x} + 2\sqrt{3x}$

    b. $3x\sqrt{5y} - 6\sqrt{5x^2y}$

    c. $\sqrt[3]{27a^3b^2} - 5a\sqrt[3]{b^2}$

    d. $\sqrt[5]{-64a^7b^3c^{10}} + 4ac\sqrt[5]{2a^2b^3c^5} + 19ac^2\sqrt[5]{2a^2b^3}$

    e. $5x\sqrt{3xy^3} + 7\sqrt{27x^3y^3} + 4\sqrt{3y}$

6. Multiply the following radical expressions and simplify the result.

    a. $\sqrt{15} \cdot \sqrt{20}$

    b. $\sqrt{3xy} \cdot \sqrt{6x}$

    c. $4\sqrt{5a^3b} \cdot 3\sqrt{2ab}$

    d. $\sqrt[3]{3a^3b^2} \cdot \sqrt[3]{18b^2}$

    e. $3x^2y\sqrt[3]{15xy^2z} \cdot 2xy^3\sqrt[3]{18xyz^5}$

    f. $(3 + 5\sqrt{7})(2 - 3\sqrt{7})$

    g. $(3 + 5\sqrt{6})(3 - 5\sqrt{6})$

7. Simplify the following radical expressions. Rationalize the denominator if necessary.

    a. $\sqrt{\dfrac{36}{2}}$

    b. $\dfrac{\sqrt{24}}{\sqrt{3}}$

    c. $\dfrac{\sqrt{5x}}{\sqrt{3x}}$

    d. $\sqrt{\dfrac{7ab}{3ac}}$

    e. $\dfrac{5x}{\sqrt[3]{2x^2y}}$

    f. $\dfrac{5}{2 + \sqrt{3}}$

g. $\dfrac{5 + 2\sqrt{x}}{3 - 4\sqrt{x}}$

h. $\dfrac{4 - \sqrt{7}}{2 + \sqrt{6}}$

i. $\dfrac{12 + 7i}{3}$

j. $\dfrac{12 + 9i}{3}$

k. $\dfrac{4 + 7i}{5i}$

l. $\dfrac{7}{2 + 3i}$

m. $\dfrac{5 + 7i}{3 - 4i}$

n. $\dfrac{2 - 9i}{4 + 3i}$

o. $\dfrac{2.5 + 6.4i}{3.3 + 8.2i}$

p. $\dfrac{1.5 + 7.25i}{3.25 - 4.5i}$

8. Find the period of a pendulum if its length is 2 ft.

9. If you want a pendulum to have a period of 2.5 seconds what must its length be?

10. Use the model from exercise 1 to estimate what month the profit for Big Jim's Mart will be $17,000.

11. Solve the following radical equations:

a. $\sqrt{5 + x} = 4$

b. $\sqrt{3x - 7} = 2$

c. $-3\sqrt{2x - 7} + 14 = -1$

d. $\sqrt{x - 4} = \sqrt{2x + 8}$

e. $\sqrt{x + 2} = \sqrt{3x - 7}$

f. $\sqrt{x - 5} - \sqrt{x} = -1$

g. $\sqrt{x - 4} = 5 + \sqrt{3x}$

h. $\sqrt{x + 5} + \sqrt{3x + 4} = 13$

i. $\sqrt[3]{2x} = 3$

j. $\sqrt[4]{5x + 2} = 2$

12. Simplify the given expressions and write your answer in terms of i.

a. $\sqrt{-25}$

b. $\sqrt{-32}$

c. $\sqrt{-4} + \sqrt{-25}$

d. $(2 + \sqrt{-5})(3 - \sqrt{-10})$

13. Perform the indicated operation and write your answer in the standard form for a complex number.

a. $(2 + 3i) + (5 + 7i)$

b. $(3.5 + 1.2i) + (2.4 - 3.6i)$

c. $(4 + 15i) - (3 + 11i)$

d. $(4.5 + 2.9i) - (1.6 - 4.2i)$

e. $(3 + 4i)(2 - 7i)$

f. $(6 + 5i)(2 + 7i)$

g. $(2 - 3i)(2 + 3i)$

h. $(2.3 + 4.1i)(3.7 - 9.2i)$

14. Solve each equation and write any complex solutions in standard form.

a. $x^2 + 25 = 0$

b. $x^2 - 4 = -20$

c. $2(x - 7)^2 + 11 = 5$

d. $3x^2 + 12x + 15 = 2$

e. $-x^2 - 4x + 6 = 15$

Chapter 6 Test

1. The speed of a sound wave in air can be modeled by
$$v(T) = 20.1\sqrt{273 + T}$$

   where $v(T)$ represents the speed of sound in air in meters per second when the temperature is T degrees Celsius.

   a. Find the speed of a sound wave at room temperature (20 degrees Celsius.)

2. A daredevil wants to free-fall from a plane for 1.5 minutes before he needs to pull his ripcord and release his parachute at 1500 feet. How high should the plane be to allow for this long of a free-fall? (see formula section 6.4, exercise 9)

3. Give the domain and range of the following functions:

   a. $f(x) = -4.5\sqrt{x}$

   b. $f(x) = 4\sqrt[3]{x}$

   c.

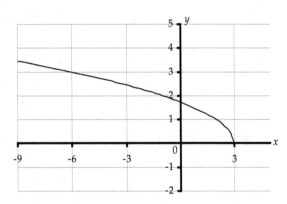

4. Simplify the following radical expressions. Rationalize the denominator if necessary.

   a. $\dfrac{\sqrt{6}}{\sqrt{5x}}$

   b. $\sqrt{\dfrac{8b}{10a}}$

   c. $\dfrac{5m}{\sqrt[3]{3mn^2}}$

   d. $\dfrac{3 - \sqrt{2}}{2 + \sqrt{5}}$

5. Simplify the following radical expressions:

   a. $\sqrt{36xy^2}$

   b. $7\sqrt{120a^2b^3}$

   c. $\sqrt[5]{-64m^3n^7p^{10}}$

6. Solve each equation and write any complex solutions in standard form.

   a. $-4(x + 5)^2 + 7 = 9$

   b. $2.3x^2 + 4.6x + 9 = 5$

7. If you want a pendulum to have a period of 3 seconds what must its length be?

8. Perform the indicated operation and simplify

   a. $5n\sqrt{6m} - 2\sqrt{24mn^2}$

   b. $2a\sqrt{7ab^5} + 7b\sqrt{28a^3b^3} + 4b\sqrt{7a}$

9. Solve the following radical equations:

   a. $2\sqrt{5x + 4} - 11 = -3$

   b. $\sqrt{x - 13} - \sqrt{x} = -1$

   c. $\sqrt{x - 7} + \sqrt{4x - 11} = 13$

   d. $\sqrt[3]{x + 5} = 4$

10. Multiply the following radical expressions and simplify the result.

    a. $\sqrt{3ab} \cdot 2\sqrt{15ac}$

    b. $\sqrt[3]{4a^4b} \cdot \sqrt[3]{18b^2}$

    c. $2xy\sqrt[3]{18xz^2} \cdot 5xz^2\sqrt[3]{6x^7yz^4}$

    d. $(5 + 2\sqrt{3})(2 - 4\sqrt{3})$

11. Perform the indicated operation and write your answer in the standard form for a complex number.

    a. $(2.7 + 3.4i) + (1.4 - 4.8i)$

    b. $(5 + 11i) - (4 - 7i)$

    c. $(7 + 2i)(3 - 5i)$

    d. $(1.5 - 4.5i)(2.25 - 6.5i)$

    e. $\dfrac{8}{4 + 5i}$

    f. $\dfrac{3 + 2i}{6 - 7i}$

12. In helium the speed of sound can be modeled by
$$v(T) = 58.8\sqrt{273 + T}$$

    where $v(T)$ represents the speed of sound in helium in meters per second when the temperature is T degrees Celsius.

    a. Find the speed of a sound wave at room temperature (20 degrees Celsius.)

    b. How does the speed of sound in air compare to the speed of sound in helium?

Chapter 1

Section 1.1

1.

   a. In 1992 there were approximately 4178 homicides of 15 - 19 year-olds in the U.S..

   b. In 2002 there were approximately 1019 homicides of 15 - 19 year-olds in the U.S..

   c. In 1982 there were approximately 7337 homicides of 15 - 19 year olds in the U.S..

3.

   a. After 5 weeks of summer the gasoline prices in Southern California will be $1.449 per gallon.

   b. Gasoline prices in Southern California will reach $1.66 per gallon after about 12 weeks of summer.

5.

   a. On sales of $2000 you will make $80 in commissions.

   b. On sales of $50,000 you will make $3920 in commissions.

   c. To make at $500 per week you will need $7250 in sales each week.

7.

   a. $C = 10 + 0.20m$

   b. If you talk for 200 minutes in one month the total cost will be $50.

   c. Your June bill would be $37 if you talked on the phone for 135 minutes that month.

9.

   a. Let C be the total cost (in dollars) for a trip to Las Vegas and d be the number of days you stay. $C = 125 + 100d$

   b. A 3 day trip to Las Vegas will cost $425.

   c. If you have $700 and gamble half of it you can only stay in Las Vegas for 2 days.

11.

   a. Let R be the total revenue (in dollars) for shooting a wedding and r be the number of rolls of film used. $R = 45r + 400$

   b. The photographer will charge $1075 for a wedding where 15 rolls of film were used.

   c. Let P be the profit (in dollars) for shooting a wedding when r rolls of film are used. $P = 26.61r - 100$

   d. The photographer will make $299.15 profit for a wedding where 15 rolls of film were used.

   e. The photographer needs to shoot 3.76 rolls of film to break even on a wedding. This implies that she needs to shoot at least 4 rolls to make any profit.

13.

   a. The population of the United States was approximately 257.49 million in 1993.

   b. In about 1998 the population of the U.S. was approximately 270 million.

   c. In about 2010 the population of the U.S. will reach 300 million.

15.

   a. About 62% of companies are still in operation after 1 year.

   b. According to this equation -10% of companies will be in business after 25 years. This is not possible.

   c. Only 35% of companies are still in business after 10 years.

17. $d = -0.45$

19. $c = 37.67$

21. $x = -1.82$

23. $m = 8$

25. $m = 0.33$

27. $d = 30.1$

29. $t = 2.27$

31. $a = \dfrac{F}{m}$

33. $F = \dfrac{I}{t}$

35. $b = y - mx$

37. $k = \dfrac{2U}{x^2}$

39. $y = \dfrac{c - ax}{b}$

Section 1.2

1.

   a. P = Profit for Quiksilver Inc., in millions of dollars.

     t = Time in years since 1990.

   b.

t	P
8	126.7
9	175.6
10	199.8
11	232.7

c.

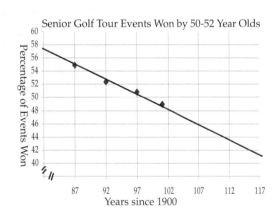

d. Quiksilver will make a profit of about $300 million in 2003.

e. Domain: [6, 13] and Range : [60, 300].

3.

a. P = The percent of Senior Golf Tour events won by 50 - 52 year olds.
t = midpoint of five year period since 1900.(i.e. $t = 87$ represents 1985 - 1989 and $t = 92$ represents 1990 - 1994).

b.

t	P
87	54.9
92	52.4
97	50.8
101*	48.9

* 2000 through Sept. 2002.

c.

Senior Golf Tour Events Won by 50-52 Year Olds

d. Between 2005 and 2009 50 - 52 year olds will win approximately 46% of Senior Golf Tour events.

e. Domain: [82, 107] and Range: [46, 57].

5.

a.

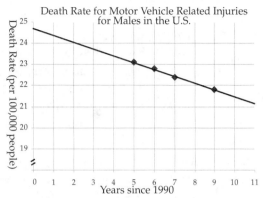

b. There will be approximately 20 deaths per 100,000 people in the U.S. in about 2004.

c. Domain: [3, 12] and Range: [21, 24].

d. In 1998 there were approximately 22 deaths per 100,000 people in the U.S..

e. The vertical intercept is about 24.75 and represents the number of deaths per 100,000 people in the U.S. in 1990.

7. Answers may vary.

a. $(0, 7)$

b. $(12, 0)$

c. This graph equals 15 when $x = -13$.

d. This graph equals –2 when $x = 15$

e. When $x = -10$ this graph equals 13.

9. Answers may vary.

a. $(8, 0)$

b. $(0, -50)$

c. The graph equals 500 when $x = 110$.

d. The graph equals –200 when $x = -30$.

e. When $x = 100$ the graph equals 450.

Section 1.3

1.

a. The slope is approximately 3.

b. $(0, -6)$

c. $(2, 0)$

d. $y = 3x - 6$

3.

a. The slope is approximately –1.5

b. $(0, 2.5)$

c. $(1.667, 0)$

d. $y = -1.5x + 2.5$

5.

a. The slope is 2.

b. $(0, 7)$

c. $y = 2x + 7$

7.

    a. The slope is –7

    b. $(0, 15)$

    c. $y = -7x + 15$

9.

    a. The slope is 4

    b. $(0, -26)$

    c. $y = 4x - 26$

11. $y = 2.25x - 1.75$

13. $y = \dfrac{-5}{14}x + \dfrac{17}{2}$

15.

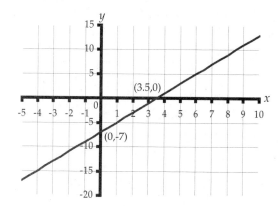

17.

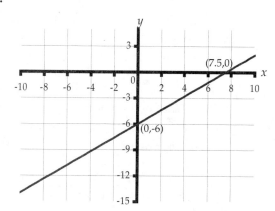

19.

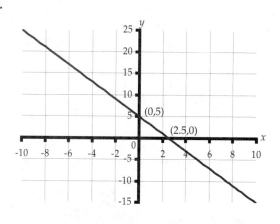

21.

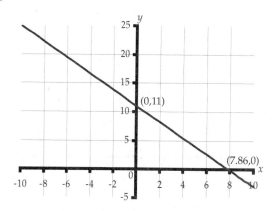

23.

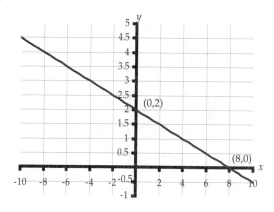

25.

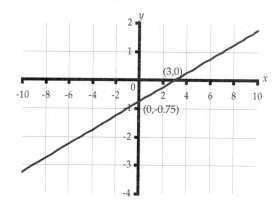

27.

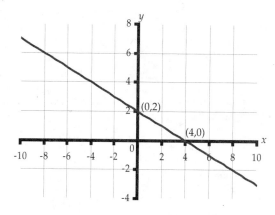

29.

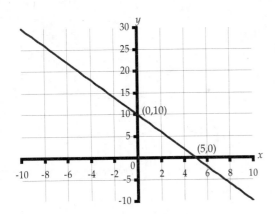

31.

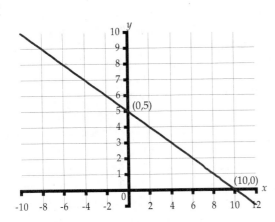

33.

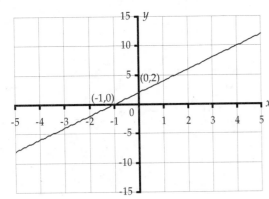

35.

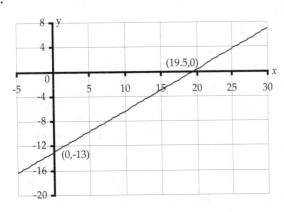

Section 1.4

1.

   a. Let t be time in years since 1990 and B be beef consumption by Americans in millions of pounds.
$$B = 325.9t + 24031$$

   b. In 1997 about 26312 million pounds of beef were consumed by Americans.

   c. Domain: $[-2, 13]$; Range $[23379, 28268]$

   d. Slope = 325.9 The amount of beef consumed by Americans increases by 325.9 million pounds per year.

3.

   a. Let t be time in years since 1990 and P be the gross profit made by Burlington Industries Inc. in millions of dollars..
$$P = -47.1t + 649.3$$

   b. Slope = –47.1 gross profit made by Burlington Industries Inc. is decreasing by $47.1 million per year.

   c. In 2003 Burlington Industries will have a gross profit of about $37 million.

5.

   a. Let t be time in years since 1980 and C be chicken consumption by Americans in millions of pounds.
$$C = 720.1t + 10561$$

   b. In 1987 about 15602 million pounds of chicken were consumed by Americans.

   c. Domain: $[-2, 22]$; Range $[9120.8, 26403]$

   d. Slope = 720.1 The amount of chicken consumed by Americans increases by approximately 720.1 million pounds per year.

7. Let t be time in years since 1990 and U, S, and F be the number of internet users in the UK, Spain and Finland respectively.
$$U = 5.74t - 39.23$$
$$S = 2.3t - 17.8$$
$$F = 0.251t - 0.577$$

9. The UK has the fastest growing internet user population since it has the largest slope of the three countries models. The UK's internet users is growing about 5.74 million users per year compared to only 2.3 million per year for Spain and 0.25 million users per year for Finland.

11.

   a. Let t be time in years since 1990 and P be the gross profit for Aiborne Inc. in millions of dollars.
$$P = -65.9t + 1263.9$$

   b. Domain: $[5, 13]$; Range $[407.2, 934.4]$

c. Slope = -65.9 The gross profit for Airborne Inc. is decreasing by 65.9 million dollars per year.

d. In 1995 Airborne Inc. had a gross profit of approximately $934.4 million.

13.

a. Let t be time in years since 1980 and G be the number of gallons of milk consumed per person in the U.S.
$$G = -0.22t + 27.6$$
This model could be adjusted up slightly to obtain a better fit, giving the model:
$$G = -0.22t + 27.7$$

b. Domain: $[-5, 20]$; Range: $[23.3, 28.8]$

c. The vertical intercept is $(0, 27.7)$ and means that in 1980 people in the U.S. consumed about 27.7 gallons of milk per person.

d. In about 1970 people in the U.S. consumed about 30 gallons of milk per person.

e. The horizontal intercept is $(125.9, 0)$ and means that in the year 2106 people in the U.S. will consume no milk. This model breakdown.

15.

a. Let t be time in years since 1980 and E be the national health expenditures by individuals in billions of dollars.
$$E = 6.79t + 58$$

b. Domain: $[-3, 22]$; Range $[37.63, 207.38]$

c. Slope = 6.79 The amount spent on health care expenses in the U.S. by individuals is increasing by approximately $6.79 billion per year.

d. In 2002 individuals in the U.S. spent about $207.38 billion on health care.

e. Individuals in the U.S. will spend about $250 billion on health care in 2008.

17.

a. Let t be time in years since 1990 and P be the population of the United States in millions.
$$P = 2.6t + 249.5$$

b. In 2000 the population of the United States was approximately 275.5 million people.

c. Domain: $[-3, 13]$; Range: $[241.7, 283.3]$

d. The vertical intercept is $(0, 249.5)$. In 1990 the U.S. population was approximately 249.5 million.

e. The U.S. population will reach 300 million in about 2010.

19.

a. Let t be time in years since 1990 and P be the stock price for IBM in dollars.
$$P = 11.655t - 44.065$$

b. In 2000 the stock price for IBM was about $72.49 per share.

c. The stock price reached $65 per share in 2000.

d. Domain: $[5, 12]$; Range: $[14.21, 95.80]$

e. Slope = 11.655 The stock price for IBM increases about $11.655 per year.

Section 1.5

1. t is the average hours you spend studying for this class per week and is the input variable. G is your letter grade in this class and is the output variable. This is a function.

3. H is the heights, in inches of children attending Mission Meadows Elementary School and is the output variable. a is the age of the students in years and is the input variable. This is not a function since two children the same age may not be the same height.

5. I is the interest earned in dollars on an investment and is the output variable. t is time in years and is the input variable. This is a function.

7. S is the song at the top of the pop charts and is the output variable. y is the year and is the input variable. This is not a function since each year there will be several songs at the top of the pop charts.

9. T is the amount of taxes in dollars you paid and is the output variable. t is the year and is the input variable. This is a function.

11. This is a function.

13. This is a function.

15. This is not a function since the input of Monday is related to two different amounts spent on lunch.

17. Domain: {5'5", 5'7", 5'10", 6'1", 6'2"}
Range: {70, 82, 86.4, 90, 91, 92}

19. The death rate from HIV for 20 year olds is 0.5 per 100,000.

21. In 1994 there were 71,558 business failures in the U.S..

23. This is a function.

25. This is a function.

27. This is not a function it will have two outputs for almost every input value.

29. This is not a function since it fails the vertical line test.

31. This is not a function since it fails the vertical line test.

33.

a. $P(\text{Wyoming}) = 0.494423$

b. $P(\text{Texas}) = 21.325018$

c. $P(\text{Ohio}) = 11.37$

35.

    a. Let $B(t)$ be the average monthly Social Security benefit in dollars t years since 1990.
$$B(t) = 25t + 595$$

    b. $B(9) = 820$ In 1999 the average monthly Social Security benefit was $820.

    c. $t = 12.2$ In about 2002 the average monthly Social Security benefit will be $900.

    d. Domain: $[0, 15]$; Range: $[595, 970]$

    e. B-intercept = 595 In 1990 the average monthly Social Security benefit was $595.

37.

    a. $f(5) = 3$

    b. $f(-10) = -27$

    c. $x = 3$

    d. Domain: All Real Numbers
Range: All Real Numbers

39.

    a. $h(5) = 12.4$

    b. $h(-123) = 12.4$

    c. Domain: All Real Numbers
Range: $y = 12.4$

41.

    a. $h(105) = 1970$

    b. $x = -45.714$

    c. Domain: All Real Numbers
Range: All Real Numbers

43.

    a. $h(5) = 30$

    b. $h(20) = 0$

    c. $x = 10$

    d. Domain: All Real Numbers
Range: All Real Numbers

    e. Vertical Intercept $(0, 40)$
Horizontal Intercept $(20, 0)$

Section 1.6

1.

    a. $T(20) = 722.51$ so in 2000 Americans ate an average of 722.51 pounds of fruits and vegetables.

    b. $F(20) = 293.72$ so in 2000 the average American ate 293.72 pounds of fruit.

    c. In 2000 the average American ate 428.79 pounds of vegetables.

    d. Let V be the average pounds of vegetables each American eats and y be years since 1980.
$$V(y) = (T - F)(y)$$
$$V(y) = 4.626y + 336.27$$

    e. $V(20) = 428.79$ so the average American at 428.79 pounds of vegetables in 2000.

    f.
$$V(23) = 442.67 \qquad V(25) = 451.92$$
$$V(30) = 475.05$$
Americans will eat an average of 442.67 pounds of vegetables per person in 2003, 451.92 pounds per person in 2005 and 475.05 pounds per person in 2010.

3.

    a. Let O be the per capita consumption of milk products in gallons per person other than whole milk in the U.S. t years since 1980.
$$O(t) = 0.342t + 11.26$$

    b. $W(10) = 10.85$ so 10.85 gallons of whole milk was consumed per person in the U.S. in 1990.

    c. $O(5) = 12.97$ so 12.97 gallons of milk products other than whole milk were consumed per person in the U.S. in 1985. $O(15) = 16.39$ so 16.39 gallons of milk products other than whole milk were consumed per person in the U.S. in 1995.

    d. Slope = -0.56 The amount of whole milk consumed per person in the U.S. is decreasing by approximately 0.56 gallons per year.

    e. M - intercept = 27.71 In 1980 27.71 gallons of milk products were consumed per person in the U.S..

5.

    a. Let $K(w)$ be the total weekly cost in dollars for week w of production.
$$K(w) = C(T(w)) = 875w + 10250$$

    b. $T(5) = 5500$ There were 5500 toys produced during week 5.

    c. $C(5000) = 13750$ The total weekly cost from production 5000 toys per week is $13,750.

    d. $K(7) = 16375$ The total weekly cost of production for week 7 was $16,375.

    e. $K(w) = 18500$ when $w = 9.4$. The weekly cost will reach and surpass $18,500 in week 10 of production.

7. $ST(d)$ is the miles driven on day d of a cross country trip.

9. $\dfrac{D}{U}(t)$ is the average amount of national debt per person in the U.S. in dollars t years since 1900.

11. $D(V(t))$ the amount of environmental damage in thousands of dollars at a national park in year t.

13.

    a. Let T be the total sales in billions of dollars from prescription drug sales t years since 1990.
$$T(t) = 17.35t - 33.85$$

b. Let M be the mail order prescription drug sales in billions of dollars t years since 1990.
$$M(t) = 3.08t - 10.68$$

c. $T(11) = 157$ In 2001 there were 157 billion dollars worth of prescription drug sales in the U.S..

d. $M(11) = 23.2$ In 2001 there were 23.2 billion dollars worth of prescription drugs sold through mail order in the U.S..

e. Let $N(t)$ be the non-mail order prescription drug sales in the U.S. in billions of dollars t years since 1990.
$$N(t) = 14.27t - 23.17$$

f. $N(11) = 133.8$ In 2001 there were 133.8 billion dollars worth of prescription drugs sold by non-mail order sales. $N(12) = 148.07$ In 2002 there were 148.07 billion dollars worth of prescription drugs sold by non-mail order sales.

15. $C(K(t))$ Cost for all children under 12yrs old who traveled on the tour in year t.

17. $C(K(t)) + A((T - K)(t))$ the total cost for all people who traveled on the tour in year t.

19.

a. The percent who are male plus the percent who are female must be 100 since every inmate is either male or female.

b. $F(t) = 0.195t + 10.621$

c. $F(5) = 11.596$ In 1995 11.596% of jail inmates in U.S. federal and state prisons were female.

d. Slope $= 0.195$ The percent of jail inmates in U.S. federal and state prisons who are female is increasing by 0.195 percentage points per year.

e. M - intercept $= 89.379$ In 1990 89.3795 of jail inmates in U.S. federal and state prisons were male.

21.

a. Let I be the percent of prescription drug expenditures paid by private insurance t years since 1990.
$$I(t) = 3.09t + 28.94$$

b. Let P be the percent of prescription drug expenditures paid by the patient t years since 1990.
$$P(t) = -3.09t + 71.06$$

c. Slope $= -3.09$ The percent of prescription drug expenditures paid by the patient is decreasing by 3.09 percentage points per year.

23.

a. $f(x) + g(x) = 7.5x - 5.5$

b. $g(x) - f(x) = 6.5x + 3.5$

c. $f(x)g(x) = 3.5x^2 - 32x + 4.5$

d. $f(g(x)) = 3.5x - 5$

e. $g(f(x)) = 3.5x - 32.5$

25.

a. $f(x) + g(x) = 4.25x + 8.85$

b. $g(x) - f(x) = 2.89x + 4.13$

c. $f(x)g(x) = 2.4276x^2 + 12.8384x + 15.3164$

d. $f(g(x)) = 2.4276x + 6.7732$

e. $g(f(x)) = 2.4276x + 14.9152$

27.

a. $f(x) + g(x) = -7.6x - 8$

b. $f(x) - g(x) = 6.4x + 1.6$

c. $f(x)g(x) = 4.2x^2 + 25.28x + 15.36$

d. $f(g(x)) = 4.2x - 0.32$

e. $g(f(x)) = 4.2x + 17.6$

29.

a. $f(2) + g(2) = 9.5$

b. $g(2) - f(2) = 16.5$

c. $f(2)g(2) = -45.5$

d. $f(g(2)) = 2$

31.

a. $f(-3) + g(-3) = -3.9$

b. $g(-3) - f(-3) = -4.54$

c. $f(-3)g(-3) = -1.3504$

d. $f(g(-3)) = -0.5096$

e. $g(f(-3)) = 7.6324$

Chapter 1 Review Exercises

1.

a. The grass is approximately 9.75 inches tall after 1 week.

b. For the grass to be 12 inches high they would want to cut the grass 10 days prior to the tournament.

2.

a. Let C be the cost in dollars to rent a Bobcat tractor from Pauley's Rental Company for h hours.
$$C = 40h + 15$$

b. It will cost $95 to rent a Bobcat tractor for 2 hours from Pauley's.

c. It will cost $975 to rent a Bobcat tractor for 3 days from Pauley's.

3.

a. The Holy Light Candle Company produced about 7.1 million candles in 1995.

b. In 1993 the Holy Light Candle Company produced about 5.98 million candles.

c. The Holy Light Candle Company produced 10 million candles in 2000.

4.

a. Let E be the amount spent in millions of New Zealand dollars on non steroidal drugs throughout New Zealand t years since 1990.
$$E(t) = -1.875t + 25.95$$

b. (13.84, 0) In about 2004 there will be no money spent on NSAIDs throughout New Zealand. This is probably model breakdown.

c. In 1994 18.45 million New Zealand Dollars was spent on NSAIDs throughout New Zealand.

d. Slope = -1.875 The amount of money spent in New Zealand on NSAIDs is decreasing by about 1.875 million New Zealand dollars per year.

5.

a. Let P be the gross profit for Costco Wholesale Corporation in millions of dollars and t be time in years since 1990.
$$P(t) = 448.24t - 704.03$$

b. The gross profit for Costco Wholesale Corporation will reach $5 billion in about 2003.

c. In 1995 the gross profit for Costco was about $1537.2 million.

d. Slope = 448.24 The gross profit for Costco Wholesale Corporation is increasing by $448.24 million per year.

6.

a. Let P be the percent of full-time workers in private industry who filed an injury case t years since 1990.
$$P(t) = -0.35t + 9.05$$

b. Slope = -0.35 The percent of full-time workers in private industry who filed an injury case is decreasing by about 0.35 percentage points per year.

c. In 2003 4.5% of full-time workers in private industry filed an injury case.

d. (0, 9.05) In 1990 9.05% of full-time workers in private industry filed an injury case.

e. (25.86, 0) In about 2016 no full-time workers in private industry will file an injury case

7.

a. Let S be the number of Pre-Kindergarten through 12th grade students in California public schools in millions and let t be time in years since 1990.
$$S(t) = 0.1129t + 4.8481$$

b. Slope = 0.1129 The number of Pre-Kindergarten through 12th grade students in California public schools is increasing by 0.1129 million students per year.

c. In 2005 California can expect to have 6.5416 million Pre-Kindergarten through 12th grade students.

8. $U(t) - C(t)$ The number of adults 20 years old or older in the United States t years since 1900.

9. $(R - C)(l)$ The profit in thousands of dollars for Luxury Limousines Inc. to produce and sell l limousines per year.

10. $ES(t)$ The total number of sick days taken by Disneyland employees in year t.

11. $W(E(t))$ is the annual workers compensation insurance costs in dollars at Disneyland in year t.

12. $(M + R)(t)$ The total amount spent on Cancer treatments and research in the U.S. in year t.

13.

a. Let H be the number of high school students in millions in California public schools and let t be time in years since 1990.
$$H(t) = 0.0436t + 1.2769$$

b. In 2005 California can expect to have 1.9309 million High School students.

c. Let E be the number of Pre-Kindergarten through 8th grade public school students in California t years since 1990.
$$E(t) = 0.0693t + 3.5712$$

d. $E(13) = 4.4721$ In 2003 California can expect about 4.4721 million Pre-Kindergarten through 8th grade students. $E(15) = 4.6107$ In 2005 California can expect about 4.6107 million Pre-Kindergarten through 8th grade students. $E(20) = 4.9572$ In 2010 California can expect about 4.9572 million Pre-Kindergarten through 8th grade students.

14.

a. Let L be the number of people in the California's labor force in millions t years since 1990.
$$L(t) = 0.37t + 13.2$$

b. Let U be the number of people in California who are considered unemployed in millions t years since 1990.
$$U(t) = -0.07t + 1.56$$

c. In 2005 there will be about 18.75 million people in California's labor force.

d. In 2005 there will be about 510,000 people in California considered unemployed. This may be too low and be model breakdown.

e. Let P be the percent of California's labor force that is considered unemployed t years since 1990.
$$P(t) = \frac{U(t)}{L(t)} = \frac{-0.07t + 1.56}{0.37t + 13.2}$$

f. In 1998 6.2% of California's labor force will be considered unemployed.
In 1999 5.6% of California's labor force will be considered unemployed.
In 2000 5.1% of California's labor force will be considered unemployed.
In 2005 2.7% of California's labor force will be considered unemployed. This is probably model breakdown since the percentage is so low.

15.

a. $T = \dfrac{V}{b}$

b. $x = \dfrac{c - by}{a}$

c. $x = \dfrac{2y - b}{a}$

16.

a.

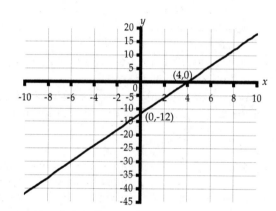

b.

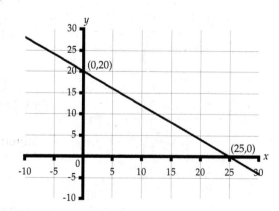

c.

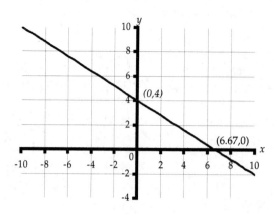

17.

a. $f(x) + g(x) = 2x + 11$

b. $f(x) - g(x) = 10x - 5$

c. $f(x)g(x) = -24x^2 + 36x + 24$

d. $f(g(x)) = -24x + 51$

e. $g(f(x)) = -24x - 4$

18.

a. $f(x) + g(x) = 2.75x - 9.08$

b. $f(x) - g(x) = 2.05x - 3.52$

c. $f(x)g(x) = 0.84x^2 - 8.877x + 17.514$

d. $f(g(x)) = 0.84x - 4.985$

e. $g(f(x)) = 0.84x - 12.972$

19.

a. $f(x) + g(x) = 4\frac{2}{5}x - 6\frac{2}{5}$

b. $f(x) - g(x) = -3\frac{3}{5}x + 7\frac{3}{5}$

c. $f(x)g(x) = 1\frac{3}{5}x^2 - \frac{2}{5}x - 4\frac{1}{5}$

d. $f(g(x)) = 1\frac{3}{5}x - 2\frac{1}{5}$

e. $g(f(x)) = 1\frac{3}{5}x - \frac{2}{5}$

20.

a. $f(4) + g(4) = 2.2857$

b. $f(4) - g(4) = 0.2857$

c. $f(4)g(4) = 1.2857$

d. $f(g(4)) = 0.857$

e. $g(f(4)) = -4.429$

21.

a. $f(-3) + g(-3) = -6.1$

b. $g(-3) - f(-3) = -7.5$

c. $f(-3)g(-3) = -4.76$

d. $f(g(-3)) = -1.58$

e. $g(f(-3)) = 6.15$

22.

  a. $f(2) + g(2) = 64$

  b. $g(2) - f(2) = -64$

  c. $f(2)g(2) = 0$

  d. $f(g(2)) = 34$

  e. $g(f(2)) = -1054$

23. $y = 4x - 1$

24. $y = -2x + 17$

25.

  a. $(0, 4)$

  b. $(1.33, 0)$

  c. Slope = -3

  d. $f(4) = -8$

  e. $f(x) = 16$ when $x = -4$

  f. $f(x) = -3x + 4$

26.

  a. $(0, 5)$

  b. $(3.33, 0)$

  c. Slope = 1.5

  d. $h(-2) = -8$

  e. $h(x) = -2$ when $x = 2$

  f. $h(x) = 1.5x + 5$

27.

  a. Slope = $\dfrac{2}{3}$

  b. $(0, 6)$

  c. $y = \dfrac{2}{3}x + 6$

Chapter 1 Test

1.

  a. Let $I(t)$ be the number of injury cases in the U.S. private industry in thousands t years since 1990.
$$I(t) = -180.5t + 6959.3$$

  b. $I(11) = 4973.3$ In 2003 there were about 4973.3 thousand injury cases in the U.S. private industry.

  c. Slope = -180.5 The number of injury cases in the U.S. private industry is decreasing by 180.5 thousand cases per year.

  d. There were about 7 million injury cases in the U.S. private industry in about 1990.

2.

  a. $T(9) = 16.74$ In 1999 New Zealand spent about 16.74 million New Zealand dollars on the treatment of diabetes.

  b. $R(t) = 10$ when $t = 7.3$ New Zealand spent about 10 million New Zealand dollars on diabetes research in 1997.

  c. Let D be the total New Zealand spends on diabetes research and treatment in millions of New Zealand dollars t years since 1990.
$$D(t) = T(t) + R(t) = 2.4t + 7.36$$

  d. $D(10) = 31.36$ New Zealand spent 31.36 million New Zealand dollars on research and treatment of diabetes.

3.

  a. $f(x) - g(x) = 2x + 24$

  b. $f(x)g(x) = 8x^2 + 6x - 119$

  c. $f(g(x)) = 8x - 11$

4.

  a. $(f + g)(4) = 14.15$

  b. $fg(-2) = 36.075$

  c. $f(g(6)) = 20.485$

  d. $g(f(0)) = -2.82$

5.

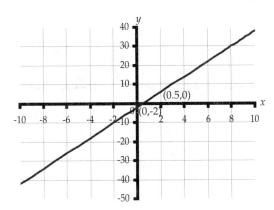

6.

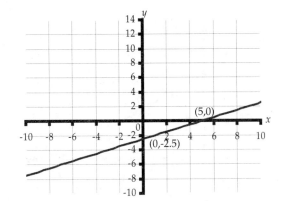

7. $x = \dfrac{c + by}{a}$

8. $y = 0.2x + 8.8$

9.

  a. John should sell 42 paintings in the sixth month.

  b. John will sell 50 paintings in the tenth month.

10. $(T-B)(t)$ is the number of girls attending the tennis camp in year t.

11. $M(B(t))$ is the number of boys matches at the camp in year t.

12. $C(T(t))$ is the total cost for the camp in year t.

13. $A(t) \cdot M(T(t))$ is the time it takes for all the matches to be played in year t.

14.

    a. Let $E(t)$ be the total operating expenses in millions of dollars for Southwest Airlines t years since 1995.
$$E(t) = 127.86t + 1176.13$$

    b. Vertical intercept = 1176.13 In 1995 the total operating expenses for Southwest Airlines was \$1173.13 million.

    c. $E(8) = 2199$ In 2003 Southwest Airlines had \$2199 million in total operating expenses.

    d. In about 1993 the total operating expenses for Southwest Airlines were about \$1 billion.

    e. Slope = 127.86 The total operating expense for Southwest Airlines is increasing by about \$127.86 million per year.

15.

    a. Slope $= -\dfrac{4}{5}$

    b. $(0, 12)$

    c. $(15, 0)$

    d. $y = -\dfrac{4}{5}x + 12$

16.

    a. Slope = 2

    b. $(0, 8)$

    c. $(0, -4)$

    d. $y = 2x + 8$

Chapter 2

Section 2.1

1.

   a. Let $E(t)$ be the value in millions of dollars of records and other magnetic media exported by the U.S. t years since 1990.

$$E(t) = -441.9t + 9781.4$$

Let $I(t)$ be the value in millions of dollars of records and other magnetic media imports to the U.S. t years since 1990.

$$I(t) = 340.7t + 1701.3$$

   b.

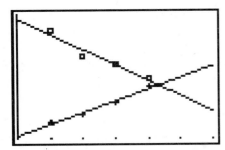

   c. The value of exports and imports of records and other magnetic media was the same in 2000 at a value of approximately $5219 million each.

3.

   a. Let $M(t)$ be the percent of white American males 25 years old or older who are college graduates t years since 1980.

$$M(t) = 0.352t + 21.74$$

Let $F(t)$ be the percent of white American females 25 years old or older who are college graduates t years since 1980.

$$F(t) = 0.558t + 12.92$$

   b.

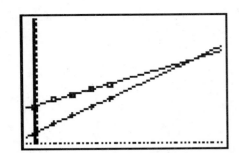

   c. In 2023 the percent of American males 25 years old or older will be the same as the percent of American females 25 years old or older. This may be model breakdown since it is so far in the future.

5.

   a.

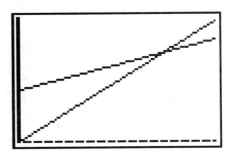

   b. Hope's Pottery will break even after producing and selling 56 vases. At this point she will have expenses of $8640 and revenue of $8680. Before this point she will lose money.

7.

   a. La Opinion will have approximately the same circulation as the Long Beach Press Telegram in 1999 with a circulation of about 104,289.

   b. La Opinion's model has a slope of 7982 and the Long Beach Press Telegram's model has a slope of 726. This means that the circulation of La Opinion is increasing much faster than the Long Beach Telegram.

9. These two salaries will only be equal if you have negative $40,000 worth of sales in a month. This is not likely so option 2 is the best salary option to take.

11. $(-7, -2)$ this is a consistent system.

13. This is an inconsistent system and has no solutions.

15. This is a dependent system and has a infinite number of solutions that solve the equation $H = 3c + 6.5$

17. Consistent system with solution $(-4, -7)$

19. Inconsistent system since the output values are always 1 unit apart.

21. Consistent system with solution $(-6.97, 12.2)$

X	Y1	Y2
-8	7	11.667
-7	12	12.167
-6	17	12.667
-7.1	11.5	12.117
-6.9	12.5	12.217
-6.98	12.1	12.177
-6.97	12.15	12.182

Y1 ☐ 5X+47

23. Consistent system with solution (15, 10)

Section 2.2

1.

   a. Let $P(t)$ be the student to teacher ratio at public schools in the U.S. t years since 1990.
$$P(t) = -0.27t + 18.68$$

      Let $R(t)$ be the student to teacher ratio at private schools in the U.S. t years since 1990.
$$R(t) = 0.11t + 14.31$$

   b. The student to teacher ration in public and private schools in the U.S. will both be about 15.5 in 2002.

3.

   a. Let $C(t)$ be the percent of Caucasians who have a college degree t years since 1990.
$$C(t) = 0.45t + 21.62$$

   b. The percent of Caucasians who have a college degree is growing by 0.45 percentage points per year.

   c. Let $A(t)$ be the percent of African Americans who have a college t years since 1990.
$$A(t) = 0.67t + 9.46$$

   d. The percent of African Americans who have a college degree is growing by 0.67 percentage points per year.

   e. In 2045 about 46.4% of both Caucasians and African Americans will have college degrees.

5. Damian needs to invest \$54,545 in the account paying 5% interest and \$95,455 in the account paying 7.2% interest.

7. Joan needs to invest \$93,750 in the account paying 5% interest and \$81,250 in the account paying 9% interest.

9. Fred needs to mix 32.4ml of the 5% solution with 12.6ml of the 30% solution to get 45ml of 12% sucrose solution.

11. $w = 6$
     $s = -6$

13. $x = -0.58$
     $y = 2.13$

15. $d = 15$
     $g = -45$

17. $w = -0.59$
     $t = 2.03$

19. $x = 0$
     $y = \dfrac{2}{11}$

21. $x = 3.7$
     $y = -4$

23. $d = 19.6$
     $W = 14.4$

25. $x = -\dfrac{5}{48}$
     $y = -\dfrac{3}{16}$

27. $c = 0$
     $d = -\dfrac{8}{7}$

29. $x = 3$
     $y = -6$

31. $x = -1.7$
     $y = 8.25$

33. $c = 2.3$
     $W = -3.27$

35. $r = -\dfrac{31}{23}$
     $c = -\dfrac{33}{46}$

Section 2.3

1.

   a. Let $F(t)$ be the number of full time faculty in thousands at U.S. higher education institutions t, years since 1980.
$$F(t) = 4.57t + 486.85$$

      Let $P(t)$ be the number of part time faculty in thousands at U.S. higher education institutions t, years since 1980.
$$P(t) = 14.82t + 167.6$$

   b. The number of part time faculty will be greater than full time in years after 2011.

3.

   a. Let $M(t)$ be the male life expectancy at birth in America t years since 1990.
$$M(t) = 0.26t + 71.6$$

      Let $F(t)$ be the female life expectancy at birth in America t years since 1990.
$$F(t) = 0.087t + 78.72$$

b. The life expectancy of males will be greater than that of females for men born after 2031.

c. Perhaps better advances in treating ailments that affect men.

5.

a. Let $M(t)$ be the percentage of births that are to teenage mothers in Massachusetts t years since 1990.
$$M(t) = -0.091t + 8.015$$

b. The percent of births that are to teenage mothers in Massachusetts is decreasing by approximately 0.091 percentage points per year.

c. Let $m(t)$ be the percentage of births that are to teenage mothers in Minnesota t years since 1990.
$$m(t) = 0.098t + 7.96$$

Let $W(t)$ be the percentage of births that are to teenage mothers in Wisconsin t years since 1990.
$$W(t) = 0.069t + 10.19$$

d. The percent of births that are to teenage mothers in Minnesota will be greater than the percent in Wisconsin after 2067.

7.

a. Let $F(m)$ be the cost in dollars for the Free-up plan from Verizon Wireless when used for m minutes.
$$F(m) = 69.99 + 0.30m$$

Let $C(m)$ be the cost in dollars for the pre-paid plan from Cingular Wireless when used for m minutes.
$$C(m) = 69.99 + 0.35m$$

Let $V(m)$ be the cost in dollars for the pre-paid plan from Virgin Mobile when m minutes are used.
$$V(m) = 79 + 0.25m$$

b. Virgin Mobile will be the cheapest plan if used for more than 181 minutes.

9. The salesperson would need to sell at least $2976.19 each month to earn at least $1225 per month.

11. Y1<Y2 when $x < 2$.

13. Y1>Y2 when $x < -7$

15. $x \leq -\dfrac{16}{3}$

17. $t > -\dfrac{1}{2}$

19. $v > -8.4917$

21. $w \leq \dfrac{415}{74}$

23. $x < -11.59$

Section 2.4

1. A 5'1" weighing 105 pounds falls into the normal range.

3. A 6' person weighing under 150 pounds is considered underweight.

5. A person 67" tall is in the normal weight range if they weigh between 121 and 159 pounds.

7. Yes this company can build 400 cruisers and 100 mountain bikes per month. This is at the 500 bikes per month limit and is under their cost limitations for a month.

9. If Bicycles Galore wants to make 500 bikes per month than they can build a maximum of about 220 mountain bikes. Beyond this their costs would be too high.

11.

a. Let n be the number of necklaces and b be the number of bracelets Theresa builds per month.
$$0.75n + 0.5b \leq 25$$
$$20n + 18b \geq 800$$

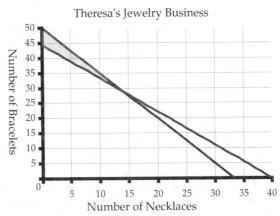

b. Theresa should make more bracelets than necklaces.

c. Theresa should make 14 necklaces and 29 bracelets so that she will have the most pairs but also meet her profit goals in the time she has per month.

13.

a. Let P be the number of power bars and D be the number of sports drinks that need to be consumed by the atheletes.

$$240P + 300D \geq 2000$$

$$30P + 70D \geq 350$$

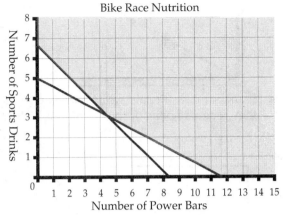

Bike Race Nutrition

b. Each athlete can carry a minimum of 3 drinks and 5 power bars.

c. If a racer carries 4 drinks they must also carry 4 power bars.

15.

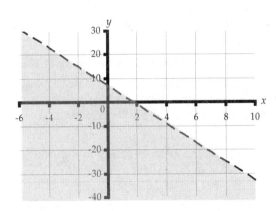

17.

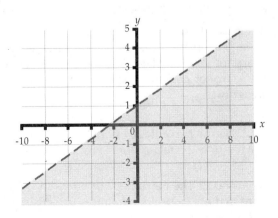

19.

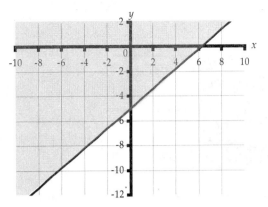

21.

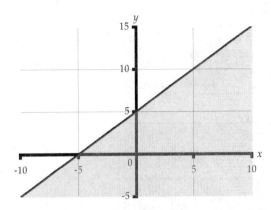

23.

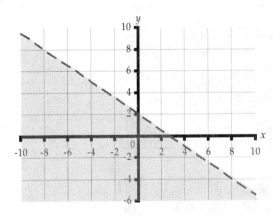

25.

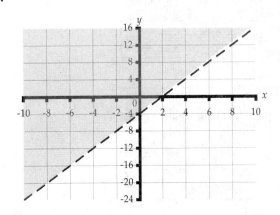

27. $y > -\dfrac{3}{2}x + 6$

29.

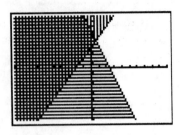

31.

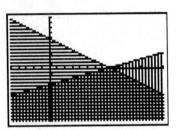

33.

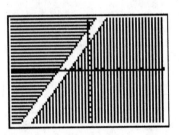

35.

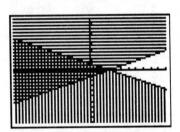

37.

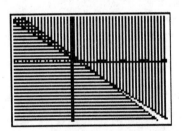

39.

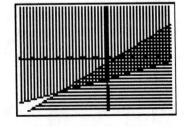

Chapter 2 Review Exercises

1.

a.

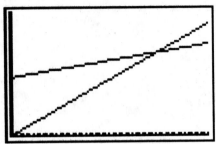

b. Frank's Show Repair will break even when they repair 45 pairs of shoes a month.

2.

a.

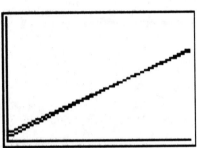

b. These two salary options will be the same when the sales reach $20,000 with a salary of $1750.

3. You must sell 640 copies in order to break even.

4. John needs to mix 60 pounds of peanuts and 40 pounds of cashews in order to make 100 pounds of mixed nuts that cost $3.00 per pound.

5.

a. Let $F(t)$ be the average salary in thousands of dollars for an NFL player t years since 1990.
$$F(t) = 120.6t + 58.1$$

Let $B(t)$ be the average salary in thousands of dollars for an NBA player t years since 1990.
$$B(t) = 230t + 680$$

b. According to these models the average salary for an NBA player was the same as the average salary for an NFL player in 1984 with an average salary of negative $624,000. This is model breakdown.

6.

a. Let D be the percentage of births in Delaware that are to teenage mothers t years since 1990.
$$D(t) = 0.29t + 11.79$$

b. Slope = 0.29 The percentage of births in Delaware that are to teenage mothers is increasing by 0.29 percentage points per year.

c. Let F be the percentage of births in Florida that are to teenage mothers t years since 1990.
$$F(t) = -0.09t + 13.81$$

d. The percentage of births that are to teenage mothers in Delaware and Florida will be the same in about 1995 with approximately 13.3% of births being to teenage mothers.

7. Consistent system. $(10, 1)$

8. Consistent system.
$$x = -\frac{57}{16}$$
$$y = -\frac{45}{16}$$

9. Consistent system.
$$d = -4.14$$
$$w = -1.27$$

10. Inconsistent system, no solution.

11. Inconsistent system, no solution.

12. The foundation should invest $1,750,000 in the account that pays 7% simple interest and $1,250,000 in the account that pays 11% simple interest.

13. Brian should use 105 gallons of the 15% solution and 45 gallons of the 5% solution to make the 150 gallons of 12% solution of test chemical AX-14.

14.
$$x = -2$$
$$y = -5$$

15.
$$t = 1$$
$$w = 2$$

16.
$$d = -3.38$$
$$c = 2.69$$

17.
$$m = 15$$
$$n = 12.5$$

18.
$$x = -0.7$$
$$y = -5.07$$

19.
$$x = 0$$
$$y = -\frac{3}{7}$$

20.
$$w = -0.59$$
$$t = 2.03$$

21.
$$f = -4$$
$$g = -5$$

22.
$$x = 0$$
$$y = \frac{1}{3}$$

23.
$$w = 100$$
$$z = -27$$

24.
$$x = 2.77$$
$$y = -6.14$$

25.

a. The percent of births to unmarried women in Sweden will be less than the percent in Norway in years after 1990.

26. $x > 12$

27. $x > 7$

28. $x \geq \dfrac{55}{3}$

29. $x \leq \dfrac{11}{12}$

30. $t > -\dfrac{16}{27}$

31. $d < -5$

32. $v > -2.54$

33. $k \leq 258.09$

34.

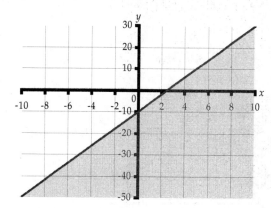

35.

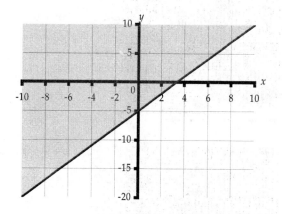

36.

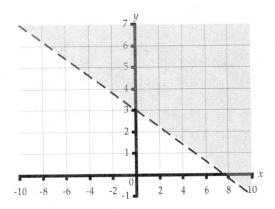

37.

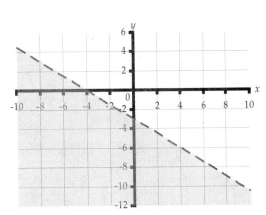

38.

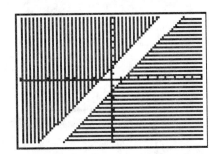

39.

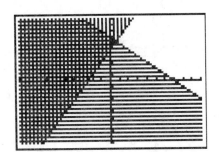

40.

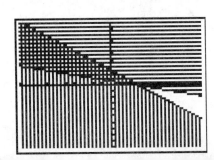

41.

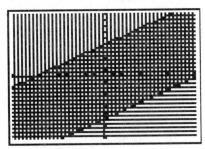

42. Let S be the number of student tickets sold and R be the number of regular admission tickets sold.

$$S + R \leq 12000$$

$$9S + 15R \geq 140000$$

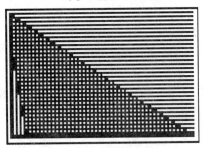

43. $y \leq \dfrac{1}{3}x - 6$

44. $y > -\dfrac{1}{2}x + 6$

Chapter 2 Test

1.

    a. Let $C(t)$ be the average hourly earnings in dollars of production workers in manufacturing industries in California t years since 1990.

$$C(t) = 0.332t + 10.953$$

    Let $c(t)$ be the average hourly earnings in dollars of production workers in manufacturing industries in Colorado t years since 1990.

$$c(t) = 0.48t + 9.92$$

    b. In 1997 production workers in manufacturing industries in both California and Colorado made an average of $13.27 per hour.

2.

    a. Let A be the amount invested in the account paying 12% and B be the amount invested in the account paying 7%.

$$A + B = 500000$$

$$0.12A + 0.07B = 44500$$

    b. Christine should invest $190,000 in the account paying 12% interest and $310,000 in the account paying 7% interest.

3. Let M be the number of hours per week Georgia needs to study for her math class and h be the number of hours per week Georgia needs to study for her history class.

$$M \geq 12$$

$$M + h \leq 20$$

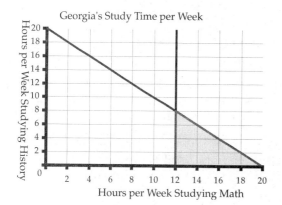

Georgia's Study Time per Week

4. Wendy should use 1.6 liters of the 5% HCL solution and 0.4 liters of the 20% HCL solution to make 2 liters of 8% HCL solution.

5. $x > 2.14$

6. $m \leq -1.81$

7. $a \geq 25.05$

8. $\begin{aligned} x &= 12 \\ y &= -2 \end{aligned}$

9. Dependent system, an infinite number of solutions.

10. Inconsistent System, no solution.

11. $\begin{aligned} g &= 3.49 \\ f &= -4.21 \end{aligned}$

12.

a. Let $I(t)$ be the time in hours per year the average person spends on the internet t years since 1990.

$$I(t) = 33.9t - 207.8$$

Let $V(t)$ be the time in hours per year the average person spends playing home video games t years since 1990.

$$V(t) = 16.5t - 88.5$$

b. Before 1997 the time the average person spent playing home video games was greater than the time they spent on the internet.

13. $x \leq 8$

14. Scott needs to sell 49 hammock stands in order to break-even.

15.

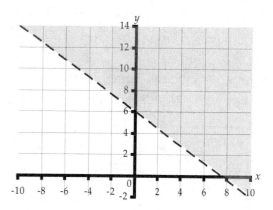

16. The revenue for cellular phone providers will be greater than that of local telephone providers after 2026.

17. $x < -4$

Chapter 3

Section 3.1

1.

   a. D = The average number of days above 70°F in San Diego California during month m.

   m = month of the year (i.e. $m = 1$ represents Jan.)

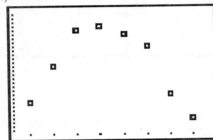

   b. A quadratic would fit best.

   c. The vertex is at about $(8, 31)$ and is a maximum point. Thus August has the most number of days on average above 70°F in San Diego California.

   d. According to the graph San Diego would expect 5 or fewer days above 70°F in January, February and March.

3.

   a.

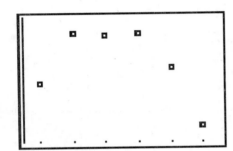

   b.

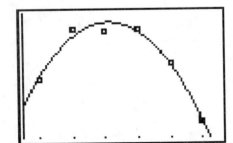

   c. This model fits the data reasonably well, the point at the top is low for a vertex but otherwise the data is shaped like a quadratic.

   d. The vertex for this model is at about $(4, 11238)$ and is a maximum point for this function.

   e. This vertex represents that in 1994 the number of cable television systems in the United States reached a maximum of 11,238.

5.

   a. Vertex: $(-2, -20)$

   b. x-intercepts: $(-8.2, 0)$ and $(4.2, 0)$

   c. y-intercept: $(0, -18)$

7.

   a. Vertex: $(4, 25)$

   b. x-intercepts: $(-1, 0)$ and $(9, 0)$

   c. y-intercept: $(0, 9)$

9. Horizontal intercepts: $(-0.4, 0)$ and $(0.8, 0)$

11. This would not be a linear or quadratic function so it is an other. (note this might be modeled with a cubic function.)

13. This data could be modeled by a linear function.

15. This data could be modeled by a quadratic function with a vertex of about $(-2, 15)$.

Section 3.2

1. Increase the value of k to bring the entire parabola up.

3. Change the value of h to be a positive number to move the parabola to the right.

5. Make a closer to zero to make the parabola wider.

7. Make k a small positive number to bring the parabola up and make h about 0 to bring the parabola to the vertical axis.

9.

   a. $N(9) = 3359$ so in 1989 about 3,359,000 people 65 years old and over were below the poverty level.

   b.

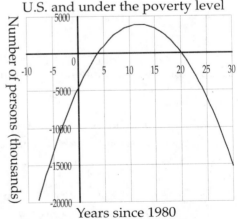

People 65 years old and older in the U.S. and under the poverty level

   c. The vertex for this model is $(12, 3890)$ and means that in 1992 the number of people 65 years old and over below the poverty level reached a maximum of 3,890,000.

   d. According to this graph there were never 4 million people 65 years old and over below the poverty level.

11.

a.

Women who experience Congestive Heart Failure

b. $H(30) = 0.071$ so 0.071% of women experience congestive heart failure.

c. The vertex of this model is $(26, 0.007)$ so at 26 years old women experience the least percent of congestive heart failure. Any age less than 26 probably would have a lower number of congestive heart failures and thus this model is probably not valid for ages less than 26.

d. According to the graph at the ages -10 and about 60 5% of women experience congestive heart failure. The -10 age does not make sense in this case and is model breakdown.

13.

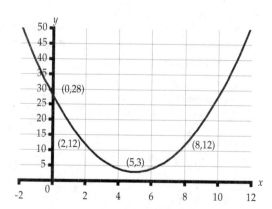

15.

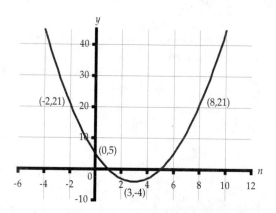

17.

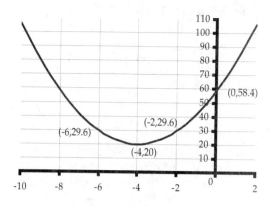

19.

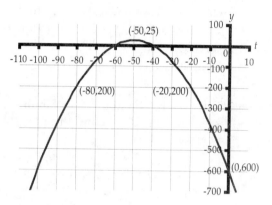

21.

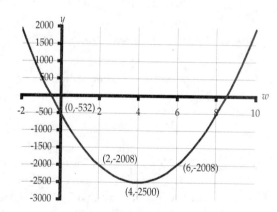

23.

a. Vertex = $(1000, 0)$
b. Wide
c. Up
d. Xmin = 0, Xmax = 2000, Ymin = 0, Ymax = 200

25.

a. Vertex = $(-10000, 5000)$
b. Wide
c. Down
d. Xmin = $-11,000$, Xmax = -9000, Ymin = 4500, Ymax = 5000

27.

    a. Vertex = (55.8, –29.7)

    b. Normal width

    c. Up

    d. Xmin = 0 , Xmax = 100 , Ymin = –30 , Ymax = 1000

Section 3.3

1.

    a. Let $T(m)$ be the average monthly low temperatures (in $^\circ$F) in Anchorage Alaska during month m. (i.e. $m = 1$ represents Jan.)
$$T(m) = -2.56(m - 7)^2 + 51$$

    b. The highest average low temperature for Anchorage Alaska is about 51°F in July.

    c. This model predicts the average low temperature in March to be 10°F.

    d. Domain: [2, 12] ; Range: [–13, 51]

3.

    a. Let $F(t)$ be the number of families in thousands in the U.S. below the poverty level t years since 1990.
$$F(t) = -75.78(t - 6)^2 + 5059$$

    b. In 2000 there were approximately 3,846,500 families in the U.S. under the poverty level.

    c. In 1996 the number of families in the U.S. under the poverty level reached a maximum of about 5,059,000.

    d. Domain: [3, 12] ; Range: [2331, 5059]

5.

    a. Let $H(t)$ be the number of hours per year the average person spent using the Internet t years since 1990.
$$H(t) = 5.7(t - 5)^2 + 5$$

    b. If you use this model for years prior to 1995 the model shows more and more hours spent on the internet as you go back in time. This is model breakdown since the internet was just beginning to take off in the early 90's.

    c. Domain: [5, 12] ; Range: [5, 284]

    d. $H(11) = 210.2$ in 2001 the average person spent 210 hours using the internet.

    e. According to this model people will spend 365 hours per year on the internet in 2003.

7. $f(x) = -4(x + 5)^2 + 8$
Domain: All Real Numbers
Range: $(-\infty, 8]$

9. $f(x) = (x - 5)^2 - 4$
Domain: All Real Numbers
Range: $[-4, \infty)$

11. $f(x) = 12(x + 55)^2 - 9000$
Domain: All Real Numbers
Range: $[-9000, \infty)$

13. Domain: All Real Numbers
Range: $(-\infty, 17]$

15. Domain: All Real Numbers
Range: $[5, \infty)$

17. Domain: All Real Numbers
Range: $[0, \infty)$

Section 3.4

1.

    a. In 1998 there were 27.2 million cassette singles shipped by major recording media manufacturers.

    b. In about 1989 and 1997 there were about 50 million cassette singles shipped by major recording media manufacturers.

    c. Vertex = (13, 85.6) In 1993 the number of cassette singles shipped by major recording media manufacturers reached a maximum of 85.6 million.

    d. Anytime prior to about 1988 is probably model breakdown and anytime after 1999 will also be since the model gives a negative number of cassette singles being shipped.

3.

    a. In 2000 personal households and non-profit organizations invested about \$5285.6 billion in time and savings deposits.

    b. According to this model personal households and non-profit organizations invested about \$7500 billion in time and savings deposits in the years 1985 and 2002. 1985 may be model breakdown.

    c. Vertex (3.5, 2176) In about 1994 personal households and non-profit organizations invested about \$2176 billion in time and savings deposits. This was the minimum amount invested around this time.

5.

    a. The company needs to make either 2 or 18 parts to make \$144 profit per part.

    b. The company needs to make either 5 or 15 parts to make \$300 profit per part.

    c. The company needs to make 10 parts to make \$400 profit per part.

7.

    a. The company needs to manufacture either 5 or 13 machines to have an average cost of \$390 per machine.

b. The company needs to manufacture either 8 or 10 machines to have an average cost of $480 per machine.

9. $(x+4)(x+5)$

11. $(t-4)(t-7)$

13. $(7m-4)(m-3)$

15. $(3w+4)(2w+7)$

17. Not factorable.

19. $w(w-2)(w-5)$

21. $x = -5 \qquad x = -1$

23. $x = 4 \qquad x = -4$

25. $t = \dfrac{10}{3} \qquad t = -1$

27. $w = \dfrac{5}{2} \qquad w = \dfrac{2}{3}$

29. $x = 5 \qquad x = -5$

31. $p = \dfrac{8}{7} \qquad p = -\dfrac{5}{4}$

33. $x = -1.5 \qquad x = -5$

35. $w = 0 \qquad w = -2 \qquad w = 5$

37. $m \approx 3.06 \qquad m \approx -3.06$

39. $(x-5)(x+5)$

41. Not factorable.

Section 3.5

1.
   a. In 1955 there was about 22.6 thousand tons of lead used in paint.
   b. In 1965 about 5,500 thousand tons of lead were used in paint. The year 1984 represents model breakdown.
   c. In 1945 we used about 51 thousand tons of lead in paint. 2004 would be model breakdown.

3.
   a. One second after launch the rocket is 186 feet high.
   b. The rocket first reaches 450 feet 2.9 seconds into the flight.
   c. The rocket will first reach a height of 600 feet about 4.95 seconds into the flight.
   d. The rocket never reaches a height of 700 feet. The rocket reaches a maximum of 627 feet.

5.
   a. In 2000 an average person spent 137 hours on the internet.
   b. In 1999 an average person spent 100 hours on the internet. 1989 would be model breakdown.
   c. In 2004 an average person will spend about 1 hour per day on the internet. 1984 would be model breakdown.

7. $w = 2.07 \qquad w = 5.93$

9. $f = 14.46 \qquad f = -10.46$

11. $c = 8 \qquad c = -3$

13. $p = -3.95 \qquad p = 2.28$

15. No real solution.

17. $(1.11, 2.48) \qquad (-39.11, 183.52)$

19. $(-5, 35) \qquad (7, 155)$

21. $(1.21, -0.72) \qquad (-2.54, -1.09)$

23. $(-0.58, -5.6) \qquad (10.58, 16.72)$

25. $(-1.67, -15.89) \qquad (3.5, 68.5)$

Section 3.6

1.
   a. $C(30) = 975$ It costs $975 to produce 30 football uniforms.
   b. Vertex = $(50, 875)$ 50 uniforms costs the least amount at $875.
   c. A school can get 103 uniforms with a budget of $1600

3.
   a. $R(9) = 148.5$ The revenue from selling 900 pairs of sunglasses is about $14,850.00.
   b. The company must sell 423 or 1,578 pairs of sunglasses to make a revenue of about $10,000.
   c. The company needs to sell 1000 pairs of sunglasses in order to maximize their revenue at $15,000.

5.
   a. $I(10) = 1962.2$ The net income for Dell in 2000 was about $1962.2 million.
   b. Dell's net income reached $1,500 million in 1999 and again in 2003.
   c. Vertex = $(10.86, 2071.18)$ Dell's net income reached a maximum of about $2068.5 million in 2001.

7.
   a. $F(5) = 768.79$ The average fuel consumption of vehicles driving the roads in 1975 was about 769 gallons per vehicle per year.
   b. $F(15) = 689.48$ The average fuel consumption of vehicles driving the roads in 1985 was about 689 gallons per vehicle per year.

c. Vertex $= (19.33, 681.51)$ The minimum fuel consumption for vehicles driving the roads was about 682 gallons per vehicle per year in 1989.

9.

a. $h(0) = 4$ The ball is 4 feet high when it is hit.

b. The ball reaches a height of 25 feet after 0.43 seconds and again on the way down after 3.07 seconds.

c. The ball reaches a maximum height of 53 feet after 1.75 seconds.

11.

a.

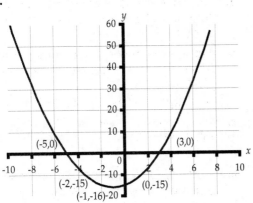

b. vertex: $(-1, -16)$

c. vertical: $(0, -15)$ horizontal: $(3, 0)$ $(-5, 0)$

d. symmetric point to the vertical intercept: $(-2, -15)$

e. Faces up

f. Domain: All Real Numbers, Range: $[-16, \infty)$

13.

a.

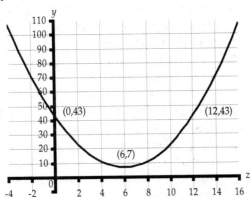

b. vertex: $(6, 7)$

c. vertical: $(0, 43)$ horizontal: none

d. symmetric point to the vertical intercept: $(12, 43)$

e. Faces up.

f. Domain: All Real Numbers, Range: $[7, \infty)$

15.

a.

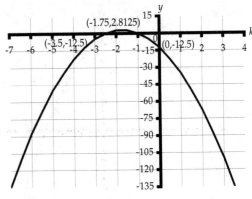

b. vertex: $(-1.75, 2.8125)$

c. vertical: $(0, -12.5)$ horizontal: $(-1, 0)$ $\left(-\dfrac{5}{2}, 0\right)$

d. symmetric point to the vertical intercept: $(-3.5, -12.5)$

e. Faces down

f. Domain: All Real Numbers
   Range: $(-\infty, 2.8125]$

17.

a.

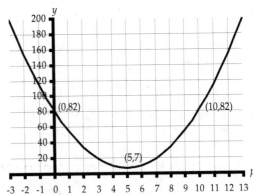

b. vertex: $(5, 7)$

c. vertical: $(0, 82)$ horizontal: none

d. symmetric point to the vertical intercept: $(10, 82)$

e. Faces up

f. Domain: All Real Numbers, Range: $[7, \infty)$

19.

a.

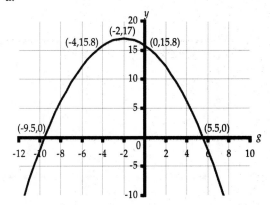

b. vertex: (−2, 17)

c. vertical: (0, 15.8)

   horizontal: (5.53, 0)   (−9.53, 0)

d. symmetric point to the vertical intercept: (−4, 15.8)

e. Faces down

f. Domain: All Real Numbers, Range: $(-\infty, 17]$

21.   (3, 10)   (−4, 10)

23.   No solution.

25.   (2.18, 17.5)   (−2.74, 18.61)

27.   (5, 9)

29.

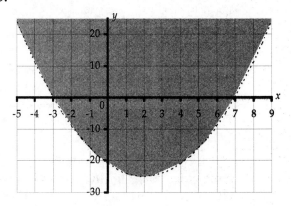

Section 3.7

1.

a. $R(8) = 81.89$ $C(8) = 50.57$ IBM revenue for 1998 was about $81.89 billion and their costs were about $50.57 billion.

b. Let $P(t)$ be the gross profit for IBM in billions of dollars t years since 1990.
$$P(t) = -0.23t^2 + 4.84t + 7.32$$

c. $P(8) = 31.32$ IBM made a gross profit in 1998 of about $31.32 billion.

d. Vertex = (10.52, 32.783) In about 2001 IBM made a maximum amount of profit at about $32.8 billion.

3.

a. $R(9) = 3380.3$ $P(9) = 430.6$ Pearson Publishing Company had 3380.0 million British Pounds in revenue and 430.6 million British Pounds of profit in 1999.

b. $C(t)$ be the cost incurred by Pearson Publishing Company in millions of British Pounds t years since 1990.
$$C(t) = -36.33t^3 + 796.14t^2 - 4605.44t + 6395.89$$

c. $C(10) = 3625.5$ Pearson Publishing Company had 3625.5 million British Pounds in costs in 2000.

5.

a. $S(100) = 60$ Car stereo producers are willing to supply 60 thousand stereos if the price is set at $100.

b. Let $R(p)$ be the revenue in thousands of dollars from selling car stereos at a price of p dollars.
$$R(p) = 0.009p^3 - 0.5p^2 + 20p$$

c. If car stereos are sold for $90 each the car manufacturers will make about $4,311,000.

7.

a. $S(25) = 33.75$ Car manufacturers are willing to supply about 33,750 Mini-Vans if they can be sold for $25,000 each.

b. Let $R(p)$ be the revenue in millions of dollars from selling Mini-Vans at a price of p thousand dollars.
$$R(p) = 0.11p^3 - 3.2p^2 + 45p$$

c. $R(31) = 1596.81$ If Mini-Vans sell for $31,000 each the car manufacturers can estimate a revenue of about $1.6 billion.

9.

a. $M(200) = 133706$ $F(200) = 141192$ There were approximately 133,706,000 men and 141,192,000 women in the U.S. in 2000.

b. Let $P(t)$ be the population in thousands of the U.S. t years since 1800.
$$P(t) = 6.51t^2 + 48.76t + 4746.16$$

c. $P(202) = 280230$ In 2002 the population of the U.S. was about 280,230,000.

d. In about 1938 the number of men and women in the U.S. was about equal at 68,203,000 each. The model also shows an equal number of men and women in 1846 with about 10,346,000 each.

e. Vertex = (−3.745, 4654.9) In about 1796 the U.S. had a minimum population of 4,655,000 people. This is not the actual minimum since the population of the U.S. would have been smaller prior to this year. This may represent the start of a reasonable domain for this function.

11.

   a. Let $U(t)$ be the number of U.S. residents who are white and under 18 years old in millions t years since 1990.
$$U(t) = -0.014t^2 + 0.524t + 51.579$$

   b. $U(12) = 56.067$ In 2002 there were approximately 56 million white U.S. residents who were under 18 years old.

13.

   a. Let $N(w)$ be the total area in square inches of an Norman Window with height of 75 inches and a width of w inches for the rectangle part.
$$N(w) = \frac{\pi}{8}w^2 + 75w$$

   b. $N(36) = 3208.94$ A norman window with a height of 75 inches and width of 36 inches will have a total area of 3208.94 square inches.

15. $3x^2$ has degree 2; $5x$ has degree 1; -7 has degree 0; the polynomial has degree 2.

17. $1.023t$ has degree 1; 6.2 has degree 0; the polynomial has degree 1.

19. $4m$ has degree 1, 8 has degree 0; the polynomial has degree 1.

21. $0.22w^5x^2y^7z^3$ has degree 17; $0.4wx^3y^4z$ has degree 9; the polynomial has degree 17.

23. $5x^2 - 3x - 7$

25. $a^2b + 2ab^2 - 17b$

27. $6x^3 + 5x^2 - 11x + 35$

29. $9x^2 + 42xy + 49y^2$

31. $5x^2 + 50x - 16$

Chapter 3 Review Exercises

1.

   a. $P(8) = 637.87$ In 1998 the population of North Dakota was approximately 638 thousand.

   b.

   c. Vertex $= (5.6, 643)$ In about 1996 the population of North Dakota reached a maximum of about 643 thousand people.

   d. The population of North Dakota was about 640,000 in about 1994 and about 1998.

2.

   a. There were approximately 17.9 thousand murders in the U.S. in 1996.

   b. Vertex $(2.5, 23)$. In about 1993 the most murders occurred in the U.S. at 23 thousand.

   c. In 1997 and 1983 there were about 14,500 murders in the U.S.

3.

   a.

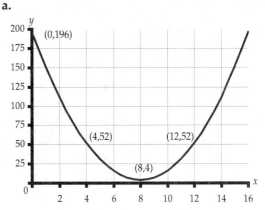

   b.

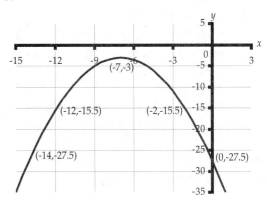

4.

   a. Let $J(t)$ be the number of juveniles in thousands arrested for possession of drugs t years since 1990.
$$J(t) = -3095(t - 7)^2 + 124683$$

   b. Domain: [1, 11] Range: [13263, 124683]

   c. In 2000 there were approximately 96,828,000 juveniles arrested for drug possession.

   d. The juvenile arrests were down to 50,000,000 again in about 2002.

5.

   a. Let $R(t)$ be the obligations of the U.S. Department of Commerce for research and development in millions of dollars t years since 1990.
$$R(t) = 17(t - 8.2)^2 + 982$$

   b. Domain: [4, 12] ; Range: [982, 1982]

   c. $R(8) = 982.68$ In 1998 the research and development obligations of the U.S. Department of Commerce was approximately $983 million.

   d. The research and development obligations for the U.S. Department of Commerce will reach $1.5 billion in about 2021. 1975 is an unreasonable solution and represents model breakdown.

6.

   a. In 1995 the median sales price of a new home in the western U.S. was $142.31 thousand dollars.

   b. In 2003 the median sales price of a new home in the western U.S. reached $250,000.

   c. Vertex: (2.73, 136.73) In about 2003 the median sales price of a new home in the western U.S. reached a low of $136,730.

7.

   a. $x = \dfrac{4}{3}$

   b. $x = -\dfrac{2}{3}$ $x = 1$

8.

   a.

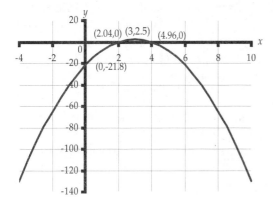

   b.

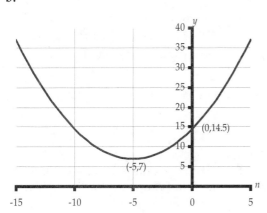

9.

   a. (−0.65, 9.6)   (1.15, 20.4)

   b. (−1.464, −12.32)   (5.464, 22.32)

10. (−4, 3) and (2, 6)

11. (3, 9) and (5, 9)

12.

   a. The R & D federal funding at John Hopkins University was about $778.31 million in 1999. At the University of Washington the federal funding was about $382.79 million.

   b. Let $D(t)$ be the difference in the federal funding at John Hopkins University from that of the University of Washington in millions of dollars t years after 1990.
$$D(t) = J(t) - W(t)$$
$$D(t) = 13.38t^3 - 267.06t^2 + 1749.66t - 3473.58$$

   c. In 2000 John Hopkins University had $697.02 million more in federal funding for their research and development.

13.

   a. $2x^2y - 2xy - 13y^2$

   b. $6x^2 - 13x - 63$

   c. $15x^2 - xy - 28y^2$

Chapter 3 Test

1.

   a. $V(15) = 13.796$ In 1995 there were approximately 13.8 million violent crimes in the U.S.

   b.

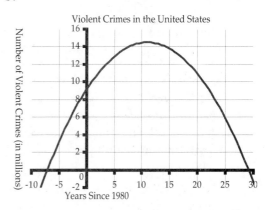

   c. Vertex = (11, 14.5) In 1991 the number of violent crimes in the U.S. was at a maximum of 14.5 million.

   d. According to this graph there were 10 million violent crimes in 1981 and again in 2001.

2. (−6, 4) and (4, 8)

3.

   a. $x = -\dfrac{7}{3}$ $x = 4$

   b. $x = \dfrac{7}{4}$ $x = \dfrac{5}{2}$

4.

a. Let $O(t)$ be the total outlays in billions of dollars for national defense and veterans benefits by the U.S. t years since 1990.

$$O(t) = 1.9(t-6)^2 + 308$$

b. Domain: [1, 11] Range: [308, 355.5]

c. In 1998 the total outlays for national defense and veterans benefits by the U.S. were about $315.6 billion.

d. Total outlays for national defense and veterans benefits by the U.S. will reach half a trillion dollars in about 2006.

5.

a. $S(10) = 447.08$ In 2000 there were approximately 447 thousand science/engineering graduate students in doctoral programs.

b. Let $M(t)$ be the number of male science/engineering graduate students in doctoral programs in thousands t years since 1990.

$$M(t) = 0.347t^3 - 5.643t^2 + 22.147t + 242.359$$

c. $M(10) = 246.5$ In 2000 there were approximately 246.5 thousand male science/engineering graduate students in doctoral programs.

6.

a. Let $R(t)$ be the revenue for the U.S. commercial space industry from satellite manufacturing in billions of dollars t years since 1990.

$$R(t) = -1.225(t-8)^2 + 11.8$$

b. Domain: [6, 10]; Range: [6.9, 11.8] In this case we did not go back from the data since it resulted in a very small revenue in 1995 and that seemed like model breakdown.

c. $R(10) = 6.9$ In 2000 the revenue from satellite manufacturing was about $6.9 billion.

d. Vertex = (8, 11.8) In 1998 the revenue from satellite manufacturing reached a maximum of $11.8 billion.

7.

a.

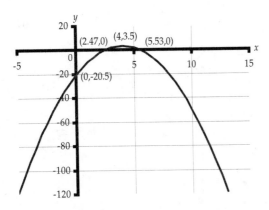

b.

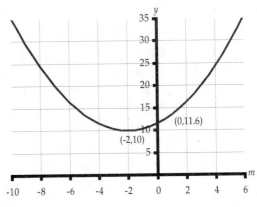

8. $(-1.222, -12.12)$ $(1, -2)$

9.

a. In 2000 there were about 1230.8 thousand privately owned single unit houses started.

b. There were 1000 thousand privately owned single unit houses started in about 2001 and in about 1997.

10.

a. In 1997 about 53.6% of murders were committed using a handgun.

b. Let $H(t)$ be the number of murders in thousands that were committed using a handgun t years since 1990.

$$H(t) = M(t)\frac{P(t)}{100}$$

$$-0.0002t^5 + 0.005t^4 - 0.0308t^3 - 0.299t^2 + 2.04t + 10.076$$

c. In 1996 there were about 9.8 thousand murders committed using a handgun.

11.

a. $x^2 + 2x - 16$

b. $9x^2y - 4xy - 2y^2 + 8$

c. $6x^2 + 10x - 56$

d. $6a^2 - 23ab + 20b^2$

12. $(-7, 4)$ and $(-4, 8)$

Chapter 4

Section 4.1

1.

  a. Let $B(h)$ be the number of bacteria after h hours have passed.
$$B(h) = 30(2)^h$$

  b. $B(12) = 122880$ after 12 hours there will be approximately 122,880 bacteria.

  c. $B(24) = 503316480$ after 24 hours there will be approximately 503,316,480 bacteria.

  d. According to the table there will be about 1 million bacteria after 15.03 hours.

X	Y1
14	491520
15	983040
16	1.97E6
15.3	1.21E6
15.2	1.13E6
15.1	1.05E6
15.03	1E6

X=14

3.

  a. Let $B(n)$ be the number of bacteria after n 15 minute intervals.
$$B(n) = 5(2)^n$$

  b. $B(12) = 20480$ after 3 hours there will be approximately 20,480 bacteria.

  c. These two models represent the same amount of exponential growth. The difference is the input variable is measured in different incriments.

5.

  a. Let $B(n)$ be the number of bacteria after n 30 minute intervals.
$$B(n) = 10(3)^n$$

  b. $B(4) = 810$ after 2 hours there will be approximately 810 bacteria.

  c. These two functions represent the same exponential growth but with two different measurements of time.

7.

  a. Let $C(t)$ be the number of centenarians in thousands in the U.S. t years after 1990.
$$C(t) = 37(2)^{\frac{t}{10}}$$

  b. $C(60) = 2368$ If this trend continues in 2050 there will be 2,368,000 centenarians in the U.S.

  c. This model is only predicting about half as many centenarians as the Census Bureau is estimating. The model may not be doing a good job of predicting this far into the future.

9.

  a. Let $P(t)$ be the population of India's Delhi territory in millions t years since 1950.
$$P(t) = 2.2(2)^{\frac{t}{20}}$$

  b. $P(55) = 14.8$ If this growth trend continues the population of India's Delhi territory will reach approximately 14.8 million people in 2005.

  c. The prediction for 2005 seems to agree with the 2001 population. This model seems to be valid at this point in time.

11.

  a. $2000(25) = 50000$ If you take option 1 you will earn \$50,000 for the 25 week temporary job.

  b. Answers may vary

  c. Let $S(w)$ be the salary in dollars you will earn in week w of this temporary job.
$$S(w) = 0.01(2)^{w-1}$$

  d. Finding $S(1)$, $S(2)$, ... , $S(25)$ and adding them up gives us a total of \$335,544.31 for the 25 week temporary job.

  e. You should choose option 2.

  f. Option 1 would pay \$40,000 and option 2 would only pay \$10,485.75 so option 1 would be better.

13.

  a. Let $R(d)$ be the percent of a Radon-222 sample left after d days.
$$R(d) = 100\left(\frac{1}{2}\right)^{d/3.825}$$

  b. $R(30) = 0.435$ After 30 days there will only be 0.435% of a Radon-222 sample left.

  c. According to the graph there will be 5% of this Radon-222 sample left after about 16.5 days.

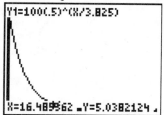

Y1=100(.5)^(X/3.825)

X=16.489862 Y=5.0382124

15.

  a. Let $B(d)$ be the percent of a Bismuth-210 sample left after d days.
$$B(d) = 100\left(\frac{1}{2}\right)^{d/5}$$

  b. $B(15) = 12.5$ After 15 days there will be 12.5% of a sample of Bismuth-210.

c. According to the table there will be about 15% of the Bismuth-210 remaining after about 13.65 days.

X	Y₁	
15	12.5	
14	14.359	
13	16.494	
13.5	15.389	
13.6	15.177	
13.7	14.968	
13.65	15.073	

X=13.65

17.

    a. This is an example of exponential growth.

    b. $h(5) = 22$

    c. $h(x) = 100$ when $x = 15$

    d. y-intercept: $(0, 10)$

19.

    a. This is an example of exponential decay.

    b. $g(7.5) = 20$

    c. $g(x) = 30$ when $x = 5$

    d. vertical intercept: $(0, 60)$

21. $f(x) = -35(7)^x$

23. $f(x) = 360\left(\dfrac{1}{2}\right)^x$

25. $f(x) = -7(3)^{x/10}$

Section 4.2

1.   113

3. w^{10}

5.   343

7.   27

9. $3b^2$

11. $\dfrac{y^9}{3x^8}$

13. $8a^3c^2$

15. $80w^{11}z^{13}$

17. $\dfrac{1}{4x^4y^6}$

19. $\dfrac{25}{9}$

21. $\dfrac{6}{7x^2y^4}$

23. $\dfrac{25}{9c^4}$

25. $\dfrac{75}{2c^3}$

27. $\dfrac{4mn^4}{p}$

29. $3125x^{10}y^{35}z^5$

31.

    a. $c^{\frac{3}{2}}$

    b. $t^{\frac{2}{3}}$

    c. $m^{\frac{3}{4}}$

33.

    a. $\sqrt[3]{r}$

    b. $\sqrt{x}$

    c. $\sqrt[3]{n^2}$

35.

    a. $\sqrt[5]{rs^2}$

    b. $\sqrt{xy^3z}$

    c. $\sqrt[3]{n^2mp^2}$

37. $c = 4$

39. $d = 5$

41. $t = -4$

43. $c = 7$

45. $m = 0$

47. $c = 3$

49. $t = 2$

51. $x = 4$

53. $w = 5$

55. $x = 2$

57. $g = 2$

59. $x = 5$

Section 4.3

1.

    a. Let $W(t)$ be the volume of water remaining in the cylinder after t seconds.
$$W(t) = 15.89(0.994)^t$$

    b. $W(360) = 1.82$ After 6 minutes there will be approximately 1.82 liters remaining in the cylinder.

c.   Domain: $[10, 360]$; Range: $[1.82, 14.96]$

d.   There will be about 1 liter remaining after 459 seconds.

3.

    a.   Let $W(t)$ be the stockpiles warheads in the U.S. arsenal t years since 1940.
$$W(t) = 0.92(1.7)^t$$

    b. $W(10) = 185.47$ In 1950 the U.S. had approximately 185 warheads. This estimate is low compared to the data given.

    c.   Domain: $[5, 20]$; Range: $[13, 37391]$

    d.   There were about 50,000 warheads in the U.S. arsenal in about 1961.

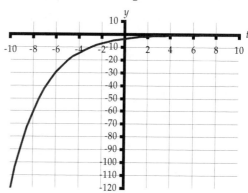

5.

    a.   Let $P(t)$ be the percent of organic material in soil after t years of overuse.
$$P(t) = 3(0.984)^t$$

    b. $P(100) = 0.5979$ After 100 years of overuse there would be only 0.6 percent of organic material left in the soil.

    c.   Domain: $[0, 200]$; Range: $[0.1, 3]$

7. $f(x) = 4.25(1.27)^x$
Domain: All Real Numbers
Range: $(0, \infty)$

9. $f(x) = 1.34(2.31)^x$
Domain: All Real Numbers
Range: $(0, \infty)$

11.

    a. a is positive
    b. b is greater than 1.
    c.   Domain: All Real Numbers
    d.   Range: $(0, \infty)$

13.

    a. a is negative
    b. b is greater than 1.
    c.   Domain: All Real Numbers
    d.   Range: $(-\infty, 0)$

15.

    a. a is negative
    b. b is less than 1.
    c.   Domain: All Real Numbers
    d.   Range: $(-\infty, 0)$

17.   The vertical intercept is $(0, -3.5)$. This graph will increase from left to right.

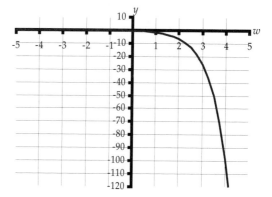

19.   The vertical intercept is $(0, -0.47)$. This graph will decrease from left to right.

Section 4.4

1.

    a. $t(N) = \dfrac{N - 4809.8}{-315.9}$ or
$$t(N) = -0.0032N + 15.2257$$

    b.   Domain: $[1019, 5125.7]$; Range: $[-1, 12]$

    c. $t(2000) = 8.89$ There were approximately 2000 homicides of 15-19 year olds in the U.S. in 1999.

3.

    a. $t(P) = \dfrac{P - 249.78}{2.57}$ or
$$t(P) = 0.389P - 97.19$$

    b. $t(260) = 3.98$ The population of the United States reached 260 million in about 1994.

    c. P is the input variable and t is the output variable.

5.

a. $y(T) = \dfrac{T - 601.39}{6.056}$ or

$y(T) = 0.165T - 99.3$

b. $y(650) = 8.03$ In 1988 Americans ate an average of 650 pounds of fruits and vegetables per person.

c. Domain: $[600, 700]$; Range: $[-0.3, 16.2]$

7. This function is not one-to-one. It fails the Horizontal Line Test.

9. This function is not one-to-one. It fails the Horizontal Line Test.

11. $g^{-1}(t) = -0.25t + 2$

13. $f^{-1}(x) = -\dfrac{7}{5}x + \dfrac{28}{5}$

15. $W^{-1}(a) = 0.4167a - 1.54$

17. $f(g(x)) = x \qquad g(f(x)) = x$ These are inverses.

19. $f(g(x)) = x + \dfrac{150}{7}$ These are not inverses.

Section 4.5

1. $f^{-1}(x) = \log_3 x$

3. $h^{-1}(c) = \log c$

5. $m^{-1}(r) = \log_5 r$

7. $\log_2 32 = 5$

9. $\log 0.1 = -1$

11. $\ln 1 = 0$

13. $\log_7 1 = 0$

15. $\log_7 343 = 3$

17. $\log_7 25 = 1.654$

19. $\log_2 0.473 = -1.08$

21. $10^3 = 1000$

23. $2^3 = 8$

25. $5^{-2} = \dfrac{1}{25}$

27. $\log_3 243 = 5$

29. $\log_b c = y$

31. $x = 1000$

33. $t = e^2$

35. $t = 243$

37. $w = 13.967$

39.

a. $g(150) = 4.6$

b. $g(x) = 5$ when $x = 250$

Section 4.6

1. $\log 5 + \log x + 2\log y$

3. $\log_7 3 + 3\log_7 x + 4\log_7 y$

5. $\log 2 + 2\log x - \log y$

7. $\ln 3 + 4\ln x + 3\ln y - \ln z$

9. $\dfrac{1}{2}(\log_{15} 3 + 4\log_{15} x + 3\log_{15} y) - 5\log_{15} z$

11. $\dfrac{2}{5}\ln m + \dfrac{3}{5}\ln p$

13. $\log(5x^2yz^3)$

15. $\log_3\left(\dfrac{ab^2}{c^5}\right)$

17. $\log_5(7\sqrt{xy})$

19. $\log_9(5\sqrt[3]{x^2y^2})$

21. $\log\dfrac{3x^4}{49y^2}$

23. $\ln\left(\dfrac{5x^5}{y^4z}\right)$

25. $\ln\left(\dfrac{\sqrt{35a^4b^3}}{c^3}\right)$

Section 4.7

1.

a. Let $C(t)$ be the number of hours the Cray C90 has been used per academic year t years since 1980.

$$C(t) = 0.424(2.027)^t$$

b. Domain: $[5, 17]$; Range: $[14.5, 69804]$

c. $C(17) = 69804$ In 1997 the Cray C90 was used about 69,804 hours.

d. $C(t) = 500000$ when $t = 19.8$ so The Cray C90 was used about 500,000 hours in 2000. This may be model breakdown since it is such a large jump in hours from those recorded in 1997.

3.

a. Let $H(t)$ be the population of humpback whales off the coast of Australia t years since 1981.
$$H(t) = 350(1.14)^t$$

b. Domain: $[-1, 15]$; Range: $[307, 2498]$

c. $H(9) = 1138.2$ In 1990 there were approximately 1138 humpback whales off the coast of Australia.

d. $H(t) = 6000$ when $t = 21.7$ If this trend continues the humpback whale population off the coast of Australia would reach 6000 in 2003.

5.

a. $E(0) = 16.89$ At the end of the pour the head of an Erdinger beer was 16.89cm. $B(0) = 13.25$ At the end of the pour the head of an Budweiser Budvar was 13.25cm. $A(0) = 13.36$ At the end of the pour the head of an Augustinerbrau was 13.36cm.

b. $E(200) = 7.577$ After 200 seconds the Erdinger beer has a head of 7.577cm. $B(200) = 2.17$ After 200 seconds the Budweiser Budvar had a head of 2.17cm. $A(200) = 3.278$ After 200 seconds the Augustinerbrau had a head of 3.278cm.

c. The Erdinger beer will be ready to drink after 705 seconds, 11 minutes 45 seconds. The Budweiser Budvar will be ready to drink after 286 seconds, 4 minutes 46 seconds. The Augustinerbrau will be ready to drink after 369 seconds, 6 minutes 9 seconds.

7.

a. Let $D(t)$ be the population of Denmark in millions t years since 1996.
$$D(t) = 5.2(1.001)^t$$

b. $D(9) = 5.25$ In 2005 Denmark's population will reach approximately 5.25 million.

c. It will take about 693 years for Denmark's population to double at this rate.

9.

a. If the interest is compounded monthly the account will have approximately $16,470.09 in it after 10 years.

b. If the interest is compounded weekly the account will have approximately $16,483.25 in it after 10 years.

c. If the interest is compounded daily the account will have approximately $16,486.65 in it after 10 years.

11.

a. If the interest is compounded daily the account will have approximately $405,465.57 in it after 20 years.

b. If the interest is compounded hourly the account will have approximately $405,517.73 in it after 20 years.

c. If the interest is compounded continuously the account will have approximately $405,520 in it after 20 years.

13. They will need an account paying about 8.67% compounded daily to double their money in 8 years.

15. $5000 will double in about 9.9 years when invested in an account paying 7% interest compounded monthly.

17. It will take about 55 years to triple the money.

19. $x = -6.208$

21. $x = 5$

23. $t = 3$

25. $n = 3$

27. $x = 2 \qquad x = -2$

29. $m = -2.926$

31. $f^{-1}(x) = \dfrac{\log\left(\dfrac{x}{5}\right)}{\log 3}$

33. $h^{-1}(x) = \dfrac{\log\left(\dfrac{x}{-2.4}\right)}{\log 4.7}$

35. $g(x) = \ln\left(\dfrac{x}{-3.4}\right)$

37. $(5.1, 30.3) \qquad (-4.9, 0.08)$

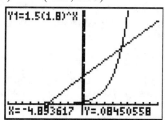

39. $(-4, -12.3)$

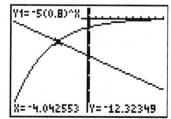

Section 4.8

1. The earthquake would be magnitude 3.3.

3. The earthquake would be magnitude 9.7.

5. The earthquake would have an intensity of 3162.3cm.

7. The earthquake would have an intensity of about 2cm.

9. The solution has a PH of about 6.4.

11. The solution has a hydrogen ion concentration of about 7.94×10^{-4} M.

13. The solution has a hydrogen ion concentration of about 4.37×10^{-2} M.

15. $x = 19.6$

17. $x = 14.43$

19. $x = 2.96$

21. $x = e^2 - 4 \approx 3.389$

23. $x = -0.342$

25. $x = 6.35$

27. $x = -5.5 \qquad x = -13.5$

29. $x = 2.44$

31. $x = 0.944 \qquad x = -2.61$

Chapter 4 Review Exercises

1.
  a. Let $P(t)$ be the population of Africa in millions t years since 1996.
$$P(t) = 731.5(1.025)^t$$
or
$$P(t) = 731.5(2)^{\frac{t}{28}}$$

  b. $P(9) = 913.54$ If this trend continues the population of Africa will reach 913.5 million in 2005.

2.
  a. Let F be the number of people who have flu symptoms d days after the start of the epidemic.
$$F(u) = 1(3)^d$$

  b. $F(14) = 4782969$ After 2 weeks 4,782,969 people would have flu symptoms. This is probably model breakdown for any one city.

3.
  a. Let $P(d)$ be the percent of Plutonium-210 left after d days.
$$P(d) = 100\left(\frac{1}{2}\right)^{d/138}$$

  b. $P(300) = 22.16$ After 300 days 22.16% of the Plutonium -210 will remain.

4. $f(x) = 5000(0.8)^x$

5. $f(x) = 0.2(7.6)^x$

6. $\dfrac{8x^{15}y^8 z}{25}$

7. 1024

8. $\dfrac{15c^5}{a^4 b^3}$

9. 1

10. $15x^4 y^7$

11. $\dfrac{b^{10}c^4}{a^6}$

12. 45

13. $\dfrac{1}{ab^8 c^2}$

14. $\dfrac{a^4}{9b^{10}c^4}$

15. $\dfrac{9x^3 y^3 z^3}{10}$

16. $(0, 5)$ is the vertical intercept and this graph will increase from left to right.

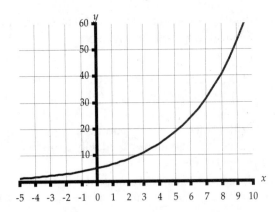

17. $(0, -0.25)$ is the vertical intercept and this graph will increase from left to right.

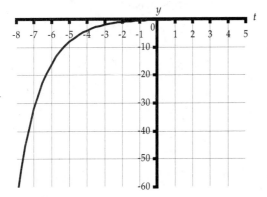

18.

  a. Let $N(t)$ be the number of non-strategic nuclear warheads stockpiled by the U.S. t years since 1950.
$$N(t) = 66.55(1.69)^t$$

  b. Domain: $[0, 10]$ Range: $[66.55, 12648]$

  c. $N(15) = 174361$ In 1965 there were about 174,361 non-strategic nuclear warheads in the U.S. stockpile. This may be model breakdown.

19.

  a. Let $C(t)$ be the counts per minute recorded on a Geiger counter measuring $^{137}\text{Ba}^m$.
$$C(t) = 3098(0.9957)^t$$

  b. $C(600) = 233.45$ After 10 minutes there would only be 233 counts per minute.

  c. Domain: $[0, 1200]$; Range: $[17.6, 3098]$

20. This is not a one-to-one function, it fails the horizontal line test.

21. This is a one-to-one function, it passes the horizontal and vertical line tests.

22. This is a one-to-one function, it passes the horizontal and vertical line tests.

23. $f^{-1}(x) = 0.714x + 5$

24. $g^{-1}(t) = -0.5t + 3$

25. $h^{-1}(x) = \dfrac{\log x}{\log 5} = \log_5 x$

26. $f^{-1}(x) = \dfrac{\log\left(\dfrac{x}{3.5}\right)}{\log 6}$

27. $g^{-1}(x) = \ln\left(\dfrac{x}{2}\right)$

28. $\ln 2 + 3\ln x + 4\ln y$

29. $\dfrac{1}{2}\log_3 5 + \dfrac{1}{2}\log_3 a + \log_3 b + \dfrac{3}{2}\log_3 c$

30. $\log 3 + 3\log x + 5\log y - 4\log z$

31. $\log(4x^3 y^2 z)$

32. $\log\left(\dfrac{2x^4 y^5}{z^2}\right)$

33. $\log_3\left(\dfrac{ab^3}{c^2}\right)$

34. $\ln\left(\dfrac{7x^2 z}{y^5 z^3}\right)$

35.

  a. $F(5) = 551.89$ In 2005 there will be only 551.89 thousand Franklin's Gulls in North America.

  b. There will be fewer than 500,000 Franklin's Gulls in North America by 2007.

  c. Conservation efforts may slow this type of decline in the population of Franklin's Gulls.

36. It will take about 11.6 years for the money to double.

37. It will take about 8.15 years for the money to double.

38. $w = 1.822$

39. $x = -0.021$

40. $x = 1.84$

41. $x = 0.466$

42. $x = 1.76 \qquad x = -1.76$

43. An earthquake of 5.7 magnitude has an intensity of 50.12cm.

44. This solution has a PH of 2.4.

45. A solution with PH of 5.6 has a hydrogen ion concentration of 2.5×10^{-6} M.

46. $x = 9998$

47. $t = 0.00258$

48. $x = 17.68$

49. $x = 7.266$

50. $x = 3.976$

Chapter 4 Test

1.

    a. Let $B(h)$ be the number of bacteria in millions on the bathroom handle h hours after 12 noon.
$$B(h) = 5(2)^h$$

    b. $B(6) = 320$ At 6pm there are about 320 million bacteria on the handle.

    c. Let $b(h)$ be the number of bacteria in millions on the bathroom handle h hours after 12 noon.
$$b(h) = 5(2)^{4h}$$

2.

    a. Let $T(m)$ be the percent of Thallium-210 left after m minutes.
$$T(m) = 100\left(\frac{1}{2}\right)^{\frac{m}{1.32}}$$

    b. $T(15) = 0.038$ After 15 minutes only 0.038% of the Thallium-210 sample will be left.

3. It will take about 20 years for the money to double.

4. The intensity of an 7.0 magnitude earthquake is 1000cm.

5. $x = -0.375$

6. $x = 11.46$

7. $x = 2.524$

8. $x = 0.413$

9. This is not a one-to-one function, it fails the horizontal line test.

10. $\dfrac{32b^{26}}{9c^2}$

11. $\dfrac{1}{2b^5c^2}$

12. $\dfrac{5x}{7y^5}$

13. $\log 16a^{17}b^{15}$

14. $\log 3 + \log x + 5\log y - \dfrac{1}{2}\log z$

15.

    a. a is negative since the graph has been reflected below the x-axis and the vertical intercept is negative.

    b. b is less than one since before it was reflected it was a decaying exponential function.

16.

    a. Let $C(t)$ be the number of CD singles in millions shipped t years since 1990.
$$C(t) = 1.16(1.79)^t$$

    b. Domain: $[2, 9]$; Range: $[3.7, 218.8]$

    c. $C(10) = 391.7$ In 2000 there were approximately 391.7 million CD singles shipped. This may be model breakdown since that is a very large number of CD singles.

    d. There were only 5 million CD singles shipped in 1992.

17. $f^{-1}(x) = 0.2x - 0.4$

18. $g^{-1}(x) = -0.4167x - 3.04167$

19. $f^{-1}(x) = \dfrac{\log x}{\log 5}$

20. $h^{-1}(x) = \dfrac{\log\left(\frac{x}{2}\right)}{\log 7}$

21. $(0, -2)$ is the vertical intercept of this graph and it will decrease from left to right.

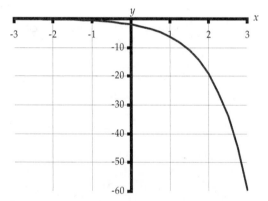

22. $(0, 40)$ is the vertical intercept of this graph and it will decrease from left to right.

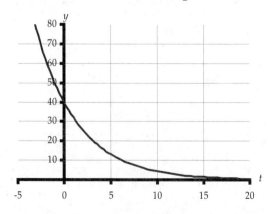

23. A solution with a pH value of 2.58 will have a hydrogen ion concentration of 2.63×10^{-3} M.

Chapter 5

Section 5.1

1.

   a. Let $C(m)$ be the per person cost in dollars for the party if m members attend the party.
$$C(m) = \frac{800}{m - 5}$$

   b. $C(45) = 20$ If 45 members attend the party the 40 non graduates would have to pay \$20 each.

   c. Domain: $[6, 100]$ Range: $[8.42, 800]$

3.

   a. Let $I(d)$ be the illumination of a light source in foot candles that is d feet away.
$$I(d) = \frac{2550}{d^2}$$

   b. $I(5) = 102$ at five feet from the light source the illumination is 102 foot candles.

   c. $I(30) = 2.83$ at 30 feet from the light source the illumination is 2.83 foot candles.

   d. The illumination will be about 50 foot candles at a distance of about 7.13 feet.

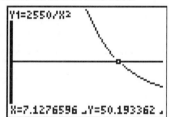

5.

   a. Let $a(m)$ be the acceleration in mps^2 of a mass of m kilograms.
$$a(m) = \frac{10}{m}$$

   b. $a(10) = 1$ The acceleration of a 10 kilogram mass under this force is $1\,\text{mps}^2$.

   c. $a(5) = 2$ The acceleration of a 5 kilogram mass under this force is $2\,\text{mps}^2$.

   d. This force can accelerate a 14.2 kilogram mass at $0.7\,\text{mps}^2$.

X	Y1
13	.76923
14	.71429
15	.66667
14.2	.70423
14.3	.6993
14.4	.69444
14.5	.68966

Y1🔲10/X

7. When the volume of this balloon is 2 cubic inches the pressure will be 10 psi.

9.

   a. 36 newtons of force applied 1 unit from the fulcrum is needed to balance the 200g weight.

   b. 4 newtons of force applied 3 units from the fulcrum is needed to balance the 200g weight.

   c. 0.36 newtons of force applied 10 units from the fulcrum is needed to balance the 200g weight.

11.

   a. $F(6) = 41.67$ so it will take 41.67 Newtons of force to lift the boulder if the force is applied only 6 inches away from the fulcrum.

   b. $F(24) = 2.6$ It only takes 2.6 Newtons of force to lift the boulder if it is applied 24 inches, 2 feet, from the fulcrum.

13.

   a. Let $A(t)$ be the average amount of national debt per person in the U.S. t years since 1970.
$$A(t) = \frac{8215.1t^2 - 23035.4t + 413525.6}{0.226t^2 + 1.885t + 204.72}$$

   b. $A(30) = 15314.21$ In 2000 the average amount of national debt per person in the U.S. was about \$15,314.21.

   c. The average amount of national debt per person was \$10,000 in about 1990.

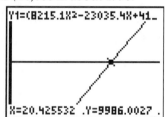

15.

   a. $B(10) = 791.76$ In 2000 the average benefit per person paid for people on the U.S. food stamp program was \$791.75.

   b. The average benefit for a person participating in the food stamp program was about \$700 in 1990 and again in 2001.

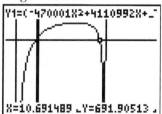

17. Domain: All Real Numbers except $x \neq -\dfrac{5}{4}$

19. Domain: All Real Numbers except
$$x \neq -4 \qquad x \neq 9$$

21. Domain: All Real Numbers except
$$x \neq 1 \qquad x \neq 8$$

23.
    a. Domain: All Real Numbers except
$$x \neq -5 \qquad x \neq 7$$
    b. $f(0) = 0$
    c. $f(x) = 5$ when $x = -4.5$ $x = 7.5$

25. Domain: All Real Numbers except
$$x \neq -5 \qquad x \neq -3$$

Section 5.2

1. $\dfrac{1}{2}$

3. $\dfrac{x+3}{x+2}$

5. $\dfrac{t+5}{t-6}$

7. $\dfrac{w-4}{w-3}$

9. $\dfrac{x-5}{2x-7}$

11. $\dfrac{x+3}{x-5}$

13. $\dfrac{2(x+5)}{x-7}$

15. $\dfrac{(x+7)^2}{(x-3)(x-9)}$

17. $-\dfrac{k+6}{k+9}$ or $\dfrac{-k-6}{k+9}$

19. $\dfrac{m+3}{m+2}$

21. $\dfrac{(x+5)(x-7)}{(x-3)(x-5)}$

23. $\dfrac{x+3}{x-8}$

25. $\dfrac{w-4}{w-8}$

27. $\dfrac{(c-5)(3c-5)}{(2c+3)(c+4)}$

29. 1

Section 5.3

1.
$$\text{LCD} = 84x^2y$$
$$\frac{49}{84x^2y} \qquad \frac{9x}{84x^2y}$$

3.
$$\text{LCD} = 69300n^2p$$
$$\frac{245m}{69300n^2p} \qquad \frac{176n^3}{69300n^2p}$$

5.
$$\text{LCD} = (x+8)(x+7)$$
$$\frac{(x+2)(x+7)}{(x+8)(x+7)} \qquad \frac{(x+8)(x-4)}{(x+8)(x+7)}$$

7.
$$\text{LCD} = (x+6)(x+5)$$
$$\frac{(x-5)(x+5)}{(x+6)(x+5)} \qquad \frac{(x-5)(x+6)}{(x+6)(x+5)}$$

9.
$$\text{LCD} = (x+9)(x+4)(x-3)$$
$$\frac{(x-2)(x+4)}{(x+9)(x+4)(x-3)} \qquad \frac{(x+7)(x+9)}{(x+9)(x+4)(x-3)}$$

11.
$$\text{LCD} = (x+3)(x+2)$$
$$\frac{(x+2)}{(x+3)(x+2)} \qquad \frac{(x+3)}{(x+3)(x+2)}$$

13.
$$\text{LCD} = (2x+5)(x-7)(x+3)$$
$$\frac{(x-5)(x+3)}{(2x+5)(x-7)(x+3)} \qquad \frac{(x+6)(x-7)}{(2x+5)(x-7)(x+3)}$$

15. 2

17. $\dfrac{13}{x-2}$

19. $\dfrac{2x^2+38}{(x+6)(x-5)}$

21. $\dfrac{-8x-34}{(x+2)(x+4)}$

23. $\dfrac{-2}{x+3}$

25. $\dfrac{3x^2-3x-29}{(x-11)(x+3)(x-4)} = \dfrac{3x^2-3x-29}{x^3-12x^2-x+132}$

27. $\dfrac{6x-52}{(x-2)(x-7)(x-8)} = \dfrac{2(3x-26)}{(x-2)(x-7)(x-8)}$

29. $\dfrac{2x^2+18x+55}{(x+9)(x-3)(x+4)} = \dfrac{2x^2+18x+55}{x^3+10x^2-3x-108}$

31. $\dfrac{6x^2-4x-14}{(2x+1)(x+3)(4x-5)} = \dfrac{6x^2-4x-14}{8x^3+18x^2-23x-15}$

33. $\dfrac{3}{x-5}$

Section 5.4

1.
  a. Let $s(t)$ be the per capita spending in dollars of California t years since 1900.
  $$s(t) = \frac{55.125t^2 - 6435.607t + 186914.286}{0.464t - 12.47}$$
  b. $s(95) = 2310.49$ In 1995 the per capita spending in California was about $2310.49 per person.
  c. $s(t) = 3000$ when $t = 102.167$ In about 2002 the per capita spending in California reached $3000 per person.

3.
  a. $s(25) = 24027.8$ In 1995 the per capita personal spending in the United States was approximately $24,028.
  b. $s(t) = 25000$ when $t = 26.5$ and $t = 329.3$ In 1997 the per capita personal spending in the United States reached about $25000. The year 2299 is model breakdown.

5. $B(t) = 800$ when $t = 9.89$ and $t = 1.91$ In 1992 and 2000 the average benefit paid to participants on the food stamp program was $800 per person.

7. A resistance of 266.67ohms will result in a current of 0.9 amp.

9.
  a. Let $a(p)$ be the per person cost in dollars for p people to attend this charity event.
  $$a(p) = \frac{4.55p + 365.00}{p}$$
  b. $a(p) = 7.50$ when $p = 123.73$ so the per person cost will be just under $7.50 per person if 124 people attend the charity event.

11.
  a. $m = \dfrac{800}{n^5}$
  b. $m = 0.78125$
  c. $n = 1.741$

13. $x = 5$

15. $w = -\dfrac{11}{10}$

17. $x = 2$ $x = \dfrac{1}{3}$

19. $x = 9$

21. $x = 5$

23. $w = -3$

25. $x = 7$ $x = -4$

27. $v = 50$

29. $d = -\dfrac{17}{4}$

31. $m = 6$ $m = -7$

33. $p = 24$

35. $c = 0.95$ $c = 43.05$

37. $x = 8$

39. $c = 5$

Chapter 5 Review Exercises

1.
  a. Let $I(d)$ be the illumination in foot candles of this light source d feet away from the source.
  $$I(d) = \frac{36000}{d^2}$$
  b. $I(40) = 22.5$ At 40 feet from the light source this light has an illumination of 22.5 foot candles.
  c. $I(d) = 50$ when $d = 26.83$ This light has an illumination of 50 foot candles at a distance of 26.83 feet from the light source.

2.
  a. $y = \dfrac{224}{x^5}$
  b. $y = 0.21875$

3.
  a. Let $F(p)$ be the entrance fee MRU should charge if they have p people compete in the math compitition.
  $$F(p) = \frac{500 + 7.5p}{p - 10}$$
  b. $F(100) = 13.89$ MRU should charge an entrance fee of $13.89 to cover their expenses.
  c. $F(p) = 10$ when $p = 240$ If MRU wants an entrance fee of only $10 they need 240 people to compete.

4.
  a. $C(5) = 27.004$ In 1995 the each American consumed an average of 27 pounds of cheese.
  b. $C(t) = 30$ when $t = 10.8$ In 2001 Americans will each an average of 30 pounds of cheese per person.

5. Domain: All Real Numbers except $x \neq 9$

6. Domain: All Real Numbers except
$$x \neq -5 \qquad x \neq 3$$

7. Domain: All Real Numbers except
$$x \neq 5 \qquad x \neq -\frac{3}{2}$$

8. Domain: All Real Numbers except
$$x \neq -6 \qquad x \neq 4$$

9. Domain: All Real Numbers except
$$x \neq -3 \qquad x \neq 6$$

10. $\dfrac{x+3}{x-2}$

11. $\dfrac{4(x+9)}{(x+3)(x-7)}$

12. $\dfrac{x+2}{x+7}$

13. $\dfrac{x+4}{x-5}$

14. $\dfrac{6}{(n+7)(n+4)}$

15. $\dfrac{v+7}{v-8}$

16. $\dfrac{4x+15}{x+6}$

17. $\dfrac{-4x+41}{(x-5)(x+2)}$

18. $\dfrac{x^2+x+16}{(x+3)(x+5)(x-7)}$

19. $\dfrac{3x^2+6x-11}{(x-7)(x+2)(x+3)}$

20. $x = -\dfrac{41}{3} = -13.67$

21. $x = 0 \qquad x = 21$

22. $x = 2.2 \qquad x = -5.37$

23. $x = -7$

24. $w = 3$

25. $x = 3$

26. $k = 2 \qquad k = -7.67$

27. $x = -2 \qquad x = \dfrac{-10}{3}$

Chapter 5 Test

1.
   a. Let $I(d)$ be the illumination in foot candles of this light source d feet away from the source.
$$I(d) = \frac{4320}{d^2}$$
   b. $I(7) = 88.16$ At 7 feet from the light source this light has an illumination of 88.16 foot candles.
   c. $I(d) = 20$ when $d = 14.696$ This light has an illumination of 20 foot candles at a distance of 14.696 feet from the light source.

2. $\dfrac{2x^2+6x}{(x+7)(x-4)}$

3. $\dfrac{x+4}{x+2}$

4. $\dfrac{2}{(w+3)(w-4)}$

5. $\dfrac{2(m+1)}{m+4}$

6. $\dfrac{8x-8}{2x-7}$

7. $\dfrac{14(x+1)}{(x-3)(x+4)}$

8. $\dfrac{6x^2+36x+2}{(x+3)(x+2)(x+7)}$

9.
   a. Domain: All Real Numbers except
$$x \neq -9 \qquad x \neq 3$$
   b. Domain: All Real Numbers except
$$x \neq -2 \qquad x \neq 4$$

10.
   a. Let $U(t)$ be the unemployment rate for the state of Florida as a decimal t years since 2000.
$$U(t) = \frac{80.5t+287.5}{141.5t+7826.8}$$
   b. $U(3) = 0.0641$ In 2003 the unemployment rate in Florida was 6.41%.
   c. $U(t) = 0.08$ when $t = 4.9$ In 2005 Florida's unemployment rate will reach 8%.

11. $x = 17$

12. $x = 19$

13. $x = 3 \qquad x = -3$

14. $x = 1$

15. $x = 9.8$

Chapter 6

Section 6.1

1.

   a. Yes a radical function seems appropriate for this data.

   b. It fits well.

   c. $C(5.5) = 8.57$ It costs about \$8.57 million to produce 550,000 heaters per month.

   d. $C(15) = 12.07$ It costs about \$12.07 million to produce 1,500,000 heaters per month.

   e. Domain: [1, 15] Range [5.49, 12.07]

3.

   a. This model fits the data relatively well.

   b. A Basilisk lizard with a body mass of 50 grams will have a leg length of about 0.061 meters.

   c. A Basilisk lizard with a body mass of 100 grams will have a leg length of about 0.077 meters.

   d. A Basilisk lizard would have a body mass of about 223 grams to have a leg length of 0.1 meters.

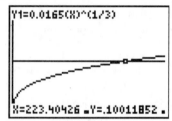

5.

   a. A butterfly with a thoracic mass of 0.05 grams can fly at a speed of about 2.92 meters per second.

   b. A butterfly with a thoracic mass of 0.12 grams can fly at a speed of about 4.93 meters per second.

   c. Range: [0.279, 12.95]

7.

   a. This is the graph of an odd root.

   b. Domain: All Real Numbers.

   c. Range: All Real Numbers.

9.

   a. This is the graph of an even root.

   b. Domain: $[-4, \infty)$

   c. Range: $[0, \infty)$

11.

   a. This is the graph of an even root.

   b. Domain: $(-\infty, -5]$

   c. Range: $[0, \infty)$

13.

   a. This is the graph of an odd root.

   b. Domain: All Real Numbers

   c. Range: All Real Numbers

15.

   a. Domain: $[0, \infty)$. Range: $[0, \infty)$

   b. Domain: $[0, \infty)$. Range: $(-\infty, 0]$

   c. Domain: $[0, \infty)$. Range: $[0, \infty)$

   d. Domain: $[0, \infty)$. Range: $(-\infty, 0]$

17.

   a. Domain: $[-8, \infty)$. Range: $[0, \infty)$

   b. Domain: $(-\infty, 10]$. Range: $[0, \infty)$

   c. Domain: $(-\infty, -11]$. Range: $[0, \infty)$

Section 6.2

1.   10

3. $5y^2$

5. -2

7. $14m^2 n$

9. $6a\sqrt{a}$

11. $36a^2 b^4 c^7 \sqrt{ac}$

13. $2xy^2$

15. $2b^2 c^5 \sqrt[4]{3a^3 c}$

17. $3tu^2 \sqrt[5]{s^3}$

19. $-3ab^2$

21. $4\sqrt{5x}$

23. $x\sqrt{y}$

25. $6\sqrt[3]{a}$

27. $5n\sqrt[5]{10m^3}$

29. $35x^2 y^3 \sqrt[3]{z^2} - 54x^2 y^2 \sqrt[3]{z^2}$

31. $-7\sqrt{2x} + 10x\sqrt{2}$

33. $7xyz^2 \sqrt{z} + 7xz^2 \sqrt{yz}$

35. $12\sqrt{2x} + 4\sqrt[3]{2x}$

37. $-3\sqrt[3]{7xy} + 3\sqrt[5]{7xy}$

Section 6.3

1. $\sqrt{21}$

3. $5\sqrt{2xy}$

5. $2x$

7. $2y\sqrt{3x}$

9. $6m^3$

11. $160m^2p\sqrt{7n}$

13. $14x^3y\sqrt[3]{20y^2}$

15. $36x^4y^6\sqrt[5]{686x^2}$

17. 2

19. $-175ab + 64$

21. 2

23. $\dfrac{x}{3y}$

25. $\dfrac{d\sqrt{21}}{3}$

27. $\dfrac{5\sqrt{14xy}}{21y}$

29. $\dfrac{\sqrt[3]{245x^2y}}{7xy}$

31. $\dfrac{5\sqrt[3]{4m^2n^2}}{2n}$

33. $\dfrac{\sqrt[3]{36xy^2}}{14xy}$

35. $\dfrac{4\sqrt[5]{216y^3z^3}}{3yz}$

37. $\dfrac{56 + 7\sqrt{6}}{58}$

39. $\dfrac{15 - 5\sqrt{2x}}{9 - 2x}$

41. $\dfrac{3x\sqrt{21} + 6\sqrt{3x} + \sqrt{7x} + 2}{1 - 27x}$

43. $\dfrac{5m\sqrt{n} + 2\sqrt{mn} + 15\sqrt{m} + 6}{9 - mn}$

45. $\dfrac{-20x\sqrt{6} - 2\sqrt{30x} + 8\sqrt{5x} + 4}{2 - 15x}$

Section 6.4

1. The car was traveling at a speed of about 67 mph.

3. The coefficient of friction for this road would be about 0.877.

5. The pendulum would have a period of about 1.9 seconds.

7. A pendulum 0.81 feet long will have a period of 1 second.

9.
   a. It will take 2.5 seconds for an object to fall 100 feet.
   b. It will take 1.77 seconds for an object to fall 50 feet.
   c. An object dropped from a height of 1600 feet it will fall for about 10 seconds.

11. If the speed of sound through air is 345mps the temperature is about 23.0 degrees Celsius.

13.
   a. A specimen with a leg length of 0.1 meters would have a body mass of about 222.6 grams.
   b. A specimen with a leg length of 0.075 meters would have a body mass of about 93.9 grams.

15.
   a. A butterfly with a thoracic mass of about 0.123 grams can fly at about 5 meters per second.
   b. A butterfly with a thoracic mass of about 0.176 grams can fly at about 6.2 meters per second.

17. $x = 23$

19. $x = 32$

21. $t = -22.5$

23. $x = 5.5$

25. $w = 1363.48$

27. $x = 9$

29. $z = -\dfrac{1}{9}$

31. $x = 36$

33. $x = -2.42$ or $x = 2.75$

35. $x = 2$

37. No solution

39. No solution

41. $x = 3$ or $x = -1$

43. $x = 105.5$

45. $x = 5$

47. $x = 24.6$

49. $x = 32$

Section 6.5

1. $10i$

3. $12i$

5. $2 - 4i$

7. $4.1i$

9. $-21 + 14i$

11. $8 + 9i$

13. $7.9 - 1.7i$

15. $3 - 4i$

17. $-5 + 7i$

19. $-4 - 3i$

21. $6.5 - 9.2i$

23. 5

25. $29 - 2i$

27. $0.74 - 20.59i$

29. $-33.33 + 21.33i$

31. 58

33. $-77 + 36i$

35. $4 + 3i$

37. $1.40 + 3.36i$

39. $\dfrac{8}{3} - \dfrac{5}{3}i$

41. $\dfrac{16}{13} - \dfrac{11}{13}i$

43. $0.58 + 0.04i$

45. $-0.17 + 1.84i$

47. $\dfrac{1082}{221} + \dfrac{197}{221}i$

49. $x = 5i$ or $x = -5i$

51. $x = 3$ or $x = -3$

53. $t = -3.4 + 4.9i$ or $t = -3.4 - 4.9i$

55. $x = 0$ or $x = 1$ or $x = -\dfrac{7}{5}$

57. $x = 0$

or $x = -4 + \dfrac{1}{3}i\sqrt{15} \approx -4 + 1.29i$

or $x = -4 - \dfrac{1}{3}i\sqrt{15} \approx -4 - 1.29i$

59. $w = 2 + \dfrac{1}{3}i\sqrt{42} \approx 2 + 2.16i$

or $w = 2 - \dfrac{1}{3}i\sqrt{42} \approx 2 - 2.16i$

Chapter 6 Review Exercises

1.
   a. $P(3) = 13.764$ Big Jim's Mart makes a profit of $13.8 thousand in March.
   b. $P(8) = 15.96$ Big Jim's Mart makes a profit of about $15.96 thousand in August.

2.
   a. $W(4) = 51.4$ A 4 year old Alpacas should weight about 51.4 kilograms.
   b. $W(a) = 60$ when $a = 5.18$ A 5 year old Alpacas would weigh about 60 kilograms.

3.
   a. Domain: $[0, \infty)$ Range: $(-\infty, 0]$
   b. Domain: $[0, \infty)$ Range: $[0, \infty)$
   c. Domain: $[0, \infty)$ Range: $[0, \infty)$
   d. Domain: $[0, \infty)$ Range: $(-\infty, 0]$
   e. Domain: All Real Numbers
       Range: All Real Numbers
   f. Domain: All Real Numbers
       Range: All Real Numbers
   g. Domain: $[5, \infty)$ Range: $[0, \infty)$

4.
   a. $12xy^2$
   b. $10a\sqrt{ab}$
   c. $6m^2n^2\sqrt{5n}$
   d. $4xy\sqrt[3]{y^2}$
   e. $2ab^2c^6$
   f. $n^2\sqrt[4]{25m^3n^3}$
   g. $-2xy^2\sqrt[3]{y}$
   h. $ac\sqrt[5]{-40a^2b^3}$

5.
   a. $7\sqrt{3x}$
   b. $-3x\sqrt{5y}$
   c. $-2a\sqrt[3]{b^2}$

d. $21ac^2 \sqrt[5]{2a^2b^3}$

e. $26xy\sqrt{3xy} + 4\sqrt{3y}$

6.

a. $10\sqrt{3}$

b. $3x\sqrt{2y}$

c. $12a^2b\sqrt{10}$

d. $3ab\sqrt[3]{2b}$

e. $18x^3y^5z^2\sqrt[3]{10x^2}$

f. $-99 + \sqrt{7}$

g. -141

7.

a. $3\sqrt{2}$

b. $2\sqrt{2}$

c. $\dfrac{\sqrt{15}}{3}$

d. $\dfrac{\sqrt{21bc}}{3c}$

e. $\dfrac{5\sqrt[3]{4xy^2}}{2y}$

f. $10 - 5\sqrt{3}$

g. $\dfrac{8x + 26\sqrt{x} + 15}{9 - 16x}$

h. $\dfrac{8 - 4\sqrt{6} + \sqrt{42} - 2\sqrt{7}}{-2}$

8. A 2 foot pendulum will have a period of about 1.57 seconds.

9. To have a pendulum with a period of 2.5 seconds it must be 5.066 feet long.

10. Big Jim's Mart will have a profit of about $17,000 in November.

11.

a. $x = 11$

b. $x = \dfrac{11}{3}$

c. $x = 16$

d. No Solution

e. $x = \dfrac{9}{2}$

f. $x = 9$

g. No solution

h. $x = 20$

i. $x = \dfrac{27}{2}$

j. $x = \dfrac{14}{5}$

12.

a. $5i$

b. $4i\sqrt{2} = 5.657i$

c. $7i$

d. $13.07 + 0.384i$

13.

a. $7 + 10i$

b. $5.9 - 2.4i$

c. $1 + 4i$

d. $2.9 + 7.1i$

e. $34 - 13i$

f. $-23 + 52i$

g. 13

h. $46.23 - 5.99i$

i. $4 + \dfrac{7}{3}i$

j. $4 + 3i$

k. $\dfrac{7}{5} - \dfrac{4}{5}i$

l. $\dfrac{14}{13} - \dfrac{21}{13}i$

m. $-\dfrac{13}{25} + \dfrac{41}{25}i$

n. $-\dfrac{19}{25} - \dfrac{42}{25}i$

o. $0.777 + 0.0079i$

p. $-0.9 + 0.98i$

14.

a. $x = 5i \qquad x = -5i$

b. $x = 4i \qquad x = -4i$

c. $x = 7 + i\sqrt{3} \qquad x = 7 - i\sqrt{3}$

d. $x = -2 + \dfrac{1}{3}i\sqrt{3} \qquad x = -2 - \dfrac{1}{3}i\sqrt{3}$

e. $x = -2 + i\sqrt{5} \qquad x = -2 - i\sqrt{5}$

Chapter 6 Test

1.

   a. The speed of sound through air at room temperature is about 344.06 meters per second.

2. The daredevil would have to jump from a height of 131,100 feet. The daredevil would die at this height.

3.

   a. Domain: $[0, \infty)$ Range: $(-\infty, 0]$

   b. Domain: All Real Numbers
Range: All Real Numbers

   c. Domain: $(-\infty, 3]$ Range: $[0, \infty)$

4.

   a. $\dfrac{\sqrt{30x}}{5x}$

   b. $\dfrac{2\sqrt{5ab}}{5a}$

   c. $\dfrac{5\sqrt[3]{9m^2n}}{3n}$

   d. $-6 + 3\sqrt{5} + 2\sqrt{2} - \sqrt{10}$

5.

   a. $6y\sqrt{x}$

   b. $14ab\sqrt{30b}$

   c. $-2np^2\sqrt[5]{2m^3n^2}$

6.

   a. $x = -5 - i\sqrt{\dfrac{1}{2}}$ $x = -5 + i\sqrt{\dfrac{1}{2}}$

   b. $x = -1 + 0.86i$ $x = -1 - 0.86i$

7. For a pendulum to have a period of 3 seconds it must be 7.3 feet long.

8.

   a. $n\sqrt{6m}$

   b. $16ab^2\sqrt{7ab} + 4b\sqrt{7a}$

9.

   a. $x = \dfrac{12}{5}$

   b. $x = 49$

   c. $x = 23$

   d. $x = 59$

10.

   a. $6a\sqrt{5bc}$

   b. $2ab\sqrt[3]{9a}$

   c. $30x^4yz^4\sqrt[3]{4x^2y}$

   d. $-14 - 16\sqrt{3}$

11.

   a. $4.1 - 1.4i$

   b. $1 + 18i$

   c. $31 - 29i$

   d. $-25.875 - 19.875i$

   e. $\dfrac{32}{41} - \dfrac{40}{41}i$

   f. $\dfrac{4}{85} + \dfrac{33}{85}i$

12.

   a. The speed of sound through helium at room temperature is about 1006.5 meters per second.

   b. The speed of sound in air is much slower than the speed of sound through helium.

Appendix F   Other Factoring Techniques

• Perfect Square Trinomials • Difference of Squares • Difference and Sum of Cubes

In this appendix we will look at several other techniques of factoring along with some special situations where you can use a pattern to factor. The key to most of these techniques is to recognize the form of the polynomial and follow the pattern to factor it. Many of these patterns can be done using the factoring techniques found in chapter 3 but are often much quicker using these patterns.

A perfect-square trinomial comes as a result of squaring a binomial. Using the distributive property and combining like terms we get the following:

$$(a+b)^2 = (a+b)(a+b) = a^2 + ab + ab + b^2 = a^2 + 2ab + b^2$$
$$(a-b)^2 = (a-b)(a-b) = a^2 - ab - ab + b^2 = a^2 - 2ab + b^2$$

If we look at the resulting trinomials we can see a pattern for a perfect square trinomial. The first and last terms of the trinomial will be perfect squares and the middle term will be either plus or minus twice the product of the first and last terms that are being squared. For factoring purposes the relationship is better seen as

$$a^2 + 2ab + b^2 = (a+b)^2$$
$$a^2 - 2ab + b^2 = (a-b)^2$$

Example 1

Factor the following perfect square trinomials:

a. $x^2 + 6x + 9$

b. $m^2 - 14m + 49$

c. $4a^2 + 20a + 25$

d. $9x^2 - 24xy + 16y^2$

Solution

a.   First we need to confirm that this is a perfect square trinomial. The first term is x squared, the last term is 3 squared, and the middle term is twice the product of these two terms ($2 \cdot 3 \cdot x$). So this trinomial can be factored into a binomial squared.
$$x^2 + 6x + 9$$
$$(x+3)^2$$

b.   The first term is m squared, the last term is 7 squared, and the middle term is twice the product of these two terms.
$$m^2 - 14m + 49$$
$$(m-7)^2$$

c.   The first term is $2a$ squared, the last term is 5 squared and the middle term is twice the product of these two terms.
$$4a^2 + 20a + 25$$
$$(2a+5)^2$$

d. The first term is $3x$ squared, the last term is $4y$ squared, and the middle term is twice the product of these two terms.

$$9x^2 - 24xy + 16y^2$$
$$(3x - 4y)^2$$

A similar pattern we can use is the difference of two squares. When multiplying two binomials, one the sum of two terms and the other the difference of those same two terms we get the difference of two squares.

$$(a + b)(a - b) = a^2 - ab + ab - b^2 = a^2 - b^2$$

From this we can see that a binomial made up of the difference of two perfect squares can be factored following the pattern:

$$a^2 - b^2 = (a + b)(a - b)$$

As you can see the factorization is the sum of the two terms multiplied by the difference of the two terms.

Example 2

Factor the following:

a. $x^2 - 9$

b. $4a^2 - 25$

c. $x^2 + 49$

d. $9m^2 - 16n^2$

Solution

a. $x^2 - 9 = x^2 - 3^2 = (x + 3)(x - 3)$

b. $4a^2 - 25 = (2a)^2 - 5^2 = (2a + 5)(2a - 5)$

c. $x^2 + 49$ is the sum of two squares not the difference of two squares and is not factorable. We can demonstrate this by considering the graph of the equation $y = x^2 + 4$

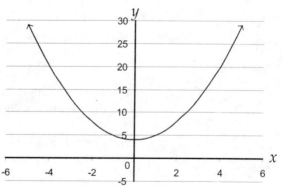

Since the graph has no horizontal intercepts this expression cannot be factored using the real numbers.

d. $9m^2 - 16n^2 = (3m)^2 - (4n)^2 = (3m + 4n)(3m - 4n)$

Remember that the sum of two squares is not factorable only the difference of two squares. Two other patterns that we can use are the sum and difference of two cubes. The sign changes in these patterns are very important and you should be very careful when using these patterns to get the signs correct.

Sum of Two Cubes

$$a^3 + b^3 = (a+b)(a^2 - ab + b^2)$$

Same signs   Opposite signs

Difference of Two Cubes

$$a^3 - b^3 = (a-b)(a^2 + ab + b^2)$$

Same signs   Opposite signs

Example 3

Factor the following difference and sum of two cubes.

a. $x^3 + 27$

b. $m^3 - 8$

c. $8a^3 + 125b^3$

d. $2p^3 - 54r^3$

Solution

a.   The first term is x cubed and the second term is 3 cubed so we can use the pattern for the sum of two cubes.

$$x^3 + 27$$
$$x^3 + 3^3$$
$$(x+3)(x^2 - 3x + 9)$$

b.   The first term is m cubed and the second term is 2 cubed so we can use the pattern for the difference of two cubes.

$$m^3 - 8$$
$$m^3 - 2^3$$
$$(m-2)(m^2 + 2m + 4)$$

c.   The first term is $2a$ cubed and the second term is $5b$ cubed so we can use the pattern for the sum of two cubes.

$$8a^3 + 125b^3$$
$$(2a)^3 + (5b)^3$$
$$(2a+5b)(4a^2 - 10ab + 25b^2)$$

d.   We will need to first factor out the 2 that is in common and then use the pattern for the difference of two cubes.

$$2p^3 - 54r^3$$
$$2[p^3 - (3r)^3]$$
$$2(p-3r)(p^2 + 3pr + 9r^2)$$

Some polynomials take several steps to factor completely or require slightly different thinking to find the key to factoring them. Always look for the greatest common factor and remove that first. Then look for a pattern that you recognize and begin factoring. Several of the patterns we have discussed can be found in more complicated expressions. The sum or difference of two cubes or the difference of two squares can be found in expressions with exponents that are multiples of two or three.

$$x^6 - y^6 = (x^3)^2 - (y^3)^2$$
$$x^6 - y^6 = (x^2)^3 - (y^2)^3$$

This expression can be looked at as either a difference of two squares or difference of two cubes. This leads to two different paths to factoring but the same result in the end. Trinomials of one variable can be of quadratic form by having the degree of the highest term be twice that of the next term and the final term be a constant.

$$a(\text{expression})^2 + b(\text{expression}) + c$$

These types of situations take practice to see so consider the following examples and follow closely the thinking behind each factorization.

Example 4

Completely factor the following:

a. $x^4 - 81$

b. $3a^6 - a^3 - 10$

c. $12w^4 + 52w^2 + 35$

d. $3x^6 - 192y^6$

Solution

a.   This is the difference of two squares since the first term is x^2 squared and the second term is 9 squared.

$$x^4 - 81$$
$$(x^2)^2 - 9^2$$
$$(x^2 + 9)(x^2 - 9) \qquad \text{The second factor is still}$$
$$\qquad\qquad\qquad\qquad\qquad \text{the difference of two squares}$$
$$(x^2 + 9)(x + 3)(x - 3) \qquad \text{so we can factor again.}$$

b.   This trinomial is quadratic in form since the first term has degree twice that of the second term and the third term is a constant. We can use a substitution for a^3 to make the trinomial appear to be quadratic and then factor and replace the a^3 back into the expression. We can use any variable for this substitution so for this problem we will use x. Letting $x = a^3$ we get the following:

$$3a^6 - a^3 - 10$$
$$3(a^3)^2 - (a^3) - 10$$
$$3x^2 - x - 10 \qquad \text{Substitute in } x \text{ and factor.}$$
$$(3x + 5)(x - 2)$$
$$(3a^3 + 5)(a^3 - 2) \qquad \text{Replace the } x \text{ with } a^3$$

c.   This trinomial is quadratic in form and we can use substitution and then factor the remaining quadratic. Using $t = w^2$ we get the following.

$$12w^4 + 52w^2 + 35$$

$$12(w^2)^2 + 52w^2 + 35$$

$$12t^2 + 52t + 35 \qquad \text{Substitute in } t \text{ and factor.}$$

$$(2t + 7)(6t + 5)$$

$$(2w^2 + 7)(6w^2 + 5) \quad \text{Replace } t \text{ with } w^2$$

d.   This can be viewed as either the difference of two squares or the difference of two cubes. If we consider it to be the difference of two cubes we end up needing to factor again using the difference of two squares to completely finish the factoring.

$$3x^6 - 192y^6$$

$$3(x^6 - 64y^6)$$

$$3[(x^2)^3 - (4y^2)^3] \qquad \text{Factor using the difference of two cubes.}$$

$$3(x^2 - 4y^2)(x^4 + 4x^2y^2 + 16y^4) \qquad \text{Finish by using the}$$

$$3(x - 2y)(x + 2y)(x^4 + 4x^2y^2 + 16y^4) \quad \text{difference of two squares.}$$

Appendix F Exercises

For Exercises 1 through 8 factor the following perfect square trinomials.

1. $x^2 + 8x + 16$

2. $w^2 + 10w + 25$

3. $9g^2 + 12g + 4$

4. $x^2 - 12x + 36$

5. $4t^2 - 28t + 49$

6. $100d^2 + 20d + 1$

7. $25x^2 + 30xy + 9y^2$

8. $49m^2 - 84mn + 36n^2$

For exercises 9 through 19 factor the following difference of two squares and difference or sum of two cubes.

9. $x^2 - 36$

10. $m^2 - 49$

11. $9k^2 - 16$

12. $x^2 + 9$

13. $m^3 - 64$

14. $x^3 + 125$

15. $8x^3 + 27$

16. $27d^3 - 64$

17. $3g^3 - 24$

18. $40x^3 + 625$

19. $50x^2 - 18$

For exercises 20 through 30 completely factor the following polynomials.

20. $r^6 - 64$

21. $16b^4 - 625c^4$

22. $8x^8 + 12x^4 + 18$

23. $6w^{10} - 27w^5 - 105$

24. $H + 6\sqrt{H} + 9$

25. $4t - 20t^{\frac{1}{2}} + 25$

26. $7g^4 - 567h^4$

27. $5w^5x^3z + 25w^3x^2z^2 - 120wxz^3$

28. $24a^3b^2 + 11a^2b^3 - 35ab^4$

29. $-7g^7h^2 - 7g^5h^4 + 140g^3h^6$

30. $a^{12} - b^{36}$